AutoCAD LT 2012
for Designers

CADCIM Technologies
525 St. Andrews Drive
Schererville, IN 46375, USA
(www.cadcim.com)

Contributing Author
Sham Tickoo
Professor
Department of Mechanical Engineering Technology
Purdue University Calumet
Hammond, Indiana, USA

CADCIM Technologies

AutoCAD LT 2012 for Designers
Sham Tickoo

Published by CADCIM Technologies, 525 St Andrews Drive, Schererville, IN 46375 USA.
© Copyright 2011 CADCIM Technologies. All rights reserved. No part of this publication may be reproduced or distributed in any form or by any means, or stored in the database or retrieval system without the prior permission of CADCIM Technologies.

ISBN 978-1-936646-14-2

www.cadcim.com

DEDICATION

*To teachers, who make it possible to disseminate knowledge
to enlighten the young and curious minds
of our future generations*

*To students, who are dedicated to learning new technologies
and making the world a better place to live in*

THANKS

*To the faculty and students of the MET Department of
Purdue University Calumet for their cooperation*

To employees of CADCIM Technologies for their valuable help

Online Training Program Offered by CADCIM Technologies

CADCIM Technologies provides effective and affordable virtual online training on various software packages including Computer Aided Design and Manufacturing (CAD/CAM), computer programming languages, animation, architecture, and GIS. The training is delivered 'live' via Internet at any time, any place, and at any pace to individuals, students of colleges, universities, and CAD/CAM training centers. The main features of this program are:

Training for Students and Companies in a Class Room Setting

Highly experienced instructors and qualified Engineers at CADCIM Technologies conduct the classes under the guidance of Prof. Sham Tickoo of Purdue University Calumet, USA. This team has authored several textbooks that are rated "one of the best" in their categories and are used in various colleges, universities, and training centers in North America, Europe, and in other parts of the world.

Training for Individuals

The cost effective and time saving initiative of CADCIM Technologies strives to deliver the training in the comfort of your home or work place, thereby relieving you from the hassles of traveling to training centers.

Training Offered on Software Packages

We provide basic and advanced training on the following software packages:

__CAD/CAM/CAE__: CATIA, Pro/ENGINEER Wildfire, SolidWorks, Autodesk Inventor, Solid Edge, NX, AutoCAD, AutoCAD LT, Customizing AutoCAD, EdgeCAM, ANSYS, and Alias

__Computer Programming__: C++, VB.NET, Oracle, AJAX, and Java

__Animation and Styling__: Autodesk 3ds Max, 3ds Max Design, and Maya

__Architecture and GIS__: Autodesk Revit Architecture, Autodesk Civil 3D, Autodesk Revit Structures, and Autodesk Map 3D

For more information, please visit the following link:
__http://www.cadcim.com__

Note

The free teaching and learning resources, mentioned in the cover page of this textbook, are available only for those who buy the textbook from our web site **www.cadcim.com** or the university/college bookstores. We need proof of purchase when you request the technical support from us.

Table of Contents

Dedication   iii
Preface   xiii

Chapter 1: Introduction to AutoCAD LT

Starting AutoCAD LT   1-2
AutoCAD LT Screen Components*   1-3
   Drawing Area   1-4
   Command Window   1-4
   Navigation Bar   1-4
   Status Bar   1-4
Invoking Commands in AutoCAD LT   1-8
   Keyboard   1-8
   Ribbon   1-9
   Application Menu   1-9
   Tool Palettes   1-10
   Menu Bar   1-10
   Toolbar   1-11
   Shortcut Menu   1-12
AutoCAD LT Dialog Boxes   1-13
Starting a New Drawing   1-14
   Open a Drawing   1-15
   Start from Scratch   1-15
   Use a Template   1-15
   Use a Wizard   1-15
Saving Your Work   1-20
   Save Drawing as Dialog box   1-21
   Using the Drawing Recovery Manager to Recover Files 1-22
Closing a Drawing   1-22
Opening an Existing Drawing   1-23
   Opening an Existing Drawing Using the Select File Dialog Box   1-23
   Opening an Existing Drawing Using the Startup Dialog Box   1-25
   Opening an Existing Drawing Using the Drag and Drop Method   1-25
Quitting AutoCAD LT   1-25
Creating and Managing Workspaces   1-26
   Creating a New Workspace   1-26
   Modifying the Workspace Settings   1-26
AutoCAD LT HELP   1-27
   Autodesk Exchange*   1-28
   Home   1-28
   Help   1-29
Additional Help Resources   1-29

Chapter 2: Getting Started with AutoCAD LT

Dynamic Input Mode*   2-2
   Enable Pointer Input   2-2
   Enable Dimension Input where possible   2-3
   Show command prompting and command input near the crosshairs   2-5
   Drafting Tooltip Appearance   2-5
Drawing Lines in AutoCAD LT   2-6
   The Close Option   2-7

The Undo Option   2-8
Invoking tools Using Dynamic INPUT/Command Prompt   2-8
Coordinate Systems   2-8
    Absolute Coordinate System   2-9
    Relative Coordinate System   2-11
    Relative Polar Coordinates   2-14
    Direct Distance Entry   2-16
Erasing Objects   2-19
Canceling and Undoing a Command   2-19
Object Selection Methods   2-20
    Window Selection   2-20
    Window Crossing Method   2-21
Drawing a Circle   2-22
BASIC Display Commands   2-25
Setting Units Type and Precision   2-26
    Specifying the Format   2-26
    Specifying the Angle Format   2-27
SETTING the Limits OF A DRAWING   2-30

Chapter 3: Starting with Advanced Sketching

Drawing Arcs   3-2
Drawing Rectangles   3-9
Drawing Ellipses   3-12
Drawing Regular Polygon   3-16
Drawing Polylines   3-17
Placing Points   3-22
Drawing Infinite Lines   3-23
Writing A Single Line Text   3-26

Chapter 4: Working with Drawing Aids

Introduction   4-2
Understanding the Concept and use of LAYERS   4-2
    Advantages of Using Layers   4-2
Working with Layers*   4-3
    Creating New Layers   4-3
    Making a Layer Current   4-4
    Controlling the Display of Layers   4-5
    Deleting Layers   4-9
Object Properties   4-11
    Changing the Color   4-12
    Changing the Linetype   4-12
    Changing the Lineweight   4-13
    Changing the Plot Style   4-13
    Properties Palette   4-13
    Quick Properties Palette   4-14
Drafting Settings dialog box   4-15
    Setting Grid   4-15
    Setting Snap   4-17
    Snap Type   4-17
Drawing Straight Lines using the Ortho Mode   4-18
Working with Object Snaps   4-19
    AutoSnap   4-19
    Endpoint   4-20

Midpoint   4-20
Nearest   4-21
Center   4-21
Tangent   4-22
Quadrant   4-22
Intersection   4-23
Apparent Intersection   4-23
Perpendicular   4-24
Node   4-25
Insertion   4-25
Snap to None   4-25
Parallel   4-26
Extension   4-26
From   4-27
Midpoint Between 2 Points   4-27
Temporary Tracking Point   4-27
Combining Object Snap Modes   4-28
Running Object Snap Mode   4-29
Overriding the Running Snap   4-29
Cycling through Snaps   4-30
Using AutoTracking   4-30
Object Snap Tracking   4-30
Polar Tracking   4-31
AutoTrack Settings   4-32
Function and Control Keys   4-32

Chapter 5: Editing Sketched Objects-I

Editing Sketches   5-2
Moving the Sketched Objects   5-2
Copying the Sketched Objects   5-3
Creating Multiple Copies   5-3
Creating a Single Copy   5-3
Offsetting Sketched Objects   5-4
Rotating Sketched Objects   5-6
Scaling the Sketched Objects   5-7
Filleting the Sketches   5-9
Chamfering the Sketches   5-12
Trimming the Sketched Objects   5-14
Extending the Sketched Objects   5-17
Stretching the Sketched Objects   5-19
Lengthening the Sketched Objects   5-20
Arraying the Sketched Objects*   5-22
Rectangular Array   5-22
Polar Array   5-29
Path Array   5-34
Mirroring the Sketched Objects   5-37
Text Mirroring   5-38

Chapter 6: Editing Sketched Objects-II

Introduction to Grips   6-2
Types of Grips   6-2
Editing a Polyline by Using Grips   6-3
Editing Gripped Objects   6-4
Changing the Properties Using the PROPERTIES Palette   6-4

Matching the Properties of Sketched Objects   6-5
Cycling Through Selection   6-5
Managing Contents Using the DesignCenter   6-6
    Autodesk Seek design content Link   6-9
    Displaying Drawing Properties   6-11
Basic Display Options   6-12
Redrawing the Screen   6-12
Regenerating Drawings   6-13
Zooming Drawings   6-13
    Realtime Zooming   6-14
    All Option   6-15
    Center Option   6-15
    Extents Option   6-16
    Dynamic Option   6-16
    Previous Option   6-17
    Window Option   6-17
    Scale Option   6-18
    Object Option   6-19
    Zoom In and Out   6-19
Panning Drawings   6-19
    Panning in Realtime   6-20

Chapter 7: Creating Text and Tables

Annotative Objects   7-2
Annotation Scale   7-2
    Assigning Annotative Property and Annotation Scales   7-2
    Customizing Annotation Scale   7-3
Multiple Annotation Scales   7-3
    Assigning Multiple Annotation Scales Manually   7-3
    Assigning Multiple Annotation Scales Automatically   7-4
Controlling the Display of Annotative objects   7-5
Creating Text   7-5
    Writing Single Line Text   7-6
Entering Special Characters   7-9
Creating Multiline Text   7-9
    Text Window   7-10
    Text Editor Tab   7-11
Editing Text   7-24
    Editing Text Using the DDEDIT Command   7-24
    Editing Text Using the Properties Palette   7-25
    Modifying the Scale of the Text   7-25
Inserting Table in the Drawing   7-25
    Table style Area   7-26
    Insert options Area   7-26
    Insertion behavior Area   7-29
    Column and row settings Area   7-29
    Set cell styles Area   7-30
Creating a New Table Style   7-30
    Starting table Area   7-31
    General Area   7-31
    Cell styles Area   7-32
Setting a Table Style As Current   7-33
Modifying a Table Style   7-34
Modifying Tables   7-34
Substituting Fonts   7-38

Specifying an Alternate Default Font — 7-39
Creating Text Styles — 7-39
Determining Text Height — 7-41
Creating Annotative text — 7-41

Chapter 8: Basic Dimensioning, Geometric Dimensioning, and Tolerancing

Need for Dimensioning — 8-2
Dimensioning in AutoCAD LT — 8-2
Fundamental Dimensioning Terms — 8-2
    Dimension Line — 8-3
    Dimension Text — 8-3
    Arrowheads — 8-3
    Extension Lines — 8-3
    Leader — 8-4
    Center Mark and Centerlines — 8-4
    Alternate Units — 8-4
    Tolerances — 8-5
    Limits — 8-5
Associative Dimensions — 8-5
Definition Points — 8-6
Annotative Dimensions — 8-7
Selecting Dimensioning Commands — 8-7
    Using the Ribbon and the Toolbar — 8-7
    Using the Command Line — 8-8
Dimensioning a Number of Objects Together — 8-8
Creating Linear Dimensions — 8-9
    DIMLINEAR Command Options — 8-10
Creating Aligned Dimensions — 8-12
Creating Arc Length Dimensions — 8-13
Creating Rotated Dimensions — 8-14
Creating Baseline Dimensions — 8-15
Creating Continued Dimensions — 8-16
Creating Angular Dimensions — 8-17
    Dimensioning the Angle between Two Nonparallel Lines — 8-18
    Dimensioning the Angle of an Arc — 8-19
    Angular Dimensioning of Circles — 8-19
    Angular Dimensioning based on Three Points — 8-19
Creating Diameter Dimensions — 8-20
Creating Radius Dimensions — 8-21
Creating Jogged Linear Dimensions — 8-21
Creating Ordinate Dimensions — 8-23
Maintaining Equal Spacing between Dimensions — 8-24
Creating Inspection Dimensions — 8-25
    Inspection Label — 8-25
    Dimension Value — 8-25
Working with True Associative Dimensions — 8-26
    Inspection Rate — 8-26
    Removing the Dimension Associativity — 8-26
    Converting a Dimension into a True Associative Dimension — 8-27
Drawing Leaders — 8-27
Multileader — 8-31
Adding leaders to existing Multileader — 8-34
Removing Leaders from Existing Multileader — 8-34
Aligning Multileaders* — 8-34

Distribute   8-35
make leader segments Parallel   8-36
specify Spacing   8-36
Use current spacing   8-36
Geometric Dimensioning and Tolerancing   8-37
Geometric Characteristics and Symbols   8-38
Adding Geometric Tolerance   8-38
Feature Control Frame   8-39
Geometric Characteristics Symbol   8-39
Tolerance Value and Tolerance Zone Descriptor   8-39
Material Condition Modifier   8-40
Datum   8-40
Complex Feature Control Frames   8-40
Composite Position Tolerancing   8-40
Projected Tolerance Zone   8-41
Creating Annotative Dimensions, Tolerances, Leaders, and Multileaders   8-44

Chapter 9: Editing Dimensions

Editing Dimensions Using Editing Tools   9-2
Editing Dimensions by Stretching   9-2
Editing Dimensions by Trimming and Extending   9-3
Flipping Dimension Arrow   9-4
Modifying the Dimensions   9-4
Editing the Dimension Text   9-6
Updating Dimensions   9-7
Editing Dimensions with Grips   9-7
Editing Dimensions using the Properties Palette   9-7
Properties Palette (Dimension)   9-7
Properties Palette (Multileader)   9-8
Model Space and Paper Space Dimensioning   9-10

Chapter 10: Dimension Styles, Multileader Styles, and System Variables

Using Styles and Variables to Control Dimensions   10-2
Creating and Restoring Dimension Styles   10-2
New Dimension Style dialog box   10-3
Controlling the Dimension Text Format   10-10
Fitting Dimension Text and Arrowheads   10-14
Formatting Primary Dimension Units   10-17
Formatting Alternate Dimension Units   10-20
Formatting the Tolerances   10-21
Creating and Restoring Multileader Styles   10-26
Modify Multileader Style dialog box   10-27

Chapter 11: Model Space Viewports, Paper Space Viewports, and Layouts

Model Space And Paper Space/Layouts   11-2
Model Space Viewports (Tiled Viewports)   11-3
Creating Tiled Viewports   11-3
Making a Viewport Current   11-5

Joining Two Adjacent Viewports   11-5
Paper space viewports (Floating Viewports)*   11-6
    Creating Floating Viewports   11-7
    Creating Rectangular Viewports   11-7
    Creating Polygonal Viewports   11-9
    Converting an Existing Closed Object into a Viewport   11-10
Temporary Model Space   11-10
Editing Viewports   11-12
    Controlling the Display of Objects in Viewports 11-12
    Locking the Display of Objects in Viewports   11-12
    Controlling the Display of Hidden Lines in Viewports   11-12
    Clipping Existing Viewports   11-13
    Maximizing Viewports   11-14
Inserting Layouts   11-16
Inserting a Layout Using The Wizard   11-18
Defining Page Settings   11-18
Controlling the Display of Annotative Objects in Viewports   11-20

Chapter 12: Plotting Drawings

Plotting Drawings in AutoCAD LT   12-2
Plotting Drawings Using the Plot Dialog Box   12-2
    Page setup Area   12-2
    Printer/plotter Area   12-3
    Paper size Area   12-4
    Number of copies Area   12-4
    Plot area Area   12-4
    Plot offset (origin set to printable area) Area   12-5
    Plot scale Area   12-5
    Plot style table (pen assignments) Area   12-6
    Shaded viewport options Area   12-6
    Plot options Area   12-6
    Preview   12-7
Adding Plotters   12-7
    The Plotter Manager Tool   12-7
Using Plot Styles   12-9
    Adding a Plot Style   12-10

Chapter 13: Hatching Drawings

Hatching   13-2
    Hatch Patterns   13-2
    Hatch Boundary   13-3
Hatching Drawings Using the Hatch Tool   13-3
Panels in the Hatch Creation Tab   13-4
    Boundaries Panel   13-4
    Pattern Panel   13-7
    Properties Panel   13-8
    Origin Panel   13-9
    Options Panel   13-10
    Match Properties   13-12
    Setting the Parameters for Gradient Pattern   13-13
Creating Annotative Hatch   13-14
Hatching the Drawing Using the Tool Palettes   13-14

Drag and Drop Method   13-15
Select and Place Method   13-15
Hatching Around Text, Dimensions, and Attributes   13-17
Editing Hatch Patterns   13-17
Using the Hatch Editor Tab   13-17
Using the HATCHEDIT Command   13-17
Trimming the Hatch Patterns   13-19
Using AutoCAD LT Editing Tools   13-21
Hatching Blocks and Xref Drawings   13-22
Other Features of Hatching   13-22

Chapter 14: Working with Blocks

The Concept of Blocks   14-2
Advantages of Using Blocks   14-2
Drawing Objects for Blocks   14-3
Converting Entities into a Block   14-4
Inserting Blocks   14-7
Creating and Inserting Annotative Blocks   14-12
Block Editor   14-15
Adding Blocks in Tool Palettes   14-16
Drag and Drop Method   14-16
Shortcut Menu   14-16
Modifying Existing Blocks in the Tool Palettes   14-17
Layers, Colors, Linetypes, and Lineweights for Blocks   14-17
Nesting of Blocks   14-18
Creating Drawing Files using the Write Block Dialog Box   14-20
Exploding Blocks Using the XPLODE Command   14-22
Renaming Blocks   14-23
Deleting Unused Blocks   14-24
Editing Constraints to Blocks   14-25

Student Projects   1

Index   1

CHAPTERS FOR FREE DOWNLOAD

The following chapters are available on the publisher's website for free download. To download the chapters, log on to www.cadcim.com and follow the path:

Textbooks > CAD/CAM > AutoCAD LT > AutoCAD LT 2012 for Designers

Chapter 15: Defining Block Attributes

Chapter 16: Understanding External References

Chapter 17: Working with Advanced Drawing Options

Chapter 18: Grouping and Advanced Editing of Sketched Objects

Preface

AutoCAD LT, developed by Autodesk Inc., is the most popular PC-CAD system available in the market. Today, over 7 million people use AutoCAD LT and other AutoCAD LT based design products. 100% of the Fortune 100 firms are Autodesk customers and 98% of the Fortune 500 firms are Autodesk customers. AutoCAD LT also facilitates customization that enables the users to increase their efficiency and improve their productivity.

The **AutoCAD LT 2012 for Designers** textbook contains a detailed explanation of AutoCAD LT 2012 commands and their applications to solve drafting and design problems. Every AutoCAD LT command is thoroughly explained with the help of examples and illustrations. This makes it easy for the users to understand its function and application in the drawing. After reading this textbook, you will be able to use AutoCAD LT commands to make a drawing, create text, create and insert symbols, dimension a drawing, apply constraints to sketches, create blocks and dynamic blocks.

The book also covers basic drafting and design concepts that provide you with the essential drafting skills to solve the drawing problems in AutoCAD LT. These include sketching, adding text, hatching, and dimensioning principles. While going through this textbook, you will discover some new unique applications of AutoCAD LT that will have a significant effect on your drawings. In addition, you will be able to understand why AutoCAD LT has become such a popular software package and an international standard in PC-CAD.

Formatting Conventions Used in the Text
Please refer to the following list for the formatting conventions used in this textbook.

Naming Conventions Used in the Text

Convention	Example
• New and enhanced features of AutoCAD LT 2012 are indicated by an asterisk symbol at the end of the feature.	**Cycling Through Selection**˙
• Command names are capitalized and bold.	Example: The **MOVE** command
• A key icon appears when you have to respond by pressing the ENTER or the RETURN key.	

- Command sequences are indented. The responses are indicated in boldface. The directions are indicated by italics and the comments are enclosed in parentheses.

Command: **MOVE**
Select object: **G**
Enter group name: *Enter a group name (the group name is group1)*

- The methods of invoking a tool/option from the **Ribbon, Menu Bar, Quick Access toolbar, Tool Palettes, Application menu,** toolbars, Status Bar, and Command prompt are enclosed in a shaded box.

Ribbon:	Draw > Line
Menu Bar:	Draw > Line
Tool Palettes:	Draw > Line
Toolbars:	Draw > Line
Command:	LINE or L

Tool

If you click on an item in a toolbar or a panel of the **Ribbon** and a command is invoked to create/edit an object or perform some action, then that item is termed as **tool**.

For example:
To Create: **Line** tool, **Circle** tool
To Edit: **Fillet** tool, **Array** tool, **Stretch** tool
Action: **Zoom** tool, **Move** tool, **Copy** tool

If you click on an item in a toolbar or a panel of the **Ribbon** and a dialog box is invoked wherein you can set the properties to create/edit an object, then that item is also termed as **tool**, refer to Figure 1.

For example:
To Create: **Define Attributes** tool, **Create** tool, **Insert** tool
To Edit: **Edit Attributes** tool, **Block Editor** tool

*Figure 1 Various tools in the **Ribbon***

Button

If you click on an item in a toolbar or a panel of the **Ribbon** and the display of the corresponding object is toggled on/off, then that item is termed as **Button**. For example, **Grid** button, **Snap** button, **Ortho** button, **Properties** button, **Tool Palettes** button, and so on; refer to Figure 2.

*Figure 2 Various buttons displayed in the Status Bar and **Ribbon***

The item in a dialog box that has a 3D shape like a button is also termed as **Button**. For example, **OK** button, **Cancel** button, **Apply** button, and so on. Refer to Figure 3 given below for the terminologies used for the components in a dialog box.

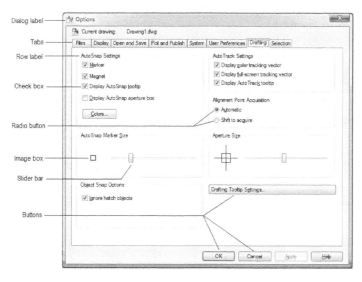

Figure 3 The components in a dialog box

Drop-down

A drop-down is one in which a set of common tools are grouped together for creating an object. You can identify a drop-down with a down arrow on it. These drop-downs are given a name based on the tools grouped in them. For example, **Circle** drop-down, **Fillet/Chamfer** drop-down, **Leader** drop-down, and so on; refer to Figure 4.

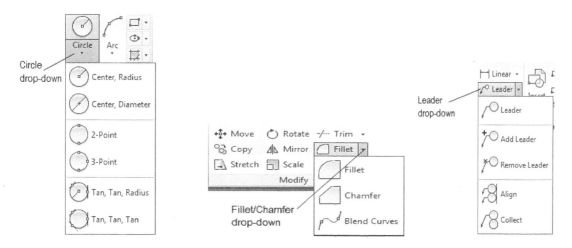

*Figure 4 The **Circle**, **Fillet/Chamfer**, and **Leader** drop-downs*

Drop-down List

A drop-down list is one in which a set of options are grouped together. You can set various parameters using these options. You can identify a drop-down list with a down arrow on it. To know the name of a drop-down list, move the cursor over it; its name will be displayed as a tool tip. For example, **Lineweight** drop-down list, **Linetype** drop-down list, **Text Style** drop-down list, and so on; refer to Figure 5.

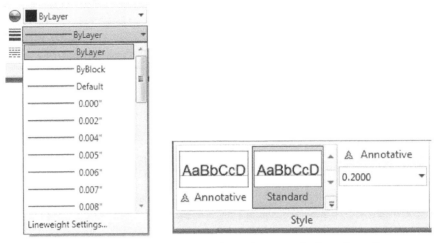

*Figure 5 The **LineWeight** and **Text Style** drop-down lists*

Options

Options are the items that are available in shortcut menu, drop-down list, Command prompt, **Properties** panel, and so on. For example, choose the **Properties** option from the shortcut menu displayed on right-clicking in the drawing area, refer to Figure 6.

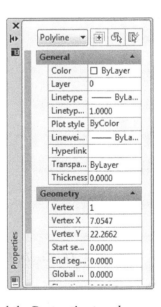

*Figure 6 Options in the shortcut menu and the **Properties** panel*

Tools and Options in Menu Bar

A menu bar consists of both tools and options. As mentioned earlier, the term **tool** is used to create/edit something or perform some action. For example, in Figure 7, the item Box has been used to create a box shaped surface, therefore it will be referred as **3 Points** tool.

Similarly, an option in the menu bar is one that is used to set some parameters. For example, in

Figure 7, the item Linetype has been used to set/load the linetype, therefore it will be referred as an option.

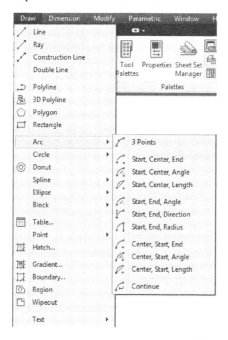
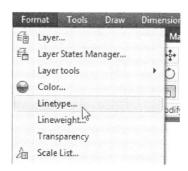

Figure 7 *Tools and options in the menu bar*

Free Companion Website

It has been our constant endeavor to provide you the best textbooks and services at affordable price. In this endeavor, we have come out with a Free Companion website that will facilitate the process of teaching and learning of AutoCAD LT 2012. If you purchase this textbook from our website (www.cadcimtech.com), you will get access to the files on the Companion website.

To access the files, you need to register by visiting the **Resources** section at *www.cadcim.com*. The following resources are available for the faculty and students in this website:

Faculty Resources

• **Technical Support**
You can get online technical support by contacting *techsupport@cadcim.com*.

• **Instructor's Guide**
Solutions to all review questions and exercises in the textbook are provided in this link to help the faculty members test the skills of the students.

• **PowerPoint Presentations**
The contents of the book are arranged in PowerPoint slides that can be used by the faculty for their lectures.

• **Drawing Files**
The drawing files used in illustration, examples, and exercises are available for free download.

Student Resources

- **Technical Support**
  You can get online technical support by contacting *techsupport@cadcim.com*.

- **Drawing Files**
  The drawing files used in illustrations and examples are available for free download.

- **Additional Students Projects**
  Various projects are provided for the students to practice.

If you face any problem in accessing these files, please contact the publisher at *sales@cadcim.com* or the author at *stickoo@purduecal.edu* or *tickoo525@gmail.com*.

Chapter *1*

Introduction to AutoCAD LT

CHAPTER OBJECTIVES

In this chapter, you will learn:
- *To start AutoCAD LT.*
- *About the components of the initial AutoCAD LT screen.*
- *To invoke AutoCAD LT commands from the keyboard, menu, toolbar, shortcut menu, Tool Palettes, and Ribbon.*
- *About the components of a dialog box in AutoCAD LT.*
- *To start a new drawing using the New tool and the Startup dialog box.*
- *To save a work using various file-saving commands.*
- *To close a drawing.*
- *To open an existing drawing.*
- *About the concept of Multiple Document Environment.*
- *To exit AutoCAD LT.*

KEY TERMS

- *Initial Setup*
- *AutoCAD LT Screen Components*
- *Ribbon*
- *Application Menu*
- *Tool Palettes*

- *Menu Bar*
- *Toolbar*
- *New*
- *Save*
- *Save As*
- *Close*

- *STARTUP*
- *Open*
- *Partial open*
- *Drawing Recovery Manager*
- *Workspaces*

- *Help*
- *Autodesk Exchange*

STARTING AutoCAD LT

After you have installed AutoCAD LT 2012, an AutoCAD LT 2012 icon is displayed on the desktop. You can start AutoCAD LT by double-clicking on it. You can also load AutoCAD LT from the Windows taskbar by choosing the **Start** button at the bottom left corner of the screen (default position). On doing so, a menu will be displayed. From this menu, choose **All Programs** to display program folders. Now, choose **Autodesk > AutoCAD LT 2012** to display AutoCAD LT programs and then choose **AutoCAD LT 2012-English** to start AutoCAD LT, see Figure 1-1.

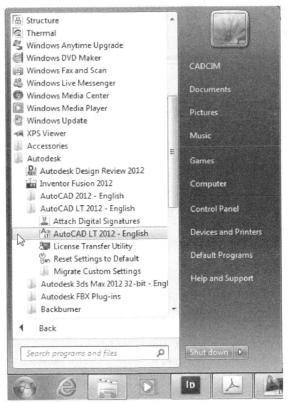

Figure 1-1   Starting AutoCAD LT 2012 using the
Start *Menu*

When you start AutoCAD LT 2012, the **Autodesk Exchange** window will be displayed, as shown in Figure 1-2. In this window, various links are available. These links provide information on enhancements, new features, products and services, subscription, and so on. You can click on a link to find information contained in that link. For example, when you click on any link in the **New in AutoCAD LT 2012** area, you can find information about new features and enhancements of AutoCAD LT 2012.

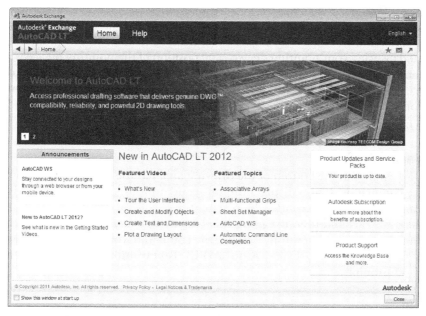

Figure 1-2 *The **Autodesk Exchange** window of AutoCAD LT 2012*

AutoCAD LT SCREEN COMPONENTS*

The components of the initial AutoCAD LT screen are drawing area, command window, menu bar, Title bar, several toolbars, model and layout tabs, and status bar (Figure 1-3). The title bar that has AutoCAD LT symbol and the current drawing name is displayed on top of the screen.

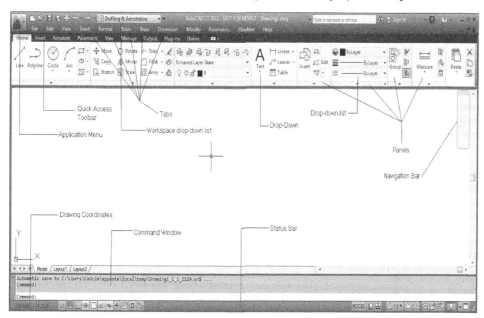

Figure 1-3 *AutoCAD LT screen components in AutoCAD LT **Drafting** & **Annotation** workspace*

Drawing Area

The drawing area covers the major portion of the screen. In this area, you can draw the objects and use the commands. To draw the objects, you need to define the coordinate points, which can be selected by using your pointing device. The position of the pointing device is represented on the screen by the cursor. There is a coordinate system icon at the lower left corner of the drawing area. The window also has the standard Windows buttons such as close, minimize, scroll bar, and so on, on the top right corner. These buttons have the same functions as for any other standard window.

Command Window

The command window at the bottom of the drawing area has the Command prompt where you can enter the commands. It also displays the subsequent prompt sequences and the messages. You can change the size of the window by placing the cursor on the top edge (double line bar known as the grab bar) and then dragging it. This way you can increase its size to see all the previous commands you have used. By default, the command window displays only three lines. You can also press the F2 key to display **AutoCAD LT Text window**, which displays the previous commands and prompts.

Tip
You can hide all toolbars displayed on the screen by pressing the CTRL+0 keys or by choosing
View > Clean Screen *from the menu bar. To turn on the display of the toolbars again, press the CTRL+0 keys. Note that the 0 key on the numeric keypad of the keyboard cannot be used for the **Clean Screen** option. You can also choose the **Clean Screen** button in the Status Bar to hide all toolbars.*

Navigation Bar

The **Navigation Bar** is displayed in the drawing area and contains navigation tools. These tools are grouped together, refer to Figure 1-4 and are discussed next.

SteeringWheels

The SteeringWheels has a set of navigation tools such as pan, zoom, and so on. You will learn more about the SteeringWheel in the later chapters.

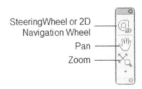

Pan

This tool allows you to view the portion of the drawing that is outside the current display area. To do so, choose this tool, press and hold the left mouse button, and then drag the drawing area. Press ESC to exit this command.

Figure 1-4 Tools in the Navigation Bar

Zoom

The tools to enlarge the view of the drawing on the screen without affecting the actual size of the objects are grouped together. You will learn more about zoom in later chapters.

Status Bar

The Status Bar is displayed at the bottom of the screen and is called Application Status Bar. It contains some useful information and buttons (see Figure 1-5) that make it easy to change the status of some AutoCAD LT functions. You can toggle between the on and off states of most of these functions by choosing them.

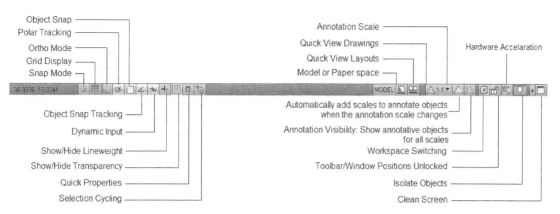

Figure 1-5 *The Status Bar displayed in the* ***Drafting & Annotation*** *workspace*

Drawing Coordinates

The information about the coordinates is displayed on the left corner of the Status Bar. You can choose this coordinate button to toggle between the on and off states. The **COORDS** system variable controls the display type of the coordinates. If the value of the **COORDS** variable is set to 0, the coordinate display is static, that is, the coordinate values displayed in the Status Bar change only when you specify a point. If the value of the **COORDS** variable is set to 1 or 2, the coordinate display is dynamic. When the variable is set to 1, AutoCAD LT constantly displays the absolute coordinates of the graphics cursor with respect to the UCS origin. The polar coordinates (length<angle) are displayed if you are in an AutoCAD LT command and the **COORDS** variable is set to 2. You can also click on the **Drawing Coordinates** area to change the coordinate status from on to off and vice versa.

Snap Mode

If the **Snap Mode** button is chosen, the snap mode is on. So, you can move the cursor in fixed increments. The F9 key acts as a toggle key to turn the snap off or on.

Grid Display

In AutoCAD LT, the grid lines are used as reference lines to draw objects. If the **Grid Display** button is chosen, the grid display is on and the grid lines are displayed on the screen. The F7 function key can be used to turn the grid display on or off.

Ortho Mode

If the **Ortho Mode** button is chosen, you can draw lines at right angles only. You can use the F8 function key to turn ortho on or off.

Polar Tracking

If you turn the polar tracking on, the movement of the cursor is restricted along a path based on the angle set as the polar angle. Choose the **Polar Tracking** button to turn the polar tracking on. You can also use the F10 function key to turn on this option. Note that turning the polar tracking on, automatically turns off the ortho mode.

Object Snap

When the **Object Snap** button is chosen, you can use the running object snaps to snap on to a point. You can also use the F3 function key to turn the object snap on or off. The status of **OSNAP** (off or on) does not prevent you from using the immediate mode object snaps.

Object Snap Tracking

When you choose this button, the inferencing lines will be displayed. Inferencing lines are dashed lines that are displayed automatically when you select a sketching tool and track a particular keypoint on the screen. Choosing this button turns the object snap tracking on or off.

Dynamic Input

The **Dynamic Input** button is used to turn the **Dynamic Input** on or off. Turning it on facilitates the heads-up design approach because in the state, all the commands, prompts, and dimensional inputs are in the drawing area and you do not need to look at the Command prompt all the time. This saves the design time and also increases the efficiency of the user. If the **Dynamic Input** mode is turned on, you will be allowed to enter the commands through the **Pointer Input** boxes, and the numerical values through the **Dimensional Input** boxes. You will also be allowed to select the command options through the **Dynamic Prompt** options in the graphics window. To turn the **Dynamic Input** on or off, use the F12 key.

Show/Hide Lineweight

Choosing this button in the Status Bar allows you to turn on or off the display of lineweights in the drawing. If this button is not chosen, the display of lineweight will be turned off.

Show/Hide Transparency

This button is available in the Status Bar and is chosen to turn on or off the transparency set for a drawing. You can set the transparency in the **Properties** panel or in the layer in which the sketch is drawn.

Quick Properties

If you select a sketched entity when this button is chosen in the Status Bar, the properties of the selected entity will be displayed in a panel.

Selection Cycling

When this button is chosen, you can cycle through the objects to be selected, if they are overlapping or close to other entities. On selecting an entity when this button is chosen, the **Selection** list box with a list of the entities that can be selected will be displayed.

Model

The **Model** button is chosen by default because you are working in the model space to create drawings. You will learn more about the model space in later chapters.

Quick View Layouts

Choose this button to display a panel from which you can choose the layout you need to invoke.

Quick View Drawings

Choose this button to display a panel from which you can choose the drawings you need to invoke.

Annotation Scale

The annotation scale controls the size and display of the annotative objects in the model space. The **Annotation Scale** button has a flyout that displays all the annotation scales available for the current drawing.

Annotation Visibility

This button is used to control the visibility of the annotative objects that do not support the current annotation scale in the drawing area.

Automatically Add Scale

This button, if chosen, automatically adds all the annotation scales that are set current to all the annotative objects present in the drawing.

Toolbar/Window Positions Unlocked

The **Toolbar/Window Positions Unlocked** button is used to lock and unlock the positions of toolbars and windows. When you click on this icon, a shortcut menu is displayed. Choosing the **Floating Toolbars/Panels** option allows you to lock the current position of the floating toolbars. A checkmark will be displayed in the shortcut menu on the type of toolbars that are currently locked. Choosing the **Docked Toolbars/Panels** option from the shortcut menu allows you to lock the current position of all the docked toolbars. Similarly, you can lock or unlock the position of floating and docked windows, such as the **Properties** window or the **Tool Palettes**. If you move the cursor on the **All** option, a cascading menu is displayed that provides the option to lock and unlock all the toolbars and windows.

Note

*The **LOCKUI** system variable is responsible for the locking and unlocking of the toolbars and windows. The following are the values of the system variable:*

Lockui<0> No toolbar or window locked
Lockui<1> Locks all docked toolbars
Lockui<2> Locks all docked windows
Lockui<4> Locks all floating toolbars
Lockui<8> Locks all floating windows

Hardware Acceleration On

This button is used to set the performance of the software to an acceptable level.

Isolate Objects

This button is used to hide or isolate objects from the drawing area. On choosing this button, a flyout will be displayed with two options. Choose the required option from this flyout and then select the objects to hide or isolate. To end the isolation or display a hidden object, click this button again and choose the **End Object Isolation** option.

Drawing Status Bar

The **Drawing Status Bar** is displayed between the drawing area and the command window. Choose the **Application Status Bar Menu** arrow and choose the **Drawing Status Bar** option from the flyout; the **Drawing Status Bar** will be displayed, refer to Figure 1-6. Turn on the **Drawing Status Bar**; the **Annotation Scale**, **Annotation Visibility**, and **Automatically Add Scale** buttons will move automatically to the **Drawing Status Bar**. If you turn off the **Drawing Status Bar**, these buttons will move back to the **Application Status Bar**.

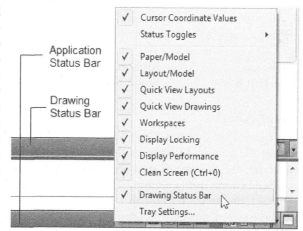

Figure 1-6 The Drawing Status Bar

Tray Settings

Choose the **Tray Settings** option from the flyout displayed on clicking the arrow in the **Application Status Bar**; the **Tray Settings** dialog box will be displayed. You can control the display of icons and notifications in the tray at the right end of the status bar by selecting appropriate options.

Clean Screen

The **Clean Screen** button is at the lower right corner of the screen. This button, when chosen, displays an expanded view of the drawing area by hiding all the toolbars except the command window, Status Bar, and menu bar. The expanded view of the drawing area can also be displayed by choosing **View > Clean Screen** from the menu bar or by using the CTRL+0 keys. Choose the **Clean Screen** button again to restore the previous display state.

Status Toggles

You can hide the display of some of the buttons in the Status Bar. To do so, right-click on the **Application Status Bar**; a shortcut menu will be displayed. Move the cursor on the **Status Toggles** option in the shortcut menu; a cascading menu will be displayed. Clear the check mark near the names of the corresponding buttons in the cascading menu.

Plot/Publish Details Report Available

This icon is displayed when some plotting or a publishing activity was performed in the background. When you click on this icon, the **Plot and Publish Details** dialog box, which provides the details about the plotting and publishing activity, will be displayed. You can copy this report to the clipboard by choosing the **Copy to Clipboard** button from the dialog box.

Manage Xrefs

The **Manage Xrefs** icon is displayed whenever an external reference drawing is attached to the selected drawing. This icon displays a message and an alert whenever the Xreffed drawing needs to be reloaded. To find detailed information regarding the status of each Xref in the drawing and the relation between the various Xrefs, click on the **Manage Xrefs** icon; the **External References Palette** will be displayed.

INVOKING COMMANDS IN AutoCAD LT*

On starting AutoCAD LT, when you are in the drawing area, you need to invoke AutoCAD LT commands to perform any operation. For example, to draw a line, first you need to invoke the **LINE** command and then define the start point and the endpoint of the line. Similarly, if you want to erase objects, you must invoke the **ERASE** command and then select the objects for erasing. AutoCAD LT has provided the following methods to invoke the commands:

Keyboard	**Ribbon**	**Application Menu**	**Tool Palettes**
Tool Palettes	**Menu bar**	**Shortcut menu**	**Toolbar**

Keyboard

You can invoke any AutoCAD LT command from the keyboard by typing the command name and then pressing the ENTER key. As you type the first letter of a command, AutoCAD LT displays all available commands starting with that letter. If the **Dynamic Input** is on and the cursor is in the drawing area, by default, the command will be entered through the **Pointer Input** box. The **Pointer Input** box is a small box displayed on the right of the cursor, as shown in Figure 1-7. However, if the cursor is currently placed on any toolbar or menu bar, or if the **Dynamic Input** is turned off, the command will be entered through the Command prompt. Before you enter a command, the Command prompt is displayed as the last line in the command window area. If it is not displayed, you must cancel the existing command by pressing the ESC (Escape) key. The following example shows how to invoke the **LINE** command using the keyboard:

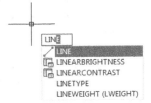

Figure 1-7 The Pointer Input box displayed when the Dynamic Input is on

Command: **LINE** or **L** [Enter]   (L is command alias)

Ribbon

In AutoCAD LT, you can also invoke a tool from the **Ribbon**. The tools for creating, modifying, and annotating the 2D & 3D designs are available in the panels instead of being spread out in the entire drawing area in different toolbars and menus, see Figure 1-8.

*Figure 1-8 The **Ribbon** for the **Drafting & Annotation** workspace*

When you start the AutoCAD LT session for the first time, by default the **Ribbon** is displayed horizontally below the **Quick Access Toolbar**. The **Ribbon** consists of various tabs. The tabs have different panels, which in turn, have tools arranged in rows. Some of the tools have small black down arrow. This indicates that the tools having similar functions are grouped together. To choose a tool, click on the down arrow; a drop-down will be displayed. Choose the required tool from the drop-down displayed. Note that if you choose a tool from the drop-down, the corresponding command will be invoked and the tool that you have chosen will be displayed in the panel. For example, to draw a circle using the **2-Point** option, click on the down arrow next to the **Center, Radius** tool in the **Draw** panel of the **Home** tab; a flyout will be displayed. Choose the **2-Point** tool from the flyout and then draw the circle. You will notice that the **2-Point** tool is displayed in place of the **Center, Radius** tool. In this textbook, the tool selection sequence will be written as, choose the **2-Point** tool from **Home > Draw > Circle** drop-down.

Choose the down arrow to expand the panel. You will notice that a push pin is available at the left end of the panel. Click on the push pin to keep the panel in the expanded state. Also, some of the panels have an inclined arrow at the lower-right corner. When you left click on an inclined arrow, a dialog box is displayed. You can define the setting of the corresponding panel in the dialog box.

You can reorder the panels in the tab. To do so, press and hold the left mouse button on the panel to be moved and drag it to the required position. To undock the **Ribbon**, right-click on the blank space in the **Ribbon** and choose the **Undock** option. You can move, resize, anchor, and auto-hide the **Ribbon** using the shortcut menu that will be displayed when you right-click on the heading strip. To anchor the floating **Ribbon** to the left or right of the drawing area in the vertical position, right-click on the heading strip of the floating **Ribbon**; the shortcut menu is displayed. Choose the corresponding option from this shortcut menu. The **Auto-hide** option will hide the **Ribbon** into the heading strip and will display it only when you move the cursor over this strip.

You can customize the display of tabs and panels in the **Ribbon**. To customize the **Ribbon**, right-click on any one of the tools in it; a shortcut menu will be displayed. On moving the cursor over one of the options, a flyout will be displayed with a tick mark before all options and the corresponding tab or panel will be displayed in the **Ribbon**. Select/clear appropriate option to display/hide a particular tab or panel.

Application Menu

The **Application Menu** is available at the top-left of the AutoCAD LT window. It contains some of the tools that are available in the **Standard** toolbar. Click the down arrow on the **Application Menu** to display the tools, as shown in Figure 1-9. You can search a command using the search field on the top of the **Application Menu**. To search a tool, enter the complete or partial name of the command in the search field; the possible tool list will be listed. If you click on a tool from the list, the corresponding command will get activated.

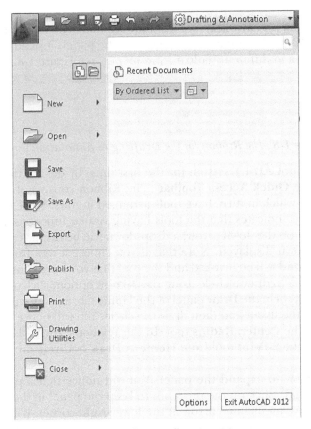

*Figure 1-9 The **Application Menu***

By default, the **Recent Document** button is chosen in the **Application Menu**. Therefore, the recently opened drawings will be listed. If you have opened multiple drawing files, choose the **Open Documents** button; the documents that are opened will be listed in the **Application Menu**. To set the preferences of the file, choose the **Options** button available at the bottom-right of the **Application Menu**. To exit AutoCAD LT, choose the **Exit** button next to the **Options** button.

Tool Palettes

AutoCAD LT has provided **Tool Palettes** as an easy and convenient way of placing and sharing hatch patterns and blocks in the current drawing. By default, the **Tool Palettes** are not displayed. Choose the **Tool Palettes** button from the **Palettes** panel in the **View** tab or choose the CTRL+3 keys to display the **Tool Palettes** as a window on the right of the drawing area. You can resize the **Tool Palettes** using the resizing cursor that is displayed when you place the cursor on the top or bottom extremity of the **Tool Palettes**. The **Tool Palettes** are discussed in detail in Chapter 13, *Hatching Drawings*.

Menu Bar

You can also select commands from the menu bar. Menu bar is not displayed by default. To display the menu bar, choose the down arrow in the **Quick Access Toolbar**; a flyout is displayed. Choose the **Show Menu Bar** option from it; the menu bar will be displayed. As you move the cursor over the menu bar, different titles are highlighted. You can choose the desired item by left-clicking on it; the corresponding menu is displayed directly under the title. You can invoke a command by left-clicking on a menu. Some of the menu items display an arrow on the right side, which indicates that they have a cascading menu. The cascading menu provides various options to execute the same AutoCAD LT command. You can display the cascading menu by choosing the menu item or by moving the arrow pointer to the right of that item. You can then choose any item from the cascading menu by highlighting the item or command and pressing the pick button of your pointing device. For example, to draw an ellipse using the **Center** option, choose the **Draw** menu and then choose the **Ellipse** option; a cascading menu will be displayed. From the cascading menu, choose the **Center** option. In this text, this command selection sequence will be referenced as choosing **Draw > Ellipse > Center** from the menu bar.

Toolbar

Toolbars are not displayed by default. To display a toolbar, choose the **View** tab in the **Ribbon** and click on **Toolbars** in the **Windows** panel; a flyout will be displayed. Move the cursor over the **AutoCAD LT** option; a list of toolbars will be displayed. Select the required toolbar. Alternatively, display the menu bar and then choose **Tools > Toolbars > AutoCAD LT** from it; a list of toolbars will be displayed. Select the required toolbar.

In a toolbar, the similar tools representing various AutoCAD LT commands are grouped together. When you move the cursor over the button of a toolbar, the button gets lifted and a three-dimensional (3D) box encloses it. The tooltip (name of the tool and related information) is also displayed below the tool. Once you have located the desired tool, left-click on it to invoke the corresponding command. For example, you can invoke the **LINE** command by choosing the **Line** tool from the **Draw** toolbar, see Figure 1-10.

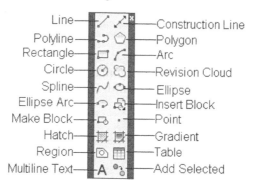

*Figure 1-10 The **Draw** toolbar*

Some of the tools in a toolbar have a small triangular arrow at the lower-right corner. This indicates that the tool has a flyout attached to it. If you press and hold the left mouse button on those tools, a flyout containing more tools will be displayed. Choose the required tool from this flyout.

Moving and Resizing Toolbars

Toolbars can be moved anywhere on the screen by placing the cursor on the strip and then dragging it to the desired location. You must hold the left mouse button down while dragging. While moving the toolbars, you can dock them to the top or sides of the screen by dropping them in the docking area. You may also prevent docking by holding the CTRL key when moving the toolbar to a desired location. You can also change the size of a toolbar by placing the cursor anywhere on the border of the toolbar where it takes the shape of a two sided arrow (Figure 1-11), and then pulling it in the desired direction (Figure 1-12). You can also customize toolbars to meet your requirements.

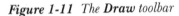

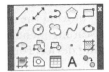

Figure 1-11 The **Draw** *toolbar*   *Figure 1-12* The **Draw** *toolbar reshaped*

Shortcut Menu

AutoCAD LT has provided shortcut menus as an easy and convenient way of invoking the recently used tools. These shortcut menus are context-sensitive, which means that the tools present in them are dependent on the place/object for which they are displayed. A shortcut menu is invoked by right-clicking and is displayed at the cursor location. You can right-click anywhere in the drawing area to display the general shortcut menu. It generally contains an option to select the previously invoked tool again, apart from the common tools for Windows, refer to Figure 1-13.

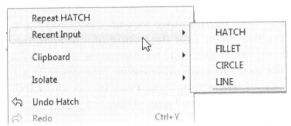

Figure 1-13 *Shortcut menu with the recently used commands*

If you right-click in the drawing area while a command is active, a shortcut menu is displayed, containing the options of that particular command. Figure 1-14 shows the shortcut menu which is displayed when the **Polyline** tool is active.

If you right-click on the **Layout** tab, a shortcut menu will be displayed, containing the options for layouts (Figure 1-15).

You can also right-click on the command window to display the shortcut menu. This menu displays the six most recently used commands and some of the window options like **Copy** and **Paste** (Figure 1-16). The commands and their prompt entries are displayed in the History window (previous command lines not visible) and can be selected, copied, and pasted in the command line using the shortcut menu. As you press the up arrow key, the previously entered commands are displayed in the command window. Once the desired command is displayed at the Command prompt, you can execute it by simply pressing the ENTER key. You can also copy and edit any previously invoked command by locating it in the History window and then selecting the lines.After selecting the desired command lines from the History window, right-click to display a shortcut menu. Choose Copy from the menu and then paste the selected lines at the end of the command line.

You can right-click on the coordinate display area of the Status Bar to display the shortcut menu. This menu contains the options to modify the display of coordinates, as shown in Figure 1-17. You can also right-click on any of the toolbars to display the shortcut menu from where you can choose any toolbar to be displayed.

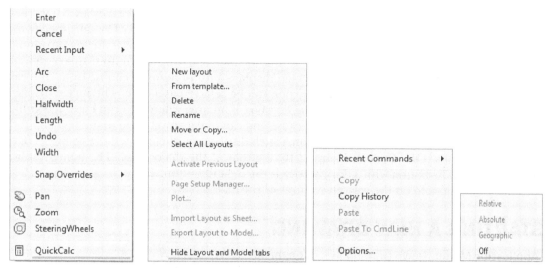

Figure 1-14 *Shortcut menu with the POLYLINE command active*

Figure 1-15 *Shortcut menu for the Layout tab*

Figure 1-16 *Command line window shortcut menu*

Figure 1-17 *The Status Bar shortcut menu*

AutoCAD LT DIALOG BOXES

There are certain commands, which when invoked, display a dialog box. A dialog box is a convenient method of interacting through user interface. When you choose an item in the menu bar with the ellipses [...], it displays the dialog box. For example, **Options** in the **Tools** menu displays the **Options** dialog box. A dialog box contains a number of parts like the dialog label, radio buttons, text or edit boxes, check boxes, slider bars, image boxes, and command buttons. These components are also referred to as tiles. Some of the components of a dialog box are shown in Figure 1-18.

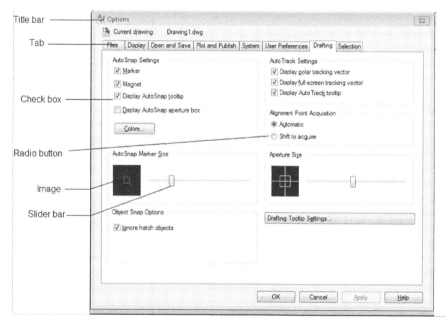

Figure 1-18 *Components of a dialog box*

You can select the desired tile using the pointing device, which is represented by an arrow when a dialog box is invoked. The titlebar displays the name of the dialog box. The tabs specify the various sections with a group of related options under them. The check boxes are toggle options for making the particular option available or unavailable. The drop-down list displays an item and an arrow on the right which when selected displays a list of items to choose from. You can make a selection in the radio buttons. Only one can be selected at a time. The image displays the preview image of the item selected. The text box is an area where you can enter a text like a file name. It is also called an edit box, because you can make any change to the text entered. In some dialog boxes, there is the [...] button, which displays another related dialog box. There are certain buttons (**OK**, **Cancel**, **Help**) at the bottom of the dialog box. The name implies their functions. The button with a dark border is the default button. The dialog box has a Help button for getting help on the various features of the dialog box.

STARTING A NEW DRAWING

Application Menu: New > Drawing	**Command:** NEW or QNEW
Quick Access Toolbar: New	**Menu Bar:** New > Drawing

You can open a new drawing using the **New** tool in the **Quick Access Toolbar**. When you invoke the **New** tool, by default AutoCAD LT will display the **Select a template file** dialog box, as shown in Figure 1-19. This dialog box displays a list of default templates available in AutoCAD LT 2012. The default template is *acadlt.dwt*, which starts the 2D drawing environment. Alternatively, you can select any other template to start a new drawing that will use the settings of the selected template. You can also open any drawing without using any template either in metric or imperial system. To do so, choose the down arrow on the right of the **Open** button and select the **Open with no Template-Metric** option or the **Open with no Template-Imperial** option from the flyout.

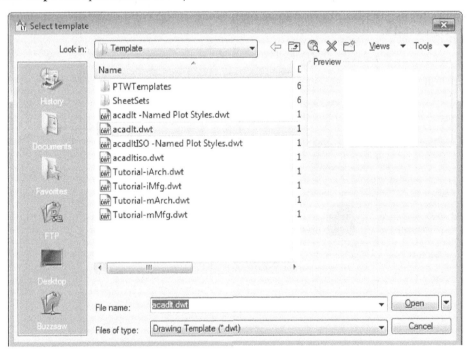

Figure 1-19 The Select a template file dialog box

You can also open a new drawing using the **Use a Wizard** and **Start from Scratch** options from the **Create New Drawing** dialog box. By default, this dialog box is not invoked. To invoke the **Create New Drawing** dialog box, enter **STARTUP** in the command window and then enter **1** as the new value for this system variable. After setting 1 as the new value for the system variable, whenever you invoke the **New** tool, the **Create New Drawing** dialog box will be displayed, as shown in Figure 1-20. The options in this dialog box are discussed next.

*Figure 1-20 The **Create New Drawing** dialog box*

Note
*If you have started a new AutoCAD LT session with the **STARTUP** variable set to 1, then the **Startup** dialog box is displayed instead of the **Create New Drawing** dialog box.*

Open a Drawing
By default, this option is not available for the **New** tool.

Start from Scratch
When you choose the **Start from Scratch** button (Figure 1-20), AutoCAD LT provides you with options to start a new drawing that contains the default AutoCAD LT setup for Imperial (*acadlt.dwt*) or Metric drawings (*acadltiso.dwt*). If you select the Imperial default setting, the limits are 12X9, text height is 0.20, and dimensions and linetype scale factors are 1.

Use a Template
When you choose the **Use a Template** button in the **Create New Drawing** dialog box, AutoCAD LT displays a list of templates, see Figure 1-21. The default template file is *acadlt.dwt* or *acadiso.dwt*, depending on the installation. You can directly start a new file in the 2D sketching environment by selecting the *acadlt.dwt* or *acadltiso.dwt* template. If you use a template file, the new drawing will have the same settings as specified in the template file. All the drawing parameters of the new drawing such as units, limits, and other settings are already set according to the template file used. The preview of the template file selected is displayed in the dialog box. You can also define your own template files that are customized to your requirements. To differentiate the template files from the drawing files, the template files have a *.dwt* extension whereas the drawing files have a *.dwg* extension. Any drawing file can be saved as a template file. You can use the **Browse** button to select other template files. When you choose the **Browse** button, the **Select a template file** dialog box is displayed with the **Template** folder open, displaying all the template files.

Use a Wizard
The **Use a Wizard** option allows you to set the initial drawing settings before actually starting a new drawing. When you choose the **Use a Wizard** button, AutoCAD LT provides you with the

option for using the **Quick Setup** or **Advanced Setup**, see Figure 1-22. In the **Quick Setup**, you can specify the units and the limits of the work area. In the **Advanced Setup**, you can set the units, limits, and the different types of settings for a drawing.

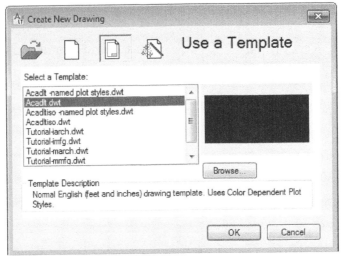

*Figure 1-21 The default templates that are displayed when you choose the **Use a Template** button*

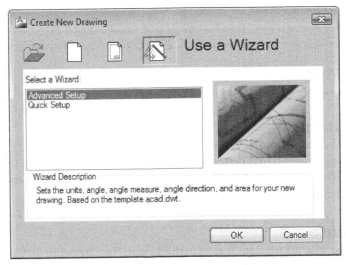

*Figure 1-22 The wizard options displayed when you choose the **Use a Wizard** button*

Advanced Setup

This option allows you to preselect the parameters of a new drawing such as the units of linear and angular measurements, type and direction of angular measurements, approximate area desired for the drawing, precision for displaying the units after decimal, and so on. When you select the **Advanced Setup** wizard option from the **Create New Drawing** dialog box and choose the **OK** button, the **Advanced Setup** wizard is displayed. The **Units** page is displayed by default, as shown in Figure 1-23.

This page is used to set the units for measurement in the current drawing. You can select the required unit of measurement by selecting the respective radio button. You will notice that the preview image is modified accordingly. The different units of measurement you can choose from are Decimal, Engineering, Architectural, Fractional, and Scientific. You can also set the precision for the measurement units by selecting it from the **Precision** drop-down list.

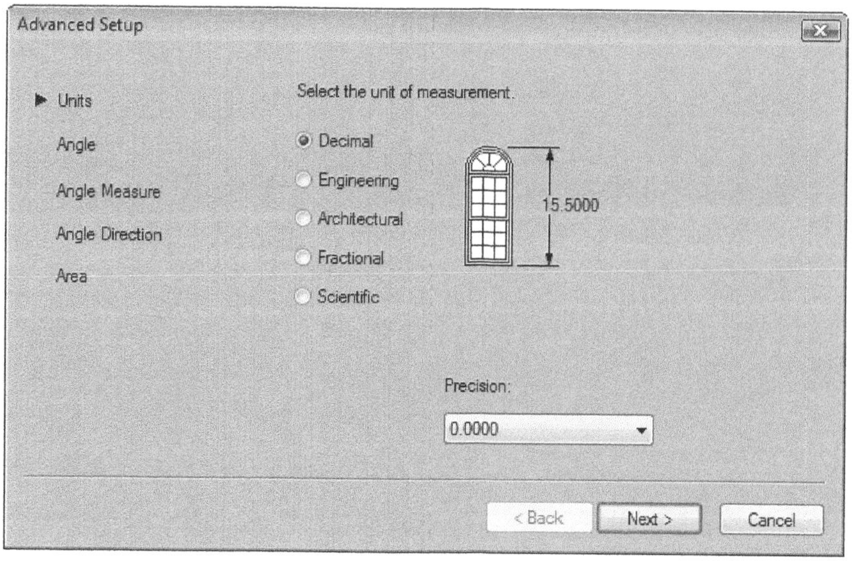

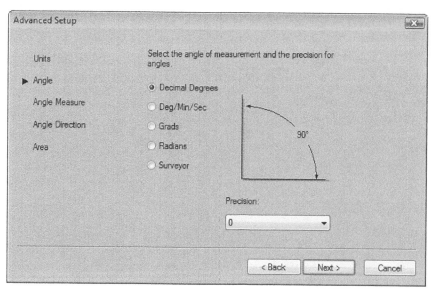

*Figure 1-23 The **Units** page of the **Advanced Setup** wizard*

Choose the **Next** button to open the **Angle** page, as shown in Figure 1-24. You will notice that an arrow appears on the left of **Angle** in the **Advanced Setup** wizard. This suggests that this page is current.

*Figure 1-24 The **Angle** page of the **Advanced Setup** wizard*

This page is used to set the units for angular measurements and its precision. The units for angle measurement are Decimal Degrees, Deg/Min/Sec, Grads, Radians, and Surveyor. The units for angle measurement can be set by selecting any one of these radio buttons as required. The preview of the selected angular unit is displayed on the right of the radio buttons. The precision format changes automatically in the **Precision** drop-down list depending on the angle measuring system selected. You can then select the precision from the drop-down list.

The next page is the **Angle Measure** page, as shown in Figure 1-25. This page is used to select the direction of the baseline from which the angles will be measured. You can also set your own direction by selecting the **Other** radio button and then entering the value in its edit box. This edit box is available when you select the **Other** radio button.

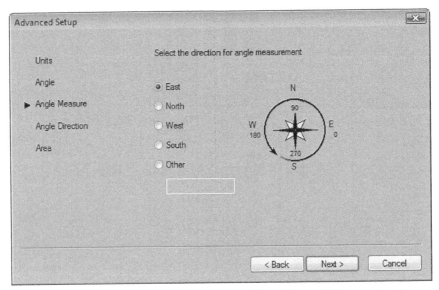

*Figure 1-25 The **Angle Measure** page of the **Advanced Setup** wizard*

Choose **Next** to display the **Angle Direction** page (Figure 1-26) to set the orientation for the angle measurement. By default the angles are positive, if measured in a counterclockwise direction. This is because the **Counter-Clockwise** radio button is selected. If you select the **Clockwise** radio button, the angles will be considered positive when measured in the clockwise direction.

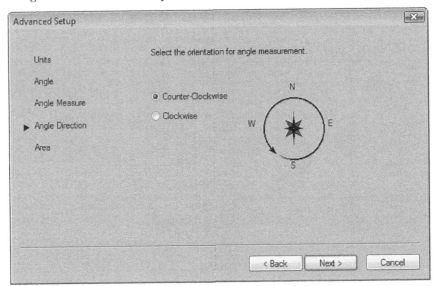

*Figure 1-26 The **Angle Direction** page of the **Advanced Setup** wizard*

To set the limits of the drawing, choose the **Next** button; the **Area** page will be displayed, as shown in Figure 1-27. You can enter the width and length of the drawing area in the respective edit boxes.

Note
*Even after you increase the limits of the drawing, the drawing display area is not increased. You need to invoke the **Zoom All** tool from the Navigation Bar to increase the drawing display area.*

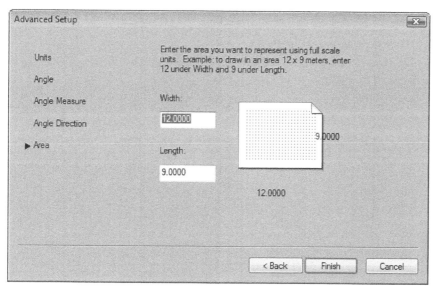

Figure 1-27 *The **Area** page of the **Advanced Setup** wizard*

Quick Setup

When you select the **Quick Setup** option and choose the **OK** button, the **QuickSetup** wizard is displayed. This wizard has two pages: **Units** and **Area**. The **Units** page is opened by default, as shown in Figure 1-28. The options in the **Units** page are similar to those in the **Units** page of the **Advanced Setup** wizard. The only difference is that you cannot set the precision for the units in this wizard.

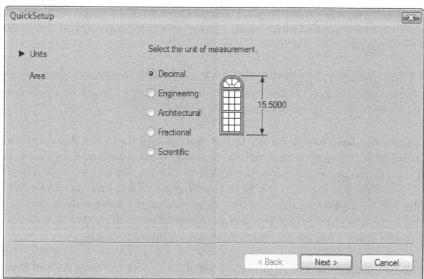

Figure 1-28 *The **Units** page of the **QuickSetup** wizard*

Choose **Next** to display the **Area** page, as shown in Figure 1-29. The **Area** page of the **QuickSetup** is similar to that of the **Advanced Setup** wizard. In this page, you can set the drawing limits.

Tip
*By default, when you open an AutoCAD LT session, a drawing opens automatically. But you can open a new drawing using options such as **Start from Scratch** and **Use a Wizard** before entering into AutoCAD LT environment using the **Startup** dialog box. As mentioned earlier, the display of the **Startup** dialog box is turned off by default. Refer to the section of **Starting a New Drawing** to know how to turn on the display of this dialog box.*

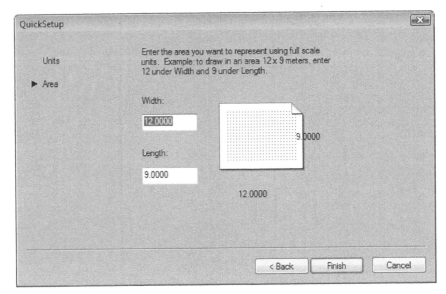

*Figure 1-29 The **Area** page of the **QuickSetup** wizard*

SAVING YOUR WORK

Application Menu: SAVEAS, SAVE	**Command:** QSAVE, SAVEAS, SAVE
Quick Access Toolbar: Save or Save As	**Menu Bar:** File > Save or Save As

You must save your work before you exit from the drawing editor or turn off your system. Also, it is recommended that you save your drawings after regular intervals, so that in the event of a power failure or an editing error, all works saved before the problem started will be retained.

AutoCAD LT has provided the **QSAVE**, **SAVEAS**, and **SAVE** commands that allow you to save your work. These commands allow you to save your drawing by writing it to a permanent storage device, such as a hard drive or in any removable drive.

When you choose the **Save** tool from the **Quick Access toolbar** or the **Application Menu**, the **QSAVE** command is invoked. If the current drawing is unnamed and you save the drawing for the first time in the present session, the **SAVEAS** command will be invoked and you will be prompted to enter the file name in the **Save Drawing As** dialog box, as shown in Figure 1-30. You can enter the name for the drawing and then choose the **Save** button. If you have saved a drawing file once and then edited it, you can use the **Save** tool to save it, without the system prompting you to enter a file name. This allows you to do a quick save.

When you choose **SaveAs** from the **Application Menu** or choose the **Save As** tool from the **Quick Access Toolbar**, the **Save Drawing As** dialog box will be displayed, similar to that shown in Figure 1-30. Even if the drawing has been saved with a file name, this tool gives you an option to save it with a different file name. In addition to saving the drawing, it sets the name of the current drawing to the file name you specify, which is displayed in the title bar. This tool is used when you want to save a previously saved drawing under a different file name. You can also use this tool when you make certain changes to a template and want to save the changed template drawing but leave the original template unchanged.

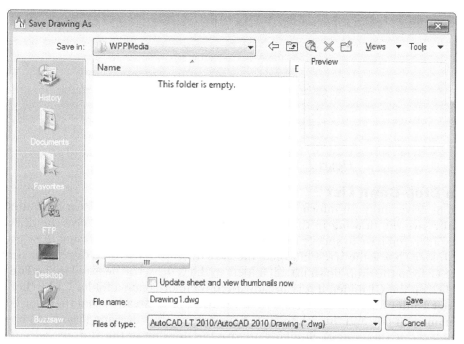

Figure 1-30 The Save Drawing As dialog box

Save Drawing As Dialog Box

The **Save Drawing As** dialog box displays the information related to the drawing files on your system. The various components of the dialog box are described next.

Places List

A column of icons is displayed on the left side of the dialog box. These icons contain the shortcuts to the folders that are frequently used. You can quickly save your drawings in one of these folders. The **History** folder displays the list of the most recently saved drawings. You can save your personal drawings in the **Documents** or the **Favorites** folder. The **FTP** folder displays the list of the various FTP sites that are available for saving the drawing. By default, no FTP sites are shown in the dialog box. To add a FTP site to the dialog box, choose the **Tools** button on the upper-right corner of the dialog box to display a shortcut menu and select **Add/Modify FTP Locations**. The **Desktop** folder displays the list of contents on the desktop. The **Buzzsaw** icons connect you to their respective pages on the Web. You can add a new folder in this list for an easy access by simply dragging the folder on to the **Places** list area. You can rearrange all these folders by dragging them and then placing them at the desired locations. It is also possible to remove the folders, which are not in frequent use. Right-click on the particular folder and then select **Remove** from the shortcut menu.

File name Edit Box

To save your work, enter the name of the drawing in the **File name** edit box by typing the file name or selecting it from the drop-down list. If you select the file name, it automatically appears in the **File name** edit box. If you have already assigned a name to the drawing, the current drawing name is taken as the default name. If the drawing is unnamed, the default name *Drawing1* is displayed in the **File Name** edit box. You can also choose the down arrow at the right of the edit box to display the names of the previously saved drawings and choose a name here.

Files of type Drop-Down List

The **Files of type** drop-down list (Figure 1-31) is used to specify the drawing format in which you want to save the file. For example, to save the file as an AutoCAD LT 2004 drawing file, select **AutoCAD 2004/LT 2004 Drawing (*.dwg)** from the drop-down list.

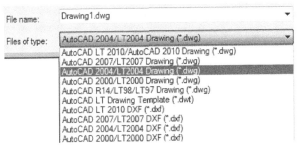

Figure 1-31 The Files of type drop-down list

Save in Drop-Down List

The current drive and path information is listed in the **Save in** drop-down list. AutoCAD LT will initially save the drawing in the default folder, but if you want to save the drawing in a different folder, you have to specify the path. For example, to save the present drawing as *house* in the *C1* folder, choose the arrow button in the **Save in** drop-down list to display the drop-down list. Select **C:** from the drop-down list; all folders in the C drive will be listed in the **File** list box. Double-click on the **C1** folder, if it is already listed there or create a folder C1 by choosing the **Create New Folder** button. Select *house* from the list, if it is already listed there, or enter it in the **File name** edit box and then choose the **Save** button. Your drawing (*house*) will be saved in the *C1* folder (*C:\C1\house.dwg*). Similarly, to save the drawing in the D drive, select **D:** in the **Save in** drop-down list.

Tip
The file name you enter to save a drawing should match its contents. This helps you to remember the drawing details and makes it easier to refer to them later. Also, the file name can be 255 characters long and can contain spaces and punctuation marks.

Using the Drawing Recovery Manager to Recover Files

The files that are saved automatically can also be retrieved by using the **Drawing Recovery Manager**. You can open the **Drawing Recovery Manager** again by choosing **Drawing Utilities > Open the Drawing Recovery Manager** from the **Application Menu** or by entering **DRAWINGRECOVERY** at the Command prompt.

If the automatic save operation is performed in a drawing and the system crashes accidentally, the next time you run AutoCAD LT, the **Drawing Recovery** message box will be displayed, as shown in Figure 1-32. The message box informs you that the program unexpectedly failed and you can open the most suitable among the backup files created by AutoCAD LT. Choose the **Close** button from the **Drawing Recovery** message box; the **Drawing Recovery Manager** is displayed on the left of the drawing area, as shown in Figure 1-33.

The **Backup Files** rollout lists the original files, the backup files, and the automatically saved files. Select a file; its preview will be displayed in the **Preview** rollout. Also, the information corresponding to the selected file will be displayed in the **Details** rollout. To open a backup file, double-click on its name in the **Backup Files** rollout. Alternatively, right-click on the file name and then choose **Open** from the shortcut menu. It is recommended that you save the backup file at the desired location before you start working on it.

CLOSING A DRAWING

You can use the **CLOSE** command to close the current drawing file without actually quitting AutoCAD LT. If you choose **Close > Current Drawing** from the **Application Menu** or enter **CLOSE** at the Command prompt, the current drawing file will be closed. If multiple drawing files are opened, choose **Close > All Drawings** from the **Application Menu**. If you have not saved the drawing after making the last changes to it and you invoke the **CLOSE** command, AutoCAD LT displays a dialog box that allows you to save the drawing before closing. This box gives you an option to discard the current drawing or the changes made to it. It also gives you an option to cancel the command. After closing the drawing, you are still in AutoCAD LT from where you can open a new or an already saved drawing file. You can also use the close button (**X**) of the drawing area to close the drawing.

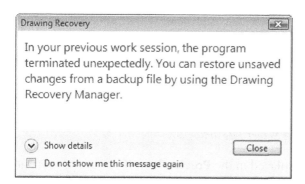

Figure 1-32 The **Drawing Recovery** *message box*

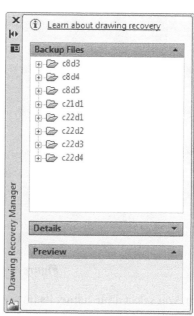

Figure 1-33 The **Drawing Recovery** *Manager*

Note
You can close a drawing even if a command is active.

OPENING AN EXISTING DRAWING

Application Menu: Open > Drawing	**Quick Access Toolbar:** Open
Menu Bar: File > Open	**Command:** OPEN

You can open an existing drawing file that has been saved previously. There are three methods that can be used to open a drawing file: by using the **Select File** dialog box, by using the **Create New Drawing** dialog box, and by dragging and dropping.

Opening an Existing Drawing Using the Select File Dialog Box

If you are already in the drawing editor and you want to open a drawing file, choose the **Open** tool from the **Quick Access Toolbar**; the **Select File** dialog box will be displayed. Alternatively, invoke the **OPEN** command to display the **Select File** dialog box, see Figure 1-34. You can select the drawing to be opened using this dialog box. This dialog box is similar to the standard dialog boxes. You can choose the file you want to open from the folder in which it is stored. You can change the folder from the **Look in** drop-down list. You can then select the name of the drawing from the list box or you can enter the name of the drawing file you want to open in the **File name** edit box. After selecting the drawing file, you can select the **Open** button to open the file. Here, you can choose *Drawing1* from the list and then choose the **Open** button to open the drawing.

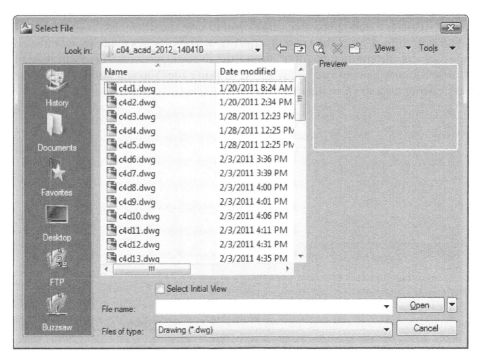

Figure 1-34 The **Select File** *dialog box*

When you select a file name, its image is displayed in the **Preview** box. If you are not sure about the file name of a particular drawing but know the contents, you can select the file names and look for the particular drawing in the **Preview** box. You can also change the file type by selecting it in the **Files of type** drop-down list. Apart from the *dwg* files, you can open the *dwt* (template) files or the *dxf* files. You have all the standard icons in the **Places** list that can be used to open drawing files from different locations. When you click on the down arrow at the right of the **Open** button, refer to Figure 1-35; a drop-down list is displayed. You can choose a method for opening the file using this drop-down list. These methods are discussed next.

Open Read-Only

To view a drawing without altering it, you must select the **Open Read-Only** option from the drop-down list. In other words, read only protects the drawing file from changes. AutoCAD LT does not prevent you from editing the drawing, but if you try to save the opened drawing with the original file name, AutoCAD LT warns you that the drawing file is write protected. However, you can save the edited drawing to a file with a different file name using the **SAVEAS** command. This way you can preserve your drawing.

Select Initial View

A view is defined as the way you look at an object. Select the **Select Initial View** check box if you want to load a specific view initially when AutoCAD LT loads the drawing. This option will work, if the drawing has saved views. This is generally used while working on a large complicated drawing, in which you want to work on a particular portion of the drawing. You can save that particular portion as a view and then select it to open the drawing next time. You can save a desired view, by using AutoCAD LT's **VIEW** command (see "**Creating Views**", Chapter 6). If the drawing has no saved views, selecting this option will load the last view. If you select the **Select Initial View** check box and then the **OK** button, AutoCAD LT will display the **Select Initial View** dialog box. You can select the view name from this dialog box, and AutoCAD LT will load the drawing with the selected view displayed.

Tip
*Apart from opening a drawing from the **Startup** dialog box or the **Select File** dialog box, you can also open a drawing from the **Application Menu**. By default, the **Recent Documents** option is chosen in the **Application Menu**, so the most recently opened drawings will be displayed and you can open the required file from it.*

It is possible to open an AutoCAD LT 2000 drawing in AutoCAD LT 2012. When you save this drawing, it is automatically converted and saved as an AutoCAD LT 2012 drawing file.

Opening an Existing Drawing Using the Startup Dialog Box

If you have configured the settings to show the **Startup** dialog box by setting the **STARTUP** system variable value as **1**, the **Startup** dialog box will be displayed every time you start a new AutoCAD LT session. The first button in this dialog box is the **Open a Drawing** button. When you choose this button, a list of the most recently opened drawings will be displayed for you to select from, see Figure 1-35. The **Browse** button displays the **Select File** dialog box, which allows you to browse to another file.

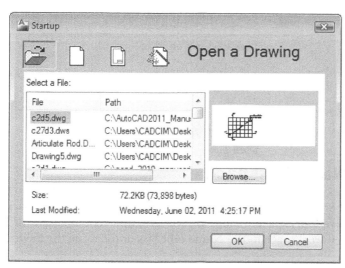

Figure 1-35 List of the recently opened drawings

Note
*The display of the dialog boxes related to opening and saving drawings will be disabled, if the **STARTUP** and the **FILEDIA** system variables are set to 0. The initial value of these variables is 1.*

Opening an Existing Drawing Using the Drag and Drop Method

You can also open an existing drawing in AutoCAD LT by dragging it from the Window Explorer and dropping it into AutoCAD LT. If you drop the selected drawing in the drawing area, the drawing will be inserted as a block and as a result you cannot modify it. But, if you drag the drawing from the Window Explorer and drop it anywhere other than the drawing area, AutoCAD LT opens the selected drawing.

QUITTING AutoCAD LT

You can exit the AutoCAD LT program by using the **EXIT** or **QUIT** command. Even if you have an active command, you can choose **Exit AutoCAD LT 2012** from the **Application Menu** to quit the AutoCAD LT program. In case the drawing has not been saved, it allows you to save the work first through a dialog box. Note that if you choose **No** in this dialog box, all the changes made in the current list till the last save will be lost. You can also use the close button (**X**) of the main AutoCAD LT window (present in the title bar) to end the AutoCAD LT session.

CREATING AND MANAGING WORKSPACES

A workspace is defined as a customized arrangement of **Ribbon**, toolbars, menus, and window palettes in the AutoCAD LT environment. You can create your own workspaces, in which only specified toolbars, menus, and palettes are available. When you start AutoCAD LT, by default, the **Drafting & Annotation** workspace is the current workspace. You can select any other predefined workspace from the **Workspace** drop-down list available in the title bar, next to the **Quick Access Toolbar**, see Figure 1-36. You can also set the workspace from the flyout that will be displayed on choosing the **Workspace Switching** button on the Status Bar or by choosing the required Workspace from the menu bar. You can also choose the workspace using the toolbar.

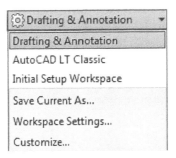

Figure 1-36   The predefined workspaces

Creating a New Workspace

To create a new workspace, customize the **Ribbon** and invoke the palettes to be displayed in the new workspace. Next, select the **Save Current As** option from the **Workspace** drop-down list in the titlebar; the **Save Workspace** dialog box will be displayed, as shown in Figure 1-37. Enter the name of the new workspace in the **Name** edit box and choose the **Save** button.

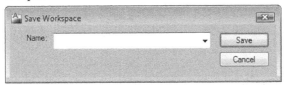

*Figure 1-37   The **Save Workspace** dialog box*

The new workspace is now the current workspace and is added to the drop-down list in the title bar. Likewise, you can create workspaces based on your requirement and switch from one workspace to the other by selecting the name from the drop-down list in the **Workspaces** toolbar or the drop-down list in the title bar.

Modifying the Workspace Settings

AutoCAD LT allows you to modify the workspace settings. To do so, select the **Workspace Settings** option in the **Workspace** drop-down list in the title bar; the **Workspace Settings** dialog box will be displayed, as shown in Figure 1-38. All workspaces are listed in the **My Workspace** drop-down list. You can make any of the workspaces as My Workspace by selecting it in the **My Workspace** drop-down list. You can also choose the **My Workspace** button from the **Workspaces** toolbar to change the current workspace to the one that was set as My Workspace in the **Workspace Settings** dialog box. The other options in this toolbar are discussed next.

Chapter 1

Menu Display and Order Area

The options in this area are used to control the display and the order of display of workspaces in the **Workspace** drop-down list. By default, workspaces are listed in the sequence of their creation. To change the order, select a workspace and choose the **Move Up** or **Move Down** button. To control the display of the workspaces, you can select or clear the check boxes. You can also add a separator between workspaces by choosing the **Add Separator** button. A separator is a line that is placed between two workspaces in the **Workspace** drop-down list in the title bar, as shown in Figure 1-39.

*Figure 1-38 The **Workspace Settings** dialog box*

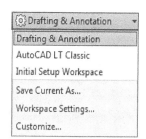

*Figure 1-39 The **Workspace** drop-down list after adding separators*

When Switching Workspaces Area

By default, the **Do not save changes to workspace** radio button is selected in this area. This ensures that while switching the workspaces, the changes made in the current workspace will not be saved. If you select the **Automatically save workspace changes** radio button, the changes made in the current workspace will be automatically saved when you switch to the other workspace.

AutoCAD LT'S HELP

Titlebar: ? > Help   **Shortcut Key:** F1   **Command:** HELP or ?

You can get the on-line help and documentation about the working of AutoCAD LT 2012 commands from the **Help** menu in the title bar, see Figure 1-40. You can also access the **Help** menu by pressing the F1 function key. An **InfoCenter** bar is displayed at the top right corner in the title bar that will help you sign into the Autodesk Online services, see Figure 1-41. You can also access AutoCAD LT community by using certain keywords. Some important options in the **Help** menu are discussed next.

*Figure 1-40 The **Help** menu*

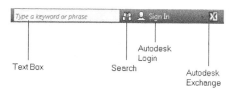

*Figure 1-41 The **InfoCenter** bar*

Customer Involvement Program

This option is used to share information about your system configuration and uses of Autodesk products with Autodesk. The collected information is used by Autodesk for the improvement of Autodesk software.

About

This option gives you information about the Release, Serial number, Licensed to, and also the legal description about AutoCAD LT.

Autodesk Exchange*

Autodesk Exchange enables you to learn the new features in AutoCAD LT 2012 through videos and text, get connected to the AutoCAD LT network, share information and designs, and so on. On choosing the **Exchange** button from the title bar, the **Autodesk Exchange** window will be displayed, as shown in Figure 1-42. In this window, there are two tabs, **Home** and **Help**. These tabs are discussed next.

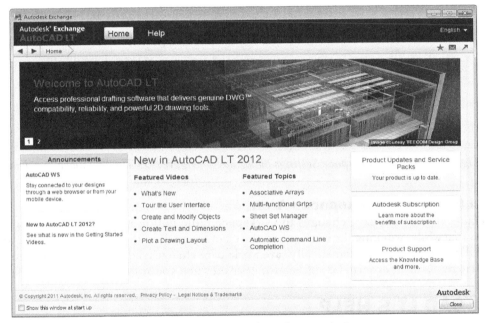

Figure 1-42 The Autodesk Exchange window

Home

This tab is chosen by default. Using this tab, you can overview the videos and topics on new features of AutoCAD LT 2012, tour the user interface, get connected to AutoCAD LT WS, and so on. The **Featured Videos** and **Featured Topics** areas are displayed in this tab, and these areas are discussed next.

Featured Videos

In the **Featured Videos** area, links to the videos showing the use of the new features of AutoCAD LT are displayed. When you choose **What's New** from the **Featured Videos** area, the video related to all latest enhancements starts playing in the **What's New** page, refer to Figure 1-43. In this window, a list of videos related to each latest enhancement is also displayed on the right. You can play any of these videos. Also, you can take a tour of the user interface of AutoCAD LT 2012 by clicking on the **Tour the User Interface** link. Note that when you click on any of the links in the **Home** tab, the **Help** tab is automatically activated.

*Figure 1-43 The **What's New** page*

Featured Topics

In the **Featured Topics** area, the text links are provided to explain new features of AutoCAD LT. There are five links available in this area. By using these links, you can find information about many important topics like **Associative Arrays**, **Multi-functional Grips**, **AutoCAD LT WS**, and so on.

Help

On choosing the **Help** tab in the **Autodesk Exchange** window, the **Browse Help** page will be displayed, as shown in Figure 1-44. The entire help documentation on AutoCAD LT 2012 is available in this page. You can search information about any command or tool on this page. As the feature is provided online, you cannot access this page without an active internet connection. If you press the F1 key while offline, an internet explorer window will be displayed with help topics, as shown in Figure 1-45. This window has all the information that is available in the online help window, except the videos and other internet-linked topics.

ADDITIONAL HELP RESOURCES

1. You can get help for a command while working by pressing the F1 key. The help html containing information about the command is displayed. You can exit the dialog box and continue with the command.

2. You can get help about a dialog box by choosing the **Help** button in that dialog box.

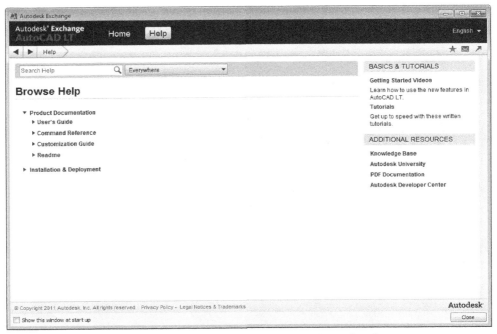

Figure 1-44 The **Browse Help** page in the **Help** tab

3. Autodesk has provided several resources that you can use to get assistance with your AutoCAD LT questions. The following is a list of some of the resources:

   a. Autodesk website *http://www.autodesk.com*
   b. AutoCAD LT Technical Assistance website *http://www.autodesk.com/support*
   c. AutoCAD LT Discussion Groups website *http://discussion.autodesk.com/index.jspa*

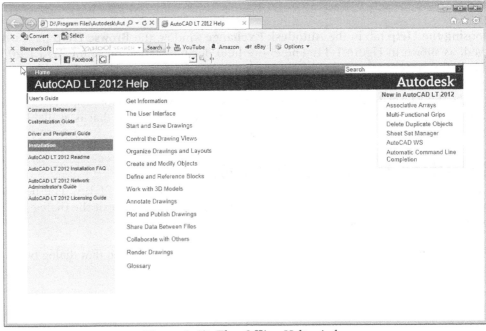

Figure 1-45 The *Offline Help window*

4. You can also get help by contacting the author, Prof. Sham Tickoo, at *stickoo@purduecal.edu* and *tickoo525@gmail.com*.

5. You can download AutoCAD LT drawings, programs, and special topics by registering yourself at the faculty's website by visiting: *http://cadcim.com/FacultyBooks_Page.aspx*

Self-Evaluation Test

Answer the following questions and then compare them to those given at the end of this chapter:

1. You can press the F3 key to display the **AutoCAD LT** text window, which displays the previous commands and prompts. (T/F)

2. If a drawing was partially opened and saved previously, it is not possible to open it again with the same layers and views. (T/F)

3. If the current drawing is unnamed and you save the drawing for the first time, the **Save** tool will prompt you to enter the file name in the **Save Drawing As** dialog box. (T/F)

4. The _____ displays a message and an alert whenever Autodesk provides the latest information regarding software updates and their other products.

5. If you want to work on a drawing without altering the original drawing, you must select the _____ option from the **Open** drop-down list in the **Select File** dialog box.

6. You can use the _____ command to close the current drawing file without actually quitting AutoCAD LT.

Review Questions

Answer the following questions:

1. The shortcut menu invoked by right-clicking in the command window displays the most recently used commands and some of the window options such as **Copy**, **Paste**, and so on. (T/F)

2. The file name that you enter to save a drawing in the **Save Drawing As** dialog box can be 255 characters long, but cannot contain spaces and punctuation marks. (T/F)

3. You can close a drawing in AutoCAD LT 2012 even if a command is active. (T/F)

4. Which one of the following combination of keys should be pressed to hide all toolbars displayed on the screen?

    (a) CTRL+3   (b) CTRL+0
    (c) CTRL+5   (d) CTRL+2

5. Which of the following commands is used to exit from the AutoCAD LT program?

    (a) **QUIT**   (b) **END**
    (c) **CLOSE**   (d) None of these

6. Which of the following options in the **Startup** dialog box is used to set the initial drawing settings before actually starting a new drawing?

    (a) **Start from Scratch**   (b) **Use a Template**
    (c) **Use a Wizard**   (d) None of these

7. When you choose **Save** from the **File** menu or choose the **Save** tool in the **Quick Access** toolbar, which of the following commands is invoked?

    (a) **SAVE**   (b) **LSAVE**
    (c) **QSAVE**   (d) **SAVEAS**

8. By default, the angles are positive if measured in the _____ direction.

9. You can change the size of toolbars by placing the cursor anywhere on the _____ of the toolbar where it takes the shape of a double-sided arrow.

10. To differentiate the template files from the drawing files, the template files have the _____ extension, whereas the drawing files have the _____ extension.

11. You can also use _____ and _____ instead of dragging and dropping the objects from one drawing to another while multiple drawings are opened.

Answers to Self-Evaluation Test

1. F, 2. F, 3. T, 4. Communication Center, 5. Open Read-Only, 6. CLOSE

Chapter 2

Getting Started with AutoCAD LT

CHAPTER OBJECTIVES

In this chapter, you will learn:
* *To draw lines by using the Line tool.*
* *About various coordinate systems used in AutoCAD LT.*
* *To clear the drawing area by using the Erase tool.*
* *About the two basic object selection methods: Window and Window Crossing.*
* *To draw circles by using various tools.*
* *To use the Zoom and Pan tools.*
* *To set up units by using the UNITS command.*
* *To set up and determine limits for a given drawing.*

KEY TERMS

* *Dynamic Input*
* *Line*
* *Coordinate Systems*
* *Absolute Coordinate System*

* *Relative Coordinate System*
* *Direct Distance Entry*
* *Erase*
* *Object Selection*

* *Circle*
* *Zoom*
* *Pan*
* *Units Format*
* *Options*

* *Plot*
* *Limits*

DYNAMIC INPUT MODE

In AutoCAD LT, the **Dynamic Input** mode allows you to enter the commands through the pointer input and the dimensions using the dimensional input. When this mode is turned on, all prompts are displayed at the tooltip as dynamic prompts and you can select the command options through the dynamic prompt. The settings for the **Dynamic Input** mode are done through the **Dynamic Input** tab of the **Drafting Settings** dialog box. To invoke the **Drafting Settings** dialog box, right-click on the **Dynamic Input** button in the Status Bar; a shortcut menu will be displayed. Choose the **Settings** option from the shortcut menu; the **Drafting Settings** dialog box will be displayed, as shown in Figure 2-1. The options in this tab are discussed next.

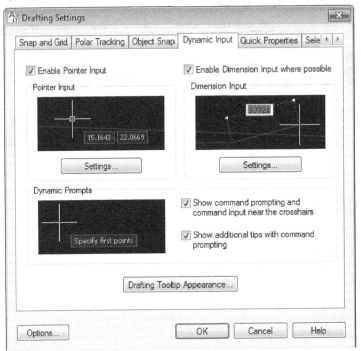

*Figure 2-1   The **Dynamic Input** tab of the **Drafting Settings** dialog box*

Enable Pointer Input

If the **Enable Pointer Input** check box selected, you can enter the commands through the pointer input. Figure 2-2 shows the **CIRCLE** command entered through the pointer input. If this check box is cleared, the **Dynamic Input** will be turned off and commands have to be entered through the Command prompt, in a way similar to the old releases of AutoCAD LT. With this release of AutoCAD LT, if you enter any alphabet at the **Dynamic Input**, all tools whose names start with the entered alphabet will be displayed in a list at the **Dynamic Input**, see Figure 2-2.

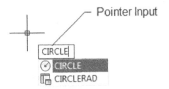

Figure 2-2 Entering a command using the pointer input

On choosing the **Settings** button from the **Pointer Input** area, the **Pointer Input Settings** dialog box is displayed as shown in Figure 2-3. The radio buttons in the **Format** area of this dialog box are used to set the default settings for specifying the other points, after specifying the first point. By default, the **Polar format** and **Relative coordinates** radio buttons are selected. As a result, the coordinates will be specified in the polar form and with respect to the relative coordinates system. You can select the **Cartesian format** radio button to enter the coordinates in cartesian form. Likewise, if you select the **Absolute coordinates** radio button, the numerical entries will be measured with respect to the absolute coordinate system.

The **Visibility** area in the **Pointer Input Settings** dialog box is used to set the visibility of the coordinates tool tips. By default, the **When a command asks for a point** radio button is selected. You can select the other radio buttons to modify this display.

Enable Dimension Input where possible

This check box is selected by default. As a result, the dimension input field is displayed in the graphics area showing the preview of that dimension. Figure 2-4 displays the dimension input fields. The options under the Dynamic prompt will be available when you press the down Arrow key from the keyboard. The dotted lines shows the geometric parameters like length, radius, or diameter corresponding to that dimension. Figure 2-4 shows a line being drawn using the **Pline** command. The two dimension inputs that are shown are for the length of the line and the angle with a positive direction of the X axis.

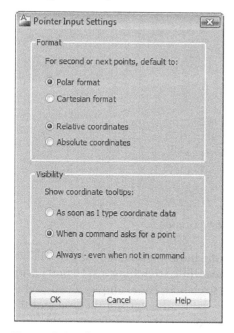

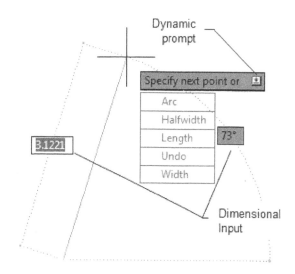

Figure 2-3 The *Pointer Input Settings* dialog box

Figure 2-4 Input fields displayed when the *Enable Dimension Input where possible* check box is selected

Using the TAB key, you can toggle between the dimension input fields. As soon as you have specified one dimension and moved to the other, the previous dimension will be locked. If the **Enable Dimensional Input where possible** check box is cleared, the preview of dimensions will not be displayed. You can only enter the dimensions in the dimension input fields below the cursor, as shown in Figure 2-5. Choose the **Settings** button from the **Dimension Input** area to display the **Dimension Input Settings** dialog box, as shown in Figure 2-6.

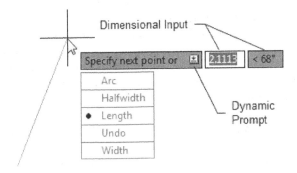

Figure 2-5 Input fields displayed when the
Enable Dimension Input where possible
check box is cleared

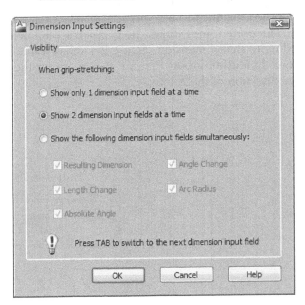

*Figure 2-6 The **Dimension Input Settings** dialog box*

By default, the **Show 2 dimension input fields at a time** radio button is selected. As a result, two dimension input fields will be displayed in the drawing area while stretching a sketched entity. The two input fields will depend on the entity that is being stretched. For example, if you stretch a line using one of its endpoints, the input field will show the total length of the line and the change in its length. Similarly, while stretching a circle using a grip on its circumference, the input fields will show the total radius and the change in the radius. You can set the priority to display only one input field or various input fields, simultaneously, by selecting their respective check boxes.

Tip
If multiple dimension input fields are available, use the TAB key to switch between the dimension input fields

Show command prompting and command input near the crosshairs

If this check box is selected, the prompt sequences will be dynamically displayed near the crosshairs. Whenever a blue arrow appears at the pointer input, it suggests that the access options are available. To access these options, press the down arrow key to see the dynamic prompt listing all options. In the dynamic prompt, you can use the cursor or the down arrow key to jog through the options. A black dot will appear before the option that is currently active. In Figure 2-5, the **Length** option is currently active. Press ENTER to confirm the polyline creation with the **Length** option.

Drafting Tooltip Appearance

When you choose the **Drafting Tooltip Appearance** button, the **Tooltip Appearance** dialog box will be displayed, as shown in Figure 2-7. This dialog box contains the options to customize the tooltip appearance. The **Colors** button is chosen to change the color of the tooltip in the model space or layouts.

The edit box in the **Size** area is used to specify the size of the tooltip. You can also use the slider to control the size of the tool tip. The preview is displayed in the **Model Preview** area and the **Layout Preview** area, as soon as the value is changed in the **Size** edit box. Likewise, the transparency of the tooltip can be controlled using the edit box or the slider in the **Transparency** area.

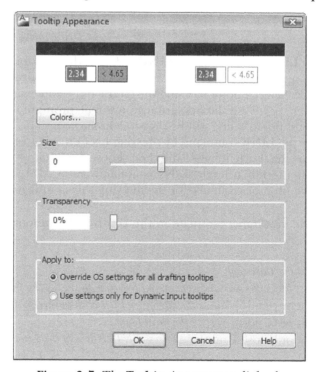

*Figure 2-7 The **Tooltip Appearance** dialog box*

Selecting the **Override OS settings for all drafting tooltips** radio button in the **Apply to** area ensures that changes made in the **Tooltip Appearance** dialog box will be applied to all drafting tooltips. If you select the **Use settings only for Dynamic Input tooltips** radio button, the changes will be applied only to the **Dynamic Input** tooltips. For example, if you change any of the parameters using the **Tooltip Appearance** dialog box and select the **Use settings only for Dynamic Input tooltips** radio button, the tooltips for the dynamic input will be modified, but for the polar tracking it will consider the original values. On the other hand, if you select the **Override OS settings for all drafting tooltips** radio button, the tooltips displayed for the polar tracking will also be modified based on the values in the **Tooltip Appearance** dialog box.

DRAWING LINES IN AutoCAD LT

Ribbon: Home > Draw > Line   **Toolbar:** Draw > Line   **Menu Bar:** Draw > Line
Tool Palettes: Draw > Line   **Command:** LINE or L

The most commonly used fundamental object in a drawing is line. In AutoCAD LT, a line is drawn between two points by using the **LINE** command. You can invoke the **LINE** command by choosing the **Line** tool from the **Draw** panel of the **Home** tab in the **Ribbon**, as shown in Figure 2-8. Besides this, you can choose the **Line** tool from the **Draw** tab of the **Tool Palettes**. To invoke the **Tool Palettes**, choose the **Tool Palettes** button from the **Palettes** panel in the **View** tab, as shown in Figure 2-9. Alternatively, you can invoke the **LINE** command by choosing the **Line** tool from the **Draw** toolbar, as shown in Figure 2-10. However, the **Draw** toolbar is not displayed by default. To invoke this toolbar, choose **View > Windows > Toolbars > AutoCAD LT** from the **Ribbon**.

*Figure 2-8 The **Line** tool in the **Draw** panel*

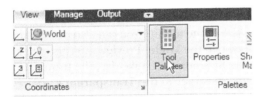

*Figure 2-9 Invoking the **Tool Palettes** from the **Palettes** panel.*

*Figure 2-10 The **Line** tool in the **Draw** toolbar*

You can also invoke the **Line** tool by entering **LINE** or **L** (L is the alias for the LINE command) at the Command prompt. On invoking the **Line** tool, you will be prompted to specify the starting point of the line. Select a point by using the mouse or by entering its coordinates at the command prompt. After specifying the first point, you will be prompted to specify the second point. Specify the second point; a line will be drawn. You may continue specifying points and draw lines or terminate the **LINE** command by pressing ENTER, ESC, or SPACEBAR. You can also right-click to display the shortcut menu and then choose the **Enter** or **Cancel** option from it to exit the **Line** tool. After terminating the **LINE** command, AutoCAD LT will again display the Command prompt. The prompt sequence for the drawing shown in Figure 2-11 is given next.

Start a new file with the *acadlt.dwt* template in the **Drafting & Annotation** or **AutoCAD LT Classic** workspace.

Command: *Choose the **Line** tool*
Specify first point: *Move the cursor (mouse) and left-click to specify the first point.*
Specify next point or [Undo]: *Move the cursor and left-click to specify the second point.*
Specify next point or [Undo]: *Specify the third point.*
Specify next point or [Close/Undo]: Enter *(Press ENTER to exit the **Line** tool.)*

Note
When you specify the start point of the line by pressing the left mouse button, a rubber band line stretches between the selected point and the current position of the cursor. This line is sensitive to the movement of the cursor and helps you select the direction and the placement of the next point for the line.

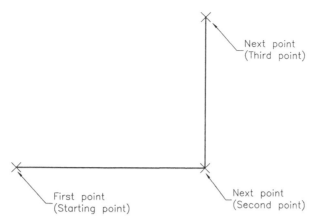

*Figure 2-11 Drawing lines using the **Line** tool*

Tip
*To clear the drawing area and draw new drawings, choose the **Erase** tool from the **Modify** panel in the **Home** tab or type **ERASE** at the Command prompt and press ENTER; the cross hairs will change into a box called pick box and you will be prompted to select objects. You can select an object by positioning the pick box on it and then by pressing the left mouse button. After selecting the objects, press ENTER to terminate the **ERASE** command; the selected objects will be erased. If you enter **All** at the **Select objects** prompt and press ENTER, all objects in the screen will be erased. You can use the **U (undo)** command to undo the last command. Alternatively, choose the **Undo** button from the **Quick Access Toolbar** to undo the last command. (See "Erasing Objects" discussed later in this chapter.)*

The **LINE** command has the following two options. They are discussed next.

Close   Undo

The Close Option

After drawing two continuous lines by using the **Line** tool, you will notice that the **Close** option is displayed at the Command prompt. The **Close** option is used to join the current point to the start point of the first line when two or more continuous lines are drawn. If you are specifying the endpoint by using the mouse, then click at the start point of the first line or enter **C** at the Command prompt, as given in the Command prompt below.

Command: *Choose the **Line** tool*
_line Specify first point: *Pick the first point.*
Specify next point or [Undo]: *Pick the second point.*
Specify next point or [Undo]: *Pick the third point.*
Specify next point or [Close/Undo]: *Pick the fourth point.*
Specify next point or [Close/Undo]: **C** Enter *(The fifth point joins with the first point). See Figure 2-12.*

You can also choose the **Close** option from the shortcut menu, which appears when you right-click in the drawing area.

Tip
*After exiting the **Line** tool, you may want to draw another line starting from the endpoint of the previous line. In such cases, press ENTER twice; a new line will start from the endpoint of the previous line. You can also type the @ symbol to start the line from the last point. For example, if you have drawn a circle and then immediately start the **Line** tool, the @ symbol will snap to the center point of the circle.*

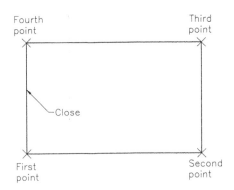

*Figure 2-12 Using the **Close** option with the **Line** tool*

The Undo Option

While drawing a line, if you have specified a wrong endpoint by mistake, then you can remove that line by using the **Undo** option of the **Line** tool. You can use this option multiple times and remove as many lines as you want. To use this option, type **Undo** (or just **U**) at the **Specify next point or [Undo]** prompt. You can also right-click to display the shortcut menu and then choose the **Undo** option from it.

Note
*By default, whenever you open a new drawing, you need to modify the drawing display area. To modify the display area, type **ZOOM** at the Command prompt and press ENTER. Then, type **ALL** and press ENTER; the drawing display is modified. You will learn more about the **ZOOM** command later in this chapter.*

INVOKING TOOLS USING DYNAMIC INPUT/COMMAND PROMPT

With this release of AutoCAD LT, if you enter any alphabet at the Command prompt or **Dynamic Input**, all tools whose names start with the entered alphabet will be displayed in a list at the Command prompt or **Dynamic Input**. For example, if you enter **L** at the Command prompt or **Dynamic Input**, all tools whose names start with the alphabet L will be displayed, refer to Figure 2-13. In this way, you can view all the tool names starting with a particular alphabet and select the required tool. In Figure 2-13, you can select the **Line** option, the **Layer** option, and so on.

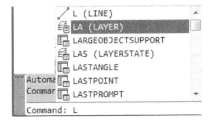

Figure 2-13 List displayed after typing L at the Command prompt

COORDINATE SYSTEMS

In AutoCAD LT, the location of a point is specified in terms of Cartesian coordinates. In this system, each point in a plane is specified by a pair of numerical coordinates. To specify a point in a plane, take two mutually perpendicular lines as references. The horizontal line is called the *X* axis, and the vertical line is called the *Y* axis. The *X* and *Y* axes divide the *XY* plane into four parts, generally known as quadrants. The point of intersection of these two axes is called the origin and the plane is called the XY plane. The origin has the coordinate values of X = 0, Y = 0. The origin is taken as the reference for locating a point on the *XY* plane. Now, to locate a point, say P, draw a vertical line intersecting the X axis. The horizontal distance between the origin and the intersection point will be called the X coordinate of P. It will be denoted as P(x). The *X* coordinate specifies how far the point is to the left or right from the origin along the *X* axis. Now, draw a horizontal line intersecting the Y axis. The vertical distance between the origin and the intersection point will be the Y coordinate of P. It will be denoted as P(y). The Y coordinate specifies how far the point is to the top or bottom from the origin along the Y axis. The intersection point of the horizontal and vertical lines is the coordinate of the point and is denoted as P(x,y). The X coordinate is positive, if measured to the right of the origin and is negative, if measured to the left of the origin. The Y coordinate is positive, if measured above the origin and is negative, if measured below the origin, see Figure 2-14.

In AutoCAD LT, the default origin is located at the lower left corner of the drawing area. AutoCAD LT uses the following coordinate systems to locate a point in an XY plane.

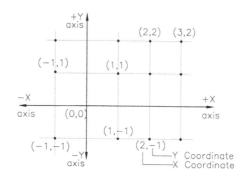

Figure 2-14 Cartesian coordinate system

1. Absolute coordinates
2. Relative coordinates
      a. Relative rectangular coordinates
      b. Relative polar coordinates
3. Direct distance entry

If you are specifying a point by entering its location at the Command prompt then you need to use any one of the coordinate systems.

Absolute Coordinate System

In the absolute coordinate system, points are located with respect to the origin (0,0). For example, a point with X = 4 and Y = 3 is measured 4 units horizontally (distance along the X axis) and 3 units vertically (distance along the Y axis) from the origin, as shown in Figure 2-15. In AutoCAD LT, the absolute coordinates are specified at the Command prompt by entering X and Y coordinates, separated by a comma. However, remember that if you are specifying the coordinates by using the **Dynamic Input** mode, you need to add # as the prefix to the X coordinate value. For example, enter #1,1 in the dynamic input boxes to use the absolute coordinate system. The following example illustrates the use of absolute coordinates at the Command prompt to draw the rectangle shown in Figure 2-16.

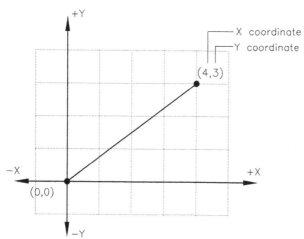

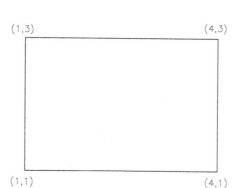

Figure 2-15 Absolute coordinate system

Figure 2-16 Lines created by using absolute coordinates

Command: *Choose the **Line** tool (Ensure that the **Dynamic Input** button is not chosen)*
_line Specify first point: **1,1** `Enter`   *(X = 1 and Y = 1.)*
Specify next point or [Undo]: **4,1** `Enter`   *(X = 4 and Y = 1.)*
Specify next point or [Undo]: **4,3** `Enter`
Specify next point or [Close /Undo]: **1,3** `Enter`
Specify next point or [Close/Undo]: **C** `Enter`

EXAMPLE 1   *Absolute Coordinate System*

Draw the profile shown in Figure 2-17 by using the Absolute Coordinate system. The absolute coordinates of the points are given in the following table. Save the drawing with the name *Exam1.dwg*.

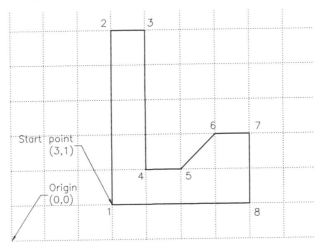

Figure 2-17 *Profile to be drawn using the absolute coordinates*

Point	Coordinates	Point	Coordinates
1	3,1	5	5,2
2	3,6	6	6,3
3	4,6	7	7,3
4	4,2	8	7,1

Start a new file with the *acadlt.dwt* template in the **Drafting & Annotation** or **AutoCAD LT Classic** workspace. Once you know the coordinates of the points, you can draw the sketch by using the **Line** tool. But, before you proceed with drawing the object, you need to turn off the **Dynamic Input** mode, if it is on by default. By doing so, you will be able to enter the command in the Command prompt. The prompt sequence is given next.

Choose the **Dynamic Input** button from the Status Bar, if it has been already chosen.

Command: ***ZOOM*** `Enter`
Specify corner of window, enter a scale factor (nX or nXP), or [All/Center/Dynamic/ Extents/Previous/Scale/Window/Object] <real time>: **ALL** `Enter`
Command: *Choose the **Line** tool* `Enter`
_ Specify first point: **3,1** `Enter`   *(Start point.)*

Specify next point or [Undo]: **3,6** [Enter]
Specify next point or [Undo]: **4,6** [Enter]
Specify next point or [Close/Undo]: **4,2** [Enter]
Specify next point or [Close/Undo]: **5,2** [Enter]
Specify next point or [Close/Undo]: **6,3** [Enter]
Specify next point or [Close/Undo]: **7,3** [Enter]
Specify next point or [Close/Undo]: **7,1** [Enter]
Specify next point or [Close/Undo]: **C** [Enter]

Choose the **Save** tool from the **Quick Access Toolbar** to display the **Save Drawing As** dialog box. Enter **Exam1** in the **File name** edit box and then choose the **Save** tool. The drawing will be saved with the specified name in the default *Documents* folder.

EXERCISE 1   *Absolute Coordinate System*

Draw the profile shown in Figure 2-18. The distance between the dotted lines is 1 unit. Enter the absolute coordinates of the points given in the following table. Then, use these coordinates to draw the same figure.

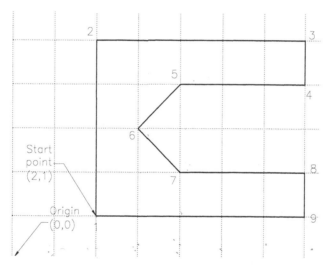

Figure 2-18 *Drawing for Exercise 1*

Point	Coordinates	Point	Coordinates
1	2, 1	6	3, 3
2	2,5	7	4,2
3	7,5	8	7,2
4	7,4	9	7,1
5	4,4		

Relative Coordinate System

There are two types of relative coordinates: relative rectangular and relative polar.

Relative Rectangular Coordinates

In the relative rectangular coordinate system, the location of a point is specified with respect to the previous point and not with respect to the origin. To enter coordinate values in terms of the Relative Rectangular Coordinate system, check whether the **Dynamic Input** is on or not. If the **Dynamic Input** is turned on, then by default the profile will be drawn using the Relative Rectangular Coordinate system. Therefore, in this case, enter the X coordinate, type comma (,), and then enter the Y coordinate. However, if the **Dynamic Input** is turned off, the coordinate values have to be prefixed by the @ symbol, so that the profile will be drawn using the Relative Rectangular Coordinate system. For example, to draw a rectangle (see Figure 2-19) of length 4 units and width 3 units and the lower left corner at the point (1,1) using the Relative Rectangular Coordinate system, you need to use the following prompt sequence:

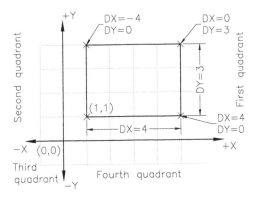

Figure 2-19 *Drawing lines using the relative rectangular coordinates*

Command: *Choose the* **Line** *tool*
_line Specify first point: **1,1** [Enter]   *(Start point)*
Specify next point or [Undo]: **@4,0** [Enter]
Specify next point or [Undo]: **@0,3** [Enter]
Specify next point or [Close/Undo]: **@-4,0** [Enter]
Specify next point or [Close/Undo]: **@0,-3** [Enter]
Specify next point or [Close/Undo]: [Enter]

Remember that if the **Dynamic Input** is on, you need to use a comma (,) after entering the first value in the Dynamic Input boxes. Else, AutoCAD LT will take coordinates in relative polar form.

Sign Convention. As just mentioned, in the relative rectangular coordinate system, the distance along the X and Y axes is measured with respect to the previous point. To understand the sign convention, imagine a horizontal line and a vertical line passing through the previous point so that you get four quadrants. If the new point is located in the first quadrant, then both the distances (DX and DY) will be specified as positive values. If the new point is located in the third quadrant, then both the distances (DX and DY) will be specified as negative values. In other words, the point will have a positive coordinate values, if it is located above or right of an axis. Similarly, the point will have a negative coordinate values, if it is located below or left of an axis.

EXAMPLE 2   *Relative Rectangular Coordinates*

Draw the profile shown in Figure 2-20 using relative rectangular coordinates. The coordinates of the points are given in the table below.

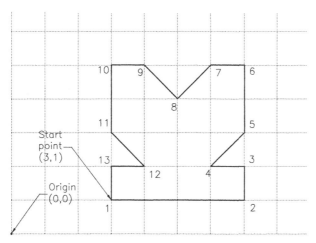

Figure 2-20 *Profile for Example 2*

Point	Coordinates	Point	Coordinates
1	3,1	8	@-1,-1
2	@4,0	9	@-1,1
3	@0,1	10	@-1,0
4	@-1,0	11	@0,-2
5	@1,1	12	@1,-1
6	@0,2	13	@-1,0
7	@-1,0	14	@0,-1

Start a new file with the *acadlt.dwt* template in the **Drafting & Annotation** or **AutoCAD LT Classic** workspace. Before you proceed, you need to make sure that the **Dynamic Input** is turned on.

Command: ***ZOOM*** Enter
Specify corner of window, enter a scale factor (nX or nXP), or
[All/Center/Dynamic/Extents/Previous/Scale/Window/Object] <real time>: **ALL** Enter
Command: *Choose the* **Line** *tool*
_line Specify first point: *Type* **3,1** *in the dynamic input boxes and press* Enter *(Start point)*
Specify next point or [Undo]: *Type* **4,0** *in the dynamic input boxes and press* Enter
Specify next point or [Undo]: *Type* **0,1** *in the dynamic input boxes and press* Enter
Specify next point or [Close/Undo]: *Type* **-1,0** *in the dynamic input boxes and press* Enter
Specify next point or [Close/Undo]: *Type* **1,1** *in the dynamic input boxes and press* Enter
Specify next point or [Close/Undo]: *Type* **0,2** *in the dynamic input boxes and press* Enter
Specify next point or [Close/Undo]: **-1,0** *and press* Enter
Specify next point or [Close/Undo]: **-1,-1** *and press* Enter

Specify next point or [Close/Undo]: **-1,1** *and press* [Enter]
Specify next point or [Close/Undo]: **-1,0** *and press* [Enter]
Specify next point or [Close/Undo]: **0,-2** *and press* [Enter]
Specify next point or [Close/Undo]: **1,-1** *and press* [Enter]
Specify next point or [Close/Undo]: **-1,0** *and press* [Enter]
Specify next point or [Close/Undo]: **0,-1** *and press* [Enter]
Specify next point or [Close/Undo]: [Enter]

EXERCISE 2   *Absolute Coordinates*

For Figure 2-21, enter the relative rectangular coordinates of the points given in the following table. Then, use these coordinates to draw the figure. The distance between the dotted lines is 1 unit.

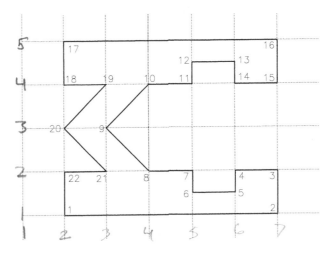

Figure 2-21 Drawing for Exercise 2

Point	Coordinates	Point	Coordinates
1	2, 1	12	5, 4.5
2	(7,1)	13	6, 4.5
3	7,2	14	6, 4
4	6,2	15	7, 4
5	6, 1.5	16	7, 5
6	5, 1.5	17	2, 5
7	5, 2	18	2, 4
8	4, 2	19	3, 4
9	3, 3	20	2, 3
10	4, 4	21	3, 2
11	5, 4	22	2, 2

Relative Polar Coordinates

In the relative polar coordinate system, the location of a point is specified by defining the distance of the point from the current point and the angle between the two points with respect to the positive *X* axis. The prompt sequence to draw a line of length 5 units whose start point is at 1,1 and inclined at an angle of 30 degrees to the *X* axis, as shown in Figure 2-22, is given next.

Command: *Choose the **Line** tool*
Specify first point: **1,1** Enter
Specify next point or [Undo]: **@5<30** Enter

If the **Dynamic Input** is on, by default the relative polar coordinate mode will be activated. Therefore, when you invoke the **Line** tool and specify the start point, two input boxes will be displayed. The second input box shows the angle value, preceded by the **<** symbol. Now, enter the distance value, press the TAB key to shift to the second input box, and then enter the angle value.

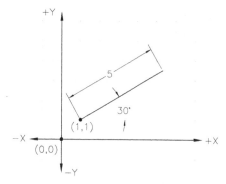

Figure 2-22 *Drawing a line by using relative polar coordinates*

Sign Convention. By default, in the relative polar coordinate system, the angle is measured from the horizontal axis as the zero degree. Also, the angle is positive, if measured in counterclockwise direction and is negative, if measured in clockwise direction. Here, it is assumed that the default setup of the angle measurement has not been changed.

Note
*You can modify the default settings of the angle measurement direction by using the **UNITS** command, which is discussed later.*

EXAMPLE 3   *Relative Polar Coordinates*

Draw the profile shown in Figure 2-23 by using the relative polar coordinates. The relative coordinate values of each point are given in the table below. The start point is located at 1.5, 1.75. Save this drawing with the name *Exam3.dwg*. The dimensions and the numbering are for reference only.

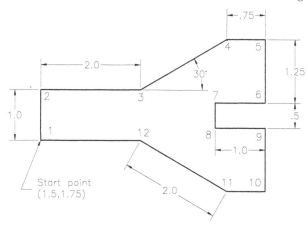

Figure 2-23 *Drawing for Example 3*

Point	Coordinates	Point	Coordinates
1	1.5,1.75	7	@1.0<180
2	@1.0<90	8	@0.5<270
3	@2.0<0	9	@1.0<0
4	@2.0<30	10	@1.25<270
5	@0.75<0	11	@0.75<180
6	@1.25<-90 (or <270)	12	@2.0<150

Start a new file with the *acadlt.dwt* template in the **Drafting & Annotation** or **AutoCAD LT Classic** workspace. Next, you need to modify the drawing display area. To do so, choose the **Zoom Extents** tool from the Navigation bar. Next, turn off the **Dynamic Input** option by choosing the **Dynamic Input** button from the Status Bar.

> Command: *Choose the **Line** tool*
> _line Specify first point: **1.5,1.75** [Enter]   *(Start point)*
> Specify next point or [Undo]: **@1<90** [Enter]
> Specify next point or [Undo]: **@2.0<0** [Enter]
> Specify next point or [Close/Undo]: **@2<30** [Enter]
> Specify next point or [Close/Undo]: **@0.75<0** [Enter]
> Specify next point or [Close/Undo]: **@1.25<-90** [Enter]
> Specify next point or [Close/Undo]: **@1.0<180** [Enter]
> Specify next point or [Close/Undo]: **@0.5<270** [Enter]
> Specify next point or [Close/Undo]: **@1.0<0** [Enter]
> Specify next point or [Close/Undo]: **@1.25<270** [Enter]
> Specify next point or [Close/Undo]: **@0.75<180** [Enter]
> Specify next point or [Close/Undo]: **@2.0<150** [Enter]
> Specify next point or [Close/Undo]: **C** [Enter] *(The last point joins with the first point.)*

To save this drawing, choose the **Save** tool from the **Quick Access Toolbar**; the **Save Drawing As** dialog box will be displayed. Enter **Exam3** in the **File name** edit box and then choose the **Save** tool; the drawing will be saved with the specified name in the **My Documents** folder.

EXERCISE 3

Draw the profile shown in Figure 2-24 by specifying points using the absolute, relative rectangular, and relative polar coordinate systems. Do not dimension the profile. They are given for reference only.

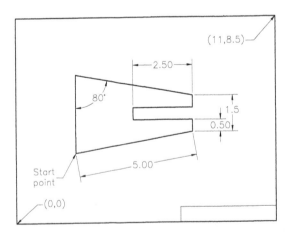

Figure 2-24 Drawing for Exercise 3

Direct Distance Entry

The easiest way to draw a line in AutoCAD LT is by using the Direct Distance Entry method. Before drawing a line by using this method, ensure that the **Dynamic Input** button is chosen in the Status Bar. Next, choose the **Line** tool; you will be prompted to specify the start point. Enter the coordinate values in the text box and press ENTER; you will be prompted to specify the next point. Now, enter the absolute length of the line and its angle with respect to the current position of the cursor in the corresponding text boxes, as shown in Figure 2-25. Note that you can use the TAB key to toggle between the text boxes. If the **Ortho** mode is on while drawing lines using this method, you can position the cursor only along the *X* or *Y* axis. If the **Dynamic Input** button is not chosen, then you need to enter the length of the line at the Command prompt. Therefore, position the cursor at the desired angle, type the length at the Command prompt, and then press ENTER, as shown in Figure 2-25.

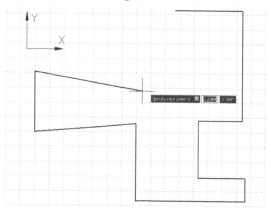

Figure 2-25 *Drawing lines using the Direct Distance Entry method*

Command: *Choose the **Line** tool*
_line Specify first point: *Start point.*
Specify next point or [Undo]: *Position the cursor and then enter distance.*
Specify next point or [Undo]: *Position the cursor and then enter distance.*

EXAMPLE 4   *Direct Distance Entry*

In this example, you will draw the profile shown in Figure 2-26, by using the Direct Distance Entry method. The start point is 2,2.

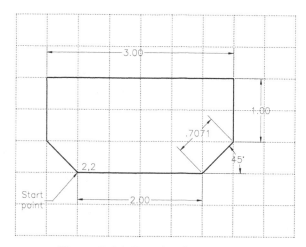

Figure 2-26 *Drawing for Example 4*

Also, you will use the polar tracking option to draw lines. The polar tracking option allows you to track the lines that are drawn at specified angles. The default angle specified for polar tracking is 90 degrees. Therefore, by default, you can track lines at an angle that is multiple of 90 degrees, such as 90, 180, 270, and 360. In this example, you need to draw lines at the angles that are multiples of 45 degrees such as 45, 90, 135, and so on. Therefore, first you need to set the polar tracking angle as 45 degrees.

Note
You will learn more about polar tracking in Chapter 4, Working with Drawing Aids.

1. Start a new file with the *acadlt.dwt* template in the **Drafting & Annotation** or **AutoCAD LT Classic** workspace.

2. To add a 45-degree angle to polar tracking, right-click on the **Polar Tracking** button on the Status Bar and then choose **45** from the shortcut menu. Again, choose the **Polar Tracking** button in the Status Bar to turn the polar tracking on.

3. Choose the **Line** tool from the **Draw** panel of the **Home** tab; you are prompted to specify the start point.

4. Enter **2,1** at the Command prompt and press ENTER; you are prompted to specify the next point.

5. Move the cursor horizontally toward the right and when the tooltip displays 0 as polar angle, type **2** and press ENTER; you are prompted to specify the next point.

6. Move the cursor at an angle close to 45 degrees and when the tooltip displays 45 as polar angle, type **0.7071** and press ENTER; you are prompted to specify the next point.

7. Move the cursor vertically upward and when the tooltip displays 90 as polar angle, type **1** and press ENTER; you are prompted to specify the next point.

8. Move the cursor horizontally toward the left and when the tooltip displays 180 as polar angle, type **3** and press ENTER; you are prompted to specify the next point.

9. Move the cursor vertically downward and when the tooltip displays 90 polar angle, type **1** and press ENTER; you are prompted to specify the next point.

10. Type **C** and press ENTER.

Tip
*To add angular values other than those displayed in the shortcut menu of polar tracking, choose **Settings** from the shortcut menu. Next, select the **Additional angles** check box in the **Polar Angle Settings** area and choose the **New** button. Enter a new value in the field that appears and then press ENTER. Choose **OK** to close the dialog box.*

EXERCISE 4 — *Direct Distance Entry*

Use the Direct Distance Entry method to draw a parallelogram. The base of the parallelogram equals 4 units, the side equals 2.25 units, and the angle equals 45-degree. Draw the same parallelogram using the absolute, relative, and polar coordinates. Note the differences and the advantages of using this method over relative and absolute coordinate methods.

ERASING OBJECTS

Ribbon: Home > Modify > Erase   **Toolbar:** Modify > Erase
Menu Bar: Modify > Erase   **Tool Palettes:** Modify > Erase
Command: ERASE or E

Sometimes, you may need to erase the unwanted objects from the objects drawn. You can do so by using the **Erase** tool. This tool is used exactly the same way as an eraser is used in manual drafting to delete the unwanted lines. To erase an object, choose the **Erase** tool from the **Modify** panel, see Figure 2-27. You can also choose the **Erase** button from the **Modify** toolbar, as shown in Figure 2-28. To invoke the **Modify** toolbar, choose **View > Windows > Toolbars > AutoCAD LT > Modify** from the **Ribbon**. On invoking the **Erase** tool, a small box, known as pick box, replaces the screen cursor. To erase the object, select it by using the pick box (see Figure 2-29); the selected object will be displayed in dashed lines and the **Select objects** prompt will be displayed again. You can either continue selecting the objects or press ENTER to terminate the object selection process and erase the selected objects. The prompt sequence is given next.

*Figure 2-27 The **Erase** tool in the **Modify** panel*

*Figure 2-28 The **Erase** tool in the **Modify** toolbar*

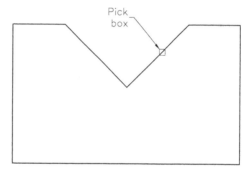

Figure 2-29 Selecting the object by positioning the pick box at the top of the object

Command: *Choose the **Erase** tool*
Select objects: *Select the first object.*
Select objects: *Select the second object.*
Select objects:

If you enter **ALL** at the **Select objects** prompt, all objects in the drawing area will be selected, even if they are outside the display area. Now, if you press ENTER, all the selected objects will be erased.

To erase objects, you can also first select the objects to be erased from the drawing and then choose the **Erase** option from this shortcut menu that is displayed on right-click in the drawing area.

CANCELING AND UNDOING A COMMAND

If you have erased an object by mistake, then to restore the erased object, enter the **OOPS** or **UNDO** command. The **OOPS** command is used to restore the objects erased by the previous **ERASE** command. The **U** (Undo) command is used to undo the action of the previously performed command.

To cancel or exit a command, press the ESC (Escape) key on the keyboard.

Chapter 2

OBJECT SELECTION METHODS

The usual method to select objects is by selecting them individually. But it will be time-consuming, if you have a number of objects to select. This problem can be solved by creating a selection set that enables you to select several objects at a time. The selection set options can be used with those tools that require object selection, such as **Erase** and **Move**. There are many object selection methods, such as **Last**, **Add**, **Window**, **Crossing**, and so on. In this chapter, you will learn two methods: **Window** and **Crossing**.

Window Selection

The window selection is one of the selection methods in which an object or group of objects are selected by drawing a window. The objects that are completely enclosed within the window are selected and the objects that lie partially inside the boundaries of the window are not selected. To select the objects by using the **Window** option after invoking a tool, type **W** at the **Select objects** prompt and press ENTER; you will prompted to specify the first corner of the window. Select the first corner and then move the cursor to specify the opposite corner. As you move the cursor, a blue color window of continuous line will be displayed. The size of this window changes as you move the cursor. Specify the opposite corner of the window; the objects that are enclosed in this window are displayed as dashed objects. Figure 2-30 shows the window drawn to select objects by using the **Window** option. The objects that will be selected are shown in dashed lines.

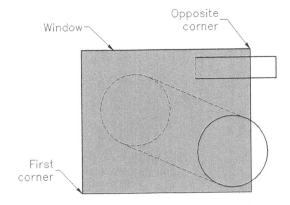

*Figure 2-30 Selecting objects using the **Window** option*

You can also invoke the **Window** option without entering **W** at the Command prompt. To do so, specify a point on the screen at the **Select objects** prompt. This is considered as the first corner of the window. Moving the cursor to the right will display a blue-shaded window. After enclosing the required objects, specify the other corner of the window. The objects that are completely enclosed within the window will be selected and displayed in dashed lines. The following is the prompt sequence for automatic window after invoking the **Erase** tool:

Command: *Choose the **Erase** tool*
Select objects: *Select a blank point as the first corner of the window.*
Specify opposite corner: *Drag the cursor to the right to select the other corner of the window.*
Select objects: [Enter]

Tip
*In AutoCAD LT, the entities are highlighted when you move the cursor over them. This feature is known as the selection preview. To set the selection preview, invoke the **Options** dialog box, choose the **Selection** tab, and then the **Visual Effects Settings** button in the **Selection Preview** area; the **Visual Effect Settings** dialog box will be displayed. Set the type of selection preview by selecting the appropriate radio button in the **Line highlighting** area of this dialog box.*

Window Crossing Method

The window crossing selection is one of the selection methods in which an object or group of objects that are completely or partially enclosed by the selection window are selected. The objects to be selected should touch the window boundaries or completely enclosed within it. To select the objects by using the window crossing method after invoking a tool, type **C** at the **Select objects** prompt and press ENTER; you will be prompted to select the first corner of the window. Select the first corner and then move the cursor to specify the opposite corner. As you move the cursor, a green color window with dashed outline is displayed. Specify the opposite corner of the window; the objects that touch the window boundaries and the objects that are enclosed by the window are selected and displayed as dashed objects. Figure 2-31 shows a window drawn to select objects by using the **Window Crossing** method. The objects that will be selected are shown in dashed lines.

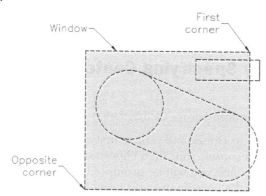

Figure 2-31 *Selecting objects using the **Window Crossing** option*

You can also invoke the **Window Crossing** method without entering **C** at the Command prompt. To do so, specify a point in the drawing area at the **Select objects** prompt and move the cursor to the left. As you move the cursor, a green color window with dashed outline will be displayed. Specify the opposite corner of the window; the objects touching the window boundary and that are enclosed within this window are selected and displayed as dashed objects. The prompt sequence for the automatic window crossing method when you choose the **Erase** tool is given next.

Select objects: *Select a blank point as the first corner of the crossing window.*
Specify opposite corner: *Drag the cursor to the left to select the other corner of the crossing window.*
Select objects: [Enter]

Tip
You can also select the objects by using the window or window crossing method before invoking a command. To do so, specify the start point of the selection window and then drag the cursor to enclose the objects in a window. If you move the cursor to the left of the start point, the window crossing method will be activated. But, if you move the cursor to the right of the start point, the window option will be activated.

If you do not invoke any tool and click to specify the first corner of the window for window selection or window crossing, the Command prompt will provide you with three selection options: **Fence**, **WPolygon**, and **CPolygon**. If you enter **FENCE** or **F** at the Command prompt, you can select objects by drawing a fence around them. If you enter **WP** at the Command prompt, you can select objects by drawing a polygon around them. If you enter **CP** at the Command prompt, you can select objects by drawing a polygon around them.

DRAWING A CIRCLE

Command: CIRCLE or C	Toolbar:	Draw > Circle
Menu Bar: Draw > Circle	Tool Palettes:	Draw > Circle
Ribbon: Home > Draw > Circle drop-down > Center, Radius		

A circle is drawn by using the **CIRCLE** command. In AutoCAD LT, you can draw a circle by using six different tools. All these tools are grouped together in the **Draw** panel of the **Ribbon**. To view these tools, choose the down arrow next to the **Center, Radius** tool in the **Draw** panel, as shown in Figure 2-32; all tools will be listed in a drop-down. Note that the tool chosen last will be displayed in the **Draw** panel. You can also invoke the **CIRCLE** command by choosing the **Circle** tool from the **Draw** toolbar or the **Tool Palettes**. The different methods to draw a circle are discussed next.

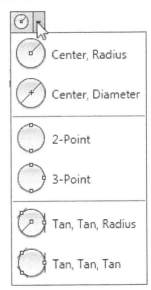

Figure 2-32 Tools in the Circle drop-down

Drawing a Circle by Specifying Center and Radius

Ribbon: Home > Draw > Circle drop-down > Center, Radius

To draw a circle by specifying its center and radius, first ensure that the **Dynamic Input** button is chosen, and then choose the **Center, Radius** tool from the **Draw** panel; you will be prompted to specify the center of the circle. Type the coordinates and press ENTER or specify the center by using the left mouse button. After specifying the center of the circle, move the cursor to define its radius; the current radius of the circle will be displayed in the dimension input box, as shown in Figure 2-33. This radius value will change as you move the cursor. Type a radius value in the dimension input box or click to define the radius; a circle of the specified radius value will be drawn.

Drawing a Circle by Specifying Center and Diameter

Ribbon: Home > Draw > Circle drop-down > Center, Diameter

To draw a circle by specifying its center and diameter, first ensure that the **Dynamic Input** button is chosen, and then choose the **Center, Diameter** tool from the **Draw** panel; you will be prompted to specify the center. Type the coordinates and press ENTER or specify the center by using the left mouse button. After specifying the center of the circle, move the cursor to define its diameter; the current diameter of the circle will be displayed in the dimension input box, as shown in Figure 2-34. This diameter value will change as you move the cursor. Type a diameter value in the dimension input box or click to define the diameter; a circle of the specified diameter value will be drawn.

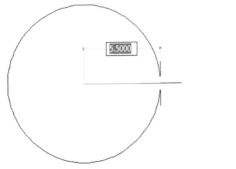

Figure 2-33 Drawing a circle by specifying the center and the radius

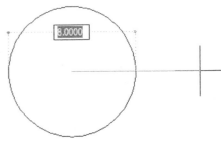

Figure 2-34 Drawing a circle by specifying the center and the diameter

Drawing a Circle by Specifying Two Diametrical Ends

Ribbon: Home > Draw > Circle drop-down > 2-Point
Command: C > 2P

You can also draw a circle by specifying its two diametrical ends, see Figure 2-35. To do so, first ensure that the **Dynamic Input** button is chosen, and then choose the **2-Point** tool from the **Draw** panel; you will be prompted to specify the first end of the diameter. Type the coordinates and press ENTER or specify the center by using the left mouse button. After specifying the center of the circle, move the cursor to define its diameter. Now, you can type the coordinates or diameter in the dimension input box.

Drawing a Circle by Specifying Three Points on a Circle

Ribbon: Home > Draw > Circle drop-down > 3-Point
Command: C > 3P

To draw a circle by specifying three points on its periphery, choose the **3-Point** tool from the **Draw** panel and specify the three points in succession. You can type the coordinates of the points or specify them by using the left mouse button. The prompt sequence to type the three coordinates on choosing the **3-Point** tool is given below.

> Specify center point for circle or [3P/2P/Ttr(tan tan radius)]: _3p Specify first point on circle: **3,3**
> Specify second point on circle: **#3,1**
> Specify third point on circle: **#4,2** *(see Figure 2-36)*

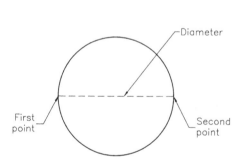

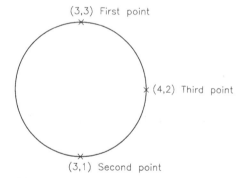

Figure 2-35 *A circle drawn by using the **2-Point** option*

Figure 2-36 *A circle drawn by using the **3-Point** option*

You can also use the relative rectangular coordinates to define the points.

Drawing a Circle Tangent to Two Objects

Ribbon: Home > Draw > Circle drop-down > Tan, Tan, Radius   **Command:** C > Ttr

An object (line, circle, or arc) is said to be tangent to a circle or an arc, if it touches the circumference of the circle or the arc at only one point. To draw a circle that has specified radius and is tangent to two objects, first ensure that the **Dynamic Input** button is chosen, and then choose the **Tan, Tan, Radius** tool from the **Draw** panel; you will be prompted to specify a point on the first object to be tangent to the circle. Move the cursor near the object to be made tangent to the circle; a tangent symbol will be displayed. Specify the first point; you will be prompted to specify a point on the second object to be made tangent to the circle. Move the cursor near the second object that is to be tangent to the circle; a tangent symbol will be displayed. Specify the second point; you will be prompted to specify the radius. Type the radius value in the dimension input box and press ENTER; a circle of the specified radius and tangent to two specified objects will be drawn.

In Figures 2-37 through 2-40, the dotted circle represents the circle that is tangent to two objects. The circle actually drawn depends on how you select the objects to be made tangent to the new circle. The figures show the effect of selecting different points on the objects. If you specify too small or large radius, you may get unexpected results or the "**Circle does not exist**" prompt.

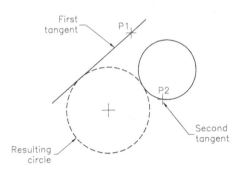

Figure 2-37 Drawing a circle tangent to two objects

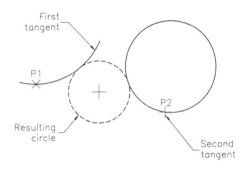

Figure 2-38 Drawing a circle tangent to two objects

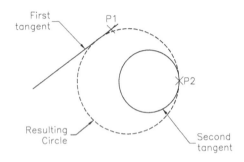

Figure 2-39 Drawing a circle tangent to two objects

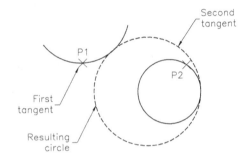

Figure 2-40 Drawing a circle tangent to two objects

Drawing a Circle Tangent to Three Objects

Ribbon:	Home > Draw > Circle drop-down > Tan, Tan, Tan

You can also draw a circle that is tangent to three objects. To do so, choose the **Tan, Tan, Tan** tool from the **Draw** panel and select the three objects in succession to which the resulting circle is to be tangent; the circle will be drawn, as shown in Figure 2-41.

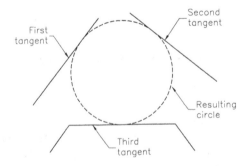

Figure 2-41 Drawing a circle tangent to three objects

EXERCISE 5   *Line and Circle*

Draw the profile shown in Figure 2-42 using various options of the **LINE** and **CIRCLE** commands. Use the absolute, relative rectangular, or relative polar coordinates for drawing the triangle. The vertices of the triangle will be used as the center of the circles. The circles can be drawn by using the **Center, Radius**, or **Center, Diameter**, or **Tan, Tan, Tan** tools. Do not apply dimensions; they are for reference only.

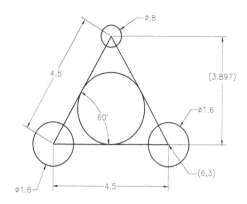

Figure 2-42 *Drawing for Exercise 5*

BASIC DISPLAY COMMANDS

Sometimes while drawing a sketch, it may be very difficult to view and alter minute details. You can overcome this problem by viewing only a specific portion of the drawing. This is done by using the **ZOOM** command. This command lets you enlarge or reduce the size of the drawing displayed on the screen. Similarly, you may need to slide the drawing view. This can be done by using the **Pan** tool. These are called display commands and are discussed next.

Zooming Drawings

The **ZOOM** command is used to enlarge or reduce the view of a drawing on the screen, without affecting the actual size of entities. In AutoCAD LT 2012, the ZOOM tools are grouped together and are available in the Navigator Bar. To invoke different **ZOOM** tools, press the down arrow next to the **Zoom Extents** tool in the Navigator Bar; all options of the **ZOOM** command will be displayed in the drop-down, as shown in Figure 2-43. You can also invoke the **ZOOM** command by choosing **View > Zoom** from the menu bar. To display the menu bar, left-click on the arrow in the **Quick Access Toolbar** and then select **Show Menu Bar**. Some **ZOOM** commands are also available in the **Standard** toolbar.

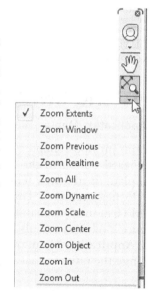

Figure 2-43 *The Zoom tools in the **Navigator Bar***

Zoom Extents

 Choose the **Zoom Extents** tool to increase or decrease the drawing display area so that all sketched entities or dimensions fit inside the current view.

Zoom Window

This is the most commonly used option of the **ZOOM** command. On choosing this tool, you need to draw a window by specifying its two opposite corners. The center of the zoom window becomes the center of the new display area and the objects in this window are magnified.

Zoom Realtime

The **Zoom Realtime** tool is used to dynamically zoom in or out a drawing. When you choose this option, the cursor will be replaced by the zoom cursor. To zoom out a drawing, press and hold the left mouse button and drag the cursor downward. Similarly, to zoom in a drawing, press and hold the left mouse button and drag the cursor upward. As you drag the cursor, the drawing display changes dynamically. After you get the desired view, exit this tool by right-clicking and then choosing **Exit** from the shortcut menu. On exiting this tool, the zoom cursor will change into cross hairs. Next, press the ESC key. You can also exit the **Zoom Realtime** tool by pressing the ESC key twice. If you have a mouse with scroll wheel, then scroll the wheel to zoom in/out the drawing.

Zoom Previous

While working on a complex drawing, you may need to zoom in a drawing multiple times to edit some minute details. After completing the editing, if you want to view the previous views, choose the **Zoom Previous** tool. You can view up to the last ten views by using the **Zoom Previous** tool.

Zoom In / Zoom Out

Choose the **Zoom In / Zoom Out** tool to increase/decrease the size of the drawing view twice/half of the original drawing size, respectively.

Note
You will learn about the other options of the ZOOM command in detail in Chapter 6.

Moving the View

You can use the **Pan** tool to move a view by sliding and placing it at the required position. To pan a drawing view, invoke the **Pan** tool from the Navigator Bar; a hand cursor will be displayed. Drag the cursor in any direction to move the drawing. To exit the **Pan** tool, right-click and then choose **Exit** from the shortcut menu. You can also press the ESC or ENTER key to exit the tool.

SETTING UNITS TYPE AND PRECISION

Application Menu: Drawing Utilities > Units	**Command:** UNITS

In the previous chapter, you learned to set units while starting a drawing by using the **Use a Wizard** option in the **Startup** dialog box. But, if you are drawing a sketch in an existing template or in a new template, you need to change the format of the units for distance and angle measurements. This is done by using the **UNITS** command. To set the units format, enter **UNITS** at the Command prompt; the **Drawing Units** dialog box will be displayed, as shown in Figure 2-44. You can also invoke this dialog box by choosing **Drawing Utilities > Units** from the **Application Menu** or by choosing **Format > Units** from the menu bar. The procedure to change the units format is discussed next.

Specifying the Format

In the **Drawing Units** dialog box, you can select the desired format of units from the **Type** drop-down list. You can select any one of the five formats given next.

Architectural (0'-01/16")   Decimal (0.00)   Engineering (0'-0.00")
Fractional (0 1/16)   Scientific (0.00E+01)

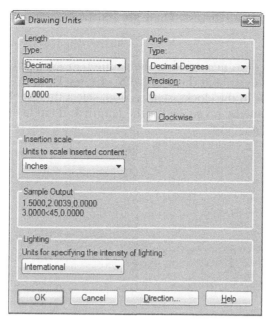

*Figure 2-44 The **Drawing Units** dialog box*

If you select the scientific, decimal, or fractional format, you can enter distance or coordinate values in any of these three formats, but not in engineering or architectural units. If you select the engineering or architectural format, you can enter distances or coordinates in any of the five formats.

Note
The inch symbol (") is optional. For example, 1'1-3/4" is the same as 1'1-3/4, and 3/4" is the same as 3/4.

Specifying the Angle Format

You can select any one of the following five angle measuring formats:

1. Decimal Degrees (0.00)   2. Deg/min/sec (0d00'00")

3. Grads (0.00g)   4. Radians (0.00r)

5. Surveyor's Units (N 0d00'00" E)

If you select any one of the first four measuring formats, you can specify the angle in the Decimal, Degrees/minutes/seconds, Grads, or Radians system, but you cannot enter the angle in Surveyor's Units system. However, if you select **Surveyor's Units**, you can enter angle values in any of the five systems. To enter a value in another system, use the appropriate suffixes and symbols, such as r (Radians), d (Degrees), or g (Grads). If you enter an angle value without indicating the symbol of a measuring system, it is taken in the current system.

In Surveyor's units, you must specify the angle that the line makes with respect to the north-south direction, as shown in Figure 2-45. For example, if you want to define an angle of 60-degree with north, in the Surveyor's units the angle will be specified as N 60d E. Similarly, you can specify angles such as S 50d E, S 50d W, and N 75d W, refer to Figure 2-45. You cannot specify an angle that exceeds 90-degree (N 120 E). Angles can also be specified in radians or grads; for example, 180-degree is equal to π (3.14159) radians. You can convert degrees into radians, or radians into degrees by using the equations given below.

radians = degrees X 3.14159/180;
degrees = radians X 180/3.14159

Grads are generally used in land surveys. There are 400 grads or 360 degree in a circle. 90 degree angle is equal to 100 grads.

In AutoCAD LT, if an angle is measured in the counterclockwise direction, then it is positive. Also, the angles are measured about the positive X axis, see Figure 2-46. If you want the angles to be measured as positive in the clockwise direction, select the **Clockwise** check box from the **Angle** area. You can specify the precision for the length and angle in the respective **Precision** drop-down lists in this dialog box.

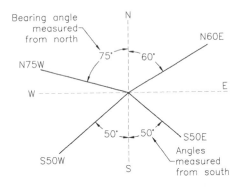

Figure 2-45 Specifying angles in Surveyor's Units

Figure 2-46 Measuring angles

Setting the Direction for Angle Measurement

As mentioned above, angles are measured about the positive X axis. This means the base angle (0-degree) is set along the east direction, see Figure 2-47. To change this base angle, choose the **Direction** button in the **Drawing Units** dialog box; the **Direction Control** dialog box will be displayed, as shown in Figure 2-48. Select the appropriate radio button to specify the direction for the base angle (0-degree).

If you select the **Other** option, you can set the direction of your choice for the base angle (0-degree) by entering a value in the **Angle** edit box or by choosing the **Pick an angle** button and picking two points to specify the angle. After specifying the base angle direction, choose the **OK** button to apply the settings.

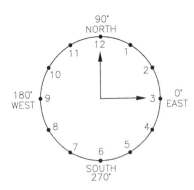

Figure 2-47 North, South, East, and West directions

*Figure 2-48 The **Direction Control** dialog box*

Tip
*If you are entering values by using the dimension input boxes that are displayed when the **Dynamic Input** option is on, then you are not required to set the base angle.*

Specifying Units for the Drawing or Block to be Inserted

To set units for a block or a drawing to be inserted, select a unit from the **Units to scale inserted content** drop-down list. Now, if you insert a block or a drawing from the **DesignCenter**, the specified unit will be applied to the block. Even if the block was created using a different measuring unit, AutoCAD LT scales it and inserts it using the specified measuring unit. If you select **Unitless** from the drop-down list, then the units specified in the **Insertion Scale** area of the **User Preferences** tab in the **Options** dialog box will be used.

Note
Inserting blocks in a drawing is discussed in detail in Chapter 14.

Sample Output

The **Sample Output** area in this dialog box shows the example of the current format used for specifying units and angles. When you change the type of length and angle measure in the **Length** and **Angle** areas of the **Drawing Units** dialog box, the corresponding example is displayed in the **Sample Output** area.

EXAMPLE 5	*Setting Units*

In this example, you will set the units of a drawing based on the specifications given below and then draw Figure 2-49.

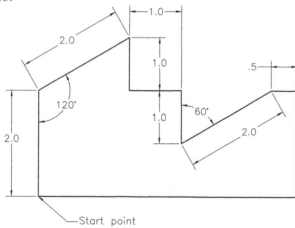

Figure 2-49 Drawing for Example 5

a. Set the units of length to fractional, with the denominator of the smallest fraction equal to 32.
b. Set the angular measurement to Surveyor's Units, with the number of fractional places for display of angles equal to zero.
c. Set the base angle (0-degree) to North and the direction of measurement of angles to clockwise.

The following steps are required to complete this example:

1. Start a new file with the *acadlt.dwt* template in the **Drafting & Annotation** or AutoCAD LT **Classic** workspace and invoke the **Drawing Units** dialog box by choosing **Drawing Utilities > Units** from the **Application Menu**. You can also invoke this dialog box by entering **UNITS** at the Command prompt.

2. In the **Length** area of this dialog box, select **Fractional** from the **Type** drop-down list. Select **0 1/32** from the **Precision** drop-down list.

3. In the **Angle** area of this dialog box, select **Surveyor's Units** from the **Type** drop-down list. From the **Precision** drop-down list, select **N 0d E**, if it has not been already selected. Also, select the **Clockwise** check box to set the clockwise angle measurement to positive.

4. Choose the **Direction** button to display the **Direction Control** dialog box. Next, select the **North** radio button. Choose the **OK** button to exit the **Direction Control** dialog box.

5. Choose the **OK** button to exit the **Drawing Units** dialog box.

6. With the units set, you need to draw Figure 2-49 by using the relative polar coordinates. Turn off the dynamic input. The prompt sequence to complete the sketch is as follows:

> Command: *Choose the* **Line** *tool*
> _line Specify first point: **2,2** [Enter]
> Specify next point or [Undo]: **@2.0<0** [Enter]
> Specify next point or [Undo]: **@2.0<60** [Enter]
> Specify next point or [Close/Undo]: **@1<180** [Enter]
> Specify next point or [Close/Undo]: **@1<90** [Enter]
> Specify next point or [Close/Undo]: **@1<180** [Enter]
> Specify next point or [Close/Undo]: **@2.0<60** [Enter]
> Specify next point or [Close/Undo]: **@0.5<90** [Enter]
> Specify next point or [Close/Undo]: **@2.0<180** [Enter]
> Specify next point or [Close/Undo]: **C** [Enter]

> Here, the units are fractional and the angles are measured from north (90-degree axis). Also, the angles are measured as positive in the clockwise direction and negative in the counterclockwise direction.

7. To modify the drawing display area, choose the **Zoom All** tool from the Navigator Bar.

SETTING THE LIMITS OF A DRAWING

Command: LIMITS

In AutoCAD LT, limits represent the drawing area and it is endless. Therefore, you need to define the drawing area before starting the drawing. In the previous chapter, you learned to set limits while starting a drawing by using the **Use a Wizard** option in the **Startup** dialog box. If you are working in a drawing by using the default template, you need to change limits. For example, the template *acadlt.dwt* has the default limits set to 12,9. To draw a rectangle of dimension 150x75 in this template, you need to change its limits to 200x100. This can be done by using the **LIMITS** command. The following is the prompt sequence of the **LIMITS** command for setting the limits to 24,18 for the *acadlt.dwt* template, which has the default limits 12,9.

> Command: **LIMITS** [Enter]
> Reset Model space limits:
> Specify lower left corner or [ON/OFF]<0.0000,0.0000>: **0,0** [Enter]
> Specify upper right corner <12.0000,9.0000>: **24,18** [Enter]

Tip

*Whenever you reset the drawing limits, the display area does not change automatically. You need to use the **All** option of the **ZOOM** command to display the complete drawing area.*

The limits of the drawing area are usually determined by the following factors:

1. The actual size of drawing.
2. The space needed for adding dimensions, notes, bill of materials, and other necessary details.
3. The space between various views so that the drawing does not look cluttered.
4. The space for the border and title block, if any.

Setting Limits

To get a good idea of how to set up limits, it is better to draw a rough sketch of a drawing. This will help in calculating the required drawing area. For example, if an object has a front view size of 5 X 5, a side view size of 3 X 5, and a top view size of 5 X 3, the limits should be set so that the drawing and everything associated with it can be easily accommodated within the set limit. In Figure 2-50, the space between the front and side views is 4 units and between the front and top views is 3 units. Also, the space between the border and the drawing is 5 units on the left, 5 units on the right, 3 units at the bottom, and 2 units at the top. (The space between the views and between the borderline and the drawing depends on the drawing.)

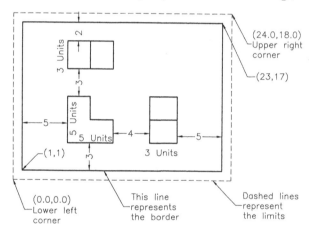

Figure 2-50 *Setting limits in a drawing*

After knowing the size of different views, the space required between views, the space between the border and the drawing, and the space required between the borderline and the edges of the paper, you can calculate the space in the following way:

$$\text{Space along } (X \text{ axis}) = 1 + 5 + 5 + 4 + 3 + 5 + 1 = 24$$
$$\text{Space along } (Y \text{ axis}) = 1 + 3 + 5 + 3 + 3 + 2 + 1 = 18$$

This shows that the limits you need to set for this drawing is 24 X 18. Once you have determined the space, select the sheet size that can accommodate your drawing. In the case just explained, you will select a D size (34 X 22) sheet. Therefore, the actual drawing limits will be 34,22.

Tip

*To display the grid, choose the **Grid Display** button in the Status Bar. By default, the grid will be displayed beyond the limits. To display the grid up to the limits, use the **Limits** option of the **GRID** command and set the **Display grid beyond Limits [Yes/No] <Yes>:** option to **No**; the grids will be displayed only up to the limits set.*

Limits for Architectural Drawings

Most architectural drawings are drawn at the scale of 1/4" = 1', 1/8" = 1', or 1/16" = 1'. You must set the limits accordingly. The following example illustrates how to calculate the limits in architectural drawings.

Given

> Sheet size = 24 X 18
> Scale is 1/4" = 1'

Calculate limits

> Scale is 1/4" = 1'
>   or 1/4" = 12"
>   or 1" = 48"
> X limit = 24 X 48
>   = 1152" or 1152 Units
>   = 96'
> Y limit = 18 X 48
>   = 864" or 864 Units
>   = 72'

Thus, the scale factor is 48 and the limits are 1152",864", or 96',72'.

EXAMPLE 6   *Setting Limits*

In this example, you will calculate the limits and determine an appropriate drawing scale factor for the drawing shown in Figure 2-51. You will plot the drawing on a 12" X 9" sheet. Assume the missing dimensions.

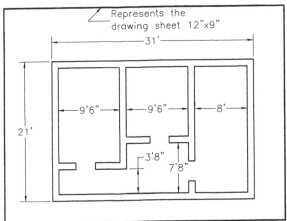

Figure 2-51 Drawing for Example 6

The calculation for the scale factor is given next.

Given or known

> Overall length of the drawing = 31'
> Length of the sheet = 12"
> Approximate space between the drawing and the edges of the paper = 2"

Calculate the scale factor

To calculate the scale factor, you have to try various scales until you find the one that satisfies the given conditions. After some experience, you will find this fairly easy to do. For this example, assume a scale factor of 1/4" = 1'.

Scale factor 1/4" = 1'   or 1" = 4'

Thus, a line 31' long will be = 31'/4' = 7.75" on paper. Similarly, a line 21' long = 21'/4' = 5.25". Approximate space between the drawing and the edges of paper = 2".

Therefore, the total length of the sheet = 7.75 + 2 + 2 = 11.75"

Similarly, the total width of the sheet = 5.25 + 2 + 2 = 9.25"

Because you selected the scale 1/4" = 1', the drawing will definitely fit in the given sheet of paper (12" x 9"). Therefore, the scale for this drawing is 1/4" = 1'.

Calculate limits

Scale factor = 1" = 48" or 1" = 4'
The length of the sheet is 12"
Therefore, X limit = 12 X 4' = 48' and Y limit = 9 X 4' = 36'

Limits for Metric Drawings

When the drawing units are in metric, you must use **standard metric size sheets** or calculate limits in millimeters (mm). For example, if the sheet size is 24 X 18, the limits, after conversion to the metric system, will be 609.6,457.2 (multiplying length and width by 25.4). You can round these numbers to the nearest whole numbers 610,457. Note that metric drawings do not require any special setup, except for the limits. Metric drawings are like any other drawings that use decimal units. Similar to architectural drawings, you can draw metric drawings to a scale. For example, if the scale is 1:20, you must calculate the limits accordingly. The following example illustrates how to calculate limits for metric drawings:

Given

Sheet size = 24" X 18"
Scale = 1:20

Calculate limits

Scale is 1:20
Therefore, scale factor = 20
X limit = 24 X 25.4 X 20 = 12192 units
Y limit = 18 X 25.4 X 20 = 9144 units

EXERCISE 6   *Setting Units and Limits*

Set the units of the drawing according to the specifications given below and then make the drawing shown in Figure 2-52 (leave a space of 3 to 5 units around the drawing for dimensioning and title block). The space between the dotted lines is 1 unit.

1. Set UNITS to decimal units, with two digits to the right of the decimal point.
2. Set the angular measurement to decimal degrees, with the number of fractional places for display of angles equal to 1.

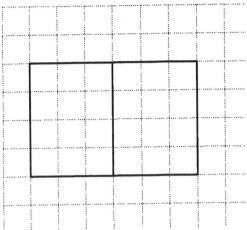

Figure 2-52 Drawing for Exercise 6

3. Set the direction to 0-degree (east) and the direction of measurement of angles to counterclockwise (angles measured positive in a counterclockwise direction).

4. Set the limits leaving a space of 3 to 5 units around the drawing for dimensioning and title block.

Self-Evaluation Test

Answer the following questions and then compare them to those given at the end of this chapter:

1. You can draw a line by specifying the length and direction of the line, using the Direct Distance Entry method. (T/F)

2. While using the **Window Crossing** method of object selection, the objects that are completely enclosed within the boundaries of the crossing box are selected. (T/F)

3. Choose the **3-Point** tool from the **Circle** drop-down to draw a circle by specifying the two endpoints of the circle's diameter. (T/F)

4. If you choose the engineering or architectural format for units in the **Drawing Units** dialog box, you can enter distances or coordinates in any of the five formats. (T/F)

5. You can erase a previously drawn line by using the _____ option of the **Line** tool.

6. Choose _____ tool from the **Circle** drop-down to draw a circle that is tangent to the two previously drawn objects.

7. The _____ tool is used to enlarge or reduce the view of a drawing without affecting the actual size of entities.

8. After increasing the drawing limits, you need to choose the _____ tool from the **Navigator Bar** to display the complete area inside the drawing area.

9. In _____ units, you must specify the bearing angle that a line makes with the north-south direction.

10. You can preview a plot before the actual plotting by using the _____ button in the **Plot** dialog box.

Review Questions

Answer the following questions:

1. In the relative rectangular coordinate system, the displacements along the X and Y axes (DX and DY) are measured with respect to the previous point and not with respect to the origin. (T/F)

2. In AutoCAD LT, by default angles are measured along the positive X axis and it will be positive if measured in the counterclockwise direction. (T/F)

3. You can also invoke the **PLOT** command by choosing **Plot** from the shortcut menu displayed on right-clicking in the Command window. (T/F)

4. The **Files** tab of the **Options** dialog box is used to store the directories in which AutoCAD LT looks for the driver, support, menu, project, template, and other files. (T/F)

5. Which of the following keys is used to terminate the **Line** tool at the **Specify next point or [Close/Undo]:** prompt?

    (a) SPACEBAR   (b) BACKSPACE
    (c) ENTER   (d) ESC

6. Which of the following **ZOOM** commands is used to zoom a drawing up to the limits or the extents, whichever is greater?

    (a) **Zoom Previous**   (b) **Zoom Window**
    (c) **Zoom All**   (d) **Zoom Realtime**

7. How many formats of units can be chosen from the **Drawing Units** dialog box?

    (a) Three   (b) Five
    (c) Six   (d) Seven

8. Which of the following input methods cannot be used to invoke the **OPTIONS** command for displaying the **Options** dialog box?

    (a) Menu   (b) Toolbar
    (c) Shortcut menu   (d) Command prompt

9. When you define a direction by specifying angle, the output of the angle does not depend on which one of the following factors?

    (a) Angular units   (b) Angle value
    (c) Angle direction   (d) Angle base

10. The _____ option of the **Line** tool can be used to join the current point with the initial point of the first line when two or more lines are drawn in succession.

11. The _____ option of drawing a circle cannot be invoked by entering the command at the Command prompt.

12. When you select any type of unit and angle in the **Length** or **Angle** area of the **Drawing Units** dialog box, the corresponding example is displayed in the _____ area of the dialog box.

13. If you want a drawing to be plotted so that it fits on the specified sheet of paper, select the _____ option in the **Plot** dialog box.

14. The _____ tab in the **Options** dialog box is used to store the details of all profiles available in the current drawing.

15. You can use the _____ command to change the settings that affect the drawing environment or the AutoCAD LT interface.

EXERCISE 7   *Relative Rectangular & Absolute Coordinates*

Invoke the **Line** tool and use the following relative rectangular and absolute coordinate values to draw the object.

Point	Coordinates
1	3.0, 3.0
2	@3,0
3	@-1.5,3.0
4	@-1.5,-3.0

Point	Coordinates
5	@3.0,5.0
6	@3,0
7	@-1.5,-3
8	@-1.5,3

EXERCISE 8   *Relative Rectangular & Polar Coordinates*

Draw the profile shown in Figure 2-53 by using the relative rectangular and relative polar coordinates of the points given in the following table. The distance between the dotted lines is 1 unit. Save this drawing with the name *C02_Exer8.dwg*.

Point	Coordinates
1	3.0, 1.0
2	_____
3	_____
4	_____
5	_____
6	_____

Point	Coordinates
7	_____
8	_____

9   _____

10   _____

11   _____

12   _____

Point	Coordinates
13	_____
14	_____
15	_____
16	_____

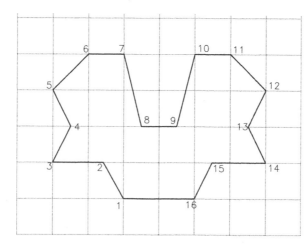

Figure 2-53 *Drawing for Exercise 8*

EXERCISE 9   Relative Polar Coordinates

For the drawing shown in Figure 2-54, enter the relative polar coordinates of the points in the following table. Then, use these coordinates to create the drawing. Do not dimension the drawing.

Point	Coordinates
1	1.0, 1.0
2	_____
3	_____
4	_____
5	_____

Point	Coordinates
6	_____
7	_____
8	_____
9	_____

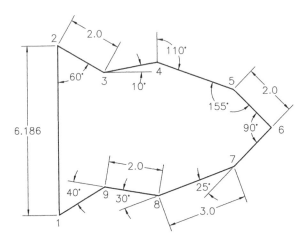

Figure 2-54 Drawing for Exercise 9

EXERCISE 10   *Line and Circle*

Draw the sketch shown in Figure 2-55 by using the **Line** and **Center,Radius** tools. The distance between the dotted lines is 1.0 unit.

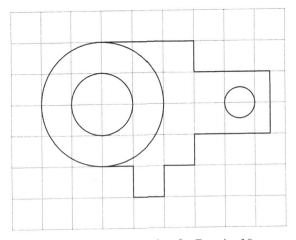

Figure 2-55 Drawing for Exercise 10

EXERCISE 11   *Line and Circle Tangent to Two objects*

Draw the sketch shown in Figure 2-56 using the **Line** and **Tan,Tan,Radius** tools.

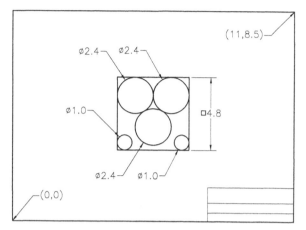

Figure 2-56 *Drawing for Exercise 11*

EXERCISE 12   *Setting Units*

Set the units for a drawing based on the following specifications.

1. Set the UNITS to architectural, with the denominator of the smallest fraction equal to 16.
2. Set the angular measurement to degrees/minutes/seconds, with the number of fractional places for the display of angles equal to 0d00'.
3. Set the direction to 0-degree (east) and the direction of measurement of angles to counterclockwise (angles measured positive in counterclockwise direction).

Based on Figure 2-57, determine and set the limits for the drawing. The scale for this drawing is 1/4" = 1'. Leave enough space around the drawing for dimensioning and title block. (HINT: Scale factor = 48 sheet size required is 12 x 9; therefore, the limits are 12 X 48, 9 X 48 = 576, 432. Use the **ZOOM** command and then select the **All** option to display the new limits.)

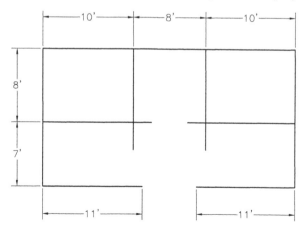

Figure 2-57 *Drawing for Exercise 12*

EXERCISE 13

Draw the sketch shown in Figure 2-58. The distance between the dotted lines is 10 feet. Determine the limits for this drawing and use the Architectural units with 0'-01/32" precision.

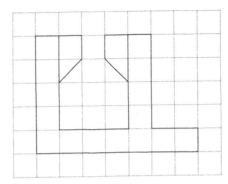

Figure 2-58 *Drawing for Exercise 13*

EXERCISE 14

Draw the object shown in Figure 2-59. The distance between the dotted lines is 5 inches. Determine the limits for this drawing and use the Fractional units with 1 1/16 precision.

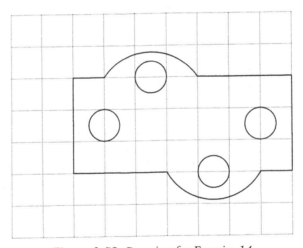

Figure 2-59 *Drawing for Exercise 14*

EXERCISE 15

Draw the object shown in Figure 2-60. The distance between the dotted lines is 1 unit. Determine the limits for this drawing and use the Decimal units with 0.00 precision.

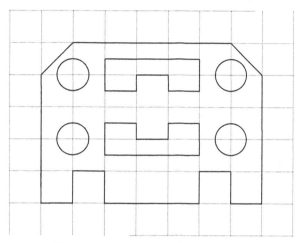

Figure 2-60 *Drawing for Exercise 15*

EXERCISE 16

Draw the object shown in Figure 2-61. The distance between the dotted lines is 10 feet. Determine the limits for this drawing and use the Engineering units with 0'0.00" precision.

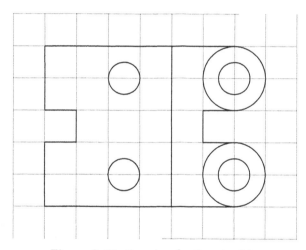

Figure 2-61 *Drawing for Exercise 16*

Problem-Solving Exercise 1

Draw the object shown in Figure 2-62, using the **Line** and **Center,Diameter** tools. In this exercise only the diameters of the circles are given. To draw the lines and small circles (Dia 0.6), you need to find the coordinate points for the lines and the center points of the circles. For example, if the center of concentric circles is at 5,3.5, then the *X* coordinate of the lower left corner of the rectangle will be 5.0 - 2.4 = 2.6.

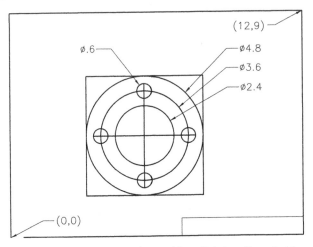

Figure 2-62 Drawing for Problem-Solving Exercise 1

Answers to Self-Evaluation Test

1. T, **2.** F, **3.** F, **4.** T, **5.** Undo, **6. Tan, Tan, Radius, 7. ZOOM, 8. Zoom All, 9.** Surveyor's, **10. Preview**

Chapter 3

Starting with Advanced Sketching

CHAPTER OBJECTIVES

In this chapter, you will learn to:
- *Draw arcs using various options.*
- *Draw rectangles, ellipses, elliptical arcs, and polygons.*
- *Draw polylines and donuts.*
- *Place points and change their style and size.*
- *Create simple text.*
- *Draw infinite lines.*
- *Write simple text.*

KEY TERMS

- *Arc*
- *Rectangles*
- *Explode*
- *Ellipse*
- *Elliptical Arc*
- *Polygon*
- *Polylines*
- *Donut*
- *FILLMODE*
- *Points*
- *DDPTYPE*
- *PDMODE*
- *XLINE*
- *Text*
- *Ray*

DRAWING ARCS

Ribbon: Home > Draw > Arc drop-down	**Toolbar: Draw > Arc**
Menu Bar: Draw > Arc	**Command:** ARC or A

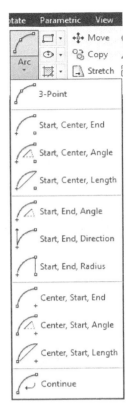

An arc is defined as a segment of a circle. In AutoCAD LT, an arc is drawn by using the **Arc** tool. There are eleven different tools to draw an arc. The tools to draw an arc are grouped together in the **Arc** drop-down of the **Draw** panel in the **Ribbon**, see Figure 3-1. You can choose the appropriate tool depending upon the parameters known and then draw the arc. Remember that the tool that was used last to create an arc will be displayed in the **Draw** panel. The different methods to draw an arc are discussed next.

Drawing an Arc by Specifying Three Points

To draw an arc by specifying the start point, endpoint, and another point on its periphery, choose the **3-Point** tool from the **Draw** panel (see Figure 3-1). On doing so, you will be prompted to specify the start point. Specify the first point or enter coordinates. Then, specify the second point and endpoint of the arc, see Figure 3-2.

Figure 3-1 The tools in the Arc drop-down

Following is the prompt sequence to draw an arc by specifying three points (You can also specify the points by using the mouse).

> Command: ***ARC*** Enter *(Ensure that dynamic input is off)*
> Specify start point of arc or [Center]: **2,2** Enter
> Specify second point of arc or [Center/End]: **3,3** Enter
> Specify end point of arc: **3,4** Enter

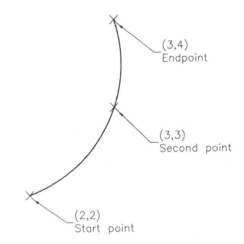

Figure 3-2 Drawing an arc using the 3-Point tool

EXERCISE 1   3-Point

Draw several arcs by using the **3-Point** tool. The points can be selected by entering coordinates or by specifying points on the screen. Also, try to create a circle by drawing two separate arcs and a single arc and notice the limitations of the **ARC** command.

Drawing an Arc by Specifying its Start Point, Center Point, and Endpoint

If you know the start point, endpoint, and center point of an arc, choose the **Start, Center, End** tool from the **Draw** panel and then specify the start, center, and end points in succession; the arc will be drawn. The radius of the arc is determined by the distance between the center point and the start point. Therefore, the endpoint is used to calculate the angle at which the arc ends. Note that in this case, the arc will be drawn in counterclockwise direction from the start point to the endpoint around the specified center, as shown in Figure 3-3.

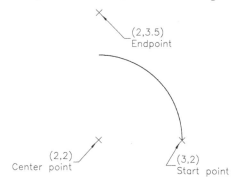

*Figure 3-3 Drawing an arc using the **Start, Center, End** tool*

Drawing an Arc by Specifying its Start Point, Center Point, and Included Angle

Included angle is the angle between the start and end points of an arc about the specified center. If you know the location of the start point, center point, and included angle of an arc, choose the **Start, Center, Angle** tool from the **Draw** panel and specify the start point, center point, and included angle; the arc will be drawn in counterclockwise direction with respect to the specified center and start point, see Figure 3-4.

If you enter a negative angle value, the arc will be drawn in clockwise direction, see Figure 3-5. Following is the prompt sequence to draw an arc by specifying the center point at (2,2), start point at (3,2), and an included angle of -60 degrees:

> Command: *Choose **Start, Center, Angle** from the **Draw** panel (Ensure that dynamic input is off)*
> _Specify start point of arc or [Center]: **3,2** Enter
> Specify second point of arc or [Center/End]: _c Specify center point of arc: **C** Enter
> Specify center point of arc: **2,2** Enter
> Specify end point of the arc or [Angle/chord Length]: _a Specify included angle: **A** Enter
> Specify included angle: **-60** Enter *see Figure 3-5*.

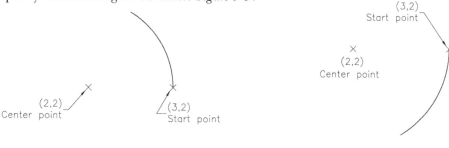

*Figure 3-4 Drawing an arc using the **Start, Center, Angle** tool*

*Figure 3-5 Drawing an arc by specifying a negative angle in the **Start, Center, Angle** tool*

EXERCISE 2   *Start, Center, Angle*

a. Draw an arc whose start point is at 6,3, center point is at 3,3, and the included angle is 240 degrees.

b. Draw the profile as shown in Figure 3-6. The distance between the dotted lines is 1.0 unit. Create the arcs by using different arc command options as indicated in the figure.

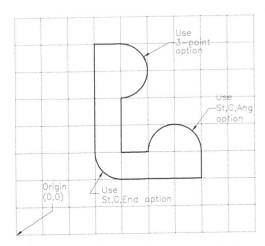

Figure 3-6 *Drawing for Exercise 2*

Drawing an Arc by Specifying the Start Point, Center Point, and Chord Length

A chord is defined as a straight line connecting the start point and endpoint of an arc. To draw an arc by specifying its chord length, choose the **Start, Center, Length** tool from the **Draw** panel and specify the start point, center point, and length of the chord in succession. On specifying the chord length, AutoCAD LT will calculate the included angle and an arc will be drawn in counterclockwise direction from the start point. A positive chord length gives the smallest possible arc with that length, as shown in Figure 3-7. This arc is known as minor arc. The included angle in a minor arc is less than 180 degrees. A negative value for the chord length results in the largest possible arc, also known as the major arc, as shown in Figure 3-8.

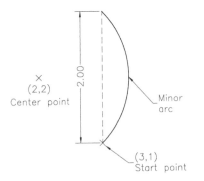

Figure 3-7 *Drawing an arc by specifying a positive chord length in the **Start, Center, Length** tool*

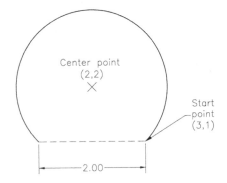

Figure 3-8 *Drawing an arc by specifying a negative chord length in the **Start, Center, Length** tool*

EXERCISE 3   *Center, Start, Length*

Draw a minor arc with the center point at (3,4), start point at (4,2), and chord length of 4 units.

Drawing an Arc by Specifying its Start Point, Endpoint, and Included Angle

To draw an arc by specifying its start point, endpoint, and the included angle, choose the **Start, End, Angle** tool from the **Draw** panel and specify the start point, endpoint, and the included angle in succession; the arc will be drawn. A positive included angle value draws an arc in the counterclockwise direction from the start point to the endpoint, as shown in Figure 3-9. Similarly, a negative included angle value draws the arc in the clockwise direction.

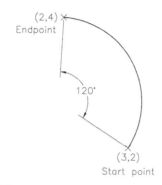

Figure 3-9 *Drawing an arc using the*
Start, End, Angle *option*

Drawing an Arc by Specifying its Start Point, Endpoint, and Direction

This option is used to draw a major or minor arc, whose size and position are determined by the distance between the start point and endpoint and the direction specified. You can specify the direction by selecting a point on a line that is tangent to the start point or by entering an angle between the start point of the arc and the end point of the tangent line.

To draw an arc by specifying its direction, choose the **Start, End, Direction** tool from the **Draw** panel and specify the start and end points in succession; you will be prompted to specify the direction. Specify a point on the line that is tangent to the start point or enter an angle between the start point of the arc and the end point of the tangent line; an arc will be drawn.

In other words, on using this option, the arc will start in the direction you specify (the start of the arc is established tangent to the direction you specify). The prompt sequence to draw an arc, whose start point is at 3,6, endpoint is at 4.5,5, and direction of -40 degrees is given next.

> Command: *Choose* **Start, End, Direction** *from the* **Draw** *panel (Ensure that dynamic input is off)*
> _arc Specify start point of arc or [Center]: **3,6** Enter
> Specify second point of arc or [Center/End]: _e Specify end point of arc: **4.5,3** Enter
> Specify center point of arc or [Angle/Direction/Radius]: _d Specify tangent direction for the start point of arc: **-40** Enter, *see Figure 3-10.*

The prompt sequence to draw an arc, whose start point is at 4,3, endpoint is at 3,5, and direction of 90 degrees, is given next.

Command: *Choose* **Start, End, Direction** *from the* **Draw** *panel (Ensure that dynamic input is off)*
_arc Specify start point of arc or [Center]: **4,3** Enter
Specify second point of arc or [Center/End]: _e Specify end point of arc: **3,5** Enter
Specify center point of arc or [Angle/Direction/Radius]: _d Specify tangent direction for the start point of arc: **90** Enter See Figure 3-11.

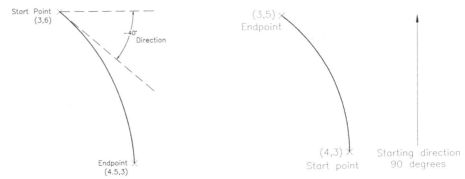

Figure 3-10 *Drawing an arc in the negative direction using the* **Start, End, Direction** *tool*

Figure 3-11 *Drawing an arc using the* **Start, End, Direction** *tool*

EXERCISE 4

a. Specify the directions and coordinates of two arcs in such a way that they form a circular figure.

b. Draw the profile shown in Figure 3-12. Create the curves by using the **ARC** command. The distance between the dotted lines is 1.0 unit and the diameter of the circles is 1 unit.

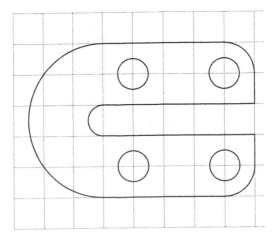

Figure 3-12 *Drawing for Exercise 4*

Drawing an Arc by Specifying its Start Point, Endpoint, and Radius

If you know the location of the start point, endpoint, and radius of an arc, choose the **Start, End, Radius** tool from the **Draw** panel and specify the start and end points; you will be prompted to specify the radius. Enter the radius value; the arc will be drawn. In this case, the arc will be drawn in counterclockwise direction from the start point. This means that a negative radius value results in a major arc (the largest arc between the two endpoints), see Figure 3-13(a). Whereas a positive radius value results in a minor arc (smallest arc between the start point and the endpoint), see Figure 3-13(b).

Drawing an Arc by Specifying its Center Point, Start Point, and Endpoint

The **Center, Start, End** tool is the modification of the **Start, Center, End** tool. You can use this tool whenever it is easier to start drawing an arc by establishing the center first. Here, the arc is always drawn in the counterclockwise direction from the start point to the endpoint, around the specified center. The prompt sequence for drawing the arc shown in Figure 3-14, which has a center point at (3,3), start point at (5,3), and endpoint at (3,5), is given next.

Command: *Choose* **Center, Start, End** *from the* **Draw** *panel.*
_arc Specify start point of arc or [Center]: _c Specify center point of arc: **3,3** `Enter`
Specify start point of arc: **5,3** `Enter`
Specify endpoint of arc or [Angle/chord Length]: **3,5** `Enter`

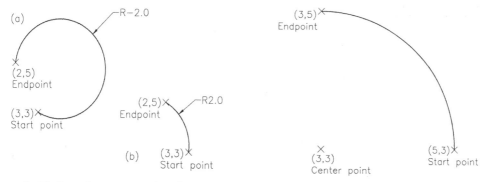

Figure 3-13 *Drawing an arc using the* **Start, End, Radius** *tool*

Figure 3-14 *Drawing an arc using the* **Center, Start, End** *tool*

Drawing an Arc by Specifying its Center Point, Start Point, and Angle

You can use the **Center, Start, Angle** tool if you need to draw an arc by specifying the center first. The prompt sequence for drawing the arc shown in Figure 3-15, which has a center point at (4,5), start point at (5,4), and included angle of 120 degrees, is given next.

Command: *Choose* **Center, Start, Angle** *from the* **Draw** *panel (Ensure that dynamic input is off)*
_arc Specify start point of arc or [Center]: _c Specify center point of arc: **4,5** `Enter`
Specify start point of arc: **5,4** `Enter`
Specify end point of arc or [Angle/chord Length]: _a Specify included angle: **120** `Enter`, see *Figure 3-15*.

Drawing an Arc by Specifying the Center Point, Start Point, and Chord Length

The **Center, Start, Length** tool is used whenever it is easier to draw an arc by establishing the center first. The prompt sequence for drawing the arc shown in Figure 3-16, that has a center point at (2,2), start point at (4,3), and length of chord as 3 is given next.

Command: *Choose* **Center, Start, Length** *from the* **Draw** *panel (Ensure that dynamic input is off)*
_arc Specify start point of arc or [Center]: **2,2** `Enter`

Specify start point of arc: **4,3** [Enter]
Specify end point of arc or [Angle/chord Length]: _l Specify length of chord: **3** [Enter], see Figure 3-16.

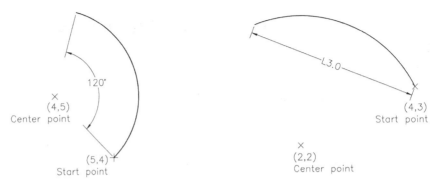

Figure 3-15 *Drawing an arc using the Center, Start, Angle tool*

Figure 3-16 *Drawing an arc using the Center, Start, Length tool*

Continue Option

To continue drawing an arc from a previously drawn arc or line, choose the **Continue** tool from the **Draw** panel; the start point and the direction of the arc will be taken from the endpoint and the ending direction of the previous line or arc. Specify the endpoint to draw an arc. If this option is used to draw arcs, each successive arc will be tangent to the previous one. This option is used to draw arcs that are tangent to a previously drawn line.

Tip
*You can also invoke the **Continue** option automatically. To do so, first draw a line or an arc and choose a tool from the **Arc** drop-down in the **Draw** panel. Now, press ENTER at the **Specify start point of arc or [Center]** prompt; the **Continue** option will be invoked automatically. The endpoint of the line or the arc drawn previously will be selected as the start point of the arc. Now, you will be prompted to specify the endpoint to complete the arc.*

EXERCISE 5

a.   Use the **Center, Start, Angle**, and **Continue** tools to draw the profiles shown in Figure 3-17.

b.   Draw the profile shown in Figure 3-18. The distance between the dotted lines is 1.0 unit. Create the radii as indicated in the drawing by using the **ARC** command options.

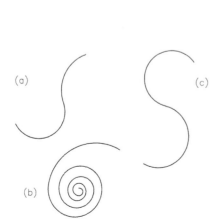

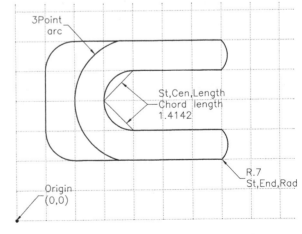

Figure 3-17 *Drawing for Exercise 5(a)*

Figure 3-18 *Drawing for Exercise 5(b)*

DRAWING RECTANGLES

Ribbon: Home > Draw > Rectangle   **Toolbar:** Draw > Rectangle
Tool Palettes: Draw > Rectangle   **Command:** RECTANG

A rectangle is drawn by choosing the **Rectangle** tool (see Figure 3-19) from the **Draw** panel. In AutoCAD LT, you can draw rectangles by specifying two opposite corners of the rectangle, by specifying the area and the size of one of the sides, or by specifying the dimensions of the rectangle. All these methods of drawing rectangles are discussed next.

Drawing Rectangles by Specifying Two Opposite Corners

On invoking the rectangle command, you will be prompted to specify the first corner of the rectangle. Enter the coordinates of the first corner or specify the start point by using the mouse. The first corner can be any one of the four corners. Next, you will be prompted to specify the other corner. Specify the diagonally opposite corner by entering the coordinates or by using the left mouse button, as shown in Figure 3-20.

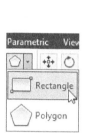
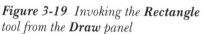
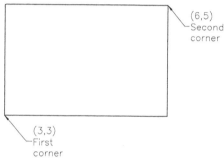

Figure 3-19 *Invoking the* **Rectangle** *tool from the* **Draw** *panel*

Figure 3-20 *Drawing a rectangle by specifying two opposite corners*

Drawing Rectangles by Specifying the Area and One Side

To draw a rectangle by specifying its area and the length of one of the sides, first specify the start point. Next, invoke the shortcut menu by right-clicking and then choose the **Area** option. Next, specify the parameters; the rectangle is drawn. Following is the prompt sequence to draw a rectangle whose start point is at 3,3, has area 15 units and length 5 units:

    Command: **RECTANG**
    Specify first corner point or [Chamfer/Elevation/Fillet/Thickness/Width]: **3,3** ⏎
    Specify other corner point or [Area/Dimensions/Rotation]: **A** ⏎
    Enter area of rectangle in current units <100.000>: **15** ⏎
    Calculate rectangle dimensions based on [Length/Width] <Length>: **L** ⏎
    Enter rectangle length <10.0000>: **5** ⏎

In the above case, the area and length of the rectangle were entered. The system automatically calculates the width of the rectangle by using the following formula:

    Area of rectangle = Length x Width
    Width = Area of rectangle/Length
    Width =15/5
    Width =3 units

Drawing Rectangles by Specifying their Dimensions

You can also draw a rectangle by specifying its dimensions. This can be done by choosing the **Dimensions** option from the shortcut menu at the **Specify other corner point or [Area/Dimensions/Rotation]** prompt and entering the length and width of the rectangle. The prompt sequence for drawing a rectangle at 3,3 with a length of **5** units and width of **3** units is given next.

> Command: **RECTANG**
> Specify first corner point or [Chamfer/Elevation/Fillet/Thickness/Width]: **3,3** Enter
> Specify other corner point or [Area/Dimensions/Rotation]: **D** Enter
> Specify length for rectangles <0.0000>: **5** Enter
> Specify width for rectangles <0.0000>: **3** Enter
> Specify other corner point or [Area/Dimensions/Rotation]: *Click on the screen to specify the orientation of rectangle.*

Here, you are allowed to choose any one of the four locations for placing the rectangle. You can move the cursor to see the four quadrants. Depending on the location of the cursor, the corner point that is specified first holds the position of either the lower left corner, the lower right corner, the upper right corner, or the upper left corner. After deciding the position, you can click to place the rectangle.

Drawing Rectangle at an Angle

You can also draw a rectangle at an angle. This can be done by entering **Rotate** at the **Specify other corner point or [Area/Dimensions/Rotation]** prompt. Then, enter the rotation angle at the next prompt. After entering the rotation angle, you can continue sizing the rectangle using any one of the above discussed methods. The prompt sequence for drawing a rectangle at an angle of 45-degree is:

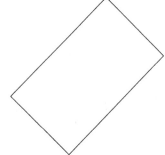

> Command: **RECTANG**
> Specify first corner point or [Chamfer/Elevation/Fillet/Thickness/Width]: *Select a point as lower left corner location.*
> Specify other corner point or [Area/Dimensions/Rotation]: **R** Enter
> Specify rotation angle or [Pick points] <current>: **45** Enter
> Specify other corner point or [Area/Dimensions/Rotation]: *Select a diagonally opposite point.*

While specifying the other corner point, you can place the rectangle in any of the four quadrants. Move the cursor in different quadrants and then select a point in the quadrant in which you need to draw the rectangle. Figure 3-21 shows a rectangle drawn at an angle of 45-degree.

Figure 3-21 Rectangle drawn at an angle

Note
Once the rotation angle has been specified, the subsequent rectangles will be drawn at that angle. If you do not want to draw the subsequent rectangles at an angle, you need to set the rotation angle to zero.

You can also set some of the parameters of a rectangle before specifying the start point. These parameters are the options in the Command Prompt and are discussed next.

Chamfer

The **Chamfer** option is used to create a chamfer, which is an angled corner, by specifying the chamfer distances, see Figure 3-22. The chamfer is created at all four corners. You can give two different chamfer values to create an unequal chamfer.

> Command: **RECTANG**
> Specify first corner point or [Chamfer/Elevation/Fillet/Thickness/Width]: **C** Enter

Specify first chamfer distance for rectangles <0.0000>: *Enter a value, d1.*
Specify second chamfer distance for rectangles <0.0000>: *Enter a value, d2.*
Specify first corner point or [Chamfer/Elevation/Fillet/Thickness/Width]: *Select a point as lower left corner.*
Specify other corner point or [Area/Dimensions/Rotation]: *Select a point as upper right corner.*

Fillet

The **Fillet** option is used to create a filleted rectangle, see Figure 3-23. You can specify the required fillet radius. The following is the prompt sequence for specifying the fillet:

Specify first corner point or [Chamfer/Elevation/Fillet/Thickness/Width]: **F** Enter
Specify fillet radius for rectangles <0.0000>: *Enter a value.*

Note that the rectangle will be filleted only if the length and width of the rectangle are equal to or greater than twice the value of the specified fillet. Otherwise, AutoCAD LT will draw a rectangle without fillets.

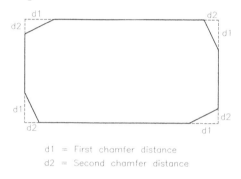

d1 = First chamfer distance
d2 = Second chamfer distance

Figure 3-22 *Drawing a rectangle with chamfers*   ***Figure 3-23*** *Drawing a rectangle with fillets*

Note
*You can draw a rectangle with chamfers or fillets. If you specify the chamfer distances first and then specify the fillet radius in the same **RECTANG** command, the rectangle will be drawn with fillets only.*

Width

The **Width** option is used to create a rectangle whose line segments have some specified width, as shown in Figure 3-24.

Specify first corner point or [Chamfer/Elevation/Fillet/Thickness/Width]: **W** Enter
Specify line width for rectangles <0.0000>: *Enter a value.*

Thickness

The **Thickness** option is used to draw a rectangle that is extruded in the Z direction by a specified value of thickness. For example, if you draw a rectangle with thickness of 2 units, you will get a cuboid whose height is 2 units, see Figure 3-25. To view the cuboid, choose **SE Isometric** from **View > Views** panel. To restore the view to the plan view, choose **Top** from **View > Views** panel.

Specify first corner point or [Chamfer/Elevation/Fillet/Thickness/Width]: **T** Enter
Specify thickness for rectangles <0.0000>: *Enter a value.*

Elevation

The **Elevation** option is used to draw a rectangle at a specified distance along the Z axis and from the *XY* plane. For example, if the elevation is 2 units, the rectangle will be drawn two units above the *XY* plane. If the thickness of the rectangle is 1 unit, you will get a rectangular box of 1 unit height, located 2 units above the *XY* plane, see Figure 3-25.

Chamfer/Elevation/Fillet/Thickness/Width/<First corner>: **E** Enter
Specify elevation for rectangles <0.0000>: *Enter a value.*

To view the rectangle in 3D space, choose **SE Isometric** from **View** > **Views** panel. To restore the view to the plan view, choose **Top** from **View** > **Views** panel.

Figure 3-24 *Drawing a rectangle of specified width*

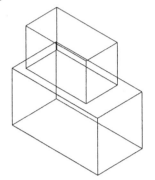

Figure 3-25 *Drawing rectangles with thickness and elevation specified*

Note
The values you enter for fillet, width, elevation, and thickness become the current values for the rectangles drawn subsequently. Therefore, you need to reset the values based on the requirement.

*A rectangle generated by using the **RECTANG** command is treated as a single object. To edit the individual lines of the rectangle, you need to explode the rectangle by using the **EXPLODE** command and then edit them.*

EXERCISE 6   *Rectangle*

Draw a rectangle of length 4 units, width 3 units, and start point at (1,1). Draw another rectangle of length 2 units and width 1 units, with its first corner at 1.5,1.5, and which is at an angle of 65-degree.

DRAWING ELLIPSES

Ribbon: Home > Draw > Ellipse drop-down	**Toolbar:** Draw > Ellipse
Tool Palettes: Draw > Ellipse	**Command:** ELLIPSE

If you cut a cone by a cutting plane at an angle and view the cone perpendicular to the cutting plane, the shape created is called an ellipse. An ellipse is created by using the **ELLIPSE** command. An ellipse can be created by using different methods and the tools to invoke these methods are grouped together in the **Draw** panel, refer to Figure 3-26. In AutoCAD LT, you can create a true ellipse, also known as a NURBS-based (Non-Uniform Rational Bezier Spline) ellipse. A true ellipse has center and quadrant points. If you select it, grips (small blue squares) will be displayed at the center and quadrant points of the ellipse. If you move one of the grips located on the perimeter of the ellipse, the size of the ellipse will be changed.

Once you invoke the **ELLIPSE** command, the **Specify axis endpoint of ellipse or [Arc/Center]** or **Specify axis endpoint of ellipse or [Arc/Center/Isocircle]** (if isometric snap is on) prompt will be displayed. The response to this prompt depends on the option you choose. The various options are explained next.

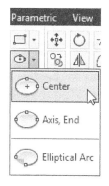

Note
*By default, the **Isocircle** option is not available in the **ELLIPSE** command. To display this option, you have to select the **Isometric snap** radio button in the **Snap and Grid** tab of the **Drafting Settings** dialog box. The **Isocircle** option will be discussed in Chapter 13.*

*Figure 3-26 Tools in the **Ellipse** drop-down in the **Draw** panel*

Drawing Ellipse Using the Center Option

To draw an ellipse by specifying its center point, endpoint of one axis, and length of other axis, choose the **Center** tool from the **Draw** panel; you will be prompted to specify the center of the ellipse. The center of an ellipse is defined as the point of intersection of the major and minor axes. Specify the center point or enter coordinates; you will be prompted to specify the endpoint. Specify the endpoint of the major or minor axis; you will be prompted to specify the distance of the other axis. Specify the distance; the ellipse will be drawn.

After specifying the endpoint of one axis, you can enter **R** at the **Specify distance to other axis or [Rotation]** prompt to specify the rotation angle around the major axis. In this case, the first axis specified is considered as the major axis. On specifying the rotation angle, the ellipse will be drawn at an angle with respect to the major axis. Note that the rotation angle should range between 0 and 89.4-degree. Figure 3-27 shows the ellipse created at different rotation angles.

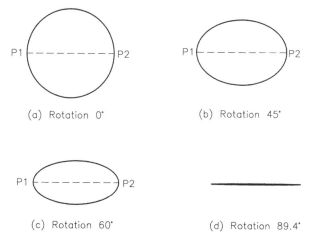

(a) Rotation 0°

(b) Rotation 45°

(c) Rotation 60°

(d) Rotation 89.4°

Figure 3-27 Rotation about the major axis

Drawing an Ellipse by Specifying its Axis and Endpoint

To draw an ellipse by specifying one of its axes and the endpoint of the other axis, choose the **Axis, End** tool from the **Draw** panel; you will be prompted to specify the axis endpoint. Specify the first endpoint of one axis of the ellipse; you will be prompted to specify the other endpoint of the axis. Specify the other endpoint of the axis. Now, you can specify the distance to other axis from the center or specify the rotation angle around the specified axis.

Figure 3-28 shows an ellipse with one endpoint of the axis located at (3,3), the other at (6,3), and the distance to the other axis as 1 unit. Figure 3-29 shows an ellipse with one endpoint of the axis located at (3,3), the other at (4,2), and the distance to the other axis as 2 units.

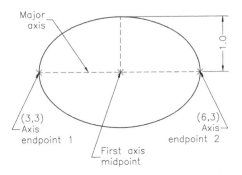

Figure 3-28 *Drawing an ellipse using the* **Axis and Endpoint** *option*

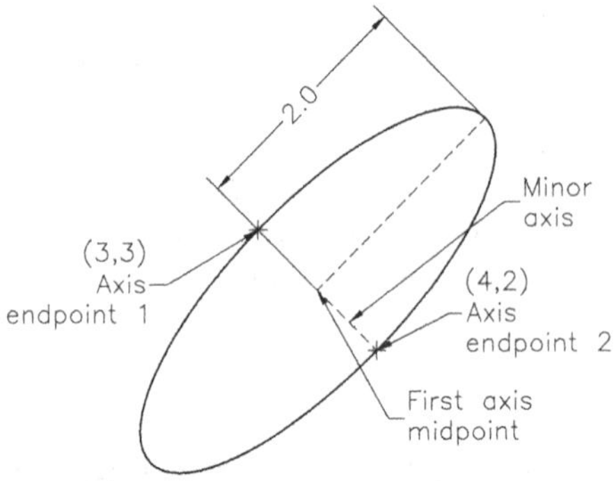

Figure 3-29 *Drawing an ellipse using the* **Axis and Endpoint** *option*

EXERCISE 7 — Ellipse

Draw an ellipse whose major axis is 4 units and the rotation around this axis is 60 degrees. Draw another ellipse whose rotation around the major axis is 15 degrees.

Drawing Elliptical Arcs

Ribbon: Home > Draw > Ellipse drop-down > Elliptical Arc	**Toolbar:** Draw > Ellipse Arc
Tool Palettes: Draw > Ellipse Arc	**Command:** ELLIPSE > Arc

In AutoCAD LT, you can draw an elliptical arc by choosing the **Elliptical Arc** tool from the **Draw** panel. On choosing this tool, you need to specify the endpoints of one of the axes, the distance to other axis from the center, and any one of the following information:

1. Start and End angles of the arc.
2. Start and Included angles of the arc.
3. Start and End parameters.

Remember that in case of elliptical arcs, angles are measured from the first point and in counterclockwise direction.

In this section, you will draw an elliptical arc by using the information given below.

a. Start angle = -45, end angle = 135
b. Start angle = -45, included angle = 225
c. Start parameter = @1,0, end parameter = @1<225

Specifying the Start and End Angles of the Elliptical Arc [Figure 3-30(a)]

> Command: *Choose the* **Elliptical Arc** *tool from the* **Draw** *panel*
> Specify axis endpoint of ellipse or [Arc/Center]: _a
> Specify axis endpoint of elliptical arc or [Center]: *Select the first endpoint*
> *Switch on the Ortho mode by pressing F8, if it is not already chosen*
> Specify other endpoint of axis: *Select the second point to the left of the first point*
> Specify distance to other axis or [Rotation]: *Select a point or enter a distance*

Specify start angle or [Parameter]: **-45** [Enter]
Specify end angle or [Parameter/Included angle]: **135** [Enter] *(Angle where arc ends.)*

Specifying the Start and Included Angles of the Elliptical Arc [Figure 3-30(b)]

Command: *Choose the **Elliptical Arc** tool from the **Draw** panel*
Specify axis endpoint of ellipse or [Arc/Center]: _a
Specify axis endpoint of elliptical arc or [Center]: *Select the first endpoint*
Specify other endpoint of axis: *Select the second point*
Specify distance to other axis or [Rotation]: *Select a point or enter a distance*
Specify start angle or [Parameter]: **-45** [Enter]
Specify end angle or [Parameter/Included angle]: **I** [Enter]
Specify included angle for arc<current>: **225** [Enter] *(Included angle.)*

Specifying the Start and End Parameters (Figure 3-30(c))

Command: *Choose the **Elliptical Arc** tool from the **Draw** panel*
Specify axis endpoint of ellipse or [Arc/Center]: _a
Specify axis endpoint of elliptical arc or [Center]: *Select the first endpoint*
Specify other endpoint of axis: *Select the second endpoint*
Specify distance to other axis or [Rotation]: *Select a point or enter a distance*
Specify start angle or [Parameter]: **P**
Specify start parameter or [Angle]: **@1,0**
Specify end parameter or [Angle/ Included angle]: **@1<225**

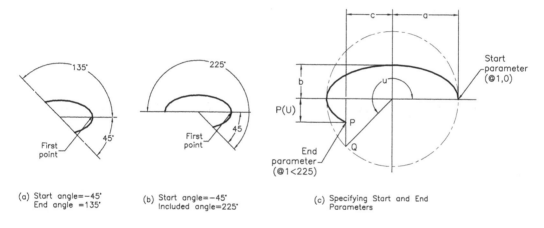

(a) Start angle=−45°
    End angle =135°

(b) Start angle=−45°
    Included angle=225°

(c) Specifying Start and End
    Parameters

Figure 3-30 Drawing elliptical arcs

EXERCISE 8   *Elliptical Arc*

a. Construct an ellipse with center at (2,3), axis endpoint at (4,6), and the other axis endpoint at a distance of 0.75 unit from the midpoint of the first axis.

b. Draw the profile shown in Figure 3-31. The distance between the dotted lines is 1.0 unit.

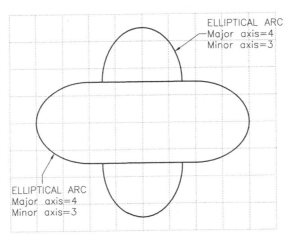

Figure 3-31 Drawing for Exercise 8

DRAWING REGULAR POLYGONS

Ribbon: Home > Draw > Polygon	**Toolbar:** Draw > Polygon
Tool Palettes: Draw > Polygon	**Command:** POLYGON

A regular polygon is a closed geometric entity with equal sides. The number of sides of a polygon varies from 3 to 1024. For example, a triangle is a three-sided polygon and a pentagon is a five-sided polygon. To draw a regular 2D polygon, choose the **Polygon** tool from the **Draw** panel; you will be prompted to specify the number of sides. Type the number of sides and press ENTER. Now, you can draw the polygon by specifying the length of an edge or by specifying the center of the polygon. Both these methods are discussed next.

Drawing a Polygon by Specifying the Center of Polygon

After you specify the number of sides and press ENTER, you will be prompted to specify the center of polygon. Specify the center point; you will be prompted to specify whether the polygon to be drawn is inscribed in a circle or circumscribed about an imaginary circle. A polygon is said to be inscribed when it is drawn inside an imaginary circle such that the vertices of the polygon touch the circle, see Figure 3-32. Whereas, a polygon is said to be circumscribed when it is drawn outside the imaginary circle such that the sides of the polygon are tangent to the circle, see Figure 3-33. Type **I** or **C** to draw an inscribed or a circumscribed polygon respectively, and press ENTER; you will be prompted to specify the radius. Specify the radius and press ENTER; a polygon will be created.

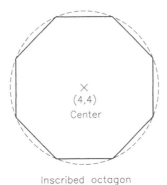

*Figure 3-32 Drawing an inscribed polygon using the **Center of Polygon** option*

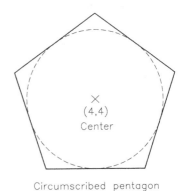

*Figure 3-33 Drawing a circumscribed polygon using the **Center of Polygon** option*

Drawing a Polygon by Specifying an Edge

To draw a polygon by specifying the length of an edge, you need to type **E** at the **Specify center of polygon or [Edge]** Command prompt and press ENTER. Next, specify the first and second endpoints of the edge in succession; the polygon will be drawn in counterclockwise direction, as shown in Figure 3-34.

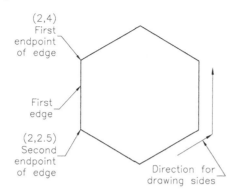

Figure 3-34 *Drawing a polygon (hexagon) using the **Edge** option*

EXERCISE 9

Draw a circumscribed polygon of eight sides by using the **Center of Polygon** method.

EXERCISE 10

Draw a polygon of ten sides by using the **Edge** option and an elliptical arc, as shown in Figure 3-35. Let the first endpoint of the edge be at (7,1) and the second endpoint be at (8,2).

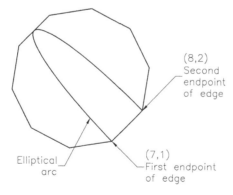

Figure 3-35 *Polygon and elliptical arc for Exercise 10*

DRAWING POLYLINES

Ribbon: Home > Draw > Polyline   **Toolbar:** Draw > Polyline
Tool Palettes: Draw > Polyline   **Command:** PLINE or PL

Etymologically, polylines means many lines. Some of the features of a polyline are listed below.

1. Polylines are thick lines with desired width. They are very flexible and can be used to draw any shape, such as a filled circle or a donut.
2. Polylines can be used to draw objects in any linetype (for example, hidden linetype).
3. Polylines are edited by using the advanced editing commands such as the **PEDIT** command.

Chapter 3

4. A single polyline object can be formed by joining polylines and polyarcs of different thicknesses.
5. It is easy to determine the area or perimeter of a polyline feature. Also, it is easy to offset a polyline when drawing walls.

To draw a polyline, you need to invoke the **PLINE** command. To do so, choose the **Polyline** tool from the **Draw** panel, see Figure 3-36. The **PLINE** command functions fundamentally like the **LINE** command, except that some additional options are provided and all segments of the polyline form a single object. After invoking the **PLINE** command and specifying the start point, the following prompt is displayed.

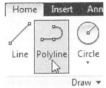

*Figure 3-36 Choosing the **Polyline** tool from the **Draw** panel*

> Specify start point: *Specify the starting point or enter its coordinates.*
> Current line-width is nn.nnnn
> Specify next point or [Arc/Halfwidth/Length/Undo/Width]:

Note that the message **Current line-width is nn.nnnn** is displayed automatically indicating that the polyline drawn will have nn.nnnn width.

When you are prompted to specify the next point, you can continue specifying the next point and draw a polyline, or depending on your requirements, the other options can be invoked. All these options are discussed next.

Next Point of Line

This is the default option that is displayed after specifying the start point and is used to specify the next point of the current polyline segment. If additional polyline segments are added to the first polyline, AutoCAD LT automatically makes the endpoint of the previous polyline segment as the start point of the next polyline segment. The prompt sequence is given next.

> Command: **PLINE** [Enter]
> Specify start point: *Specify the start point of the polyline.*
> Current line-width is 0.0000.
> Specify next point or [Arc/Halfwidth/Length/Undo/Width]: *Specify the endpoint of the first polyline segment.*
> Specify next point or [Arc/Close/Halfwidth/Length/Undo/Width]: *Specify the endpoint of the second polyline segment, or press ENTER to exit the command.*

Width

To change the current width of a polyline, enter **W** (width option) at the last prompt. You can also right-click and choose the **Width** option from the shortcut menu. On doing so, you will be prompted to specify the width at the start and end of the polyline. Specify the width of the polyline and press ENTER; the polyline will be drawn with the specified width.

The starting width value is taken as the ending width value by default. Therefore, to have a uniform polyline, you need to press ENTER at the **Specify ending width < >** prompt. However, if you specify different value for the ending width, the resulting polyline will be tapered.

For example, to draw a polyline of uniform width 0.25 unit, start point at (4,5), endpoint at (5,5), and the next endpoint at (3,3), use the following prompt sequence:

> Command: **PLINE** [Enter]
> Specify start point: **4,5** [Enter]

Current line-width is 0.0000
Specify next point or [Arc/Halfwidth/Length/Undo/Width]: **W** [Enter]
Specify starting width <current>: **0.25** [Enter]
Specify ending width <0.25>: [Enter]
Specify next point or [Arc/Halfwidth/Length/Undo/Width]: **5,5** [Enter]
Specify next point or [Arc/Close/Halfwidth/Length/Undo/Width]: **3,3** [Enter]
Specify next point or [Arc/Close/Halfwidth/Length/Undo/Width]: [Enter], *See Figure 3-37*.

Similarly, to draw a tapered polyline of starting width 0.5 units and an ending width 0.15 units, a start point at (2,4), and an endpoint at (5,4), use the prompt sequence given next.

Command: **PLINE** [Enter]
Specify start point: **2,4** [Enter]
Current line-width is 0.0000
Specify next point or [Arc/Halfwidth/Length/Undo/Width]: **W** [Enter]
Specify starting width <0.0000>: **0.50** [Enter], *See Figure 3-38*.
Specify ending width <0.50>: **0.15** [Enter]
Specify next point or [Arc/Halfwidth/Length/Undo/Width]: **5,4** [Enter]
Specify next point or [Arc/Close/Halfwidth/Length/Undo/Width]: [Enter]

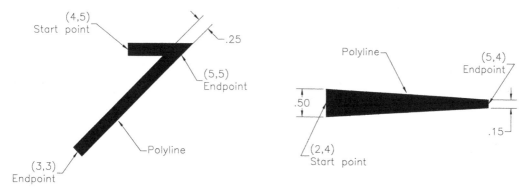

Figure 3-37 Drawing a uniform polyline using the **Polyline** tool

Figure 3-38 Drawing a tapered polyline using the **Polyline** tool

Halfwidth

The halfwidth distance is equal to the half of the actual width of a polyline. This option is invoked by entering **H** or choosing **Halfwidth** from the shortcut menu. The prompt sequence to specify the starting and ending halfwidths of a polyline is given next.

Specify next point or [Arc/Halfwidth/Length/Undo/Width]: **H** [Enter]
Specify starting half-width <0.0000>: **0.12** [Enter] *(Specify the desired starting halfwidth)*
Specify ending half-width <0.1200>: **0.05** [Enter] *(Specify the desired ending halfwidth)*

Length

The **Length** option is used to draw a new polyline segment of specified length and at the same angle as the last polyline segment or tangent to the previous polyarc segment. This option is invoked by entering **L** at the following prompt or by choosing **Length** from the shortcut menu.

Specify next point or [Arc/Close/Halfwidth/Length/Undo/Width]: **L** [Enter]
Specify length of line: *Specify the desired length of the Pline*

Undo

This option erases the most recently drawn polyline segment. It can be invoked by entering **U** at the **Specify next point or [Arc/Close/Halfwidth/Length/Undo/Width]** prompt. You can use this option repeatedly until you reach the start point of the first polyline segment. If you use this option again, the message **All segments already undone** will be displayed.

Close

This option will be available only when at least one segment of a polyline is drawn. It closes the polyline by drawing a polyline segment from the most recent endpoint to the initial start point and exits from the **PLINE** command.

Arc

This option is used to switch from polylines to polyarcs. You can also set the parameters associated with polyarcs. By default, the arc segment is drawn tangent to the previous segment of the polyline. The direction of the previous line, arc, or polyline segment is the default direction for the polyarc. On invoking the arc option, you need to choose the sub-options to draw the polyarc. Some of the sub-options to draw a polyarc are similar to that of drawing an arc. The sub-options that are different are discussed next.

Close

This option will be available only when you specify two or more than two points for creating the polyline segments. To join the start and last points of a polyline in the form of an arc, type **CL** at the **Specify endpoint of arc or [Angle/CEnter/CLose/Direction/Halfwidth/Line/Radius/Second pt/Undo/Width]** Command prompt and press ENTER; an arc will be created that will close the loop.

Direction

Usually, the arc drawn by using the **Arc** option in the **PLINE** command is tangent to the previously drawn polyline segment. In other words, the starting direction of the arc depends upon the ending direction of the previous segment. The **Direction** option is used to specify the direction of the tangent for the arc segment to be drawn. You need to specify the direction by specifying a point. The prompts are given next.

> Specify tangent direction for the start point of arc: *Specify the direction.*
> Specify endpoint of arc: *Specify the endpoint of arc.*

Halfwidth

The use of this option is similar to the option used for the polyline segment. It is used to specify the starting and ending halfwidths of an arc segment.

Line

This option is used to invoke the **Line** mode again.

Radius

This option is used to specify the radius of the arc segment. The prompt sequence for specifying the radius is given next.

> Specify endpoint of arc or [Angle/CEnter/CLose/Direction/Halfwidth/Line/Radius/Second pt/Undo/Width]: **R**
> Specify radius of arc: *Specify the radius of the arc segment.*
> Specify endpoint of arc or [Angle]: *Specify the endpoint of arc or choose an option.*

If you specify a point, the arc segment will be drawn. If you enter an angle, you will have to specify the angle and the direction of the chord at the **Specify included angle** and **Specify direction of chord for arc<current>** prompts respectively.

Second pt

This option is used to select the second point of an arc in the three-point arc option. The prompt sequence is given next.

> Specify second point of arc: *Specify the second point on the arc*
> Specify endpoint of arc: *Specify the third point on the arc*

Width

This option is used to enter the width of the arc segment. The prompt sequence for specifying the width is the same as that of the polyline. To draw a tapered arc segment, as shown in Figure 3-39, you need to enter different values at the starting width and ending width prompts.

The prompt sequence to draw an arc, whose start point is at (3,3), endpoint is at (3,5), starting width is 0.50 unit, and ending width is 0.15 unit, is given next.

> Command: **PLINE** Enter
> Specify start point: **3,3** Enter
> Current line-width is 0.0000
> Specify next point or [Arc/Halfwidth/Length/Undo/Width]: **A** Enter
> Specify endpoint of arc or [Angle/CEnter/CLose/Direction/Halfwidth/Line/Radius/Second pt/Undo/Width]: **W** Enter
> Specify starting width <current>: **0.50** Enter
> Specify ending width <0.50>: **0.15** Enter
> Specify endpoint of arc or [Angle/CEnter/CLose/Direction/Halfwidth/Line/Radius/Second pt/Undo/Width]: **3,5** Enter
> Specify endpoint of arc or [Angle/CEnter/CLose/Direction/Halfwidth/Line/Radius/Second pt/Undo/Width]: Enter

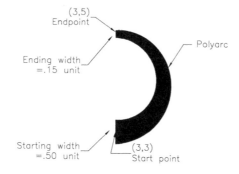

Figure 3-39 *Drawing a polyarc*

EXERCISE 11

Draw the objects shown in Figures 3-40 and 3-41 by using the polylines of different width.

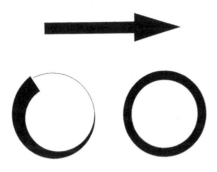

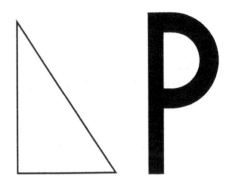

Figure 3-40 Drawing for Exercise 11

Figure 3-41 Drawing for Exercise 11

PLACING POINTS

A point is one of the basic drawing objects and is specified as a dot (a period). A point is defined as a geometric object that has no dimension and properties, except location. However, in AutoCAD LT, you can control the size and appearance (style) of a point. You will first learn to change the point style and size and then about various methods to place a point.

Changing the Point Style and Size

Ribbon: Home > Utilities > Point Style   **Command:** DDPTYPE

To change the style and size of a point, choose the **Point Style** tool from the **Utilities** panel in the **Draw** tab; the **Point Style** dialog box will be displayed, as shown in Figure 3-42. Alternatively, use the **DDPTYPE** command to invoke this dialog box. Select any one of the twenty point styles in the **Point Style** dialog box. You can specify the point size as a specified percentage of the drawing area or as an absolute size by selecting the **Set Size Relative to Screen** or **Set Size in Absolute Units** radio button respectively. After selecting the appropriate radio button, enter the point size in the **Point Size** edit box. Choose the **OK** button after specifying the parameters. Now, the points will be drawn according to the selected style and size, until you change the style and size. You can also change the point style and the point size by using the **PDMODE** and **PDSIZE** system variables respectively. The different values of **PDMODE** and the resulting style are shown in Figure 3-43.

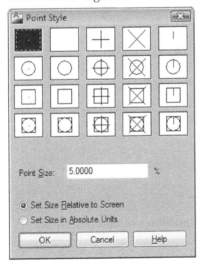

Figure 3-42 The **Point Style** dialog box

Pdmode Value	Point Style	Pdmode Value	Point Style
0		64+0=64	□
1		64+1=65	□
2	+	64+2=66	⊞
3	×	64+3=67	⊠
4	ı	64+4=68	⊡
32+0=32	○	96+0=96	⬭
32+1=33	○	96+1=97	⬭
32+2=34	⊕	96+2=98	⊕
32+3=35	⊗	96+3=99	⊠
32+4=36	⦶	96+4=100	⬭

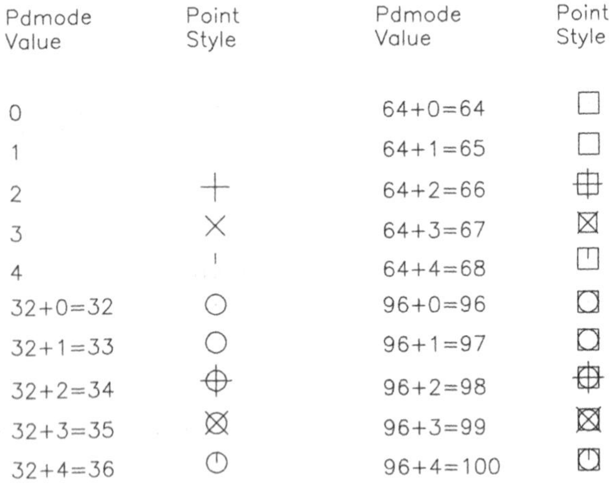

Figure 3-43 Different point styles for **PDMODE** values

Note

*On selecting the **Set Size Relative to Screen** radio button, the point size will not change when you zoom in or zoom out the drawing. However, on selecting the **Set Size in Absolute Units** radio button, the size of the point will change when you zoom in or zoom out the drawing.*

Placing Multiple Points

Ribbon: Home > Draw > Multiple Points
Menu Bar: Draw > Point > Multiple Points

To place points, choose the **Multiple Points** tool from the **Draw** panel (see Figure 3-44); the current **PDMODE** and **PDSIZE** values will be displayed and you will be prompted to specify a point. Left-click to place a point. Next, continue placing as many points as needed and then press ESC to exit the command. You can also enter the coordinate value and place a point at a particular location.

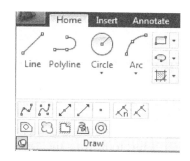

*Figure 3-44 Choosing the **Multiple Points** tool from the **Draw** panel*

Placing Points at Equal Distance

Ribbon: Home > Draw > Divide

To place points at an equal distance on an object, choose the **Divide** tool from the **Draw** panel; you will be prompted to select an object. Select an object; you will be prompted to specify the number of segments. Enter the number of segments; the points will be created on the object.

Placing Points at Specified Intervals

Ribbon: Home > Draw > Measure

You can place points at specified intervals on an object by selecting the object and specifying the length of the segment between two points. To do so, choose the **Measure** tool from the **Draw** panel; you will be prompted to select the object to measure. Select the object; you will be prompted to specify the length of the segment. Specify the length of the segment; the points will be placed at specified intervals.

EXERCISE 12   PDMODE and PDSIZE

a. Try various combinations of the **PDMODE** and **PDSIZE** variables.

b. Check the difference between the points generated by using the negative values of **PDSIZE** and the points generated by using positive values of **PDSIZE**.

DRAWING INFINITE LINES

In AutoCAD LT, you can draw a construction line or a ray that aids in construction or projection. A construction line (xline) is a 3D line that extends to infinity at both ends. As the line is infinite in length, it does not have any endpoint. Whereas, a ray is a 3D line that extends to infinity at only one end. The other end of the ray has a finite endpoint. The xlines and rays have zero extents. This means that the extents of the drawing will not change, if you use the **Zoom All** tool. Most of the object snap modes work with both xlines and rays, with some limitations. You cannot use the **Endpoint** object snap with the xline because by definition an xline does not have any endpoints. However, for rays you can use the **Endpoint** snap on one end only. Also, xlines and rays take the properties of the layer, in which they are drawn.

Tip
Sometimes, Xlines and rays when plotted like any other object may create confusion. Therefore, it is recommended to create the construction lines in a different layer altogether, such that you can recognize them easily. You will learn about layers in later chapters.

Drawing Construction Lines

Ribbon: Home > Draw > Construction Line   **Toolbar:** Draw > Construction Line
Tool Palettes: Draw > Construction Line   **Command:** XLINE

To draw a construction line that extends to infinity at both sides, choose the **Construction Line** tool from the **Draw** panel; the **XLINE** command will be invoked. The prompt sequence that is displayed on choosing this tool is as follows:

Command: **XLINE**
Specify a point or [Hor/Ver/Ang/Bsect/Offset]: *Specify an option or select a point through which the xline will pass.*

The various options in the **XLINE** command are discussed next.

Point

If you use the default option, you need to specify two points through which the xline will pass. After specifying the first point, move the cursor; a line will be attached to the cursor. On specifying the second point, an xline will be created that passes through the first and second points (Figure 3-45).

Specify a point or [Hor/Ver/Ang/Bisect/Offset]: *Specify a point.*
Specify through point: *Specify the second point.*

You can continue to select more points to create more xlines. All these xlines will pass through the first point you had selected at the **Specify a point** prompt. This point is also called the root point. Right-click or press ENTER to end the command.

Horizontal

This option is used to create horizontal xlines of infinite length that pass through the selected points. The xlines will be parallel to the *X* axis of the current UCS, see Figure 3-46. On invoking this option, a horizontal xline will be attached to the cursor and you will be prompted to select a point through which the horizontal xline will pass. Specify a point. You can continue specifying more points to draw more horizontal xlines. To exit the command, right-click or press ENTER.

Vertical

This option is used to create vertical xlines of infinite length that pass through the selected points. The xlines will be parallel to the *Y* axis of the current UCS, see Figure 3-46.

Angular

This option is used to create xlines of infinite length that pass through the selected point at a specified angle (see Figure 3-47). The angle can be specified by entering a value. You can also invoke the **Reference** option by selecting an object and then specifying an angle relative to it. The **Reference** option is useful when the actual angle is not known, but the angle relative to an existing object can be specified.

Command: _xline
_xline Specify a point or [Hor/Ver/Ang/Bisect/Offset]: **A** [Enter]
Enter angle of xline (0) or [Reference]: **R** [Enter] *(Use the **Reference** method to specify the angle)*
Select a line object: *Select a line.*
Enter angle of xline <0>: *Enter angle (the angle will be measured counterclockwise with respect to the selected line)*
Specify through point: *Specify the second point.*

Bisect

This option is used to create an xline that bisects an angle. In this case, you need to specify the vertex, start point, and endpoint of the angle. The xline will pass through the vertex and bisect the angle specified by selecting two points. The xline created using this option will lie on the plane defined by the selected points. The following is the prompt sequence for this option, refer to Figure 3-48.

Command: _xline
_xline Specify a point or [Hor/Ver/Ang/Bisect/Offset]: **B** [Enter]
Specify angle vertex point: *Enter a point (P1).*
Specify angle start point: *Enter a point (P2).*
Specify angle end point: *Enter a point (P3).*
Specify angle end point: *Select more points or press ENTER or right-click to end the command.*

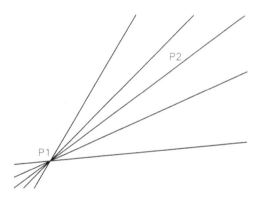

Figure 3-45 *Drawing the xlines*

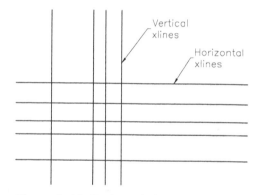

Figure 3-46 *Horizontal and vertical xlines*

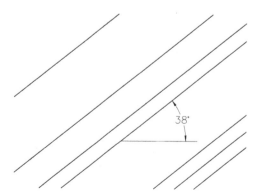

Figure 3-47 *The angular xlines*

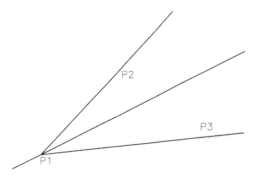

Figure 3-48 *Using the **Bisect** option to draw xlines*

Offset

The **Offset** option is used to create xlines that are parallel to a selected line/xline at a specified offset distance. You can specify the offset distance by entering a numerical value or by selecting two points on the screen. If you choose the **Through** option, the offset line will pass through the selected point. The following is the prompt sequence for this option:

Command: _xline
_xline Specify a point or [Hor/Ver/Ang/Bisect/Offset]: **O** [Enter]
Specify offset distance or [Through] <Through>: *Press ENTER to accept the **Through** option or specify a distance from the selected line object at which the xline shall be drawn.*
Select a line object: *Select the object to which the xline is drawn parallel and at a specified distance.*
Specify through point: *Select a point through which the xline should pass.*

After specifying the offset distance and selecting a line object, you need to specify the direction in which the xline has to be offset. You can continue drawing xlines or right-click or press ENTER to exit the command.

Drawing Ray

Ribbon: Home > Draw > Ray	**Command:** RAY

A ray is a 3D line similar to the xline construction line with the difference being that it extends to infinity only in one direction. It starts from a specified point and extends to infinity through the specified point. The prompt sequence is given next.

Specify start point: *Select the start point for the ray.*
Specify through point: *Specify the second point.*

Press ENTER or right-click to exit the command.

Note
When you trim an xline, it gets converted into a ray, and when a ray is trimmed, it gets converted into a line object.

WRITING A SINGLE LINE TEXT

Ribbon: Home > Annotation > Text drop-down > Single Line	**Command:** TEXT

The **TEXT** command is used to write a single line text. Although you can write more than one line of text using this command, but each line will be a separate text entity. To write text, choose the **Single Line** tool from **Home > Annotation > Text** drop-down. This tool is also available in the **Text** drop-down available in the **Text** panel of the **Annotate** tab. After invoking this command, you need to specify the start point for the text. Next, you need to specify the text height and the rotation angle. As you enter the characters, they start appearing on the screen. After typing a line if you press ENTER, the cursor will be automatically placed at the start of the next line and the prompt for entering another line will be repeated. Type another line or press ENTER again to exit the command. You can use the BACKSPACE key to edit the text on the screen while writing it. The prompt sequence is given next.

Command: **TEXT**
Current text style: "Standard" Text height: 0.2000 Annotative: No
Specify start point of text or [Justify/Style]: *Specify the starting point of the text.*
Specify height<current>: *Enter the text height.*
Specify rotation angle of text <0>: [Enter]
Enter the first line of the text in the text box displayed in the drawing window. [Enter]

Enter the second line of the text in the text box displayed in the drawing window.
Press ENTER twice to exit.

 Note
The other commands to enter text are discussed in detail in Chapter 7.

Self-Evaluation Test

Answer the following questions and then compare them to those given at the end of this chapter:

1. While drawing an arc by choosing the **Start, Center, Angle** tool, if you enter the included angle with a negative value, an arc will be drawn in the clockwise direction. (T/F)

2. After choosing the **ARC** command, if you press ENTER instead of specifying the start point, the start point and direction of the arc will be taken from the endpoint and ending direction of the previous line or the arc drawn. (T/F)

3. By using the **Single Line Text** tool, you can write more than one line of text. (T/F)

4. The start and end parameters of an elliptical arc are determined by specifying a point on the circle whose diameter is equal to the minor diameter of an ellipse. (T/F)

5. The _____ option of the **RECTANG** command is used to draw a rectangle at a specified distance from the *XY* plane along the *Z* axis.

6. If the **FILLMODE** is set to _____, only the outlines for the new polyline will be drawn.

7. You can get a _____ polyline by entering two different values at the starting width and ending width prompts.

8. Choose the _____ tool from the **Draw** panel to place points at specified intervals on an object.

9. Choose the _____ tool from the **Draw** panel to draw as many points as you want in a single command.

10. The size of a point will be taken as a percentage of the viewport size, if you enter a _____ value for the **PDSIZE** variable.

Review Questions

Answer the following questions:

1. While drawing an arc by choosing the **Start, End, Angle** tool, a negative included angle value draws the arc in the clockwise direction. (T/F)

2. When the **Continue** option of the **ARC** command is used to draw arcs, each successive arc is perpendicular to the previous one. (T/F)

3. If you specify the chamfer distances first and then specify the fillet radius in the same **RECTANG** command, the rectangle will be drawn with chamfers only. (T/F)

4. A rectangle drawn using the **Rectangle** tool is treated as a combination of different objects; therefore, the individual sides can be edited independently. (T/F)

5. On drawing an arc by choosing the **Start, Center, Length** tool, a positive chord length generates the smallest possible arc (minor arc), and the arc is always less than

   (a) 90 degree (b) 180 degree
   (c) 270 degree (d) 360 degree

6. Which one of the following options of the **Rectangle** tool is used to draw a rectangle that is extruded in the Z direction by a specified value?

   (a) **Elevation** (b) **Thickness**
   (c) **Extrude** (d) **Width**

7. Which of the following commands should be used to draw a line in 3D space that starts from a specified start point and the other end extends to infinity?

   (a) **PLINE** (b) **RAY**
   (c) **XLINE** (d) **MLINE**

8. A polygon is said to be _____, when it is drawn inside an imaginary circle and its vertices touch the circle.

9. If additional polyline segments are added to the first polyline, the _____ of the first polyline segment becomes the start point of the next polyline segment.

10. To create a solid-filled circle by using the **DONUT** tool, the value of the inside diameter of the circle should be _____.

11. Using the **DONUT** tool, you can draw a solid-filled circle by specifying the inside diameter as _____ and keeping the **FILLMODE** on.

12. The _____ option of the **XLINE** tool is used to create xlines of infinite length that are parallel to the *Y* axis of the current UCS.

13. You can use the _____ key to edit text on the screen, while writing it using the **Single Line Text** tool.

EXERCISE 13   *Arc*

Draw the sketch shown in Figure 3-49. The distance between the dotted lines is 1.0 unit. Create the radii by choosing appropriate tools from the **Arc** drop-down.

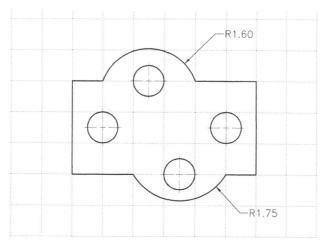

Figure 3-49 *Drawing for Exercise 13*

EXERCISE 14   *Arc*

Draw the sketch shown in Figure 3-50. The distance between the dotted lines is 1.0 unit. Create arcs by choosing appropriate tools from the **Arc** drop-down.

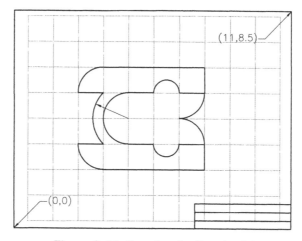

Figure 3-50 *Drawing for Exercise 14*

EXERCISE 15   *Ellipse*

Draw the sketch shown in Figure 3-51. The distance between the dotted lines is 0.5 unit. Create ellipses using the tools in the **Ellipse** drop-down.

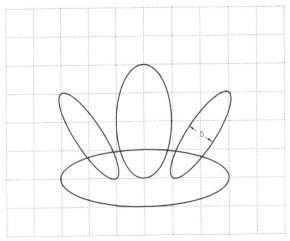

Figure 3-51 Drawing for Exercise 15

EXERCISE 16

Draw the sketch shown in Figure 3-52 using the **LINE, CIRCLE,** and **ARC** commands. The distance between the dotted lines is 1.0 unit and the diameter of the circles is 1.0 unit.

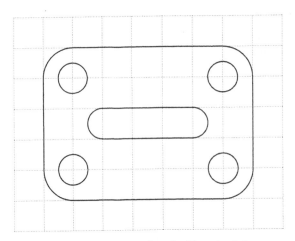

Figure 3-52 Drawing for Exercise 16

EXERCISE 17

Draw the sketch shown in Figure 3-53 using the **LINE, CIRCLE,** and **ARC** commands or their options. The distance between the grid lines is 1.0 unit and the diameter of the circle is 1.0 unit.

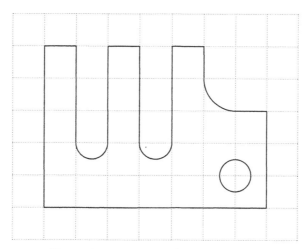

Figure 3-53 *Drawing for Exercise 17*

Problem-Solving Exercise 1 *Arc*

Draw the sketch shown in Figure 3-54. Create arcs by using the **ARC** command options indicated in the drawing. (Use the @ symbol to snap to the previous point. Example: Specify start point of arc or [Center]: @)

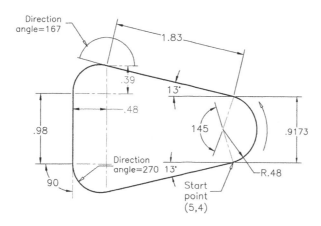

Figure 3-54 *Drawing for Problem-Solving Exercise 1*

Problem-Solving Exercise 2 *Arc*

Draw the sketch shown in Figure 3-55. Create arcs by using the **ARC** command options. The distance between the dotted lines is 0.5 unit.

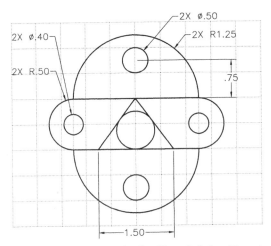

Figure 3-55 Drawing for Problem-Solving Exercise 2

Problem-Solving Exercise 3   *Arc*

Draw the sketch shown in Figure 3-56. Create arcs by using the **ARC** command options. The distance between the dotted lines is 1.0 unit.

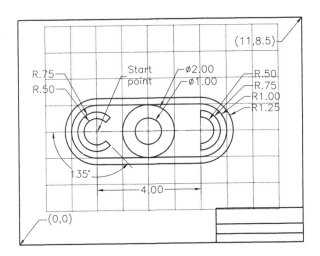

Figure 3-56 Drawing for Problem-Solving Exercise 3

Problem-Solving Exercise 4

Draw the sketch shown in Figure 3-57 by using the **POLYGON, CIRCLE,** and **LINE** commands.

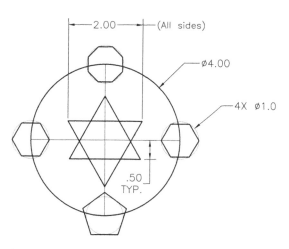

Figure 3-57 *Drawing for Problem-Solving Exercise 4*

Problem-Solving Exercise 5

Draw the sketch shown in Figure 3-58 by using different tools in the **Draw** panel. Note, Sin30=0.5, Sin60=0.866. The distance between the dotted lines is 1 unit.

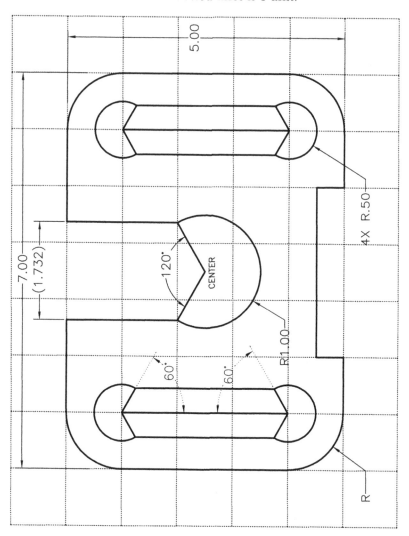

Figure 3-58 Drawing for Problem-Solving Exercise 5

Problem-Solving Exercise 6

Draw the sketch shown in Figure 3-59 by using different tools in the **Draw** panel. Also, draw the hidden lines and centerlines as continuous line. Note that the dimensions are given only for your reference.

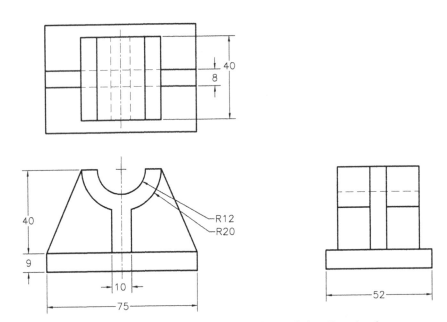

Figure 3-59 Drawing for the Problem-Solving Exercise 6

Answers to Self-Evaluation Test

1. T, **2.** T, **3.** T, **4.** F, **5. Elevation**, **6.** 0, **7.** tapered, **8. Measure**, **9. Multiple Point**, **10.** negative

Chapter 4

Working with Drawing Aids

CHAPTER OBJECTIVES

In this chapter, you will learn:
- *To set up layers, and assign colors and line type to layers.*
- *To change general object properties using the Properties toolbar.*
- *To change object properties using the PROPERTIES command.*
- *To determine the line type scaling and the LTSCALE factor for plotting.*
- *To set up Grid, Snap, and Ortho modes.*
- *To use the object snaps and running Object Snap modes.*
- *To use AutoTracking to locate keypoints in a drawing.*

KEY TERMS

- *Layer*
- *Freeze*
- *Thaw*
- *Plot Style*

- *Reconciling Layers*
- *Isolating Layers*
- *Quick Properties*

- *Global Linetype scaling*
- *Current Linetype scaling*

- *DesignCenter*
- *DSETTINGS*
- *ONSAP*

INTRODUCTION

In this chapter, you will learn about the drawing setup and the factors that affect the quality and accuracy of a drawing. This chapter contains a detailed description of how to set up layers. You will also learn about some other drawing aids, such as Grid, Snap, and Ortho. These aids help you in creating drawings accurately and quickly.

UNDERSTANDING THE CONCEPT AND USE OF LAYERS

The concept of layers can be best explained by using the concept of overlays in manual drafting. In manual drafting, different details of a drawing can be drawn on different sheets of paper or overlays. Each overlay is perfectly aligned with the others. Once all of them are placed on top of each other, you can reproduce the entire drawing. For example, in Figure 4-1, the object lines are drawn in the first overlay and the dimensions in the second overlay. You can place these overlays on top of each other and get a combined look of the drawing.

In AutoCAD LT, instead of using overlays, you can use layers. Each layer is assigned a name. You can also assign a color and a line type to a layer. For example, in Figure 4-2, the object lines are drawn in the OBJECT layer and the dimensions are drawn in the DIM layer. The object lines will be red because red has been assigned to the OBJECT layer. Similarly, the dimension lines will be green because green has been assigned to the DIM layer. You can display the layers together, individually, or in any combination.

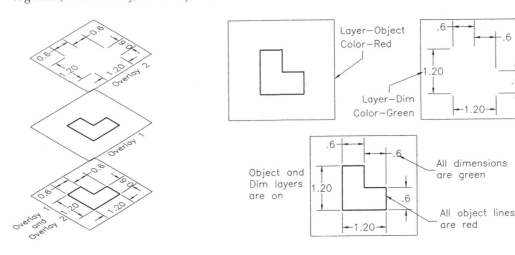

Figure 4-1 *Drawing lines and dimensions in different overlays*

Figure 4-2 *Drawing lines and dimensions in different layers*

Advantages of Using Layers

1. Each layer can be assigned a different color. Assigning a particular color to a group of objects is very important for plotting. For example, if all object lines are red, then at the time of plotting, you can assign the red color to a slot (pen) that has the desired tip width (e.g., medium). Similarly, if the dimensions are green, you can assign the green color to another slot (pen) that has a thin tip. By assigning different colors to different layers, you can control the width of lines while plotting the drawing. You can also make a layer plottable or non-plottable.

2. Layers are also useful for performing some editing operations. For example, to erase all dimensions in a drawing, you can freeze or lock all layers except the dimension layer, then select all objects by using the Window Crossing option, and erase all dimensions.

3. You can turn off a layer or freeze a layer that you do not want to be displayed or plotted.

4. You can lock a layer to prevent the user from accidentally editing the objects in it.

5. Colors also help you distinguish different groups of objects. For example, in architectural drafting, the plans for foundation, floors, plumbing, electrical work, and heating systems may be made in different layers. In electronic drafting and in PCB (printed circuit board), the design of each level of a multilevel circuit board can be drawn on a separate layer. Similarly, in mechanical engineering, the main components of an assembly can be made in one layer, other components such as nuts, bolts, keys, and washers can be made in another layer, and the annotations such as datum symbols and identifiers, texture symbols, Balloons, and Bill of Materials can be made in yet another layer.

WORKING WITH LAYERS

| **Ribbon:** | Home > Layers > Layer Properties | **Command:** | LAYER or LA |
| **Toolbar:** | Layers > Layer Properties Manager | | |

You can freeze, thaw, lock, unlock, and so on by using the **Layers** panel in the **Ribbon** (see Figure 4-3). However, to add new layers, to delete the existing layers, or to assign colors and linetypes to layers, you need to invoke the **Layer Properties Manager**. To invoke the **Layer Properties Manager**, choose the **Layer Properties** button from the **Layers** panel in the **Home** tab, or invoke it from the **Layers** toolbar (see Figure 4-4).

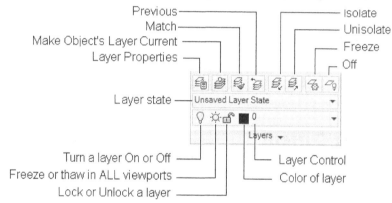

*Figure 4-3 The **Layers** panel*

*Figure 4-4 The **Layers** toolbar*

On invoking the **Layer Properties Manager**, a default layer with the name 0 is displayed. It is the current layer and any object you draw is created in it. The current layer can be recognized by the green colored tick mark in the **Status** column. There are certain features such as color, linetype, and lineweight are associated with each layer. The **0** layer has the default color as white, linetype as continuous, and lineweight as default.

Creating New Layers

To create new layers, choose the **New Layer** button in the **Layer Properties Manager**; a new layer, named Layer1, with the same properties as that of the current layer will be created and listed, as shown in Figure 4-5. Alternatively, right-click anywhere in the **Layers** list area of the **Layer Properties Manager** and then choose the **New Layer** option from the shortcut menu to create a new layer. If there are more layers and you right-click on a layer other than the current layer and then choose **New Layer** from the shortcut menu, a new layer will be created with the properties similar to the layer on which you right-clicked. To create a new layer that is automatically frozen in all viewports, choose the **New Layer VP Frozen in All Viewports** button.

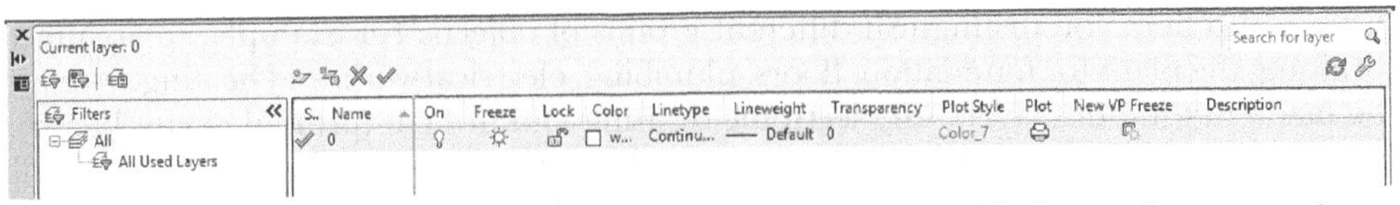

*Figure 4-5 Partial view of the **Layer Properties Manager** with the new layer created*

Naming a New Layer

New layers are created with the name layer 1, layer 2, and so on. To change or edit the name of a layer, select it, then click once in the field corresponding to the **Name** column and enter a new name. Some of the points to be remembered while naming a layer are given below.

1. A layer name can be up to 255 characters long, including letters (a-z), numbers (0-9), special characters ($ _ -), and spaces. Any combination of lower and uppercase letters can be used while naming a layer. However, characters such as <>;:,'?*|"=, and so on are not valid characters while naming a layer.

2. Layers should be named to help the user identify the contents of the layer. For example, if a layer name is HATCH, a user can easily identify it and its contents. On the other hand, if a layer's name is X261, it is hard to identify its contents.

3. Layer names should be short, but should also convey the meaning.

Tip
If you exchange drawings or provide drawings to consultants or others, it is very important that you standardize and coordinate layer names and other layer settings.

Making a Layer Current

To draw an object in a particular layer, you need to make it the current layer. There are different methods to make a layer current and they are listed below.

1. Double-click on the name of a layer in the list box in the **Layer Properties Manager**; the selected layer is made current.
2. Select the name of the layer in the **Layer Properties Manager** and then choose the **Set Current** button in the **Layer Properties Manager**.
3. Right-click on a layer in the **Layer** list box in the **Layer Properties Manager** and choose the **Set current** option from the shortcut menu displayed, see Figure 4-6.
4. Select a layer from the **Layer** drop-down list in the **Layers** toolbar or from the **Layers** panel.
5. Choose the **Make Object's Layer Current** button from the **Layers** panel; you will be prompted to select the object whose layer you want to make current. Select the required object; the layer associated with that object will become current.

On making a layer as the current layer, a green color tick mark will be displayed in the **Status** column of that layer. The name and properties of the current layer will be displayed in the **Layers** toolbar and the name of the current layer will be displayed at the upper-left corner of the **Layer Properties Manager**.

Note
*If you select more than one layer at a time using the SHIFT or CTRL key, the **Make Current** option does not appear in the shortcut menu in the **Layer Properties Manager**. This is because only one layer can be made current at a time.*

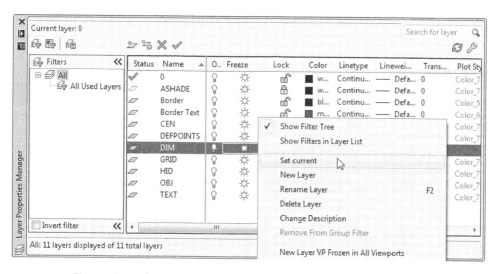

*Figure 4-6 The **Layer Properties Manager** with the shortcut menu*

Controlling the Display of Layers

You can control the display of layers by choosing the **Turn a layer On or Off**, **Freeze or thaw in ALL viewports**, and **Lock or Unlock a layer** toggle buttons in the list box of any particular layer.

Turn a layer On or Off

Choose the **Turn a layer On or Off** toggle icon (bulb) to turn a layer on or off. You can also turn the layer on or off by clicking on the **On/Off** toggle icon from the **Layer** drop-down list in the **Layers** toolbar or the **Layers** panel, as shown in Figure 4-7. The objects in the layers that are turned on are displayed and can be plotted, while the objects in the layers that are turned off are not displayed and cannot be plotted. However, you can perform the operations such as drawing and editing of the objects in the layer that has been turned off. You can turn the current layer off, but AutoCAD LT will display a message box informing you that the current drawing layer has been turned off.

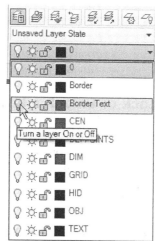

Figure 4-7 Turning off the Border Text layer

Freeze or thaw in ALL Viewports

Sometimes in an architectural drawing, you may not need the door tag, window tag, or surveyor data to be displayed, so that they are not changed. These types of information or entities can be placed in a particular layer and that layer can be frozen. You cannot edit the entities in the frozen layer. Also, frozen layers are invisible and cannot be plotted. To freeze a layer, select it and choose the **Freeze or thaw in ALL viewports** toggle icon (sun/snowflakes) in the **Layer Properties Manager**. Note that the current layer cannot be frozen. You can also select the **Freeze or thaw in ALL viewports** toggle icon in the **Layers** panel of the **Ribbon** or in the **Layers** toolbar to freeze or thaw a layer. The **Thaw** option negates the effect of the **Freeze** option, and the frozen layers are restored to normal. The difference between the usage of the **Off** option and the **Freeze** option is that in using the **Freeze** option, the layer is frozen and the entities in the frozen layer are not regenerated thereby saving time.

New VP Freeze

On choosing the **Layout** tab, you will observe that a default viewport is displayed. You can also create new viewports anytime during the design. If you want to freeze some layers in all the subsequent new viewports, select the layers, and then choose the **New VP Freeze** toggle icon.

The selected layers will be frozen in all the subsequently created viewports, without affecting the existing viewports.

VP Freeze

This icon will be available only if you invoke the **Layer Properties Manager** in the **Layout** tab, see Figure 4-8. The **Freeze or thaw in current viewport** icon will also be available the **Layer** drop-down list in the **Layers** panel of the **Ribbon** or in the **Layers** toolbar. If there are multiple viewports, make a viewport as the current viewport by double-clicking in it and freeze or thaw the selected layer in it by choosing the **VP Freeze** icon in the **Layout Properties Manager**. However, a layer that is frozen in the model space cannot be thawed in the current viewport.

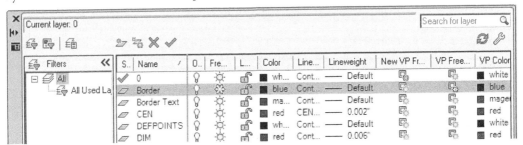

*Figure 4-8 Partial view of the **Layer Properties Manager** with the **VP Freeze** icon*

Tip
*To increase or decrease the width of column headings in the **Layer Properties Manager**, place the cursor on the separator that is between column headings; the cursor turns into a two-sided arrow. Now, press and hold the left mouse button and then drag the cursor to the right or left. This way you can change the width of the column headings.*

Lock or Unlock a Layer

While working on a drawing, if you want to avoid editing some objects on a particular layer but still need to have them visible, use the **Lock/Unlock** toggle icon to lock the layer. However, you can still use the objects in the locked layer for **Object Snaps** and inquiry commands such as **LIST**. You can also make the locked layer as the current layer and draw objects on it. Note that you can also plot a locked layer. The **Unlock** option negates the **Lock** option and allows you to edit objects on the layers that were previously locked.

Make a Layer Plottable or Nonplottable

By default, you can plot all layers, except the layers that are turned off or frozen. If you do not want to plot a layer that is not turned off or frozen, select the layer and choose the **Plot** icon (printer). This is a toggle icon, therefore you can choose this icon again to plot the layer.

Tip
*The faster and convenient way to make a layer current and control the display features of the layer (**On/Off**, **Freeze/Thaw**, **Lock/Unlock**) is by using the **Layer** drop-down list in the **Layers** panel.*

Assigning Linetype to a Layer

By default, continuous linetypes are assigned to a layer, if no layer is selected while creating a new layer. Otherwise, new layer takes the properties of the selected layer. To assign a new linetype to a layer, click on the field under the **Linetype** column of that layer in the **Layer Properties Manager**; the **Select Linetype** dialog box showing the linetypes loaded on your computer will be displayed. Select the new linetype and then choose the **OK** button; the selected linetype will be assigned to the layer.

If you are opening the **Select Linetype** dialog box for the first time, only the **Continuous** linetype will be displayed, as shown in Figure 4-9.

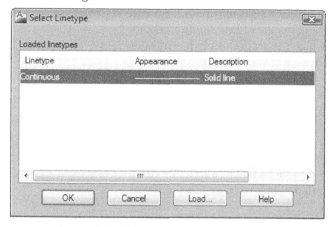

Figure 4-9 The Select Linetype dialog box

You need to load linetypes and then assign them to layers. To load linetypes, choose the **Load** button in the **Select Linetype** dialog box; the **Load or Reload Linetypes** dialog box will be displayed, see Figure 4-10. This dialog box displays all linetypes in the *acadlt.lin* or *acadltiso.lin* file. In this dialog box, you can select a single linetype, or a number of linetypes by pressing and holding the SHIFT or CTRL key and then selecting the linetypes. After selecting the linetypes, choose the **OK** button; the selected linetypes are loaded in the **Select Linetype** dialog box. Now, select the desired linetype and choose **OK**; the selected linetype is assigned to the selected layer.

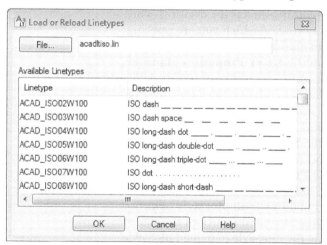

Figure 4-10 The Load or Reload Linetypes dialog box

Assigning Transparency to a Layer

By default, no transparency is assigned to a layer, if **Layer 0** is selected while creating that layer. Otherwise, new layer takes the transparency of the selected layer. To assign transparency to a layer, click on the **Transparency** field of that layer; the **Layer Transparency** dialog box will be displayed. Select the required transparency level from the **Transparency Value (0-90)** drop-down list and choose **OK**. You can also enter a value in this drop-down list. Now, if you place an object on this layer, the object will have a faded color according to the specified transparency value.

Assigning Color to a Layer

To assign a color to a layer, select the color swatch in that layer in the **Layer Properties Manager**; the **Select Color** dialog box will be displayed. Select the desired color and then choose the **OK** button; the selected color will be assigned to the layer.

Assigning Lineweight to a Layer

Lineweight is used to give thickness to objects in a layer. For example, if you create a sectional plan, you can assign a layer with a larger value of lineweight to create the objects through which the section is made. Another layer with a lesser lineweight can be used to show the objects through which the section does not pass. This thickness is displayed on the screen if the display of the lineweight is on. The lineweight assigned to an object can also be plotted. To assign a lineweight to a layer, select the layer and then click on the lineweight associated with it; the **Lineweight** dialog box will be displayed, see Figure 4-11. Select a lineweight and then choose **OK** from this dialog box to return to the **Layer Properties Manager**.

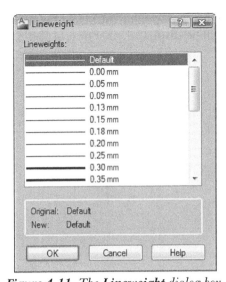

*Figure 4-11 The **Lineweight** dialog box*

Tip
*Remember that the **Linetype Control**, **Lineweight Control**, **Color Control**, and **Plot Style Control** list boxes in the **Properties** panel should display **ByLayer** as the current property of objects. This is to ensure that the objects drawn in a layer take the properties assigned to the layer in which they are drawn.*

Assigning Plot Style to a Layer

The plot style is a group of property settings such as color, linetype, and lineweight that can be assigned to a layer. The assigned plot style affects the drawings while plotting only. The drawing, in which you are working, should be in a named plot style mode (*.stb*) to make the plot style available in the **Layer Properties Manager**. If the **Plot Style** icon in the dialog box is not available, then you are in a color-dependent mode (*.ctb*). To make this icon available, choose the **Options** button from the **Application Menu**; the **Options** dialog box will be displayed. Choose the **Plot and Publish** tab from this dialog box. Next, choose the **Plot Style Table Settings** button to invoke the **Plot Style Table Settings** dialog box. In this dialog box, select the **Use named plot style** radio button from the **Default plot style behavior for new drawings** area and then exit both the dialog boxes. After changing the plot style to named plot style dependent, you have to start a new AutoCAD LT session to apply this setting. Start a new AutoCAD LT session with templates like *acad -Named Plot Styles* and invoke the **Layer Properties Manager**. You will notice that the default plot style is **Normal**, in which the color, linetype, and lineweight are BYLAYER. To assign a plot style to

*Figure 4-12 The **Select Plot Style** dialog box*

a layer, select the layer and then click on its plot style; the **Select Plot Style** dialog box will be displayed, as shown in Figure 4-12. In this dialog box, you can select a specific plot style from the **Plot styles** list of available plot styles. Plot styles need to be created before you can use them (see Chapter 12, *Plotting Drawings*). Choose **OK** to return to the **Layer Properties Manager**.

Note
When you are in a viewport, you can override the color, linetype, lineweight, and plot style settings assigned to a selected layer for the particular viewport (current viewport). These settings for

all other viewports and model space will remain unaffected. All these overrides are highlighted in different background colors. Also, the icon of the selected layer under the **Status** *column will change indicating that some of the properties of the selected layer have been overridden by the new ones (see Chapter 11, Model Space Viewports, Paper Space Viewports, and Layouts).*

Tip
You can also change the plot style mode from the command line by using the **PSTYLEPOLICY** *system variable. A value of 0 sets it to the color-dependent mode and a value of 1 sets it to the named mode.*

Deleting Layers

You can delete a layer by selecting it and then choosing the **Delete Layer** button in the **Layer Properties Manager**. Remember that you cannot a delete a layer that contains any object. Additionally, you cannot delete layers 0, Defpoints (created while dimensioning), Ashade (created while rendering), current layer, and an Xref-dependent layer.

EXAMPLE 1			*Layers*

Set up three layers with the following linetypes and colors. Then create the drawing shown in Figure 4-13(without dimensions).

Layer Name	Color	Linetype	Lineweight
Obj	Red	Continuous	0.012"
Hid	Yellow	Hidden	0.008"
Cen	Green	Center	0.006"

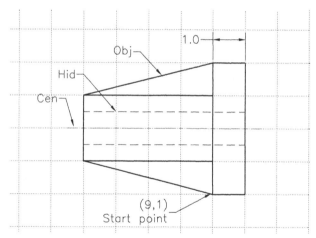

Figure 4-13 *Drawing for Example 1*

In this example, assume that the limits and units are already set. Before drawing the lines, you need to create layers and assign colors, linetypes, and lineweights to them. Also, depending on the objects that you want to draw, you need to set a layer as the current layer. In this example, you will create layers by using the **Layer Properties Manager**. You will use the **Layer** drop-down list in the **Layers** panel to set a layer as the current layer and then draw the figure.

1. As the lineweights specified are given in inches, first you need to change their units, if they are in millimeters. To do so, invoke the **Lineweight Settings** dialog box by right-clicking on the **Show/Hide Lineweight** button on the Status Bar and then choose the **Settings** option from the shortcut menu. Select the **Inches [in]** radio button in the **Units for Listing** area of the dialog box and then choose the **OK** button.

2. Choose the **Layer Properties** button from the **Layers** panel in the **Home** tab of the **Ribbon** to display the **Layer Properties Manager**. The layer **0** with default properties is displayed in the list box.

3. Choose the **New Layer** button; a new layer (Layer1) with the default properties is displayed in the list box. Change the default name, **Layer1** to **Obj**.

4. Left-click on the **Color** field of this layer; the **Select Color** dialog box is displayed. Select the **Red** color and then choose **OK**; red color is assigned to the **Obj** layer.

5. Left-click on the **Lineweight** field of the **Obj** layer; the **Lineweight** dialog box is displayed. Select **0.012"** and then choose **OK**; the selected lineweight is assigned to the **Obj** layer.

6. Again, choose the **New Layer** button; a new layer (Layer1) with properties similar to that of the **Obj** layer is created. Change the default name to **Hid**.

7. Left-click on the **Color** field of this layer; the **Select Color** dialog box is displayed. Select the **Yellow** color and then choose **OK**.

8. Left-click on the **Linetype** field of the **Hid** layer; the **Select Linetype** dialog box is displayed. If the **HIDDEN** linetype is not displayed in the dialog box, choose the **Load** button; the **Load and Reload Linetypes** dialog box is displayed. Select **HIDDEN** from the list and choose the **OK** button from the **Load and Reload Linetypes** dialog box. Next, select **HIDDEN** from the **Select Linetype** dialog box and then choose **OK**.

9. Left-click on the **Lineweight** field of the **Hid** layer; the **Lineweight** dialog box is displayed. Select **0.008"** and then choose **OK**; the selected lineweight is assigned to the **Hid** layer.

10. Similarly, create the new layer **Cen** and assign the color **Green**, linetype **CENTER**, and lineweight **0.006"** to it.

11. Select the **Obj** layer and then choose the **Set Current** button to make the **Obj** layer current, see Figure 4-14. Choose the **Close** button to exit the dialog box.

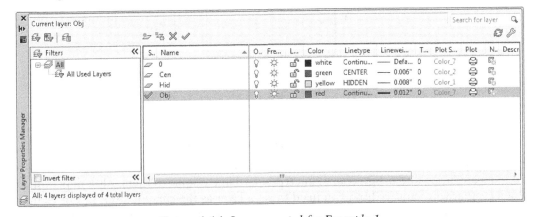

Figure 4-14 Layers created for Example 1

12. Choose the **Show/Hide Lineweight** button from the Status Bar to turn on the display of the lineweights of the lines to be drawn.

13. Choose the **Dynamic Input** button from the Status Bar to turn it on.

14. Choose the **Line** button from the **Draw** panel and draw solid lines in the drawing shown in Figure 4-13. Make sure the start point of the line is at 9,1. You will notice that a continuous line is drawn in red color. This is because the **Obj** layer is the current layer and red color is assigned to it.

15. Click the down arrow in the **Layer** drop-down list available in the **Layers** panel to display the list of layers and then select the **Hid** layer from the list to make it current, as shown in Figure 4-15.

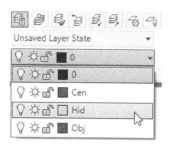

16. Draw two hidden lines; the lines are displayed in yellow color with hidden linetype.

17. Draw the center line; the centerline is displayed in yellow color with hidden linetype. This is because the **Hid** layer is the current layer.

*Figure 4-15 Selecting the **Hid** layer from the **Layers** panel to set it as the current layer*

18. Now, select the centerline and then select the **Cen** layer from the **Layer** drop-down list available in the **Layers** panel; the color and linetype of the centerline is changed.

EXERCISE 1   *Layers*

Set up layers with the following linetypes and colors. Then make the drawing (without dimensions) as shown in Figure 4-16. The distance between the dotted lines is 1 unit.

Layer Name	Color	Linetype
Object	Red	Continuous
Hidden	Yellow	Hidden
Center	Green	Center
Dimension	Blue	Continuous

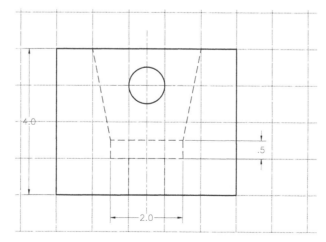

Figure 4-16 Drawing for Exercise 1

OBJECT PROPERTIES

Drawing entities have properties such as color, linetype, lineweight, and plot style based on the layer it is associated with. However, you can change these properties by using the **Properties** palette or the **Properties** panel in the **Home** tab of the **Ribbon**. By default, the **By Layer** option will be selected in the **Object Color**, **Lineweight**, and **Linetype** drop-down lists of the **Properties** panel in the **Ribbon**. Therefore, the properties set in the current layer will be applied to the entities in it. The procedure to change the properties of the selected objects is discussed next.

Changing the Color

Select the object whose color you want to change; the current color of the object will be displayed in the **Object Color** drop-down list. To change this color, select the down arrow in the **Object Color** drop-down list, as shown in Figure 4-17, and select a new color; the selected color will be applied to the object. If you want to assign a color that is not displayed in the list, select the **Select Colors** option; the **Select Color** dialog box will be displayed. You can select the desired color in this dialog box, and then choose the **OK** button.

To set a color other than the one set in the current layer as the current color, choose a color from the **Object Color** drop-down list without selecting an object. Now, all new objects will be drawn in this color.

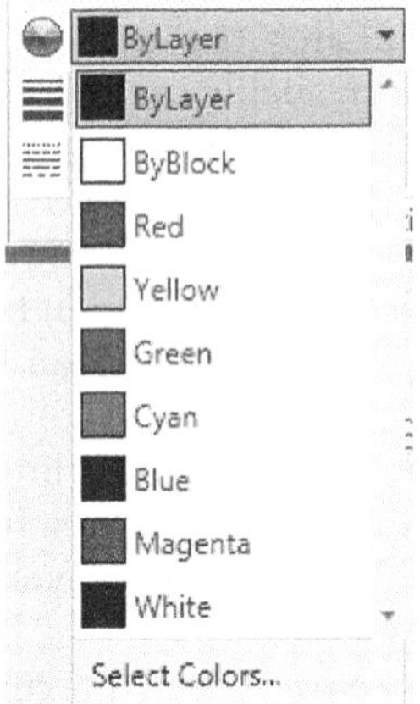

Changing the Linetype

To set a linetype other than the one set in the current layer as the current linetype, select a linetype from the **Linetype** drop-down list in the **Properties** panel from the **Home** tab, as shown in Figure 4-18. Now, all objects will be drawn in this linetype.

*Figure 4-17 Different colors in the **Object Color** drop-down list*

To assign a linetype that is not displayed in the list, choose the **Other** option; the **Linetype Manager** dialog box will be displayed, as shown in Figure 4-19. By default, the **ByLayer**, **ByBlock**, and **Continuous** linetypes will be listed in this dialog box. To load other linetypes, choose the **Load** button; the **Load or Reload Linetypes** dialog box will be displayed. Select a linetype in this dialog box; they will be displayed in the **Linetype Manager** dialog box. Next, select the required linetype from this dialog box and choose **OK**. You can also make a linetype current by using the **Current** button in the **Linetype Manager** dialog box.

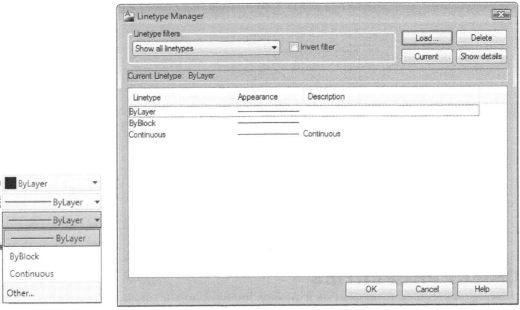

*Figure 4-18 The **Line type** drop-down list*

*Figure 4-19 The **Linetype Manager** dialog box*

Changing the Lineweight

To change the lineweight of a selected object, select a different lineweight value from the **Lineweight** drop-down list in the **Properties** panel. Also, you can set a new lineweight as current by selecting it from the list. To assign a lineweight value that is not listed in the drop-down list, select the **Lineweight Settings** option from the **Lineweight** drop-down list; the **Lineweight Settings** dialog box will be displayed, as shown in Figure 4-20. You can also invoke this dialog box by choosing the **Settings** option from the shortcut menu that is displayed on right-clicking on the **Hide/Show Lineweight** button on the Status Bar. In this dialog box, set the current lineweight for the objects. You can change the units for the lineweight and also the

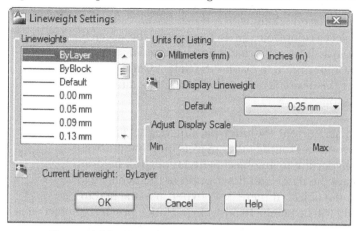

Figure 4-20 *The Lineweight Settings dialog box*

display of lineweights for the current drawing. Lineweights are displayed in pixel widths and depending on the lineweight value chosen, the lineweights are displayed if the **Display Lineweight** check box is selected. For a large drawing, displaying lineweight increases the regeneration time, and therefore the corresponding check box should be cleared. As mentioned earlier, you can also turn the display of lineweights to on or off directly from the Status Bar by choosing the **Hide/Show Lineweight** button. The value set in the **Adjust Display Scale** slider bar also affects the regeneration time. You can keep the slider bar at **Max** for getting a good display of different lineweights on the screen in the Model space; otherwise, keep it at **Min** for a faster regeneration.

Changing the Plot Style

You can change the plot style by using the **Plot Style** drop-down list. The options in this drop-down list will be available only if you are using the named plot style modes. To change the plot style, select a plot style from the **Plot Style** drop-down list in the **Properties** panel. Also, you can also set a new plot style as current by selecting it from the drop-down list.

Properties Palette

| **Ribbon:** View > Palettes > Properties | **Command:** PROPERTIES, CH, MO |
| **Toolbar:** Standard > Properties | |

The **Properties** palette is used to set the current properties and to change the general properties of the selected objects. The **Properties** palette (see Figure 4-21) is displayed on choosing the **Properties** button from the **Palettes** panel. It can also be invoked by right-clicking on an object and then choosing the **Properties** option from the shortcut menu. Right-clicking in the **Properties** palette displays a shortcut menu from where you can choose Allow Docking or Hide to dock or hide the palette.

When you select an object, the **Properties** palette displays the properties of the selected object. Depending on the object selected, the properties differ. If you change the properties in the **Properties** palette without selecting any object, the current properties will be changed in the **Properties** panel in the **Home** tab. Now, if you draw an object, it will have the properties set in the **Properties** palette.

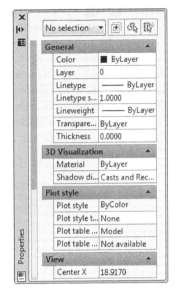

When you select **Color** from the **General** list, the color of the selected object is displayed, along with a down arrow. Click the down arrow and select a color from the list to assign to the selected object. If you want to assign a color that is not displayed in the list, choose the **Select Color** option to display the **Select Color** dialog box. You can select the desired color in this dialog box, and then choose the **OK** button.

Similarly, you can set current the linetype, lineweight, linetype scale, and other properties for the other objects individually. You can also assign a hyperlink to an object. The **Hyperlink** field in this window displays the name and description of the hyperlink, if any, assigned to the object. If there is no hyperlink attached to

Figure 4-21 The Properties palette

the object, this field will be blank. To add a hyperlink to a selected object, click on this field; the [**...**] button will be displayed in this field. Choose the [**...**] button; the **Insert Hyperlink** dialog box will be displayed where you can enter the path of the URL or the file that you want to link to the selected object.

Note
*You can enter the **CHPROP** command at the command line to change the properties of an object. You can also change the general properties of an object by using the **Properties** option of the **CHANGE** command.*

*The system variables **CECOLOR**, **CELTYPE**, and **CELWEIGHT** control the current color, linetype, and lineweight of an object. You can set the properties of objects current by using these variables from the command line.*

When you set the property of an object current, it does not consider the property of the layer, in which the object will be drawn.

EXERCISE 2   *Object Properties*

Draw a hexagon on the **Obj** layer in red. Keep the linetype hidden. Now, use the **Properties** palette to change the layer, the color to yellow, and the linetype to continuous.

Quick Properties Palette

Status Bar: Quick Properties

In AutoCAD LT, you can view some of the properties of the selected entity in the **Quick Properties** palette or in the **Properties** palette. To view the properties, keep the **Quick Properties** button chosen in the Status Bar and then select an entity; some of the properties of the selected entity will be displayed in the **Quick Properties** palette. Alternatively, enter **QP** at the Command prompt or the **Dynamic Input** to invoke the **Quick Properties** palette. You can change the properties that are displayed in the **Quick Properties** palette. Figure 4-22 shows the **Quick Properties** palette that is displayed on selecting a line.

If you select multiple objects of different types, then in the drop-down list available in the **Quick Properties** palette, the name of the objects will be defined as **All** and the number of selected entities will be displayed in parenthesis. After selecting multiple entities, you can also select a particular type of object from the drop-down list to view the properties of the particular object type.

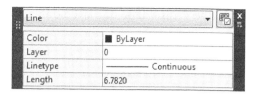

*Figure 4-22 The **Quick Properties** palette*

To set the properties displayed in the **Quick Properties** palette, right-click on the **Quick Properties** button in the Status Bar and choose the **Settings** option; the **Drafting Settings** dialog box will be displayed with the **Quick Properties** tab chosen. You can specify the display of the object type, the position of palette on invoking, and the height of palette by selecting a suitable option in this dialog box.

You can customize the **Quick Properties** palette such that it displays the required properties of a selected entity. To do so, choose the **Customize** button available next to the drop-down list; the **Customize User Interface** dialog box will be displayed. In the dialog box, different object types and their corresponding properties will be displayed on the right. If you select an object type, you will notice that the check boxes of some of the properties are selected. The properties, whose check boxes are selected, will be listed in the **Quick Properties** palette. You can also select the check boxes of the properties that you want to be displayed in the **Quick Properties** palette. If you place the cursor over an entity and pause, a tooltip, called the rollover tooltip, will be displayed. You can synchronize the properties displayed in the rollover tooltip and the **Quick Properties** panel. To do so, invoke the **Customize User Interface** dialog box, right-click on the **Rollover Tooltips** subnode in it, and choose the **Synchronize with Quick Properties** option.

DRAFTING SETTINGS DIALOG BOX

Command: DSETTINGS

You can use the **Drafting Settings** dialog box to set the drawing modes such as Grid, Snap, Object Snap, Polar, Object Snap tracking, and Dynamic Input. All these modes help you draw accurately and also increase the drawing speed. You can right-click on the **Snap Mode**, **Grid Display**, **Ortho Mode**, **Polar Tracking**, **Object Snap**, **3D Object Snap**, **Object Snap Tracking**, **Dynamic Input**, **Quick Properties**, or **Selection Cycling** button in the Status Bar to display a shortcut menu. In this shortcut menu, choose **Settings** to display the **Drafting Settings** dialog box, as shown in Figure 4-23. This dialog box has seven tabs: **Snap and Grid**, **Polar Tracking**, **Object Snap**, **3D Object Snap**, **Dynamic Input**, **Quick Properties**, and **Selection Cycling**. On starting AutoCAD LT, these tabs have default settings. You can change them according to your requirements.

Setting Grid

Grid lines are the checked lines on the screen at predefined spacing, see Figure 4-24. In AutoCAD LT 2012, by default, the grids are displayed as checked lines. In the earlier versions, the grids were displayed as dotted lines, see Figure 4-25. To display the grids as dotted lines, select the **2D model space** check box in the **Grid style** area. These dotted lines act as a graph that can be used as reference lines in a drawing. You can change the distance between grid lines as per your requirement. If grid lines are displayed within the drawing limits, it helps to define the working area. The grid also gives you an idea about the size of the drawing objects. By default, the grid will be displayed beyond the limits. To display the grid up to the limits, use the **GRID** command and set the **Display grid beyond Limits [Yes/No] <Yes>:** option to **No**.

Chapter 4

Now, the grids will be displayed only up to the limits set.

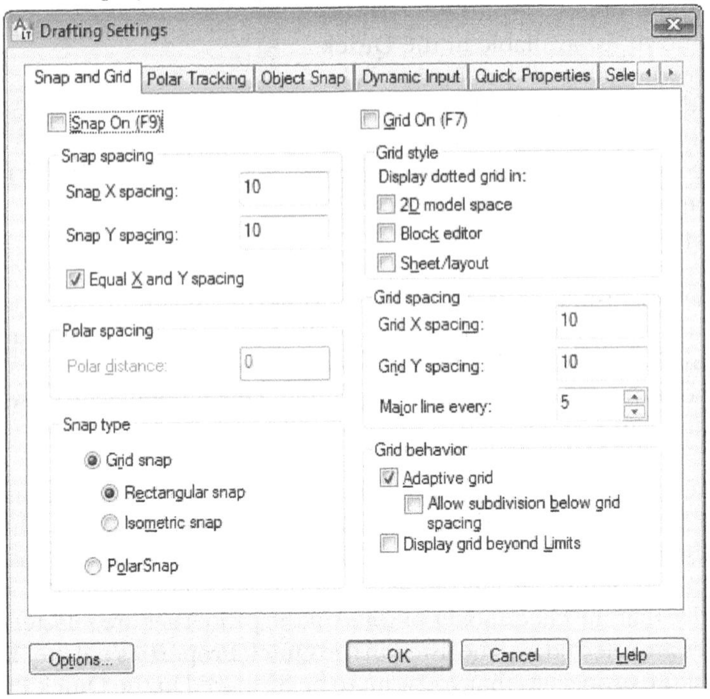

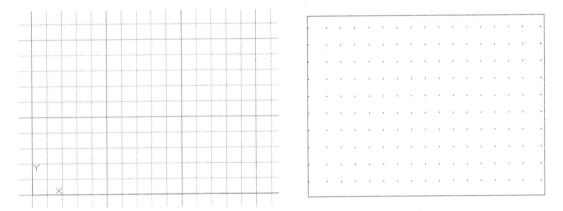

Figure 4-23 The **Drafting Settings** *dialog box*

Figure 4-24 *Grid as checked lines*   *Figure 4-25* *Grid as dots*

Grid On (F7): Turning the Grid On or Off

You can turn the grid display on/off by using the **Grid On** check box in the **Drafting Settings** dialog box. You can also turn the grid display on/off by choosing the **Grid Display** button in the Status Bar or by using the F7 key. **Grid Display** is a toggle button. When the grid display is turned on after it has been turned off, the grid is set to the previous grid spacing.

Grid X Spacing and Grid Y Spacing

The **Grid X spacing** and **Grid Y spacing** edit boxes in the **Drafting Settings** dialog box are used to define the desired grid spacing along the X and Y axes. For example, to set the grid spacing to 0.5 units, enter **0.5** in the **Grid X spacing** and **Grid Y spacing** edit boxes. You can also enter different values for the horizontal and vertical grid spacing, see Figure 4-26. If you specify only the grid X spacing value and then choose the **OK** button in the dialog box, the corresponding Y spacing value will automatically be set to match the X spacing value. Therefore, if you want different X and Y spacing values as shown in Figure 4-27, clear the **Equal X and Y spacing** check box in the **Snap spacing** area, and enter different X and Y spacing values.

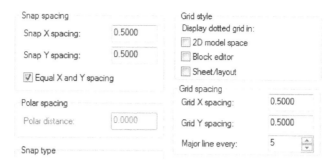

 Note
Grids are especially effective in drawing when the objects in the drawing are placed at regular intervals.

*Figure 4-26 The **Grid Spacing** area of the **Drafting Settings** dialog box*

Setting Snap

After displaying the grid, you need to switch on the snap mode so that the cursor snaps to the snap point. The snap points are invisible points (see Figure 4-28) that are created at the intersection of invisible horizontal and vertical lines. A snap point is independent of the grid spacing and the two can have equal or different values. Therefore, when the snap mode is on, the cursor moves in specified intervals from one point to another. You can turn on the snap mode even when the grid lines are invisible. To set snap spacing, enter the X and Y values in the corresponding edit boxes in the **Snap spacing** area of the **Snap and Grid** tab in the **Drafting Settings** dialog box, refer to Figure 4-26.

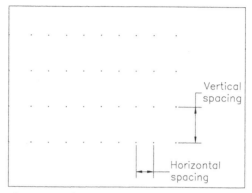

Figure 4-27 Creating unequal grid spacing

You can turn the snap mode on/off by selecting the **Snap On** check box from the **Drafting Settings** dialog box. You can also turn the snap on or off by choosing the **Snap Mode** button in the Status Bar, or from the shortcut menu displayed by right-clicking on the **Snap Mode** button in the Status Bar, or by using the function key F9 as a toggle key.

Snap Type

There are two snap types, **PolarSnap** and **Grid snap**. On selecting **Grid snap**, the cursor snaps along the grid. The **Grid snap** is either of the **Rectangular snap** type or of the **Isometric snap** type. Rectangular snap is the default snap and has been discussed earlier. The other types are discussed next.

Isometric Snap

The isometric mode is used to make isometric drawings. In isometric drawings, the isometric axes are at angles 30, 90, and 150 degrees. The isometric snap/grid enables you to display the grid lines along these axes, see Figure 4-29. Select the **Isometric snap** radio button in the **Snap type** area of the **Drafting Settings** dialog box to set the snap grid to the isometric mode. The default mode is off (standard). Once you select the **Isometric snap** radio button and choose **OK** in the dialog box, the cursor aligns with the isometric axis. You will notice that the X spacing is not available for this option. You can change the vertical snap and grid spacing by entering values in the **Snap Y spacing** and **Grid Y spacing** edit boxes. While drawing in isometric mode, you can adjust the cursor orientation to the left, top, or right plane of the drawing by using the F5 key. The procedure to create drawings using the **Isometric snap** option is discussed in later chapters.

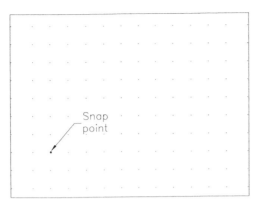

Figure 4-28 *Invisible Snap grid*

Figure 4-29 *Isometric Snap grid*

PolarSnap

The polar snap is used to snap points at a specified distance along the polar alignment angles. To set the snap mode as polar, select the **PolarSnap** radio button in the **Snap type** area; the **Polar distance** edit box will be enabled and the snap spacing options will be disabled. Enter a value for the distance in the **Polar distance** edit box and choose the **OK** button. If this value is zero, AutoCAD LT takes the same value as specified for Snap X spacing earlier. Now, if you draw a line, the cursor snaps along an imaginary line according to the Polar tracking angles that are relative to the last point selected. The polar tracking angle can be set in the **Polar Tracking** tab of the **Drafting Settings** dialog box (discussed later in this chapter).

For example, select the **PolarSnap** radio button and enter **0.5** in the **Polar distance** edit box. Choose the **Polar Tracking** tab and enter **30** in the **Increment angle** drop-down list and then choose the **OK** button. Choose the **Snap Mode** and **Polar Tracking** buttons in the Status Bar. Invoke the **Line** tool and select the start point anywhere on the screen. Now if you move the cursor at angles in multiples of 30-degree, a dotted line will be displayed and if you move the cursor along this dotted line, a small cross mark will be displayed at a distance of 0.5 (polar snap).

DRAWING STRAIGHT LINES USING THE ORTHO MODE

The **Ortho** mode is used to draw lines at right angles only. You can turn the Ortho mode on or off by choosing the **Ortho Mode** button in the Status Bar, by using the function key F8, or by using the **ORTHO** command. When the **Ortho** mode is on and you move the cursor to specify the next point, a rubber-band line is connected to the cursor in horizontal (parallel to the *X* axis) or vertical (parallel to the *Y* axis) direction. To draw a line in the Ortho mode, specify the start point at the **Specify first point** prompt. To specify the second point, move the cursor and specify a desired point. The line drawn will be either vertical or horizontal, depending on the direction in which you move the cursor, see Figures 4-30 and 4-31.

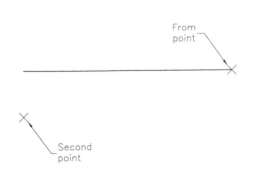

Figure 4-30 *Drawing a horizontal line using the ORTHO mode*

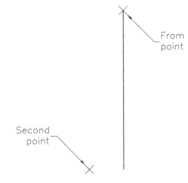

Figure 4-31 *Drawing a vertical line using the ORTHO mode*

Tip
*You can use the buttons in the Status Bar (at the bottom of the graphics area) to toggle between on or off for the different drafting functions like **Snap**, **Grid**, and **Ortho**.*

WORKING WITH OBJECT SNAPS

Toolbar: Object Snap

Object snaps are one of the most useful features of AutoCAD LT. They improve your performance and the accuracy of the drawing. Also, drafting is much simpler than it normally would be. The term object snap refers to the cursor's ability to snap exactly to a geometric point on an object. The advantage of using object snaps is that you do not have to specify an exact point. For example, to snap the midpoint of a line, use the **Midpoint** object snap and move the cursor closer to the object; a marker (in the form of a geometric shape, a triangle for Midpoint) will automatically be displayed at the mid point. Click to snap the mid point.

Object snaps recognize only the objects that are visible on the screen, which include the objects on the locked layers. The objects on the layers that are turned off or frozen are not visible, and they cannot be used for object snaps.

Object snapping can be done by using the **Object Snap modes** shortcut menu. To invoke this shortcut menu, choose a tool, press and hold the SHIFT key, and then right-click, see Figure 4-32. You can also do object snapping by using the **Object Snap** toolbar shown in Figure 4-33. Alternatively, you can invoke the **Object Snap modes** shortcut menu when you are inside any other sketching command. For example, invoke the **Center,Radius** tool from the **Draw** panel and then right-click to invoke the shortcut menu. From the shortcut menu, choose the **Snap Overrides** option to display the **Object Snaps** shortcut menu. The following are the object snap modes in AutoCAD LT.

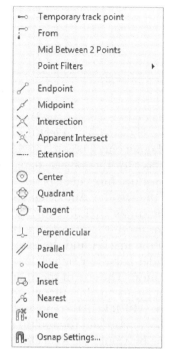

*Figure 4-32 The **Object snap** modes shortcut menu*

Endpoint	Center
Perpendicular	Nearest
Midpoint	Quadrant
Parallel	None
Intersection	Tangent
Insert	From
Apparent Intersection	Extension
Node	
Midpoint Between two points	

AutoSnap

The AutoSnap feature controls various characteristics for the object snap. As you move the target box over the object, AutoCAD LT displays the geometric marker corresponding to the shapes shown in the **Object Snap** tab of the **Drafting Settings** dialog box. You can change different AutoSnap settings such as attaching a target box to the cursor when you invoke any object snap, or change the size and color of the marker. These settings can be changed from the **Options** dialog box (**Drafting** tab). You can invoke the **Options** dialog box from the **Application Menu**, or by entering **OPTIONS** at the Command prompt. You can also invoke the dialog box by choosing the **Options** button in the **Drafting Settings** dialog box. After invoking the **Options**

Chapter 4

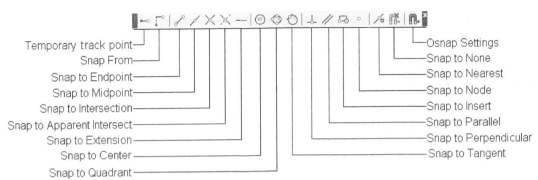

*Figure 4-33 The **Object Snap** toolbar*

dialog box, choose the **Drafting** tab in this dialog box; the **AutoSnap Settings** will be displayed, see Figure 4-34. Select the **Marker** check box to toggle the display of the marker. Select the **Magnet** check box to toggle the magnet that snaps the crosshairs to the particular point of the object for that object snap. You can use the **Display AutoSnap tooltip** and **Display AutoSnap aperture box** check boxes to toggle the display of the tooltip and the aperture box. Note that if the **Display AutoSnap tooltip** check box is selected in the **Options** dialog box and you move the cursor over an entity, after invoking a tool, the autosnap marker will be displayed. Now, do not move the cursor; the name of the object snap will be displayed. You can change the size of the marker and the aperture box by moving the **AutoSnap Marker Size** and **Aperture Size** slider bars, respectively. You can also change the color of the markers by choosing the **Colors** button. The size of the aperture is measured in pixels (short form of picture elements). Picture elements are dots that make up the screen picture. The aperture size can also be changed using the **APERTURE** command. The default value for the aperture size is 10 pixels. The display of the marker and the tooltip is controlled by the **AUTOSNAP** system variable. The following are the bit values for **AUTOSNAP**.

Bit Values	Functions
0	Turns off the Marker, AutoSnap Tooltip, and Magnet
1	Turns on the Marker
2	Turns on the AutoSnapTooltip
4	Turns on the Magnet
47	Turns on the Marker, AutoSnap Tooltip, and Magnet

The basic functionality of Object Snap modes is discussed next.

Endpoint

The **Endpoint** Object Snap mode is used to snap the cursor to the closest endpoint of a line or an arc. To use this Object Snap mode, invoke a draw tool such as **Line** and select the **Endpoint** button and move the cursor (crosshairs) anywhere close to the endpoint of the object; a marker will be displayed at the endpoint. Click to select that point; the endpoint of the object will be snapped. If there are several objects near the cursor crosshairs, the endpoint of the object that is closest to the crosshairs will be snapped. However, if the **Magnet** is on, you can move to grab the desired endpoint. Figure 4-35 shows the cursor snapping the end point of a circle. The dotted line is the proposed line to be drawn.

Midpoint

The **Midpoint** Object Snap mode is used to snap the midpoint of a line or an arc. To use this Object Snap mode, select the **Midpoint** osnap and select an object anywhere; the midpoint of the object will be snapped. Figure 4-36 shows the cursor snapping to the midpoint of a line. The dotted line is the proposed line to be drawn.

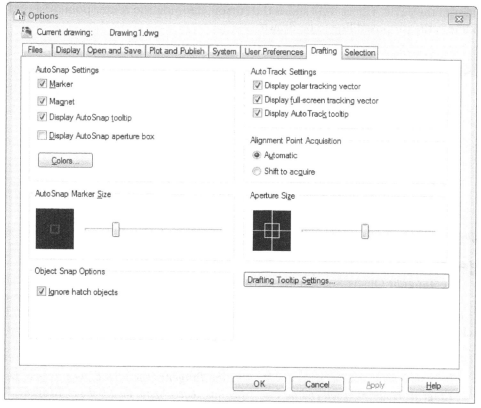

*Figure 4-34 The **Drafting** tab in the **Options** dialog box*

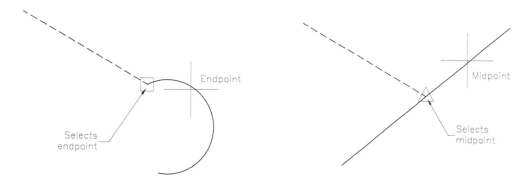

*Figure 4-35 The **Endpoint** Object Snap mode*   *Figure 4-36 The **Midpoint** Object Snap mode*

Nearest

The **Nearest** Object Snap mode is used to select a point on an object (line, arc, circle, or ellipse) that is visually closest to the crosshairs. To use this mode, invoke a tool, choose the **Nearest** object snap, and move the crosshairs near the intended point on the object; a marker will be displayed. Left-click to snap that point. Figure 4-37 shows the cursor snapping the point in a line. The dotted line is the proposed line to be drawn.

Center

The **Center** Object Snap mode is used to snap the cursor to the center point of an ellipse, circle, or arc. After choosing this option, move the cursor on the circumference of a circle or an arc; a marker will be displayed at the center of the circle. Left-click to snap the center of the circle. Figure 4-38 shows the cursor snapping the center point of a circle. The dotted line is the proposed line to be drawn.

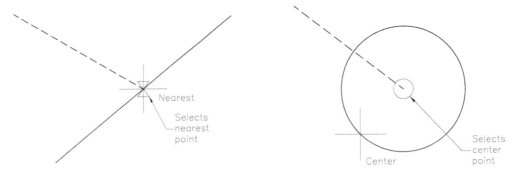

*Figure 4-37 The **Nearest** Object Snap mode*   *Figure 4-38 The **Center** Object Snap mode*

Tangent

The **Tangent** Object Snap mode is used to snap the cursor to the tangent point of an existing ellipse, circle, or arc. To use this object snap mode, place the cursor on the circumference of a circle or an arc and select it. Figure 4-39 shows the cursor selecting the circle. The dashed line is the proposed tangential line.

Note
*If the start point of a line is defined by using the **Tangent** Object Snap, the tip shows **Deferred Tangent**. However, if you end the line using this Object Snap, the tip shows **Tangent**.*

Figure 4-40 shows the use of the **Nearest**, **Endpoint**, **Midpoint**, and **Tangent** Object Snap modes.

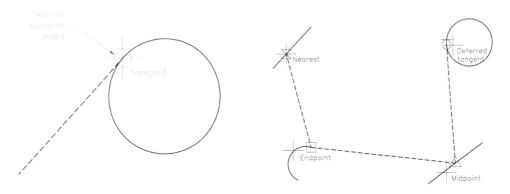

*Figure 4-39 The **Tangent** Object Snap mode*   *Figure 4-40 Using the **Nearest**, **Endpoint**, **Midpoint**, and **Tangent** Object Snap modes*

Quadrant

The **Quadrant** Object Snap mode is used to snap the cursor to the quadrant point of an ellipse, an arc, or a circle. A circle has four quadrants, and each quadrant subtend an angle of 90 degrees. Therefore, the quadrant points are located at 0, 90, 180, and 270-degree positions. If the circle is inserted as a block (see Chapter 14) and rotated, the quadrant points will also be rotated by the same degree, see Figures 4-41 and 4-42.

To use this object snap, position the cursor on the circle or arc closest to the desired quadrant and click when the marker is displayed. Figure 4-43 shows the cursor selecting the third quadrant and the proposed line.

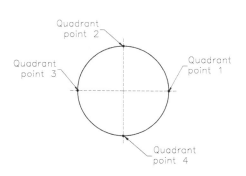

Figure 4-41 *Location of the circle quadrants*

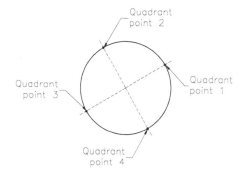

Figure 4-42 *Quadrants in a rotated circle*

Intersection

The **Intersection** Object Snap mode is used to snap the cursor to a point where two or more lines, circles, ellipses, or arcs intersect. To use this object snap, move the cursor to the desired intersection point such that the intersection is within the target box and click when the intersection marker is displayed. Figure 4-44 shows the cursor selecting the intersection point and the dotted line is the proposed line.

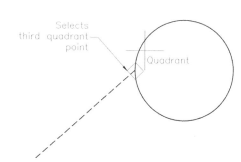

Figure 4-43 *The **Quadrant** Object Snap mode*

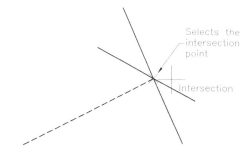

Figure 4-44 *The **Intersection** Object Snap mode*

After setting the **Intersection** Object Snap mode, if the cursor is close to an object and not close to actual intersection, the **Extended Intersection** tooltip will be displayed. If you select this object, you need to select another object. Move the cursor close to another object; the intersection point will be snapped. Left-click to select the intersection point. But, if the object selected second does not intersect with the object selected first, then the cursor will snap to the extended intersection point, as shown in Figure 4-45. The extended intersections are virtual intersection which are formed if a line or an arc is extended.

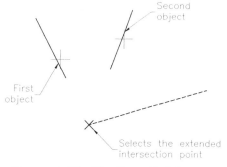

Figure 4-45 *The **Extended Intersection** Object Snap mode*

Apparent Intersection

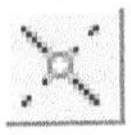

The **Apparent Intersection** Object Snap mode is used to select the projected intersections of two objects in 3D space. Sometimes, two objects appear to intersect one another in the current view, but in 3D space they do not actually intersect. The **Apparent Intersection** snap mode is used to select such intersections. This mode works on wireframes in 3D space. If you use this object snap mode in 2D, it works like an extended intersection.

Perpendicular

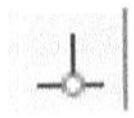

The **Perpendicular** Object Snap mode is used to draw a line perpendicular to or from another line, or normal to or from an arc or a circle, or to an ellipse. After invoking the **Line** tool, if you choose this mode and then select an object, a perpendicular line will be attached to the cursor. Move the cursor and place the line, as shown in Figure 4-46. But, after invoking the **Line** tool, if you select the start point of the line first and then choose the **Perpendicular** snap mode, you need to select an object. On doing so, AutoCAD LT selects a point such that the resulting line is perpendicular to the selected object, as shown in Figure 4-47.

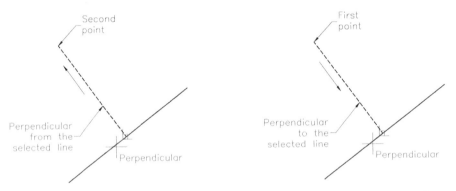

Figure 4-46 Selecting the perpendicular snap first

Figure 4-47 Selecting the start point first and then the perpendicular snap

Figure 4-48 shows the use of the various object snap modes.

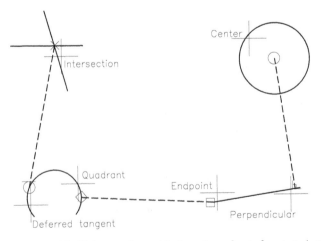

Figure 4-48 Using various object snap modes to locate points

EXERCISE 3   *Quadrant & Tangent*

Draw the sketch shown in Figure 4-49. P1 and P2 are the center points of the top and bottom arcs. The space between the dotted lines is 1 unit.

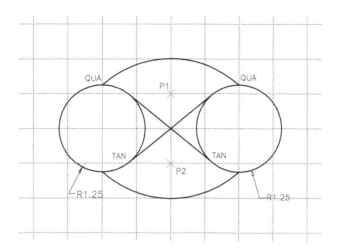

Figure 4-49 Drawing for Exercise 3

Node

You can use the **Node** Object Snap mode to snap the points placed by using the **Multiple Points**, **Divide**, or **Measure** command. Figure 4-50 shows the three points placed by using the **Multiple Points** command, the dotted line indicates the proposed line to be drawn, and the **Node** tooltip displayed on moving the cursor close to a point.

Insertion

The **Insertion** Object Snap mode is used to snap to the insertion point of a text, shape, block, attribute, or attribute definition. The insertion point is the point with respect to which a text, shape, or a block is inserted. Figure 4-51 shows the insertion point of the text and a block. The dotted line is the proposed line to be drawn.

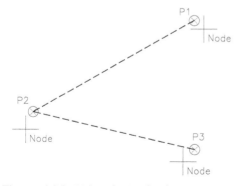 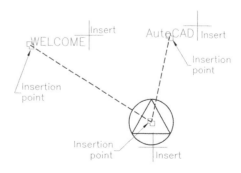

*Figure 4-50 Using the **Node** object snap*   *Figure 4-51 The **Insertion** object snap*

Snap to None

The **Snap to None** Object Snap mode is used to turn off any running object snap (see the section "Running Object Snap Mode" that follows) for one point only. The following example illustrates the use of this Object Snap mode.

Chapter 4

Invoke the **Drafting Settings** dialog box and select the **Object Snap** tab. Select the **Midpoint** and **Center** check boxes. This sets the object snap to midpoint and center. Now, to draw a line whose start point is closer to the endpoint of another line, invoke the **Line** tool and move the cursor to the desired position on the previous line. The cursor automatically snaps to the midpoint of the line. You can disable this automatic snap by choosing the **Snap to None** object snap from the **Object Snap** toolbar.

Parallel

When you need to draw a line parallel to a line or a polyline, use the **Parallel** Object Snap. For example, when you are working with the **Line** tool, and you have to draw a line parallel to the one already drawn, you can use the **Parallel** object snap mode as discussed next.

1. Choose **Line** from the **Draw** toolbar.
2. Select a point on the screen.
3. Choose the **Parallel** button from the **Object Snap** toolbar.
4. Move the cursor close to the reference object and pause for a while; the parallel tooltip appears on it, indicating that the line has been selected.
5. Now, move the cursor at an angle parallel to the line; an imaginary parallel line (construction line) appears, on which you can select the next point. As you move the cursor on the construction line, a tooltip with relative polar coordinates is displayed near the cursor. This helps you to select the next point. The line thus drawn will be parallel to the selected object, as shown in Figure 4-52.

Extension

The **Extension** Object Snap mode is used to locate a point on the proposed extension path of a line or an arc (Figure 4-53). It can also be used with intersection to determine the extended intersection point. To snap a point by using this snap mode, choose the **Line** tool from the **Draw** toolbar, and then choose the **Snap to Extension** button from the **Object Snap** toolbar. Briefly pause at the end of the line or the arc; a small plus sign (+) or a tooltip will appear at the end of the line or the arc, indicating that it has been selected. If you move the cursor along the line, a temporary extension path will be displayed and the tooltip displays the relative polar coordinates from the end of the line. Select a point or enter a distance to begin a line and then select another point to finish the line.

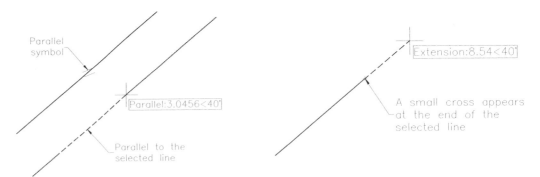

Figure 4-52 *Using the **Parallel** Object Snap mode*

Figure 4-53 *Using the **Extension** Object Snap mode*

Tip
*While using the **Parallel** object snap mode, you can choose more than one line as reference lines that are indicated by a plus sign. Depending upon the direction in which you move the cursor, AutoCAD LT will choose any one of these reference lines and the chosen line will be marked with the parallel symbol in place of the plus sign.*

*Similarly, while using the **Extension** object snap mode, you can choose more than one endpoint as the reference.*

From

The **From** Object Snap mode is used to locate a point relative to a given point (Figure 4-54). For example, to locate a point that is 2.5 units up and 1.5 units right from the endpoint of a given line, you can use the **From** object snap as follows:

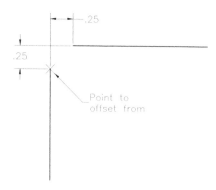

*Figure 4-54 Using the **From** Object Snap mode to locate a point*

Command: *Choose the **Line** tool.*
Specify first point: *Choose the **Snap From** button from the **Object Snap** toolbar.*
_from Base point: *Choose the **Snap to Endpoint** button from the **Object Snap** toolbar.*
_endp of *Specify the endpoint of the given line*
<Offset>: *@***1.5,2.5**

> **Note**
> *The **From** Object Snap mode cannot be used as the running object snap.*

Midpoint Between 2 Points

This Object Snap mode is used to select the midpoint of an imaginary line drawn between two selected points. Note that this Object Snap mode can only be invoked from the shortcut menu. To understand the working of this Object Snap mode, refer to the sketch shown in Figure 4-55. In this sketch, there are two circles and you need to draw another circle with the center point at the midpoint of an imaginary line drawn between the center points of two existing circles. The following is the prompt sequence:

Command: *Choose the **Center,Radius** tool*
Specify center point for circle or [3P/2P/Ttr (tan tan radius)]: *Right-click and choose **Snap Overrides > Midpoint Between 2 Points** from the shortcut menu*
_m2p First point of mid: *Snap the center of the left circle*
Second point of mid: *Snap the center of the right circle*
Specify radius of circle or [Diameter] <current>: *Specify the radius of the new circle*

Temporary Tracking Point

The **Temporary track point** is used to locate a point with respect to two different points. If you choose this option and then select a point and move the cursor, an orthogonal imaginary line will be displayed either horizontally or vertically. Then, you need to select another point to display another orthogonal imaginary line in the other direction. The required point will be located where these two imaginary lines intersect. You can also use this option along with the other Object Snap modes. To locate a point, invoke the **Line** tool from the **Draw** toolbar and then use the temporary tracking as follows.

Specify first point: *Choose the **Temporary track point** button from the **Object Snap** toolbar.*
Specify temporary OTRACK point: *Choose the **Snap to Midpoint** button from the **Object Snap** toolbar.*
Select the midpoint of the line and move the cursor horizontally toward the right.
Specify first point: *Choose the **Temporary Tracking Point** button from the **Object Snap** toolbar.*
Specify temporary OTRACK point: *Choose the **Snap to Endpoint** button from the **Object Snap** toolbar.*
Select the upper endpoint of the line and move the cursor vertically down.

As you move the cursor down, both the horizontal and vertical imaginary lines will be displayed, as shown in Figure 4-56. Select their intersection point and then draw the line.

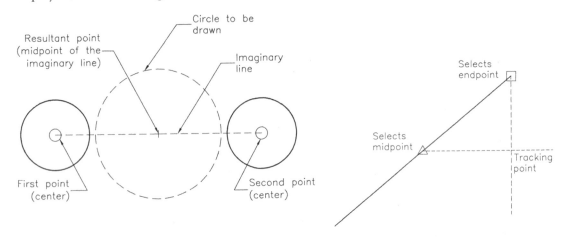

Figure 4-55 Using the **Midpoint Between 2 Points** *Object Snap mode to locate a point*

Figure 4-56 Using temporary tracking point

Combining Object Snap Modes

You can also combine the snaps from the command line by separating the snap modes with a comma. In this case, AutoCAD LT searches for the specified modes and grabs the point on the object that is closest to the point where the object is selected. The prompt sequence for using the **Midpoint** and **Endpoint** object snaps is given next.

Command: *Choose the* **Line** *tool*
_line Specify first point: **MID, END** Enter   *(MIDpoint or ENDpoint object snap.)*
of: *Select the object*

 Note
In reference to object snaps, "line" generally includes xlines, rays, and polyline segments, and "arc" generally includes polyarc segments.

EXERCISE 4

Draw the sketch shown in Figure 4-57. The space between the dotted lines is 1 unit.

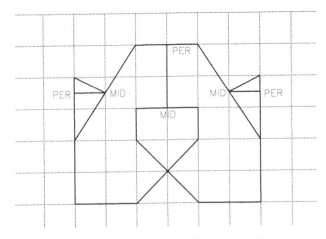

Figure 4-57 Drawing for Exercise 4

RUNNING OBJECT SNAP MODE

Toolbar: Object Snap > Osnap Settings   **Command:** OSNAP

In the previous sections, you have learned to use object snaps to snap to different points of an object. The object snaps are to be selected from the toolbar or from the shortcut menu. One of the drawbacks of this method is that you have to select them every time, even if you are using the same snap mode again. This problem can be resolved by using **running object snaps**. The Running Osnap can be invoked from the **Object Snap** tab of the **Drafting Settings** dialog box (Figure 4-58). If you choose the **Osnap Settings** button from the toolbar, or enter **OSNAP** at the Command line, or choose **Settings** from the shortcut menu displayed on right-clicking on the **OSNAP** button in the Status Bar, the **Object Snap** tab will be displayed in the **Drafting Settings** dialog box. In this tab, you can set the running object snap modes by selecting the check boxes next to the snap modes. For example, to set **Endpoint** as the running Object Snap mode, select the **Endpoint** check box and then the **OK** button in the dialog box.

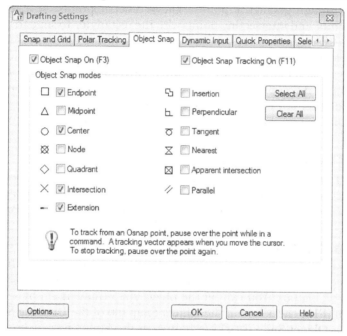

Figure 4-58 The **Drafting Settings** *dialog box (**Object Snap** tab)*

Once you set the running Object Snap mode, a marker will be displayed when you move the crosshairs over the key points. If you have selected a combination of modes, AutoCAD LT selects the mode that is closest to the crosshairs. For example, if you have selected the **Endpoint**, **Midpoint**, and **Center** check boxes in the dialog box and move the cursor over a line, the endpoint or the midpoint will be displayed, depending upon the position of the crosshair. Similarly, if you place the cursor over the circumference of a circle, the center will be displayed. The running Object Snap mode can be turned on or off without losing the object snap settings by choosing the **OSNAP** button in the Status Bar. You can also accomplish this by pressing the function key F3 or CTRL+F keys.

Overriding the Running Snap

When you select the running object snaps, all other Object Snap modes are ignored unless you select another Object Snap mode. Once you select a different osnap mode, the running OSNAP mode is temporarily overruled. After the operation has been performed, the running OSNAP mode becomes active again. If you want to discontinue the current running Object Snap mode completely, choose the **Clear all** button in the **Drafting Settings** dialog box. If you want to temporarily disable the running object snap, choose the **OSNAP** button (off position) in the Status Bar.

If you override the running object snap modes for a point selection and do not find a point to satisfy the override Object Snap mode, AutoCAD LT displays a message to this effect. For example, if you specify an override Object Snap mode of Center and no circle, ellipse, or arc is found at that location, AutoCAD LT will display the message "**No center found for specified point. Point or option keyword required**".

Cycling through Snaps

AutoCAD LT displays the geometric marker corresponding to the shapes shown in the **Object snap settings** tab of the **Drafting Settings** dialog box. You can use the TAB key to cycle through the snaps. For example, if you have a circle with an intersecting rectangle as shown in Figure 4-60 and you want to snap to one of the geometric points on the circle, you can use the TAB key to cycle through geometric points. The geometric points for a circle are the center point, quadrant points, and intersecting points with the rectangle. To snap to one of these points, first you need to set the running object snaps (center, quadrant, and intersection object snaps) in the **Drafting Settings** dialog box. Then, invoke a tool and move the cursor over the objects; AutoSnap displays a marker and a tooltip. You can cycle through the snap points by pressing the TAB key. For example, if you press the TAB key while the aperture box is on the circle and the rectangle (near the lower left intersection point), the intersection, center, and quadrant points will be displayed one by one. Left-click to select the required key point

USING AUTOTRACKING

When using AutoTracking, the cursor moves along temporary paths to locate key points in a drawing. It can be used to locate points with respect to other points or objects in the drawing. There are two types of AutoTracking options: **Object Snap Tracking** and **Polar Tracking**.

Object Snap Tracking

Object Snap Tracking is used to track the movement of the cursor along the alignment paths based on the Object Snap points (running osnaps) are selected in the **Object Snap** tab of the **Drafting Settings** dialog box. You can set the object snap tracking on by selecting the **Object Snap Tracking On (F11)** check box in the **Object Snap** tab of the **Drafting Settings** dialog box or by choosing the **Object Snap Tracking** button in the Status Bar, or by using the function key F11.

The direction of a path is determined by the motion of the cursor or the point you select on an object. For example, to draw a circle whose center is located at the intersection of the imaginary lines passing through the center of two existing circles (Figure 4-59), you can use AutoTracking. To do so, select **Center** in the **Object Snap** tab of the **Drafting Settings** dialog box and turn on the **Object Snap** button in the Status Bar. Now, activate the object tracking by choosing the **Object Snap Tracking** button in the Status Bar. Choose the **Center,Radius** button from the **Draw** toolbar and pause the cursor at the center of the first circle till the marker or a plus sign is displayed. Then, move it horizontally to get the imaginary horizontal line. Move the cursor toward the second circle; the horizontal path disappears. Now, place the cursor for a while at the center of the second circle and move it vertically to get the imaginary vertical line. Move the cursor along the vertical alignment path and when you are in line with the other circle, the horizontal path will also be displayed. Select the intersection of the two alignment paths. The selected point becomes the center of the circle. Then, enter radius or specify a point.

Similarly, you can use AutoTracking in combination with the **Midpoint** object snap to locate the center of the rectangle and then draw a circle (Figure 4-60).

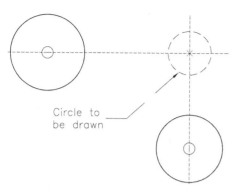

Figure 4-59 *Using **AutoTracking** to locate a point (center of circle)*

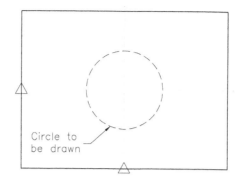

Figure 4-60 *Using **AutoTracking** to locate a point (midpoint of rectangle)*

Note

*Object tracking works only when **OSNAP** is on and some running object snaps have been set.*

Polar Tracking

Polar Tracking is used to locate points on an angular alignment path. Polar tracking can be selected by choosing the **Polar Tracking** button in the Status Bar, by using the function key F10, or by selecting the **Polar Tracking On (F10)** check box in the **Polar Tracking** tab of the **Drafting Settings** dialog box (Figure 4-61). Polar Tracking constrains the movement of the cursor along a path that is based on the polar angle settings. For example, if the **Increment angle** list box value is set to 15-degree in the **Polar Angle Settings** area, the cursor will move along the alignment paths that are multiples of 15-degree (0, 15, 30, 45, 60, and so on) and a tooltip will also display the distance and angle. Selecting the **Additional angles** check box and choosing

Figure 4-61 *The **Polar Tracking** tab in the **Drafting Settings** dialog box*

the **New** button allow you to add an additional angle value. The imaginary path will also be displayed at these new angles, apart from the increments of the increment angle selected. For example, if the increment angle is set to **15** and you add an additional angle of **22**, the imaginary path will be displayed at 0, 15, 22, 30, 45, and the increments of 15. Polar tracking is on only when the Ortho mode is off.

In the **Drafting Settings** dialog box (**Polar Tracking** tab), you can set the polar tracking to absolute or relative to the last segment. If you select the **Absolute** radio button, the base angle is taken from 0. If you select the **Relative to last segment** radio button, the base angle for the increments is set to the last segment drawn. You can also use Polar tracking together with Object tracking (Otrack). You can select the **Track using all polar angle settings** radio button in the dialog box.

AutoTrack Settings

You have different settings while working with autotracking. These settings can be specified in the **Drafting** tab of the **Options** dialog box (see Figure 4-61). If you choose the **Options** button in the **Polar Tracking** tab of the **Drafting Settings** dialog box, the **Options** dialog box with the **Drafting** tab chosen will be displayed. You can use the **Display polar tracking vector** check box to toggle the display of the angle alignment path for Polar tracking. You can also use the **Display full-screen tracking vector** check box to toggle the display of a full-screen construction line for Otrack. You can use the **Display AutoTrack tooltip** check box to toggle the display of tooltips with the paths. You can also use the **TRACKPATH** system variable to set the path display settings.

Tip
*You need the **Options** dialog box quite frequently to change different drafting settings. When you choose the **Options** button from the **Drafting Settings** dialog box, it directly opens the required tab. After making changes in the dialog box, choose the **OK** button to get back to the **Drafting Settings** dialog box. The **Options** button is available in all the three tabs of the **Drafting Settings** dialog box.*

FUNCTION AND CONTROL KEYS

You can also use the function and control keys to change the status of the coordinate display, Snap, Ortho, Osnap, tablet, screen, isometric planes, running Object Snap, Grid, Polar, and Object tracking. The following is a list of functions and their control keys.

F1	Help	F2	Graphics Screen/AutoCAD LT Text Window
F3	Osnap On/Off (CTRL+F)	F4	Tablet On/Off
F5	Isoplane top/right/left (CTRL+E)	F7	Grid On/Off (CTRL+G)
F8	Ortho On/Off (CTRL+L)	F9	Snap On/Off (CTRL+B)
F10	Polar tracking On/Off	F11	Object Snap tracking
F12	Dynamic Input On/Off		

Self-Evaluation Test

Answer the following questions and then compare them to those given at the end of this chapter:

1. The layers that are turned off are displayed on the screen but cannot be plotted. (T/F)

2. The drawing, in which you are working, should be in the named plot style mode (*.stb*) to make the plot style available in the **Layer Properties Manager**. (T/F)

3. The grid pattern appears within the drawing limits, which helps define the working area. (T/F)

4. If a circle is inserted as a rotated block, the quadrant points are not rotated by the same amount. (T/F)

5. You can change the plot style mode from the command prompt by using the _____ system variable.

6. The _____ command enables you to set up an invisible grid that allows the cursor to move in fixed increments from one snap point to another.

7. The _____ snap works along with polar and object tracking only.

8. The _____ Object Snap mode is used to select the projected or visual intersections of two objects in 3D space.

9. The _____ can be used to locate a point with respect to two different points.

10. You can set the priority between the keyboard entry and the object snap through the _____ tab of the **Options** dialog box.

Review Questions

Answer the following questions:

1. You cannot enter different values for the horizontal and vertical grid spacing. (T/F)

2. You can lock a layer to prevent a user from accidentally editing the objects in it. (T/F)

3. When a layer is locked, you cannot use the objects in it for Osnaps. (T/F)

4. The thickness given to the objects in a layer, by using the **Lineweight** option, is displayed on the screen and can be plotted. (T/F)

5. Which of the following options is not displayed in the **Layer** shortcut menu in the **Layer Properties Manager** when you select more than one layer by using the SHIFT key?

    (a) **New Layer**   (b) **Select All**
    (c) **Make Current**   (d) **Clear All**

6. Which of the following function keys acts as a toggle key for turning the grid display on or off?

    (a) F5   (b) F6
    (c) F7   (d) F8

7. Which one of the following object snap modes is used to turn off any running object snap for one point only?

    (a) **NODe**   (b) **NONe**
    (c) **From**   (d) **NEArest**

Chapter 4

8. Which of the following object snap modes cannot be used as the running object snap?

   (a) **EXTension**   (b) **PARallel**
   (c) **From**   (d) **NODe**

9. Which of the following keys can be used to cycle through different running object snaps?

   (a) ENTER   (b) SHIFT
   (c) CTRL   (d) TAB

10. While working on a drawing, you can save all layers with their current properties' settings anytime under one name and then restore them later using the _____ button in the **Layer Properties Manager**.

11. You can use the _____ window to locate the drawing data with the help of the search tools and then use it in your drawing.

12. The _____ function key is used to turn on/off the **Objest Snap** mode.

13. The difference between the usage of the **Off** option and the **Freeze** option is that in the **Freeze** option the frozen layers are not _____ by the computer while regenerating the drawing.

14. The size of the aperture is measured in _____.

15. In the **Extension** object snap mode, when you move the cursor along a path, a temporary extension path and the tooltip is displayed with the cursor. The tooltip displays _____ coordinates from the end of the line.

EXERCISE 5 — Line type and Object Color

Set up layers with the following linetypes and colors. Then make the drawing, as shown in Figure 4-62. The distance between the dotted lines is 1.0 unit.

Layer name	Color	Linetype
Object	Red	Continuous
Hidden	Yellow	Hidden
Center	Green	Center

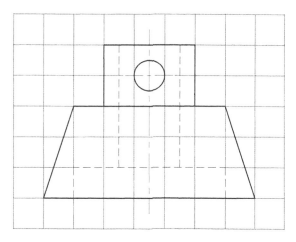

Figure 4-62 *Drawing for Exercise 5*

EXERCISE 6   *Line type and Object Color*

Set up layers, linetypes, and colors, as given in Exercise 5. Then make the drawing shown in Figure 4-63. The distance between the dotted lines is 1.0 unit.

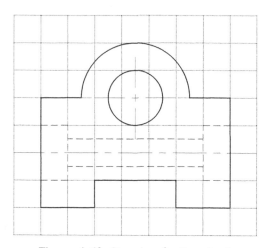

Figure 4-63 *Drawing for Exercise 6*

Chapter 4

EXERCISE 7   *Line type and Object Color*

Set up layers, linetypes, and colors and then make the drawing shown in Figure 4-64. The distance between the dotted lines is 1.0 unit.

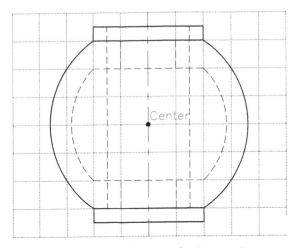

Figure 4-64 Drawing for Exercise 7

EXERCISE 8   *Line type and Object Color*

Set up layers, linetypes, and colors and then make the drawing shown in Figure 4-65. Use the object snaps as indicated.

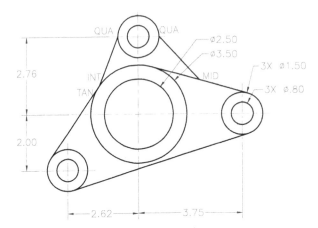

Figure 4-65 Drawing for Exercise 8

Problem-Solving Exercise 1

Draw the object shown in Figure 4-66. First draw the lines and then draw the arcs using the appropriate **ARC** command options.

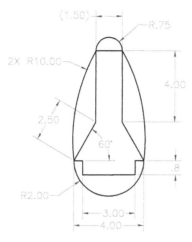

Figure 4-66 *Drawing for Problem-Solving Exercise 1*

Problem-Solving Exercise 2

Draw the object shown in Figure 4-67. First draw the front view (bottom left) and then the side and top views. Assume the missing dimensions.

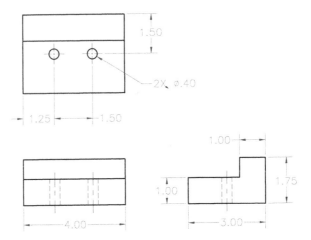

Figure 4-67 *Drawing for Problem-Solving Exercise 2*

Answers to Self-Evaluation Test

1. F, **2.** T, **3.** T, **4.** F, **5. PSTYLEPOLICY, 6.** SNAP, **7.** Polar, **8. Apparent Intersection, 9. Temporary Tracking, 10. User Preferences**

Chapter 5

Editing Sketched Objects-I

CHAPTER OBJECTIVES

In this chapter, you will learn:
- *To use the Move and Copy tools.*
- *To copy objects using the ARRAY command.*
- *About various editing and measuring tools.*

KEY TERMS

- *Move*
- *Copy*
- *Offset*
- *Chamfer*

- *Trim*
- *Extend*
- *Stretch*
- *Array*

- *Rotate*
- *Mirror*
- *Scale*
- *Lengthen*

EDITING SKETCHES

To use AutoCAD LT efficiently, you need to know the editing commands and how to use them. In this section, you will learn about the editing commands. These commands can be invoked from the **Ribbon**, toolbar, or by using the Command prompt. Some of the editing commands such as **ERASE** and **OOPS** have been discussed in Chapter 2 (Getting Started with AutoCAD LT). The rest of them will be discussed in this chapter.

MOVING THE SKETCHED OBJECTS

Ribbon:	Home > Modify > Move	**Command:** MOVE
Toolbar:	Modify > Move	

The **Move** tool is used to move one or more objects from their current location to a new location without changing their size or orientation. On invoking this tool from the **Modify** panel, as shown in Figure 5-1, you will be prompted to select the objects to be moved. Select the object by using any one of the selection techniques discussed earlier; you will be prompted to specify the base point. The base point is the reference point with respect to which the object will be picked and moved. It is recommended to select the base point on the object selected to be moved. On specifying the base point, you will be prompted to specify the second point of displacement. This is the new location where you want to move the object. On specifying this point, the selected objects will move to this point. Figure 5-2 shows the objects moved by using the **Move** tool. The prompt sequence that will be followed on choosing the **Move** tool from the **Modify** panel is given next.

> Select objects: *Select the objects to be moved.*
> Select objects: Enter
> Specify base point or [Displacement] <Displacement>: *Specify the base point to move the selected object(s).*
> Specify second point or <use first point as displacement>: *Specify the second point or press ENTER to use the first point.*

If you press ENTER at the **Specify second point of displacement or <use first point as displacement>** prompt, AutoCAD LT interprets the first point as the relative value of the displacement in the *X* axis and *Y* axis directions. This value will be added in the *X* and *Y* axis coordinates and the object will be automatically moved to the resultant location. For example, draw a circle with its center at (3,3) and then select the center point of the circle as the base point. Now, at the **Specify second point of displacement or <use first point as displacement>** prompt, press ENTER. You will notice that the circle is moved such that its center is now placed at 6,6. This is because 3 units (initial coordinates) are added along both the X and Y directions.

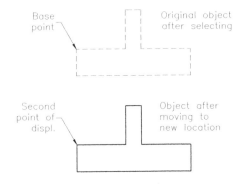

*Figure 5-1 Invoking the **Move** tool from the **Modify** panel*

Figure 5-2 Moving the objects to a new location

COPYING THE SKETCHED OBJECTS*

Ribbon: Home > Modify > Copy   **Toolbar:**   Modify > Copy
Command: COPY

The **Copy** tool is used to copy an existing object. This tool is used to make the copies of the selected objects and place them at the specified location. On invoking this tool, you need to select the objects and then specify the base point. Next, you need to specify the second point where the copied objects have to be placed. Figure 5-3 shows the objects copied by using this tool. The prompt sequence that will be followed when you choose the **Copy** tool from the **Modify** panel is given next.

Select objects: *Select the objects to copy.*
Select objects: Enter
Specify base point or [Displacement/mOde]<Displacement>: *Specify the base point.*
Specify second point or Array <use first point as displacement>: *Specify a new position on the screen using the pointing device or by entering coordinates.*
Specify second point or [Array/Exit/Undo] <Exit>: Enter

Creating Multiple Copies

On specifying the second point, the copy of the selected object will be created and you will be prompted again to specify the second point. You can continue specifying the second point for creating multiple copies of the selected entities, as shown in Figure 5-4. You can use **U (Undo)** to undo the last copied instance at any stage of the **COPY** command. After entering **U**, you can again specify the position of the last instance. The prompt sequence for creating multiple copies of an object by using the **Copy** tool is given next.

Specify base point or displacement: *Specify the base point.*
Specify second point or <use first point as displacement>: *Specify a point for placement.*
Specify second point or <Exit/Undo>: *Specify another point for placement.*
Specify second point or <Exit/Undo>: *Specify another point for placement.*
Specify second point or <Exit/Undo>: Enter

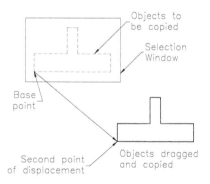

Figure 5-3 The objects copied by using the COPY tool

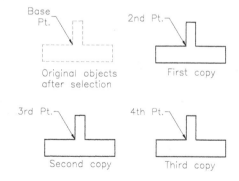

Figure 5-4 Making multiple copies

Creating a Single Copy

By default, AutoCAD LT creates multiple copies of the selected objects. However, you can also create a single copy of the selected object. To create a single copy of the selected object, choose the **mOde** option from the shortcut menu at the **Specify base point or [Displacement/mOde] <current>** prompt. Next, choose the **Single** option from the shortcut menu at the **Enter a copy mode option [Single/Multiple] <current>** prompt. On specifying the second point of displacement, a copy will be placed at that point. Now, you can exit the **Copy** tool.

Chapter 5

EXERCISE 1   *Copy*

In this exercise, you will create the drawing shown in Figure 5-5. Use the **COPY** command for creating the drawing.

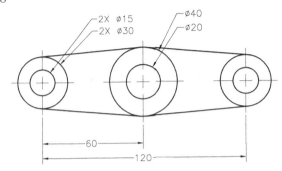

Figure 5-5 *Drawing for Exercise 1*

OFFSETTING SKETCHED OBJECTS

Ribbon: Home > Modify > Offset   **Toolbar:** Modify > Offset
Command: OFFSET

You can use the **Offset** tool to draw parallel lines, polylines, concentric circles, arcs, curves, and so on (Figure 5-6). However, you can offset only one entity at a time. While offsetting an object, you need to specify the offset distance and the side to offset, or specify the distance through which the selected object has to be offset. Depending on the side to offset, the resulting object will be smaller or larger than the original object. For example, while offsetting a circle if the offset side is toward the inner side of the perimeter, the resulting circle will be smaller than the original one. The prompt sequence that will follow when you choose the **Offset** tool from the **Modify** panel is given next.

Current settings: Erase source=No Layer=Source OFFSETGAPTYPE=0
Specify offset distance or [Through/Erase/Layer] <Through>: *Specify the offset distance*
Select object to offset or [Exit/Undo]<Exit>: *Select the object to offset*
Specify point on side to offset or <Exit/Multiple/Undo>: *Specify a point on the side to offset*
Select object to offset or [Exit/Undo]<Exit>*Select another object to offset or press* ⏎.

Through Option

While offsetting the entities, the offset distance can be specified by entering a value or by specifying two points. The distance between these two points will be used as the offset distance. The **Through** option is generally used to create orthographic views. In this case, you do not need to specify a distance; you need to specify an offset point, see Figure 5-7. The offset distance is stored in the **OFFSETDIST** system variable. A negative value indicates that the offset value is set to the **Through** option. Using this option, you can offset lines, arcs, 2D polylines, xlines, circles, ellipses, elliptical arcs, rays, and planar splines. If you try to offset objects other than these, the message **Cannot offset that object** is displayed.

Erase Option

The **Erase** option is used to specify whether the source object has to be deleted or not. Enter **Yes** at the **Erase source object after offsetting** prompt to delete the source object after creating the offset. The prompt sequence that will follow when you choose the **Erase** option is given next.

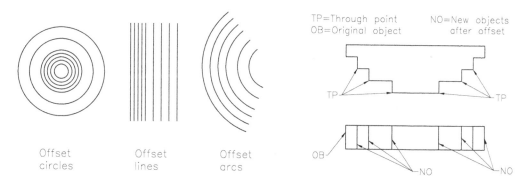

Figure 5-6 *Using the **OFFSET** command multiple times to create multiple offset entities*

Figure 5-7 *Using the **Through** option*

Current settings: Erase source=No Layer=Source OFFSETGAPTYPE=0
Specify offset distance or [Through/Erase/Layer] <current>: **E**
Erase source object after offsetting? [Yes/No] <No>: **Y**
Specify offset distance or [Through/Erase/Layer] <current>:

Layer Option

The **Layer** option is used to specify whether the offset entity will be placed in the current layer or the layer of the source object. The prompt sequence to offset the entity in the **Source** layer is given next.

Current settings: Erase source=Yes Layer=Current OFFSETGAPTYPE=0
Specify offset distance or [Through/Erase/Layer] <current>: **L**
Enter layer option for offset objects [Current/Source] <Current>: **S**
Specify offset distance or [Through/Erase/Layer] <current>:

EXERCISE 2   Offset

Use the **Offset** tool to draw entities shown in Figures 5-8 and 5-9.

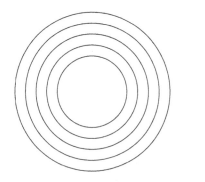

Figure 5-8 *Drawing for Exercise 2 (a)*

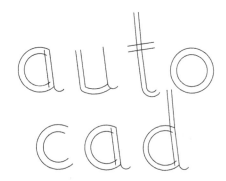

Figure 5-9 *Drawing for Exercise 2 (b)*

Chapter 5

ROTATING SKETCHED OBJECTS

Ribbon: Home > Modify > Rotate **Toolbar:** Modify > Rotate
Command: ROTATE

While creating designs, sometimes you have to rotate an object or a group of objects. You can accomplish this by using the **Rotate** tool. On invoking this tool, you will be prompted to select the objects and the base point about which the selected objects will be rotated. You should be careful in selecting the base point, if the base point is not located on the known object. After you specify the base point, you need to enter the rotation angle. By default, a positive angle results in a counterclockwise rotation, whereas a negative angle results in a clockwise rotation (Figure 5-10). The **Rotate** tool can also be invoked from the shortcut menu by selecting an object and right-clicking in the drawing area and choosing **Rotate** from the shortcut menu.

If you need to rotate objects with respect to a known angle, you can do so by using the **Reference** option in two different ways. The first way is to specify the known angle as the reference angle, followed by the proposed angle to which the objects will be rotated (Figure 5-11). Here the object is first rotated clockwise about the *X* axis, through the reference angle. Then the object is rotated through the new angle from this reference position in a counterclockwise direction. The prompt sequence is given next.

Current positive angle in UCS: ANGDIR=*current* ANGBASE=*current*
Select objects: *Select the objects for rotation.*
Select objects: Enter
Specify base point: *Specify the base point.*
Specify rotation angle or [Copy/Reference]<current>: **R** Enter
Specify the reference angle <0>: *Enter reference angle.*
Specify the new angle or [Points]: *Enter new angle or enter* **P** *to select two points for specifying the angle value.*

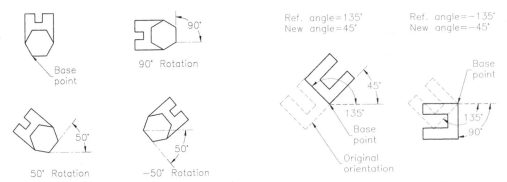

Figure 5-10 *Rotation of objects in different rotation angles*

Figure 5-11 *Rotation using the **Reference** option*

The other method is used when the reference angle and the new angle are not known. In this case, you can use the edges of the original object and the reference object to specify the original object and the reference angle, respectively. Figure 5-12 shows a model and a line created at an unknown angle. In this case, this line will be used as a reference object for rotating the object. In such cases, remember that the base point should be taken on the reference object. This is because you cannot define two points for specifying the new angle. You have to directly enter the angle value or specify only one point. Therefore, the base point will be taken as the first point and the second point can be defined for a new angle. Figure 5-13 shows the model after rotating it with reference to the line such that the line and the model are inclined at similar angles. The prompt sequence to rotate the model shown in Figure 5-12 is given next.

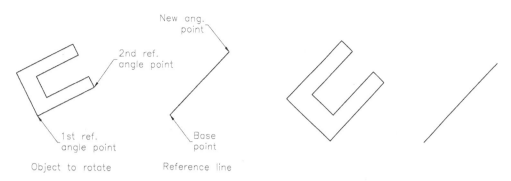

Figure 5-12 *Rotating the model using a reference line*

Figure 5-13 *The model after rotating with reference to the line*

Current positive angle in UCS: ANGDIR=*current* ANGBASE=*current*
Select objects: *Select the object for rotation.*
Select objects: [Enter]
Specify base point: *Specify the base point as the lower endpoint of the line, see Figure 5-12.*
Specify rotation angle or [Copy/Reference]<current>: **R** [Enter]
Specify the reference angle <0>: *Specify the first point on the edge of the model, see Figure 5-12.*
Specify second point: *Specify the second point on the same edge of the model, see Figure 5-12.*
Specify the new angle or [Points]<0>: *Select the other endpoint of the reference line, see Figure 5-12.*

You can also specify a new angle by entering a numeric value at the **Specify the new angle** prompt.

If you want to retain the original object and create a copy while rotating, use the **Copy** option. The source entity is retained in its original orientation and a new instance is created and rotated through the specified angle. The prompt sequence for the **Copy** option is given next.

Current positive angle in UCS: ANGDIR=*counterclockwise* ANGBASE=0
Select objects: *Select the object for rotation.*
Select objects: [Enter]
Specify base point: *Specify a base point about which the selected objects will be rotated.*
Specify rotation angle or [Copy/Reference] <current>: **C** [Enter]
Rotating a copy of the selected objects.
Specify rotation angle or [Copy/Reference] <current>: *Enter a positive or negative rotation angle, or specify a point.*

SCALING THE SKETCHED OBJECTS

Ribbon: Home > Modify > Scale	**Toolbar:** Modify > Scale
Command: SCALE	

Sometimes you need to change the size of objects in a drawing. You can do so by using the **Scale** tool. This tool dynamically enlarges or shrinks a selected object about a base point, keeping the aspect ratio of the object constant. This means that the size of the object will be increased or reduced equally in the X, Y, and Z directions. The dynamic scaling property allows you to view the object as it is being scaled. This is a useful and time saving editing tool because instead of redrawing objects to the required size, you can scale the objects. Another advantage of this tool is that if you have dimensioned the drawing, they will also change accordingly. You can also invoke the **Scale** tool from the shortcut menu by right-clicking in the drawing area and choosing the **Scale** tool. The prompt sequence that will follow when you choose the **Scale** tool is given next.

> Select objects: *Select the objects to be scaled.*
> Select objects: [Enter]
> Specify base point: *Specify the base point, preferably a known point.*
> Specify scale factor or [Copy/Reference]<current>: *Specify the scale factor.*

The base point will not move from its position and the selected object(s) will be scaled with respect to the base point, as shown in Figures 5-14 and 5-15. To reduce the size of an object, the scale factor should be less than 1 and to increase its size, the scale factor should be greater than 1. You can enter a scale factor or select two points to specify a distance as a factor. When you select two points to specify a distance as a factor, the first point should be on the referenced object.

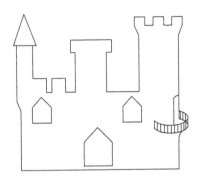

Figure 5-14 *Original object*   *Figure 5-15* *Objects after scaling to 0.5 of the actual size*

Sometimes, it is time-consuming to calculate the relative scale factor. In such cases, you can scale the object by specifying a desired size in relation to the existing size (a known dimension). In other words, you can use a reference length. This can be done by entering **R** at the **Specify scale factor or [Copy/Reference]** prompt. Then, you can either specify two points to specify the length or enter a length. At the next prompt, enter the length relative to the reference length. For example, if a line is 2.5 units long and you want its length to be 1.00 unit, then instead of calculating the relative scale factor, you can use the **Reference** option. The prompt sequence for using the **Reference** option is given next.

> Select objects: *Select the object to scale.*
> Select objects: [Enter]
> Specify base point: *Specify the base point.*
> Specify scale factor or [Copy/Reference]<current>: **R** [Enter]
> Specify reference length <1>: *Specify the reference length.*
> Specify new length [Point]: *Specify the new length or enter **P** to select two points for specifying the angle value.*

Similar to the **Rotate** tool, you can also scale one object by using the reference of another object. Again, in this case also, the base point has to be taken on the reference object as you can define only one point for the new length.

You can use the **Copy** option to retain the source object and scale the copied instance of the source object. The prompt sequence for using the **Copy** option is given next.

> Select objects: *Select the object to scale.*
> Select objects: [Enter]
> Specify base point: *Specify the base point.*

Specify scale factor or [Copy/Reference] <current>: **C** ⏎
Scaling a copy of the selected objects.
Specify scale factor or [Copy/Reference] <current>: *Specify the scale factor.*

Tip
If you need to change the dimensions of all objects with respect to other units, you can use the ***Reference*** *option of the* ***SCALE*** *command to correct the error. To do so, select the entire drawing by using the* ***ALL*** *selection option. Next, specify the* ***Reference*** *option, and then select the endpoints of the object whose desired length is known. Specify the new length; all objects in the drawing will be scaled automatically to the desired size.*

FILLETING THE SKETCHES

Ribbon: Home > Modify > Fillet/Chamfer drop-down   **Toolbar:** Modify > Fillet
Command: FILLET

The edges in a model are generally filleted to reduce the area of stress concentration. The **Fillet** tool helps you form round corners between any two entities that form a sharp vertex. As a result, a smooth round arc is created that connects the two objects. A fillet can also be created between two intersecting or parallel lines as well as non-intersecting and nonparallel lines, arcs, polylines, xlines, rays, splines, circles, and true ellipses. The fillet arc created will be tangent to both the selected entities. The default fillet radius is 0.0000. Therefore, after invoking this tool, you first need to specify the radius value. The prompt sequence displayed on choosing the **Fillet** tool from the **Fillet/Chamfer** drop-down in the **Modify** panel (Figure 5-16) is given next.

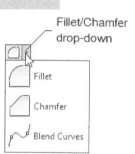

Figure 5-16 Tools in the Fillet/Chamfer drop-down

Current Settings: Mode= TRIM, Radius= 0.0000
Select first object or [Undo/Polyline/Radius/Trim/Multiple]:

Creating Fillets Using the Radius Option

The fillet you create depends on the radius distance specified. The default radius is 0.0000. You can enter a distance or specify two points. The new radius you enter becomes the default radius and remains in effect until changed. Note that the **FILLETRAD** system variable controls and stores the current fillet radius. The default value of this variable is 0.0000. The prompt sequence that is displayed on invoking the **Fillet** tool is given next.

Select first object or [Undo/Polyline/Radius/Trim/Multiple]: **R** ⏎
Specify fillet radius <current>: *Enter a value or press ENTER to accept the current value.*

Tip
A fillet with a zero radius has sharp corners and is used to clean up lines at corners if they overlap or have a gap.

Creating Fillets Using the Select First Object Option

This is the default method to fillet two objects. As the name implies, it prompts for the first object required for filleting. The prompt sequence to use this option is given next.

Current Settings: Mode= TRIM, Radius= modified value
Select first object or [Undo/Polyline/Radius/Trim/Multiple]: *Specify the first object.*

Select second object or shift-select to apply corner: *Select the second object or press the SHIFT key while selecting the object to create sharp corner.*

The **Fillet** tool can also be used to cap the ends of two parallel as well as non-parallel lines, see Figure 5-17. The cap is a semicircle whose radius is equal to half the distance between the two parallel lines. The cap distance is calculated automatically when you select the two parallel lines for filleting. You can select lines by using the **Window**, **Window Crossing**, or **Last** option, but to avoid unexpected results, select the objects by picking them individually. Also, selection by picking objects is necessary in the case of arcs and circles that have the possibility of more than one fillet. They are filleted closest to the selected points, as shown in Figure 5-18.

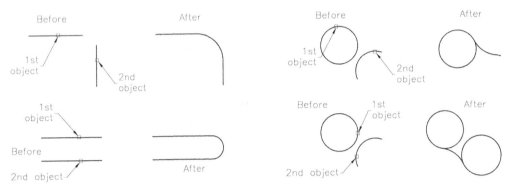

Figure 5-17 *Filleting the parallel and non-parallel lines*

Figure 5-18 *Using the FILLET command on circles and arcs*

Creating Fillets Using the Trim Option

When you create a fillet, an arc is created and the selected objects are either trimmed or extended at the fillet endpoint. This is because the **Trim** mode is set to **Trim**. If it is set to **No Trim**, they are left intact. Figure 5-19 shows a model filleted with the **Trim** mode set to **Trim** and **No Trim**. The prompt sequence is given next.

Select first object or [Undo/Polyline/Radius/Trim/Multiple]: **T** ⏎
Specify Trim mode option [Trim/No trim] <current>: *Enter **T** to trim edges, **N** to leave them intact. You can also choose the required option from the dynamic preview.*

Creating Fillets Using the Polyline Option

If an object is created by using the **Polyline** or **Rectangle** tools, then the object will be a polyline. You can fillet all sharp corners in a polyline by using the **Polyline** option of the **Fillet** tool, as shown in Figure 5-20. On selecting this option after specifying the fillet radius,

you will be prompted to select a polyline. Select the polyline; all vertices of the polyline will be filleted with the same fillet radius. The prompt sequence for using this option is given next.

Current Settings: Mode= *current*, Radius= *current*
Select first object or [Undo/Polyline/Radius/Trim/Multiple]: **P** ⏎
Select 2D polyline: *Select the polyline.*

Creating Fillets Using the Multiple Option

When you invoke the **Fillet** tool, by default, a fillet is created between a pair of entities only. However, with the help of the **Multiple** option, you can add fillets to more than a pair of entities. On selecting this option, you will be prompted to select the first object and then the second object. On selecting two objects, a fillet will be created between the two entities and again you will be prompted to select the first object and then the second object. This prompt will continue until you press ENTER to terminate the **Fillet** tool. The prompt sequence to use this option is given next.

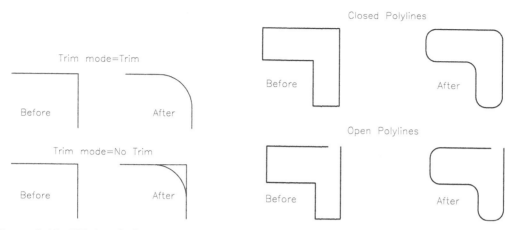

Figure 5-19 *Filleting the lines with the Trim mode set to Trim and No Trim*

Figure 5-20 *Filleting closed and open polylines*

Current Settings: Mode= TRIM, Radius= current
Select first object or [Undo/Polyline/Radius/Trim/Multiple]: **M** Enter
Select first object or [Undo/Polyline/Radius/Trim/Multiple]: *Specify the first object of one set.*
Select second object or shift-select to apply corner: *Select the second object or press down the SHIFT key while selecting the object to create sharp corner.*
Select first object or [Undo/Polyline/Radius/Trim/Multiple]: *Specify the first object of the other set.*
Select second object or shift-select to apply corner: *Select the second object or press down the SHIFT key while selecting the object to create sharp corner.*
Select first object or [Undo/Polyline/Radius/Trim/Multiple]: *Specify the first object of the other set or press* Enter

Note
*Use the **Undo** option to undo the fillet created.*

Filleting Objects with a Different UCS
The **Fillet** tool also fillets the objects that are not in the current UCS plane. To create a fillet for these objects, AutoCAD LT automatically changes the UCS transparently so that it can generate a fillet between the selected objects.

Setting the TRIMMODE System Variable
The **TRIMMODE** system variable eliminates any size restriction on the **Fillet** tool. By setting **TRIMMODE** to **0**, you can create a fillet of any size without actually cutting the existing geometry. Also, there is no restriction on the fillet radius. This means that the fillet radius can be larger than one or both objects that are being filleted. The default value of this variable is 1.

Note
TRIMMODE = 0 *Fillet or chamfer without cutting the existing geometry.*
TRIMMODE = 1 *Extend or trim the geometry.*

CHAMFERING THE SKETCHES

Ribbon: Home > Modify > Fillet/Chamfer drop-down > Chamfer   **Toolbar:** Modify > Chamfer
Command: CHAMFER

 Chamfering the sharp corners is another method of reducing the areas of stress concentration in a model. Chamfering is defined as the process by which the sharp edges or corners are beveled. The size of a chamfer depends on its distance from the corner. If a chamfer is equidistant from the corner in both directions, it is a 45-degree chamfer. A chamfer can be drawn between two lines that may or may not intersect. This command also works on a single polyline. In AutoCAD LT, the chamfers are created by defining two distances or by defining one distance and the chamfer angle.

The prompt sequence that will follow when you choose the **Chamfer** tool from the **Fillet/Chamfer** drop-down in the **Modify** panel is given next.

> (TRIM mode) Current chamfer Dist1 = 0.0000, Dist2 = 0.0000
> Select first line or [Undo/Polyline/Distance/Angle/Trim/mEthod/Multiple]:

The different options to create chamfers are discussed next.

Creating Chamfer Using the Distance Option

To create chamfer by entering the distances, enter **D** at the **Select first line or [Undo/Polyline/ Distance/Angle/Trim/Method/mUltiple]** prompt. Next, enter the first and second chamfer distances. The first distance is the distance of the corner calculated along the edge selected first. Similarly, the second distance is calculated along the edge that is selected last. The new chamfer distances remain in effect until you change them. Instead of entering the distance values, you can specify two points to indicate each distance, see Figure 5-21. The prompt sequence is given next.

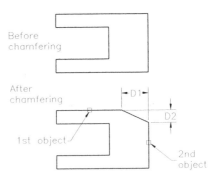

Figure 5-21 Chamfering the model using the Distance option

> Select first line or [Undo/Polyline/Distance/ Angle/Trim/mEthod/Multiple]: **D** ⏎
> Specify first chamfer distance <0.0000>: *Enter a distance value or specify two points.*
> Specify second chamfer distance <0.0000>: *Enter a distance value or specify two points.*

Note
*If Dist 1 and Dist 2 are set to zero, the **Chamfer** tool will extend or trim the selected lines so that they end at the same point.*

*The first and second chamfer distances are stored in the **CHAMFERA** and **CHAMFERB** system variables. The default value of these variables is 0.0000.*

Creating Chamfer Using the Select First Line Option

In this option, you need to select two nonparallel objects so that they are joined with a beveled line. The size of a chamfer depends on the values of the two distances. The prompt sequence to do so is given next.

> (TRIM mode) Current chamfer Dist1 = current, Dist2 = current
> Select first line or [Undo/Polyline/Distance/Angle/Trim/mEthod/Multiple]: *Specify the first line.*

Select second object or shift-select to apply corner: *Select the second object or press down the SHIFT key while selecting the object to create sharp corner.*

Creating Chamfer Using the Polyline Option

Similar to the **Fillet** tool, you can chamfer all sharp corners in a polyline by using the **Polyline** option of the **Chamfer** tool, as shown in Figure 5-22. The prompt sequence to chamfer the polylines is given next.

(TRIM mode) Current chamfer Dist1 = current, Dist2 = current
Select first line or [Undo/Polyline/Distance/Angle/Trim/mEthod/Multiple]: **P** Enter
Select 2D polyline or [Distance/Angle/Method]: *Select the polyline.*

Creating Chamfer Using the Angle Option

The other method of creating a chamfer is by specifying the distance and the chamfer angle, as shown in Figure 5-23. The prompt sequence to do so is given next.

Select first line or [Undo/Polyline/Distance/Angle/Trim/mEthod/Multiple]: **A** Enter
Specify chamfer length on the first line <current>: *Specify a length.*
Specify chamfer angle from the first line <current>: *Specify an angle.*

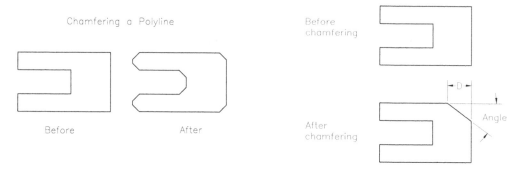

Figure 5-22 *Chamfering a polyline*   **Figure 5-23** *Chamfering using the Angle option*

Creating Chamfer Using the Trim Option

On selecting the **Trim** option, the selected objects are either trimmed or extended to the endpoints of the chamfer line or left intact. The prompt sequence to invoke this option is given next.

Select first line or [Undo/Polyline/Distance/Angle/Trim/mEthod/Multiple]: **T** Enter
Enter Trim mode option [Trim/No Trim] <current>:

Creating Chamfer Using the Method Option

On using this option, you can toggle between the **Distance** method and the **Angle** method for creating a chamfer. The current settings of the selected method will be used for creating the chamfer. The prompt sequence to create the chamfer is given next.

Select first line or [Undo/Polyline/Distance/Angle/Trim/mEthod/Multiple]: **E** Enter
Enter trim method [Distance/Angle] <current>: *Enter **D** for the **Distance** option, A for the **Angle** option.*

Note
*If you set the value of the **TRIMMODE** system variable to **1** (default value), the objects will be trimmed or extended after they are chamfered and filleted. If **TRIMMODE** is set to zero, the objects will be left untrimmed.*

Chapter 5

Creating Chamfers Using the Multiple Option

When you invoke the **Chamfer** tool, by default, a chamfer is created between a pair of entities only. However, with the help of the **Multiple** option, you can add chamfers to multiple pairs. On selecting this option, you will be prompted to select the first line and then the second line. On selecting the two lines, the chamfer will be created. Next, you will again be prompted to select the first line and then the second line. This prompt will continue until you press ENTER to terminate the **Chamfer** tool. The prompt sequence that follows to create multiple chamfers is given next.

(TRIM mode) Current chamfer Dist1 = current, Dist2= current
Select first line or [Undo/Polyline/Distance/Angle/Trim/mEthod/Multiple]: **M** Enter
Select first line or [Undo/Polyline/Distance/Angle/Trim/mEthod/Multiple]: *Specify the first line of one set.*
Select second object or shift-select to apply corner: *Select the second object or press the SHIFT key while selecting the object to create sharp corner.*
Select first line or [Undo/Polyline/Distance/Angle/Trim/mEthod/Multiple]: *Specify the first line of the other set.*
Select second object or shift-select to apply corner: *Select the second object or press the SHIFT key while selecting the object to create sharp corner.*
Select first line or [Undo/Polyline/Distance/Angle/Trim/mEthod/Multiple]: *Specify the first line of the other set or press* **ENTER** *to terminate the* **Chamfer** *tool.*

Setting the Chamfering System Variables

The chamfer modes, distances, length, and angle can also be set by using the following variables:

CHAMMODE = 0 Distance/Distance (default)
CHAMMODE = 1 Length/Angle
CHAMFERA Sets first chamfer distance on the first selected line (default = 0.0000)
CHAMFERB Sets second chamfer distance on the second selected line (default = 0.0000)
CHAMFERC Sets the chamfer length (default = 0.0000)
CHAMFERD Sets the chamfer angle from the first line (default = 0)

TRIMMING THE SKETCHED OBJECTS

Ribbon: Home > Modify > Trim   **Toolbar:** Modify > Trim
Command: TRIM

When creating a design, you may need to remove the unwanted and extended edges. Breaking individual objects takes time if you are working on a complex design with many objects. In such cases, you can use the **Trim** tool. This command is used to trim the objects that extend beyond a required point of intersection. When you invoke this tool from the **Trim/Extend** drop-down in the **Modify** panel (Figure 5-24), you will be prompted to select the cutting edges or boundaries. These edges can be lines, polylines, circles, arcs, ellipses, xlines, rays, splines, text, blocks, or even viewports. There can be more than one cutting edge and you can use any selection method to select them. After the cutting edge or edges are selected, you must select each object to be trimmed. An object can be both a cutting edge and an object to be trimmed. You can trim lines, circles, arcs, polylines, splines, ellipses, xlines, and rays. The prompt sequence to trim objects is given next.

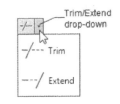

Figure 5-24 Tools in the **Trim/Extend** *drop-down*

Current settings:Projection=UCS Edge=Extend

Select cutting edges...
Select objects or <select all>: *Select the cutting edges.*
Select objects: `Enter`
Select object to trim or shift-select to extend or [Fence/Crossing/Project/Edge/eRase/Undo]:

Various options used to trim objects are discussed next.

Select object to trim Option

On selecting this option, you have to specify the objects you want to trim and the side from which the objects will be trimmed. This prompt is repeated until you press ENTER. This way you can trim several objects on invoking this tool once. The prompt sequence to use this option is given next.

Current settings: Projection= UCS Edge= Extend
Select cutting edges...
Select objects or <select all>: *Select the first cutting edge.*
Select objects: *Select the second cutting edge.*
Select objects: `Enter`
Select object to trim or shift-select to extend or [Fence/Crossing/Project/Edge/eRase/Undo]: *Select the first object.*
Select object to trim or shift-select to extend or [Fence/Crossing/Project/Edge/eRase/Undo]: *Select the second object. (Figure 5-25)*
Select object to trim or shift-select to extend or [Fence/Crossing/Project/Edge/eRase/Undo]: `Enter`

Shift-select to extend Option

This option is used to switch from trim mode to the extend mode. It is used to extend an object instead of trimming. In case the object to be extended does not intersect with the cutting edge, you can press the SHIFT key and then select the object to be extended; the selected edge will be extended taking the cutting edge as the boundary for extension. Note that you need to click near the endpoint that is closest to the cutting edge.

Edge Option

This option is used to trim those objects that do not intersect the cutting edges, but they intersect if the cutting edges were extended, see Figure 5-26.

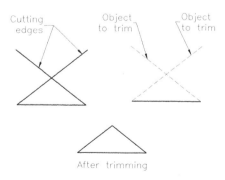

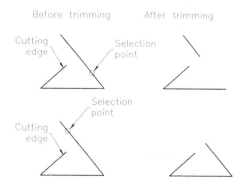

*Figure 5-25 Using the **TRIM** command*

*Figure 5-26 Trimming an object using the **Edge** option (**Extend**)*

The prompt sequence for using the **Edge** option is given next.

Current settings: Projection= UCS Edge= Extend
Select cutting edges...
Select objects: *Select the cutting edge.*
Select objects: [Enter]
Select object to trim or shift-select to extend or [Fence/Crossing/Project/Edge/eRase/
Undo]: **E** [Enter]
Enter an implied edge extension mode [Extend/No extend] <current>: **E** [Enter]
Select object to trim or shift-select to extend or [Fence/Crossing/Project/Edge/eRase/Undo]:
Select object to trim.

Project Option

The **Project** option is used to trim those objects that do not intersect the cutting edges in 3D
space, but do visually appear to intersect in a particular UCS or the current view. The prompt
sequence to invoke this option is given next.

Select object to trim or shift-select to extend or [Fence/Crossing/Project/Edge/eRase/
Undo]: **P** [Enter]
Enter a projection option [None/Ucs/View] <current>:

The **None** option is used whenever the objects to be trimmed intersect the cutting edges in
3D space. The **UCS** option is used to project the objects to the *XY* plane of the current UCS,
while the **View** option is used to project the objects to the current view direction (trims to their
apparent visual intersections).

Fence Option

As discussed in earlier chapters, the **Fence** option is used for the selection purpose. Using the
Fence option, all the objects crossing the selection fence are selected. The prompt sequence for
the **Fence** option is given next.

Select object to trim or shift-select to extend or [Fence/Crossing/Project/Edge/eRase/
Undo]: **F** [Enter]
Specify first fence point: Specify the first point of the fence
Specify next fence point or [Undo]: Specify the second point of the fence
Specify next fence point or [Undo]: Specify the third point of the fence
Specify next fence point or [Undo]: [Enter]

Crossing Option

The **Crossing** option is used to select the entities by using a crossing window. On using this
option, the objects touching the window boundaries or completely enclosing them are selected.
The prompt sequence to trim objects using this option is given next.

Select object to trim or shift-select to extend or [Fence/Crossing/Project/Edge/eRase/
Undo]: **C** [Enter]
Specify first corner: *Select the first corner of the crossing window.*
Specify opposite corner: *Select the opposite corner of the crossing window.*

Erase Option

The **Erase** option in the **Trim** tool is used to erase the entities without canceling the **Trim**
tool.

Select object to trim or shift-select to extend or [Fence/Crossing/Project/Edge/eRase/
Undo]: **R** [Enter]
Select objects to erase or <exit>: *Select object to erase.*

Select objects to erase: *Select object to erase or* [Enter]
Select objects to erase: [Enter]

Undo Option

If you want to remove the previous change made by the **Trim** tool, enter **U** at the **Select object to trim or [Fence/Crossing/Project/Edge/eRase/Undo]** prompt.

EXERCISE 3	Fillet, Chamfer, and Trim

Draw the top illustration in Figure 5-27 and then use the **Fillet**, **Chamfer**, and **Trim** tools to obtain the next illustration given in the same Figure. Assume the missing dimensions.

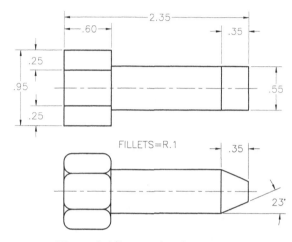

Figure 5-27 *Drawing for Exercise 6*

EXTENDING THE SKETCHED OBJECTS

Ribbon: Home > Modify > Trim/Extend drop-down > Extend	
Toolbar: Modify > Extend	**Command:** EXTEND

The **Extend** tool may be considered as the opposite of the **Trim** tool. You can trim objects using the **Trim** tool. Whereas, you can extend lines, polylines, rays, and arcs to connect to other objects by using the **Extend** tool. However, you cannot extend closed loops. The command format of the **Extend** tool is similar to that of the **Trim** tool. You are required to select the boundary edges first. The boundary edges are those objects that the selected lines or arcs extend to meet. These edges can be lines, polylines, circles, arcs, ellipses, xlines, rays, splines, text, blocks, or even viewports. The prompt sequence that will follow when you choose the **Extend** tool is given next.

Current settings: Projection= UCS, Edge=Extend
Select boundary edges...
Select objects or <select all>: *Select boundary edges.*
Select objects: [Enter]
Select object to extend or shift-select to trim or [Fence/Crossing/Project/Edge/Undo]:

Various options used to extend the objects are discussed next.

Select object to extend Option

In this option, you have to specify the object that you want to extend to the selected boundary (Figure 5-28). This prompt is repeated until you press ENTER. Note that you can select a number of objects in a single **EXTEND** command.

Shift-select to trim Option

This option is used to switch to the trim mode in the **Extend** tool, if two entities are intersecting. You can press the SHIFT key and then select the object to be trimmed. In this case, the boundary edges are taken as the cutting edges.

Project Option

The **Project** option is used to extend objects in the 3d space. The prompt sequence that will follow when you choose the **Extend** tool is given next.

> Current settings: Projection= UCS Edge= Extend
> Select boundary edges...
> Select objects or <select all>: *Select boundary edges.*
> Select objects: [Enter]
> Select object to extend or shift-select to trim or [Fence/Crossing/Project/Edge/Undo]: **P** [Enter]
> Enter a projection option [None/UCS/View] <current>:

The **None** option is used whenever the objects to be extended intersect with the boundary edge in 3D space. If you want to extend those objects that do not intersect the boundary edge in 3D space, use the **UCS** or **View** option. The **UCS** option is used to project the objects to the *XY* plane of the current UCS, while the **View** option is used to project the objects to the current view.

Edge Option

You can use this option whenever you want to extend the objects that do not actually intersect the boundary edge, but would intersect its edge if the boundary edges were extended (Figure 5-29). If you enter **E** at the prompt, the selected object is extended to the implied boundary edge. If you enter **N** at the prompt, only those objects that would actually intersect the real boundary edge are extended (the default). The prompt sequence to use this option is given next.

> Current settings: Projection= UCS Edge= Extend
> Select boundary edges...
> Select objects or <select all>: *Select the boundary edge.*
> Select objects: [Enter]
> Select object to extend or shift-select to trim or [Fence/Crossing/Project/Edge/Undo]: **E** [Enter]
> Enter an implied extension mode [Extend/No extend] <current>: **E** [Enter]
> Select object to extend or shift-select to trim or [Project/Edge/Undo]: *Select the line to extend.*

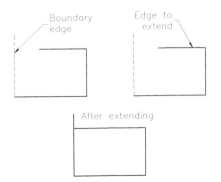

Figure 5-28 Extending an edge

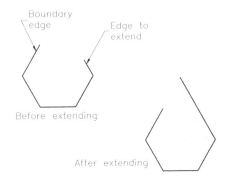

*Figure 5-29 Extending an edge using the **Edge** option (**Extend**)*

Note
The function of the Fence and Crossing options in the Extend tool is the same as that in the Trim tool.

Undo Option

If you want to remove the previous change created by the **Extend** tool, enter **U** at the **Select object to extend or [Fence/Crossing/Project/Edge/Undo]:** prompt.

Trimming and Extending with Text, Region, or Spline

The **Trim** and **Extend** tools can be used with text, regions, or splines as edges (Figure 5-30). This makes the **Trim** and **Extend** tools the most useful editing tools. The **Trim** and **Extend** tools can also be used with arcs, elliptical arcs, splines, ellipses, 3D Pline, rays, and lines. The system variables **PROJMODE** and **EDGEMODE** determine how the **Trim** and **Extend** tools are executed, see Figure 5-31. The values that can be assigned to these variables are discussed next.

Value	PROJMODE	EDGEMODE
0	True 3D mode	Use regular edge without extension (default)
1	Project to current UCS *XY* plane (default)	Extend the edge to the natural boundary
2	Project to current view plane	

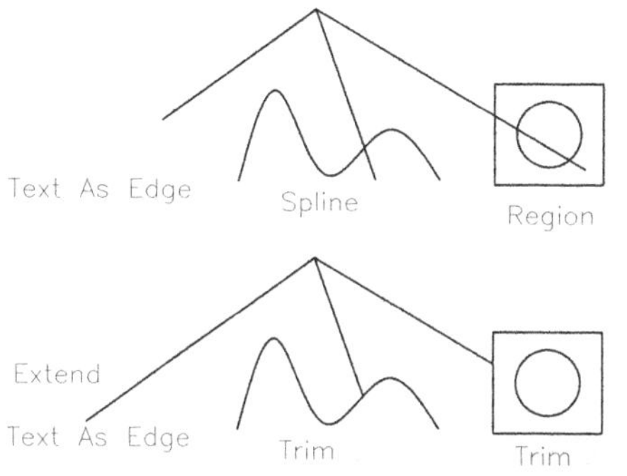

Figure 5-30 Using the TRIM and EXTEND commands with text, spline, and region

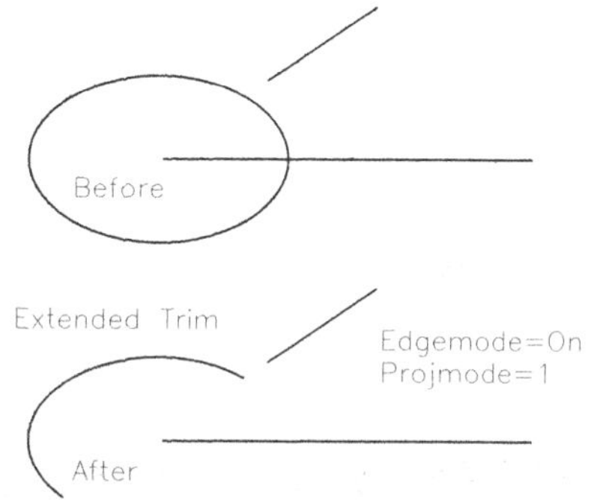

Figure 5-31 Using the PROJMODE and EDGEMODE option to trim

STRETCHING THE SKETCHED OBJECTS

Ribbon: Home > Modify > Stretch	**Toolbar:** Modify > Stretch
Command: STRETCH	

This tool can be used to lengthen objects, shorten them, and alter their shapes, see Figure 5-32. To invoke this tool, choose the **Stretch** tool from the **Modify** panel; you will be prompted to select objects. Use the **Crossing** or **CPolygon** selection method to select the objects to be stretched. After selecting the objects, you will be prompted to specify the base point of displacement. Select the portion of the object that needs to be stretched; you will be prompted to specify the second point of displacement. Specify the new location; the object will lengthen or shorten.

It is recommended to use **Crossing** or **CPolygon** selection method and select the objects to stretch, because if you use any window selection method, those objects that cross the window will not get selected, and the selected objects will be moved but not stretched. The object selection and stretch specification process of **STRETCH** is a little unusual. You are really specifying two things: first, you are selecting objects. Second, you are specifying the portions of those selected objects to be stretched. You can use a **Crossing** or **CPolygon** selection to simultaneously specify both, or you can select objects by any method, and then use any window or crossing specification to specify what parts of those objects to stretch. Objects or portions of the selected objects completely within the window or crossing specification are moved. If the selected objects cross the window or crossing specification, their defining points within the window or crossing specification are moved, their defining points outside the window or crossing specification remain fixed, and the parts crossing the window or the crossing specification are stretched. Only the last window or the crossing specification determines what is stretched or moved. Figure 5-32 illustrates the usage of a crossing selection to simultaneously select two angled lines and specify that their right ends will be stretched. Alternatively, you can select the lines by any method and then use a Crossing selection (which will not actually select anything) to specify that the right ends of the lines will be stretched.

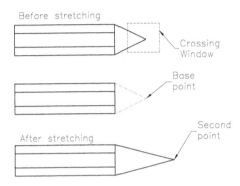

Figure 5-32 *Stretching the entities*

Note
The regions and solids cannot be stretched. If you select them, they will move instead of getting stretched.

LENGTHENING THE SKETCHED OBJECTS

Ribbon: Home > Modify > Lengthen	**Command:** LENGTHEN

Like the **Trim** and **Extend** tools, the **LENGTHEN** command can also be used to extend or shorten lines, polylines, elliptical arcs, and arcs. The **LENGTHEN** command has several options that allow you to change the length of objects by dynamically dragging the object endpoint, entering the delta value, entering the percentage value, or entering the total length of the object. This command also allows the repeated selection of the objects for editing. The prompt that will follow when you invoke the **LENGTHEN** command is given next.

Select an object or [DElta/Percent/Total/DYnamic]:

Select an object Option

This is the default option that returns the current length or the included angle of the selected object. If the object is a line, AutoCAD LT returns only the length. However, if the selected object is an arc, AutoCAD LT returns the length and the angle. The same prompt sequence will be displayed, after you select the object.

DElta Option

The **DElta** option is used to increase or decrease the length or angle of an object by defining the distance or angle by which the object will be extended. The delta value can be entered by entering a numerical value or by specifying two points. A positive value will increase (Extend) the length of the selected object; whereas a negative value will decrease it (Trim), see Figure 5-33. The prompt sequence to change the length of the object is given next.

Select an object or [DElta/Percent/Total/DYnamic]: **DE** [Enter]
Enter delta length or [Angle] <current>: *Enter A for angle.*
Enter delta angle <current>: *Specify the delta angle.*
Select object to change or [Undo]: *Select the object to be extended.*
Select object to change or [Undo]: [Enter]

Percent Option

The **Percent** option is used to extend or trim an object by defining the change as a percentage of the original length or the angle, see Figure 5-33. The current length of the line is taken as 100 percent. If you enter a value more than 100, the length will increase by that amount. Similarly, if you enter a value less than 100, then the length will decrease by that amount. For example, the numerical value150 will increase the length by 50 percent and the numerical value 75 will decrease the length by 25 percent of the original value (negative values are not allowed).

Total Option

The **Total** option is used to extend or trim an object by defining the new total length or angle, see Figure 5-33. For example, if you enter a total length of 1.25, AutoCAD LT will automatically increase or decrease the length of the object so that the new length is 1.25. The value can be entered by entering a numerical value or by specifying two points. The object is shortened or lengthened with respect to the endpoint that is closest to the selection point. The selection point is determined from where the object was selected.

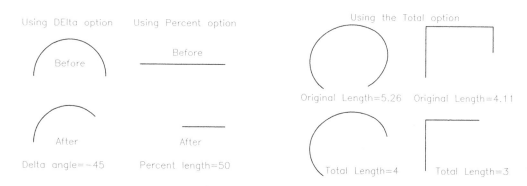

*Figure 5-33 Using the **DElta**, **Percent**, and **Total** options*

Tip
*By default, the **Lengthen** tool is not available in the **Modify** toolbar. To add the **Lengthen** tool in the **Modify** toolbar, right-click on any toolbar to display the shortcut menu. Next, choose **Customize** from the shortcut menu to display the **Customize User Interface** dialog box. Select the **Modify** option in the **Filter the command list by category** drop-down list; all tools that can be added or are currently available in the **Modify** toolbar will be displayed. Drag the **Lengthen** button from the **Command list** area to the **Modify** toolbar in the drawing area. Choose the **OK** button from the **Customize User Interface** dialog box.*

DYnamic

The **DYnamic** option allows you to dynamically change the length or angle of an object by specifying one of the endpoints and dragging it to a new location. The other end of the object remains fixed and unaffected by dragging. The angle of lines, radius of arcs, and shape of elliptical arcs remain unaffected on using this option.

ARRAYING THE SKETCHED OBJECTS*

Command:	ARRAY

In some drawings, you may need to create an object multiple times in a rectangular or circular arrangement. This type of arrangement can be obtained by creating an array of objects. An array is defined as the method of creating multiple copies of a selected object and arranging them in a rectangular or circular fashion. For example, to draw six chairs around a table, you can draw each chair separately or use the **Copy** tool to make multiple copies of the chair. But this is a very tedious process and also in this case, the alignment of the chairs will have to be adjusted. On the other hand, you can obtain the circular or rectangular arrangement of chairs easily by using the **Array** tool. All you have to do is to create one chair, and the remaining five will be created and arranged automatically around the table by using the **Array** tool. This method is more efficient and less time-consuming. In this type of arrangement, each resulting

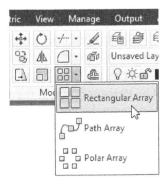

Figure 5-34 Tools in the Array drop-down

element of the array can be controlled separately. The arrays can be created by using the **Array** drop-down, refer to Figure 5-34. You can use this drop-down to create a rectangular, polar, or path array. The prompt sequence to be followed to create an array of an object is given next.

Command: **ARRAY**
Select objects: *Select the object*
Select objects: Specify opposite corner:
Select objects: [Enter]
Enter array type [Rectangular/PAth/POlar] <Rectangular>:

At the last prompt, you can specify the type of array to be created. The different types of arrays that can be created using the **ARRAY** tool are discussed next.

Rectangular Array

Ribbon:	Home > Modify > Array drop-down > Rectangular Array
Toolbar:	Modify > Rectangular Array

A rectangular array is formed by making copies of the selected object along the *X* and *Y* directions of an imaginary rectangle (along rows and columns). To create a rectangular array, choose the **Rectangular Array** tool from the **Modify** panel; you will be prompted to select objects. Select the objects to be arrayed and press ENTER; you will be prompted to specify the opposite corner to specify the number of items in the array. Move the cursor and click in the drawing window to specify the opposite corner; you will be prompted to specify the spacing. Enter the value of spacing or click to specify the spacing for the array. Next, press ENTER or X; the array of the selected object will be created, refer to Figure 5-35. This figure also shows the location of the cursor while specifying the opposite corner. The prompt sequence to create the rectangular array of an object is given next.

Command: **ARRAYRECT**

Select objects: *Select the object*
Specify opposite corner: 1 found
Select objects: [Enter]
Type = Rectangular Associative = Yes
Specify opposite corner for number of items or [Base point/Angle/Count] <Count>: *Click to specify the opposite corner*
Specify opposite corner to space items or [Spacing] <Spacing>: *Enter the spacing or click to specify the spacing*
Press ENTER to accept or [ASsociative/Base point/Rows/Columns/Levels/eXit]<eXit>: *Press [Enter] or* **X**

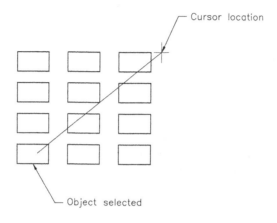

Figure 5-35 Reactangular array created

While specifying the opposite corner, if you move the cursor along the vertical or horizontal direction, the array will be created in the specified direction. Figures 5-36 and 5-37 shows the array created in the vertical and horizontal directions, respectively.

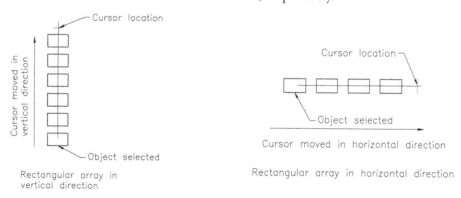

Figure 5-36 A vertical rectangular array created

Figure 5-37 A horizontal rectangular array created

Rectangular Array Options

There are three options to create a rectangular array. These options are displayed at the **Specify opposite corner for number of items or [Base point/Angle/Count] <Count>:** Command prompt. These options are discussed next.

Base point. This option is used to specify the base point of the array to be created. You can specify the base point by selecting a keypoint on the selected object. By default, the centroid is used as the base point for the array. However, you can specify any other point than the centroid of the object as the base point of the array. The prompt sequence that will follow when you invoke the **Base point** command is given next. In this prompt, the **Key point** option has been used.

    Command: **ARRAYRECT**
    Select objects: *Select the object*
    Specify opposite corner: 1 found
    Select objects: [Enter]
    Type = Rectangular Associative = Yes
    Specify opposite corner for number of items or [Base point/Angle/Count] <Count>: **B** [Enter]
    Specify base point or [Key point] <centroid>
    : **K** [Enter]
    Specify a key point on a source object as the
    base point: *Select any keypoint on the object*

Angle. This option is used to specify the rotation angle of the array, refer to Figure 5-38. If you enter **A** at the **Specify opposite corner for number of items or [Base point/Angle/Count] <Count>:** Command prompt, you will be prompted to specify the row axis angle. Enter the required angle value and then specify the opposite corner to specify the number of items. The prompt sequence that will follow when you invoke the **Angle** command is given next.

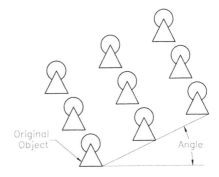

Figure 5-38 Rotated rectangular array

    Specify opposite corner for number of items or [Base point/Angle/Count] <Count>: **A**
    [Enter]
    Specify row axis angle <current>: *Enter the angle value* [Enter]
    Specify opposite corner for number of items or [Base point/Angle/Count] <Count>: *Click to specify the opposite corner*

Count. This option is used to specify the number of rows and columns in the array. If you enter **C** at the **Specify opposite corner for number of items or [Base point/Angle/Count] <Count>:** Command prompt, you will be prompted to specify the number of rows. Enter the number of rows in the array and press ENTER; you will be prompted to specify the number of columns in the array. Enter the number of columns and press ENTER; you will be prompted to specify the opposite corner or the spacing between the components of the array. Click to specify the opposite corner or enter the spacing at the Command prompt to create the array.

    Specify opposite corner for number of items or [Base point/Angle/Count] <Count>: **C**
    [Enter]
    Enter number of rows or [Expression] <current>: *Specify the number of rows*
    Enter number of columns or [Expression] <current>: *Specify the number of columns*
    Specify opposite corner to space items or [Spacing] <Spacing>: *Click to specify the opposite corner or specify the spacing between the components of the array*

You can also specify the number of columns and rows by using expressions or mathematical formulae. Figure 5-39 shows a rectangular array of three rows and six columns.

You can also specify the associativity of the objects in the array. Associativity determines whether the objects of the array are dependent upon each other or not. To specify the associativity, enter

ASSOCIATIVE at the **Press Enter to accept or [ASsociative/Base point/Rows/Columns/ Levels/eXit]<eXit>:** Command prompt; you will be prompted to specify whether the objects of the resultant array will be associative or non-associative. Enter **Yes** at the Command prompt to make the objects of the array associative. The associative array behaves as a single block. If you enter **No** at the Command prompt, the objects of the resultant array will be non-associative. If you edit one of the objects in the non-associative array, the other objects in the array will not be affected. After creating the array, press ENTER or X to exit the **ARRAYRECT** command.

All aforementioned options for creating a rectangular array are also available at the **Dynamic Input**, see Figure 5-40, provided you have chosen the **Dynamic Input** button from the status bar.

Editing the Associative Rectangular Array with Grips

You can change the number of rows, columns, and the distance between the objects in the associative array dynamically. To do so, select an object from the array; grips will be displayed on it, refer to Figure 5-41. If you hover the cursor over the parent grip of a multiple row and column array, a tooltip with two options, **Move** and **Level Count** will be displayed, as

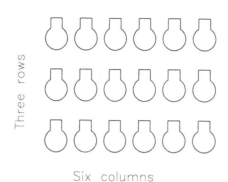

Figure 5-39 Rectangular array of three rows and six columns

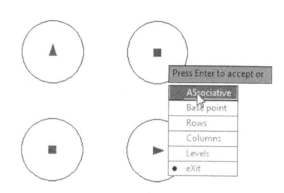

Figure 5-40 Dynamic input options for rectangular array

shown in Figure 5-42. Choose the **Move** option from the tooltip to move the array. If you choose the **Level Count** option from the tooltip, you will be prompted to specify the number of levels. Levels allow you to create a 3D array. Specify the number of levels at the Command prompt or in the **Dynamic Input**; the 3D array will be created. You can view the 3D array in any of the isometric views. The isometric views can be invoked by using the options in the **Views** panel of the **View** tab in the **Ribbon**.

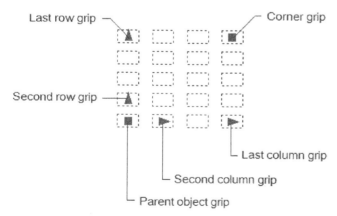

Figure 5-41 Grips of a rectangular array

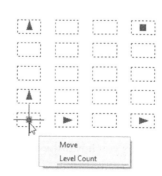

Figure 5-42 The parent grip tooltip

If you hover the cursor over the corner grip of the rectangular array, a tooltip with two options, **Row and Column Count** and **Total Row and Column Spacing**, will be displayed, as shown in Figure 5-43. Choose the **Row and Column Count** option from the tooltip to change the number of rows and columns in the array. Note that the array created using this option will have equal number of rows and columns. If you choose the **Total Row and Column Spacing** option, you will be prompted to specify the spacing between the rows and columns. Specify the distance value; the array with equal spacing between the objects in the rows and columns will be created.

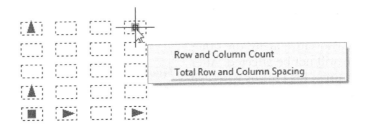

Figure 5-43 *The corner grip tooltip*

Hover the cursor over the second column grip of the rectangular array. If the **Dynamic Input** option is turned on, the value between the two columns will be displayed in the graphics window, refer to Figure 5-44. Click on the grip; an edit box will be displayed in the graphics window. Enter a value in this edit box to specify the spacing between the columns of the array. If the **Dynamic Input** is turned off, you can specify the spacing between the columns by entering values at the Command prompt or by clicking in the graphics window.

Hover the cursor over the grip on the last column; a tooltip with three options, **Column Count**, **Total Column Spacing**, and **Axis Angle** will be displayed, as shown in Figure 5-45. Choose the **Column Count** option from the tooltip; an edit box showing the total number of columns will be displayed. If you choose the **Total Column Spacing** option, you will be prompted to specify the spacing between the columns. If the **Dynamic Input** is turned off, you can specify the spacing between the columns by entering a value at the Command prompt or by clicking in the graphics window. If you choose the **Axis Angle** option, you will be prompted to specify the axis angle. Specify the required angle at the **Dynamic Input** or the Command prompt and press ENTER.

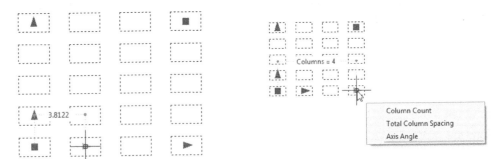

Figure 5-44 *Distance between two columns*   *Figure 5-45* *The last column grip tooltip*

Similarly, if you hover the cursor over the grip on the second row or the last row of the rectangular array, the options related to row count, row spacing, and axis angle will be displayed. These options are used to specify the parameters for rows of the array. Figure 5-46 shows a rectangular array with specific distances between rows and columns.

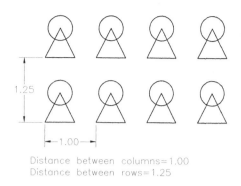

Figure 5-46 *A rectangular array with rows and columns at specific distance*

Editing the Associative Rectangular Array using the Array Contextual Tab

You can also edit the associative rectangular array by using the **Array** contextual tab that will be displayed when you select the rectangular array. The **Array** (Rectangular) contextual tab is shown in Figure 5-47.

Figure 5-47 *The Array (Rectangular) contextual tab*

The different panels and options corresponding to them in this tab are discussed next.

Type. This panel displays the type of array to be modified.

Columns. This panel displays three options which are used for changing the number of columns, the distance between two columns, and the total distance between the first and last columns. The descriptions of these options are the same as those discussed in the previous topic.

Rows. This panel displays the options for changing the number of rows, the distance between two rows, and the total distance between the first and last rows. You can also specify the incremental elevation between the rows.

Levels. This panel displays three options for changing the number of levels, the distance between two levels, and the total distance between the first and last levels. The levels allow you to create a 3D array.

Properties. The **Base Point** tool in the **Properties** panel allows you to change the base point of the array.

Options. There are three tools in the **Options** panel: **Edit Source**, **Replace Item**, and **Reset Array**. These options are discussed next.

Edit Source. The **Edit Source** tool is used to edit the source of the array. On choosing this tool, you will be prompted to select an item in the array. Select any object in the array that will act as the source of the array. On selecting an item, the **Array Editing State** message box will be displayed, as shown in Figure 5-48, prompting you either to edit the source object or exit the editing state. Choose **OK** in this message box; the **Edit Array** panel will be added to the **Home** tab of the **Ribbon**, indicating that you are now in the editing mode. Next, modify the source object geometry. On modifying the source object geometry, you will notice that the other items of the array are also modified. Next, choose **Save Array** from the **Edit Array** panel; the changes made in the array will be saved.

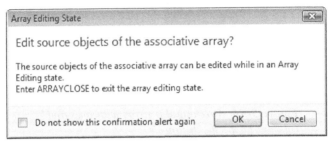

*Figure 5-48 The **Array Editing State** message box*

Figure 5-49 shows the rectangular array of a triangle and Figure 5-50 shows the source of the array being edited.

Replace Item. This tool is used to replace an item in the array with another item. On choosing this tool, you will be prompted to select the replacement object. Select the replacement object and press ENTER; you will be prompted to specify the base point of the replacement object. Click to specify the base point of the replacement object. You can also specify a keypoint as the base point of the replacement object. To do so, enter **K** at the command prompt and then select any keypoint from the array. After specifying the base point, you will be prompted to specify the item to be replaced. Select an item from the array; the selected item will be replaced with the replacement item. You can continue replacing rest of the items in the array by selecting them. Figure 5-51 shows a rectangular array and the replacement object. Figure 5-52 shows the objects of the array after replacing with the selected object.

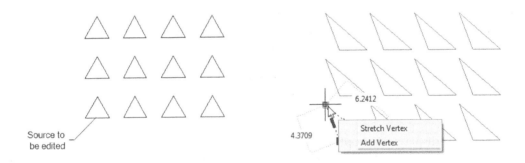

Figure 5-49 A rectangular array   *Figure 5-50 Source of the array being edited*

Reset Array. This tool is used to restore the objects that have been deleted from the array. If you have made any replacements in the array, those replacements can also be reverted by using this tool.

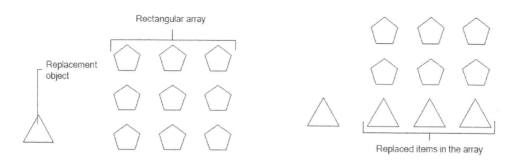

Figure 5-51 *Array with the replacement object*

Figure 5-52 *Replaced items in the first row of the array*

Polar Array

Ribbon:	Home > Modify > Array drop-down > Polar Array
Toolbar:	Modify > Rectangular Array > Polar Array

Polar array is an arrangement of objects around a point in circular pattern. A polar array can be created by choosing the **Polar Array** tool from the **Modify** panel. When you choose this tool, you will be prompted to select objects. Select objects to be arrayed; you will be prompted to specify the center point of the array. Select the center point of the array; you will be prompted to specify the number of items. Specify the number of items and press ENTER; you will be prompted to specify the fill angle. Enter an angle value at the Command prompt and then press ENTER; the polar array will be created, and you will prompted to exit the **Polar Array** tool. Press ENTER or X to exit the tool. Figure 5-53 shows a polar array with its center.

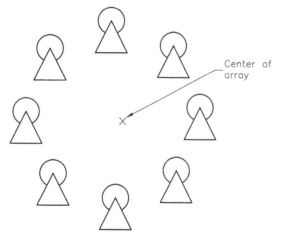

Figure 5-53 *Polar array created*

The prompt sequence to create the polar array of an object is given next.

Command: **ARRAYPOLAR**
Select objects: *Select the object*
Select objects: Enter
Type = Polar Associative = Yes
Specify center point of array or [Base point/Axis of rotation]: *Click to specify the center point of array*
Enter number of items or [Angle between/Expression] <current>: *Enter the number of items to be created*
Specify the angle to fill (+ =ccw, -=cw) or [EXpression] <current>: *Enter the fill angle*
Press Enter to accept or [ASsociative/Base point/Items/Angle between/Fill angle/ROWs/Levels/ROTate items/eXit]<eXit>: **X** Enter

Polar Array Options

There are two options used for creating a polar array. These options are displayed at the **Specify center point of array or [Base point/Axis of rotation]:** Command prompt. These options are discussed next.

Base point. This option is used to specify the base point of the polar array. You can specify the base point by clicking on the graphics window or by selecting a keypoint on the selected object. By default, the centroid is used as the base point for the array. You can also click in the drawing window to specify the base point of the array. The prompt sequence followed while using the **Base point** command is given next. In this prompt, the **Key point** option has been used.

> Command: **ARRAYPOLAR**
> Select objects: *Select the object*
> Specify opposite corner: 1 found
> Select objects: Enter
> Type = Polar Associative = Yes
> Specify center point of array or [Base point/Axis of rotation]: **B** Enter
> Specify base point or [Key point] <centroid> : **K** Enter
> Specify a key point on the source object as the base point: *Select any keypoint on the object*

Axis of rotation. This option is used to specify the rotation angle of the array, refer to Figure 5-54. If you enter **A** at the **Specify center point of array or [Base point/Axis of rotation]:** Command prompt, you will be prompted to specify the first point on the axis of rotation. Click to specify the first point; you will be prompted to specify the second point on the axis of rotation. Click to specify the second point; the preview of the polar array depending upon the axis of rotation will be displayed. You can also specify the first and second points of the axis of rotation by using the **Dynamic Input**.

The prompt sequence followed while using the **Axis of rotation** option is given next.

> Specify center point of array or [Base point/Axis of rotation]: **A** Enter
> Specify first point on axis of rotation: *Click to specify the first point*
> Specify second point on axis of rotation: *Click to specify the second point*

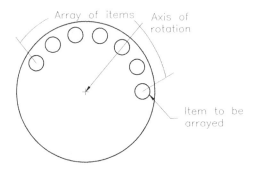

Figure 5-54 Polar array created around the axis of rotation

After specifying the required polar array option, you will be prompted to enter the number of items to be created. The prompt sequence to enter the number of items in the polar array is given next.

> Enter number of items or [Angle between/Expression] <current>:

As evident from the Command prompt, you can specify the number of items in various ways. The first way is that you can enter the number of items directly at the Command prompt. The second way to specify the number of items is that you can enter the angle between the items in the polar array. If you enter **ANGLE** or **A** at the Command prompt, you will be prompted to enter the angle between the items. Specify the angle value at the Command prompt and press ENTER. You can also specify the angle by using expressions or mathematical formulae. Another way of specifying the number of items of the polar array is by specifying the fill angle at the **Specify number of items or [Fill angle/Expression] <current>:** Command prompt. This command prompt is displayed when you enter the angle between the items in the polar array. The third method to specify the number of items is to use expressions. The prompt sequence to specify the number of items in the polar array of an object is given next. In this prompt sequence, the **Angle between** option is used.

Command: **ARRAYPOLAR**
Select objects: Select the objects to be arrayed
Select objects: Enter
Type = Polar Associative = Yes
Specify center point of array or [Base point/Axis of rotation]: *Click to specify the center point of the array*
Enter number of items or [Angle between/Expression] <current>: **A** Enter
Specify angle between items or [EXpression] <current>: *Enter the angle value*
Specify number of items or [Fill angle/Expression] <current>: *Enter the number of items of the polar array*
Press ENTER to accept or [ASsociative/Base point/Items/Angle between/Fill angle/ROWs/Levels/ROTate items/eXit]<eXit>: **X** Enter

If you enter **F** at the **Specify number of items or [Fill angle/Expression] <current>:** Command prompt, you will be prompted to specify the fill angle. Enter the fill angle; all items of the polar array will be adjusted within the specified fill angle value. You can specify the direction of the polar array either clockwise or counterclockwise. If you enter a positive angle value at the Command prompt, the polar array will be created in the counterclockwise direction. If you enter a negative angle value, the polar array will be created in the clockwise direction.

After specifying all options for the polar array, enter X at the **Press Enter to accept or [ASsociative/Base point/Items/Angle between/Fill angle/ROWs/Levels/ROTate items/eXit]<eXit>:** Command prompt to exit the **Polar Array** tool. All options in the Command prompt, except the **ROWs** and **Levels**, have already been discussed. The **ROWs** option is used to specify the number of items in the radially outward direction, whereas the **Levels** option is used to create a 3D polar array. You can view the 3D polar array in any of the isometric views.

Figure 5-55 shows a polar array created by specifying the number or items and the angle between the items. Figure 5-56 shows a polar array created by specifying the number or items and the fill angle.

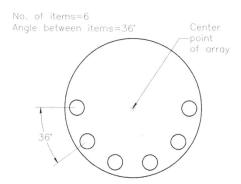
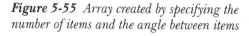
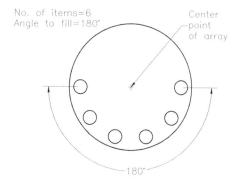

Figure 5-55 *Array created by specifying the number of items and the angle between items*

Figure 5-56 *Array created by specifying the number of items and the fill angle*

In an array, you can also make the objects associative. Associativity determines whether the objects of the array will be dependent upon each other or not. To specify the associativity, enter **ASSOCIATIVE** or **AS** at the **Press Enter to accept or [ASsociative/Base point/Items/Angle between/Fill angle/ROWs/Levels/ROTate items/eXit]<eXit>:** Command prompt. On doing so, you will be prompted to specify whether the objects of the array created will be associative or non-associative. Enter **Yes** at the Command prompt to make the objects of the array associative. An associative array behaves as a single block. If you enter **No** at the Command prompt, the objects of the array created will be non-associative. If you edit one of the objects in the non-associative array, the other objects in the array will not be affected. After creating the array, press ENTER or X to exit the **ARRAYPOLAR** command.

All aforementioned options for creating the polar array will also be available at the **Dynamic Input**, provided the **Dynamic Input** button is chosen in the status bar.

Editing the Associative Polar Array with Grips

You can change the number of rows, levels, and the fill angle between the objects in the associative array dynamically. To do so, select an object from the array; the grips will be displayed on the array, as shown in Figure 5-57. If you hover the cursor over the parent grip of a multiple row array, a tooltip with two options, **Stretch Radius** and **Level Count**, will be displayed, as shown in Figure 5-58. Choose the **Stretch Radius** option from the tooltip to change the radius of the array. If you choose the **Level Count** option from the tooltip, you will be prompted to specify the number of levels. Specify the number of levels at the Command prompt or at the **Dynamic Input**; the 3D array will be created. You can view the 3D array in any of the isometric views. The isometric views can be invoked by using the options in the **Views** panel of the **View** tab in the **Ribbon**.

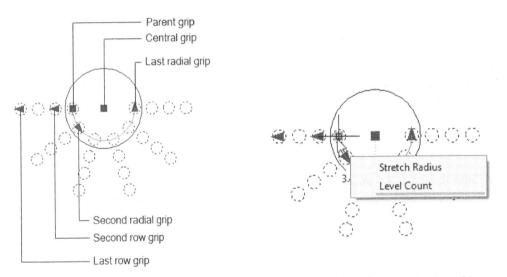

Figure 5-57 Grips of a polar array   *Figure 5-58 The parent grip tooltip*

If you hover the cursor over the second radial grip of the polar array, the angle between the parent item and the second items of the array will be displayed, as shown in Figure 5-59. If you click at this time, an edit box will be displayed and you will be prompted to specify the angle between the items. Enter the desired angle value in this edit box.

If you hover the cursor over the last grip of the polar array, a tooltip with two options, **Item Count** and **Fill Angle**, will be displayed, as shown in Figure 5-60. If you choose **Item Count** from the tooltip, an edit box will be displayed and you will be prompted to specify the number of items. Enter the number of items in this edit box. If you choose **Fill Angle** from the tooltip, an edit box will be displayed and you will be prompted to specify the fill angle. Enter the fill angle in this edit box.

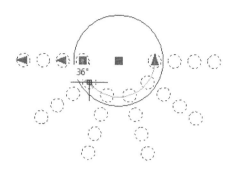

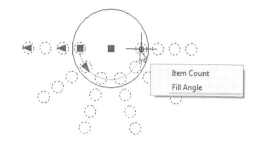

Figure 5-59 *Angle displayed between the parent and second radial grips*

Figure 5-60 *Tooltip displayed on the last radial grip*

If you hover the cursor over the second row grip of the polar array, the current distance between two rows will be displayed, as shown in Figure 5-61. Click on this grip; an edit box will be displayed and you will be prompted to specify the distance between the two rows. Enter the new value in this edit box to specify the distance between the two rows.

If you hover the cursor over the last row grip of the polar array, a tooltip with two options, **Row Count** and **Total Row Spacing**, will be displayed, as shown in Figure 5-62. If you choose **Row Count** from the tooltip, an edit box will be displayed and you will be prompted to specify the number of rows. Specify the number of rows in the edit box to determine the number of rows in the array. If you choose **Total Row Spacing** from the tooltip, an edit box will be displayed and you will be prompted to specify the distance between the first and last row. Enter the desired value in this edit box.

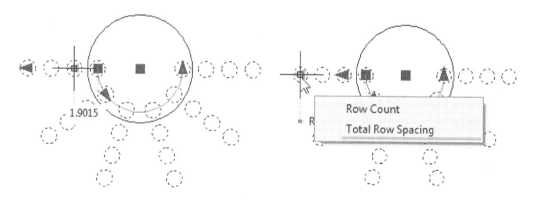

Figure 5-61 *Distance displayed between parent and second row grips*

Figure 5-62 *Tooltip displayed on the last row grip*

In case of single row polar array, if you hover the cursor over the parent object, a tooltip with three options, **Stretch Radius, Row Count**, and **Level Count**, will be displayed. You can specify the radius, number of rows, and the number of levels with these options.

Editing the Associative Polar Array using the Array Contextual Tab
You can also edit the associative polar array by using the **Array** contextual tab that will be displayed when you select the polar array. The **Array** contextual tab is shown in Figure 5-63.

Chapter 5

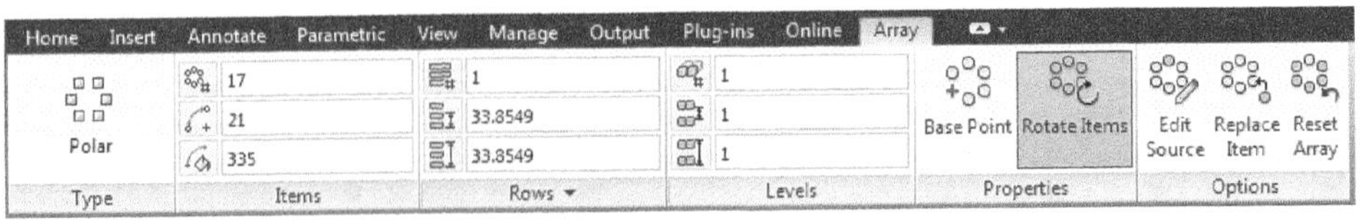

Figure 5-63 *The **Array** (Polar) contextual tab*

The different panels and their corresponding options in this tab are discussed next.

Type
This panel displays the type of array to be modified.

Items
This panel displays three options that are used for changing the number of items, angle between two items, and total fill angle between the first and last items. These options are the same as those discussed in the previous topic.

Rows
This panel displays the options that are used for changing the number of rows, distance between two rows, and total distance between the first and last rows of the polar array. You can also specify the incremental elevation between the rows.

Levels
This panel displays three options that are used for changing the number of levels, distance between two levels, and total distance between the first and last levels. The levels allow you to create a 3D array.

Properties
By default, the **Rotate Items** button is chosen in this panel. As a result, the polar array will be created on rotating the items. Choose the **Base Point** tool if you want to change the base point of the array.

Options
There are three tools in the **Options** panel: **Edit Source**, **Replace Item**, and **Reset Array**. The options in this panel function in a way similar to the options in **Options** panel of the rectangular array.

Path Array

Ribbon:	Home > Modify > Array drop-down > Path Array
Toolbar:	Modify > Rectangular Array > Path Array

In AutoCAD LT, you can create an array of objects along a path called path arrays. The path can be a line, polyline, circle, helix, and so on. To create a path array, choose the **Path Array** tool from the **Modify** panel. On doing so, you will be prompted to select objects. Select the objects to be arrayed and press ENTER; you will be prompted to select the path curve along which the object will be arrayed. Select the path curve; the preview of the path array will be displayed. You will notice that as you move the cursor, the number of items get arranged on the path and you will be prompted to enter the number of items in the array. Enter the desired number at the Command prompt and press ENTER; you will be prompted to specify the distance between the items along the path. You will notice that the spacing between the objects gets adjusted as you move the cursor. Specify the distance at the Command prompt and press ENTER; the array of the selected item will be created along the path and you will be prompted to exit the **Path Array** tool. Press ENTER to accept or X to exit the tool. Figure 5-64 shows the item and the path curve and Figure 5-65 shows the path array created.

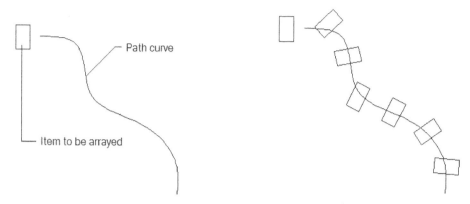

Figure 5-64 *Item and the path curve*   **Figure 5-65** *Path array created*

The prompt sequence to create the path array of an object is given next.
> Command: **ARRAYPATH**
> Select objects: *Select the object*
> Select objects: [Enter]
> Type = Path Associative = Yes
> Select path curve: *Select the path*
> Enter number of items along path or [Orientation/Expression] <Orientation>: *Specify the number of items of the path array*
> Specify the distance between items along path or [Divide/Total/Expression] <Divide evenly along path>: *Enter the distance value between the items*
> Press Enter to accept or [ASsociative/Base point/Items/Rows/Levels/Align items/Z direction/eXit]<eXit>: **X** [Enter]

For creating a path array, you need to specify the orientation of the items along the path curve. If you enter **O** or **Orientation** at the **Enter number of items along path or [Orientation/Expression] <Orientation>:** Command prompt, you will be prompted to specify the base point. You can click at the desired point on the graphics window to specify the base point by the using a keypoint on the source object. You can also use the endpoint of the path curve as the base point. On specifying the base point, you will be prompted to specify the direction along which you have to align the object in the path. You can specify the alignment direction at the **Specify direction to align with path or [2Points/NORmal] <current>:** prompt. Click to specify the alignment direction with the path; the preview of the array will be displayed. You can also specify the alignment direction by specifying two points. This can be done by entering **2P** at the **Specify direction to align with path or [2Points/NORmal] <current>:** prompt. If you enter **NOR** at the **Specify direction to align with path or [2Points/NORmal] <current>:** prompt, the items will be oriented normal to the path and you will be prompted to specify the number of items. Specify the number of items to be created and press ENTER. Figures 5-66 and 5-67 show the path arrays created with the aligned direction and normal orientation of items, respectively.

Chapter 5

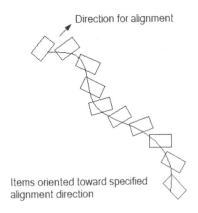

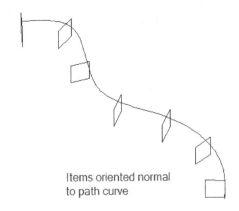

Figure 5-66 *Path array created with aligned direction orientation*

Figure 5-67 *Path array created with normal orientation of items*

After you have specified the number of items to be created, you need to specify the distance between the items at the **Specify the distance between items along path or [Divide/Total/Expression] <Divide evenly along path>:** prompt. You can either enter a value or use other options at this prompt to specify the distance between items. If you enter **D** at the command prompt, the specified number of items will be placed in equally-spaced arrangement along the path, as shown in Figure 5-68. If you enter **T** at the Command prompt, you will be prompted to specify the total distance between the first and last items. Enter the required value at the command prompt and press ENTER; the path array will be created within the specified distance, as shown in Figure 5-69. You can also specify the distance between the items by using mathematical expressions or formulae.

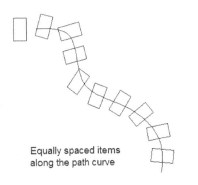

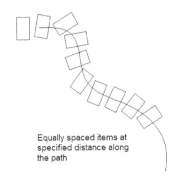

Figure 5-68 *Path array created using the* **Divide** *option*

Figure 5-69 *Path array created using the* **Total** *option*

The prompt sequence to create the path array of an object by specifying the distance between the items by using the **Divide** option is given next.

Command: **ARRAYPATH**
Select objects: *Select the object*
Select objects: [Enter]
Type = Path Associative = Yes
Select path curve: *Select the path*
Enter number of items along path or [Orientation/Expression] <Orientation>: Specify the number of items to be created
Specify the distance between items along path or [Divide/Total/Expression] <Divide evenly along path>: **D** [Enter]

Press Enter to accept or [ASsociative/Base point/ Items/Rows/Levels/Align items/Z direction/ eXit]<eXit>: **X**

All options discussed here for creating the path array are also available at the **Dynamic Input**, see Figure 5-70, which will be available only if the **Dynamic Input** button is chosen from the status bar.

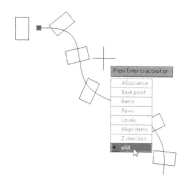

Editing the Associative Path Array

Like rectangular and polar arrays, you can edit the associative path array by using either the grips or the **Array** contextual tab. The **Array** (Path) contextual tab, as shown in Figure 5-71, will be displayed when you select the path array. Most of the options in the **Array** contextual tab function the same way as those in the rectangular and polar arrays. The rest of the options are discussed next.

Figure 5-70 Dynamic input options for path array

*Figure 5-71 The **Array** (Path) contextual tab*

Properties
By default, the **Align Items** and **Z Direction** tools are chosen in this panel. As a result, the path array will be aligned tangent to the path. Also, the original Z direction of the objects will be maintained in case the path is 3-dimensional. You can also use the **Measure** tool to specify the distance between the items of the path array.

MIRRORING THE SKETCHED OBJECTS

Ribbon: Home > Modify > Mirror   **Toolbar:** Modify > Mirror
Command: MIRROR

The **Mirror** tool is used to create a mirror copy of the selected objects. The objects can be mirrored at any angle. This tool is helpful in drawing symmetrical figures. On invoking this tool, you will be prompted to select objects. On selecting the objects to be mirrored, you will be prompted to enter the first point of the mirror line and the second point of the mirror line. A mirror line is an imaginary line about which the objects are mirrored. You can specify the endpoints of the mirror line by specifying the points in the drawing area or by entering their coordinates. The mirror line can be specified at any angle. On selecting the first point of the mirror line, the preview of the mirrored objects will be displayed. Next, you need to specify the second endpoint of the mirror line, as shown in Figure 5-72. On selecting the second endpoint, you will be prompted to specify whether you want to delete the source object or not. Enter **Yes** to delete the source object and **No** to retain the source object, see Figure 5-73.

Chapter 5

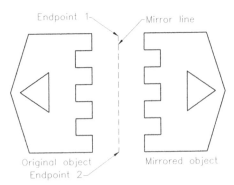

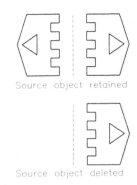

Figure 5-72 *Creating a mirror image of an object by using the* **Mirror** *tool*

Figure 5-73 *Retaining and deleting old objects after mirroring*

The prompt sequence that will follow when you choose this tool is given next.

Select objects: *Select the objects to be mirrored.*
Select objects: Enter
Specify first point of mirror line: *Specify the first endpoint.*
Specify second point of mirror line: *Specify the second endpoint.*
Erase source objects? [Yes/No] <N>: *Enter* **Y** *for deletion,* **N** *for retaining previous objects.*

To mirror the objects at some angle, define the mirror line accordingly. For example, to mirror an object such that the mirrored object is placed at an angle of 90-degree from the original object, define the mirror line at an angle of 45-degree, see Figure 5-74.

Text Mirroring

By default, the **Mirror** tool reverses all objects, except the text. But, if you want the text to be mirrored (written backward) then you need to modify the value of the **MIRRTEXT** system variable. This variable has two values that are given next (Figure 5-75).

1 = Text is reversed in relation to the original object.
0 = Restricts the text from being reversed with respect to the original object. This is the default value.

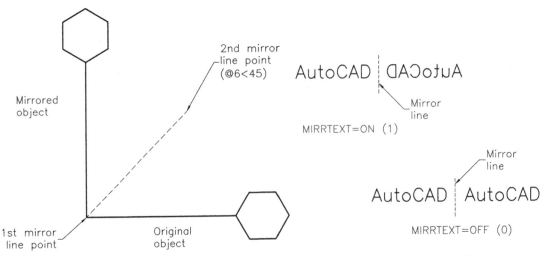

Figure 5-74 *Mirroring the object at an angle*

Figure 5-75 *Using the* **MIRRTEXT** *system variable for mirroring the text*

Self-Evaluation Test

Answer the following questions and then compare them to those given at the end of this chapter:

1. When you shift a group of objects by using the **Move** tool, the size and orientation of those objects will get changed. (T/F)

2. The **Copy** tool is used to make copies of the selected object, leaving the original object intact. (T/F)

3. A fillet cannot be created between two parallel and non-intersecting lines. (T/F)

4. On selecting an object after invoking the **Break** tool, the selection point becomes the first break point. (T/F)

5. You can create small or large circles, ellipses, and arcs by using the _____ tool, depending on the side to be offset.

6. The _____ tool prunes the objects that extend beyond the required point of intersection.

7. The offset distance is stored in the _____ system variable.

8. Instead of specifying the scale factor, you can use the _____ option to scale an object with reference to another object.

9. If the _____ system variable is set to 1, the mirrored text is not reversed with respect to the original object.

10. There are three types of arrays: _____ , _____ , and _____ .

Review Questions

Answer the following questions:

1. In the case of the **Through** option of the **Offset** tool, you do not need to specify a distance; you simply have to specify an offset point. (T/F)

2. While creating a fillet by using the **Fillet** tool, the extrusion direction of the selected object must be parallel to the Z axis of the UCS. (T/F)

3. In AutoCAD LT, you can rotate a rectangular array. (T/F)

4. Which of the following tools is used to change the size of an existing object with respect to an existing entity?

    (a) **Rotate**   (b) **Scale**
    (c) **Move**   (d) None of these

5. Which of these options of the **Lengthen** tool is used to modify the length of the selected entity such that irrespective of the original length, the entity acquires the specified length?

    (a) **DElta**   (b) **DYnamic**
    (c) **Percent**   (d) **Total**

6. If a selected object is within a window or crossing specification, the _____ tool works like the **Move** tool.

7. Which of the following commands is used to copy an existing object using a base point to another drawing?

    (a) **COPY**   (b) **COPYBASE**
    (c) **MOVE**   (d) None of these

8. The _____ option of the **Extend** tool is used to extend objects to the implied boundary.

9. If a polyline is not closed and while creating a fillet by using the **Fillet** tool with the **Polyline** option selected, the _____ corner is not filleted.

10. When the chamfer distance is zero, the chamfer created is in the form of a _____ .

EXERCISE 4   *Divide*

Create the drawing shown in Figure 5-76. Use the **Divide** tool to divide the circle and use the **NODE** object snap to select the points. Assume the dimensions of the drawing.

Figure 5-76 Drawing for Exercise 4

EXERCISE 5

Create the drawing shown in Figure 5-77 and save it. Assume the missing dimensions.

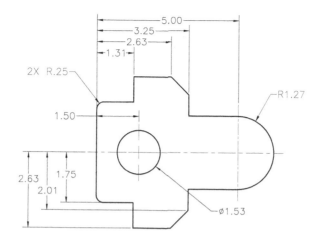

Figure 5-77 *Drawing for Exercise 5*

EXERCISE 6

Create the drawing shown in Figure 5-78 and save it.

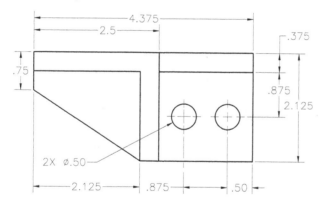

Figure 5-78 *Drawing for Exercise 6*

EXERCISE 7

Create the drawing shown in Figure 5-79 and save it.

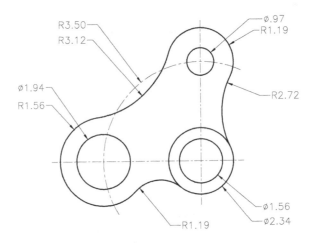

Figure 5-79 *Drawing for Exercise 7*

EXERCISE 8

Create the drawing shown in Figure 5-80 and save it. Assume the missing dimensions.

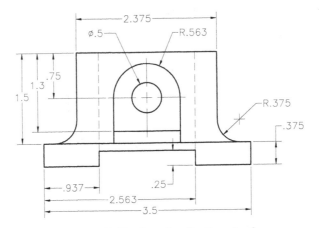

Figure 5-80 *Drawing for Exercise 8*

Problem-Solving Exercise 1

Create the drawing shown in Figure 5-81 and save it. Assume the missing dimensions.

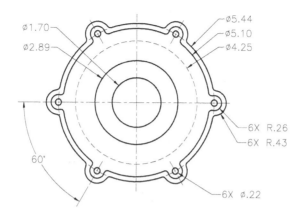

Figure 5-81 *Drawing for Problem-Solving Exercise 1*

Problem-Solving Exercise 2

Create the drawing shown in Figure 5-82 and save it. Assume the missing dimensions.

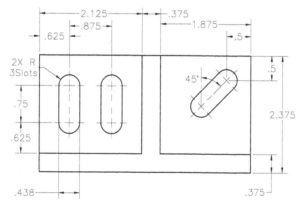

Figure 5-82 *Drawing for Problem-Solving Exercise 2*

Problem-Solving Exercise 3

Draw the dining table and chairs, as shown in Figure 5-83 and save the drawing. Assume the missing dimensions.

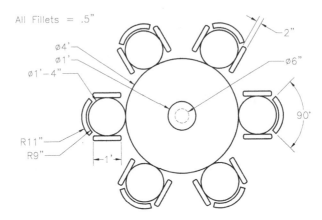

Figure 5-83 *Drawing for Problem-Solving Exercise 3*

Problem-Solving Exercise 4

Draw a reception table with chairs, as shown in Figure 5-84 and save the drawing. The dimensions of the chairs are the same as those used in Problem-Solving Exercise 3.

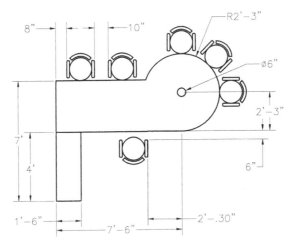

Figure 5-84 *Drawing for Problem-Solving Exercise 4*

Problem-Solving Exercise 5

Draw a center table with chairs, as shown in Figure 5-85, and save the drawing. The dimensions of the chairs are the same as those used in Problem-Solving Exercise 3.

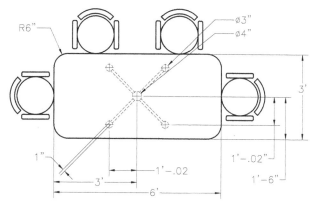

Figure 5-85 *Drawing for Problem-Solving Exercise 5*

Problem-Solving Exercise 6

Create the drawing shown in Figure 5-86 and save it. Refer to the note given in the drawing to create an arc of radius 30.

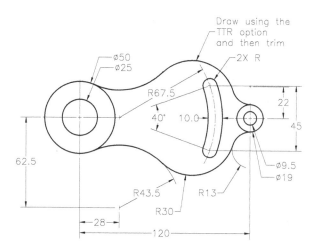

Figure 5-86 *Drawing for Problem-Solving Exercise 6*

Problem-Solving Exercise 7

Create the drawing shown in Figure 5-87 and save it.

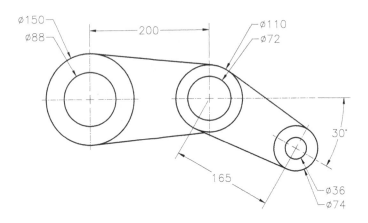

Figure 5-87 *Drawing for Problem-Solving Exercise 7*

Problem-Solving Exercise 8

Create the drawing shown in Figure 5-88 and save it.

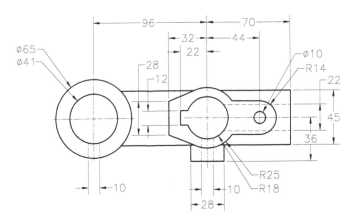

Figure 5-88 *Drawing for Problem-Solving Exercise 8*

Answers to Self-Evaluation Test

1. F, **2.** T, **3.** F, **4.** T, **5. OFFSET**, **6. TRIM**, **7. OFFSETDIST**, **8. Reference**, **9. MIRRTEXT**, **10. Rectangular, Polar, Path**

Chapter 6

Editing Sketched Objects-II

CHAPTER OBJECTIVES

In this chapter, you will learn:
* *To use grips.*
* *To use the Match Properties tool to match properties of the selected objects.*
* *To manage contents using the DesignCenter.*
* *To use the REDRAW and REGEN commands.*
* *To use the ZOOM command and its options.*
* *To use the PAN and VIEW commands.*
* *To use Sheet Set Manager.*

KEY TERMS

* *Grips*
* *Properties Panel*
* *Quick Select*
* *DesignCenter*

* *Area*
* *Distance*
* *Locate Point*
* *List*

* *Time*
* *Status*
* *Regen*
* *Redraw*

* *Zoom*

INTRODUCTION TO GRIPS

Grips provide a convenient and quick means of editing objects. Grips are small squares that are displayed on the key points of an object when the object is selected, as shown in Figure 6-1. If the grips are not displayed on selecting an object, invoke the **Options** dialog box, choose the **Selection** tab, and select the **Enable grips** check box. Using grips, you can stretch, move, rotate, scale, and mirror objects, change properties, and load the Web browser. The number of grips depends on the selected object. For example, a line has three grip points and an arc has three triangular grips along with the small square grips. The triangular grips point towards the direction, in which the arc can be edited dynamically. Similarly, a circle has five grip points and a dimension (vertical, horizontal, or inclined) has five grips. Note that the **Noun/verb selection** check box will be selected in the **Selection modes are** of the **Selection** tab of the **Options** dialog box. On clearing this selection box the small square (aperture box) will not be displayed at the intersection of crosshairs.

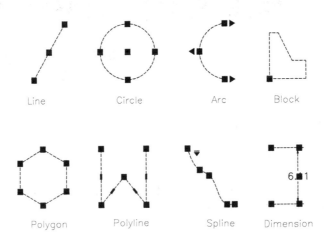

Figure 6-1 Grips displayed on various objects

TYPES OF GRIPS

Grips are classified into three types: unselected grips, hover grips, and selected grips. The selected grips are also called hot grips. When you select an object, the grips are displayed at the definition points of the object and object is displayed as dashed line. These grips are called unselected grips and displayed in blue. Now, move the cursor over an unselected grip, and pause for a second, the grip will be displayed in orange. These grips are called hover grips. Dimensions corresponding to a hover grip are displayed when you place the cursor on the grip, as shown in Figure 6-2.

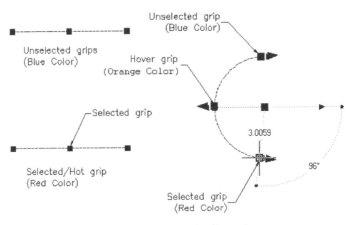

Figure 6-2 Hover grip dimensions

If you select a grip, it is displayed in red color and called as hot grips. Once the grip is hot, the object can be edited. To cancel the grip, press ESC twice. If you press ESC once, the hot grip changes to an unselected grip.

Editing a Polyline by Using Grips

In AutoCAD LT, when you select a polyline, three grips are displayed in each segment of the polyline. You can edit the polyline by using these grips. To do so, move the cursor on one of the grips and pause for a while; a tooltip will be displayed, as shown in Figure 6-3. To stretch the polyline, choose the **Stretch Vertex** option and specify a new point; the polyline will be stretched. After choosing the **Stretch Vertex** option, you can also invoke the **Base Point** or **Copy** option from the shortcut menu as discussed earlier.

To add a new vertex, choose the **Add Vertex** option from the tooltip, as shown in Figure 6-4; you will be prompted to specify a new vertex point. Specify a point; a new vertex will be added between the selected vertex and the next vertex, as shown in Figure 6-5. However, if the selected vertex is the last vertex, then a new segment will be added to the last vertex.

To remove a vertex, move the cursor over the vertex to be removed and choose the **Remove Vertex** option from the tooltip displayed.

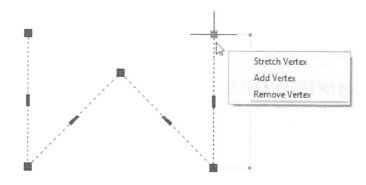

Figure 6-3 *Tooltip displayed near the grip*

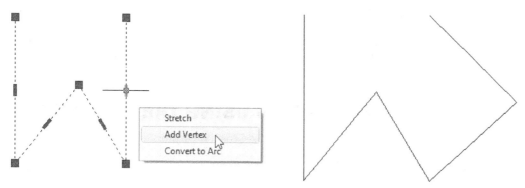

Figure 6-4 *Choosing the **Add Vertex** option from the tooltip*

Figure 6-5 *Polyline after adding a new vertex*

If you place the cursor on the middle grip, the tooltip will display the **Convert to Arc** option instead of the **Remove Vertex** option. Choose this option to convert (see Figure 6-6) the selected line to an arc. On choosing this option, you will be prompted to specify the midpoint of the arc. Specify a point on the periphery of the arc; the line will be converted to an arc, as shown in Figure 6-7. If you have drawn an arc using the **Polyline** tool or converted a polyline to an arc, you can convert the arc back to the line by choosing the **Convert to Line** option from the tool tip that is displayed on placing the cursor on the middle grip of the arc.

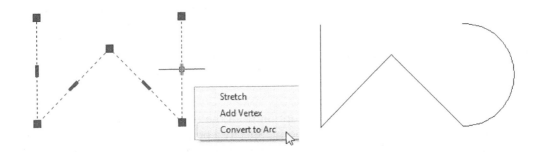

Figure 6-6 *Selecting the* ***Convert to Arc*** *option from the tooltip*

Figure 6-7 *Polyline after converting a line to an arc*

Tip
After choosing an option from the tooltip, you can cycle through the options in the tooltip by pressing the CTRL key .

EDITING GRIPPED OBJECTS

You can also edit the properties of the gripped objects by using the **Properties** panel in the **Home** tab, see Figure 6-8. When you select objects without invoking a tool, the grips (rectangular boxes) will be displayed on the selected objects. The gripped objects are highlighted and will display grips (rectangular

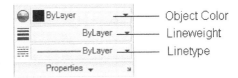

Figure 6-8 *The* ***Properties*** *panel*

boxes) at their grip points. For example, to change the color of the gripped objects, select the **Object Color** drop-down list in the **Properties** panel and then select a color from it. The color of the gripped objects will change to the selected color. Similarly, to change the layer, lineweight, or linetype of the gripped objects, select the required linetype, lineweight, or layer from the corresponding drop-down lists. If the gripped objects have different colors, linetypes, or lineweights, the **Object Color**, **Linetype**, and **Lineweight** drop-down lists will appear blank. You can also change the plot style of the selected objects using this panel.

CHANGING THE PROPERTIES USING THE PROPERTIES PALETTE

Ribbon: View > Palettes > Properties
Command: PROPERTIES
Toolbar: Quick Access > Properties

As mentioned earlier, each object has properties associated with it such as the color, layer, linetype, line weight, and so on. You can modify these properties by using the **Properties** palette. To view this palette, choose the **Properties** button from the **Palettes** tab in the **View** tab; the **Properties** palette will be displayed, as shown in Figure 6-9. The **Properties** palette can also be displayed when you double-click on the object to be edited. The contents of the **Properties** palette change depending upon the objects selected. For example, if you select a text entity, the related properties such as its height, justification, style, rotation angle, obliquing factor, and so on, will be displayed.

The **Properties** palette can also be invoked from the shortcut menu. To do so, select an entity and right-click in the drawing area. Choose the **Properties** option from the shortcut menu. If you select more than one entity, the common properties of the selected entities will be displayed in the **Properties** palette. To change the properties of the selected entities, click in the cell next to the name of the property and change the values manually. Alternatively, you can choose from the available options in the drop-down list, if one is available. You can cycle through the options by double-clicking in the property cell.

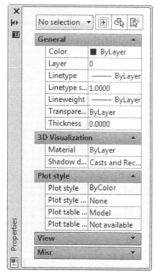

 Note
*Some of the options of the **Properties** palette have been explained in Chapter 4. Other options are explained in detail in later chapters.*

MATCHING THE PROPERTIES OF SKETCHED OBJECTS

*Figure 6-9 The **Properties** palette for editing the properties of an entity*

Ribbon: Home > Clipboard > Match Properties	**Command:** MATCHPROP
Quick Access Toolbar: Match Properties (*Customize to Add*)	

The **Match Properties** tool is used to apply properties like color, layer, linetype, and linetype scale of a source object to the selected objects. On invoking this tool, you will be prompted to select the source object and then the destination objects. The properties of the destination objects will be replaced with the properties of the source object. This is a transparent tool and can be used when another tool is active. The prompt sequence that will follow when you choose the **Match Properties** tool is given next.

Select source object: *Select the source object.*
Current active settings: Color Layer Ltype Ltscale Lineweight TransparencyThickness PlotStyle Dim Text Hatch Polyline Viewport Table Material Shadow display Multileader
Select destination object(s) or [Settings]:

If you select the destination object in the **Select destination object(s) or [Settings]** prompt, the properties of the source object will be forced on it. If you select the **Settings** option, the **Property Settings** dialog box will be displayed, as shown in Figure 6-10. The properties displayed are those of the source object. You can use this dialog box to edit the properties that are copied from the source to destination objects.

CYCLING THROUGH SELECTION

In AutoCAD LT, you can cycle through the objects to be selected if they are overlapping or close to other entities. This new feature helps in selecting the entities easily and quickly. To enable this feature, choose the **Selection Cycling** button in the Status Bar. Now, if you move the cursor near an entity that has other entities nearby it, then the selection cycling symbol will be displayed, as shown in Figure 6-11. If you select anyone of the entities when the selection cycling symbol is displayed, the **Selection** list box with a list of the entities will be displayed, as shown in Figure 6-12. You can select the entities from the **Selection** list box.

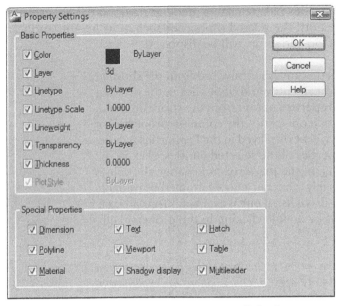

*Figure 6-10 The **Property Settings** dialog box*

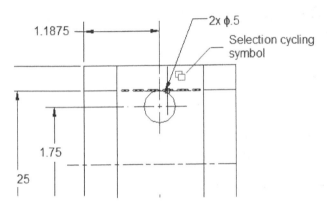
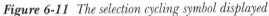

Figure 6-11 The selection cycling symbol displayed

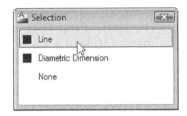

*Figure 6-12 The **Selection** list box*

MANAGING CONTENTS USING THE DesignCenter

Ribbon: View > Palettes > DesignCenter   **Command:** ADCENTER
Menu bar: Tools > Palettes > DesignCenter

The **DesignCenter** window is used to locate and organize drawing data, and to insert blocks, layers, external references, and other customized drawing content. These contents can be selected from either your own files, local drives, a network, or the Internet. You can even access and use the contents between the files or from the Internet. You can use the **DesignCenter** to conveniently drag and drop any information that has been previously created into the current drawing. This powerful tool reduces the repetitive tasks of creating information that already exists. To invoke the **DesignCenter** window, choose the **DesignCenter** tool from the **Palettes** panel; the **DesignCenter** window will be displayed, see Figure 6-13.

To move the **DesignCenter**, drag the title bar located on the left of the window. To resize it, click on the borders and drag them to the right or left. Right-clicking on the title bar of the window displays a shortcut menu to move, resize, close, dock, and hide the **DesignCenter** window. The

Auto-Hide button on the title bar acts as a toggle for hiding and displaying the **DesignCenter**. Also, double-clicking on the title bar of the window docks the **DesignCenter** window. To use this option, make sure that the **Allow Docking** option is selected from the shortcut menu that is displayed on right-clicking on the title bar.

Note
*The **DesignCenter** can be turned on and off by pressing the CTRL+2 keys.*

Figure 6-14 shows the buttons in the **DesignCenter** toolbar. When you choose the **Tree View Toggle** button on the **DesignCenter** toolbar, it displays the **Tree View** (Left Pane) with a tree view of the contents of the drives. If the tree view is not displayed, you can also right-click in the window and choose **Tree** from the shortcut menu that is displayed. Now, the window is divided into two parts, the **Tree View** (left pane) and the **Palette** (right pane). The **Palette** displays folders, files, objects in a drawing, images, Web-based content, and custom content. You can also resize both the **Tree View** and the **Palette** by clicking and dragging the bar between them to the right or the left.

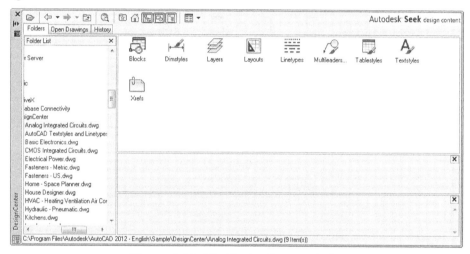

*Figure 6-13 The **DesignCenter** window*

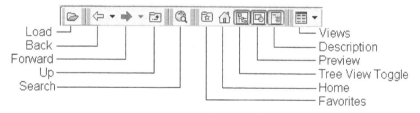

*Figure 6-14 The **DesignCenter** toolbar*

The **DesignCenter** has four tabs below the **DesignCenter** toolbar buttons. They are **Folders**, **Open drawings**, **History**, and **DC Online**. The description of these tabs is given next.

Folders Tab
The **Folders** tab lists all folders and files in the local and network drives. When this tab is chosen, the **Tree View** displays the tree view of the contents of the drives and the **Palette** displays various folders, and files in a drawing, images, and the Web-based content in the selected drive.

In the **Tree View**, you can browse the contents of any folder by clicking on the plus sign (+) adjacent to it to expand the view. Further, expanding the contents of a file displays the categories such as **Blocks**, **Dimstyles**, **Layers**, **Layouts**, **Linetypes**, **Textstyles**, and **Xrefs**. Clicking on any one of these categories in the **Tree View** displays the listing under the selected category in the **Palette** (Figure 6-15). Alternately, right-clicking on a particular folder, file, or category of the file contents displays a shortcut menu.

Choose the **Explore** option in this shortcut menu to further expand the selected folder, file, or category of contents to display the listing of the contents respectively. Choosing the **Preview** button from the toolbar displays an image of the selected object or file in a **Preview pane** below the Palette. Choosing the **Description** button displays a brief text description of the selected item, if it has one in the **Description** box. When you click on a specific block name in the palette, its preview image and description that was defined earlier when creating the block are displayed in the **Preview pane** and the **Description box**, respectively.

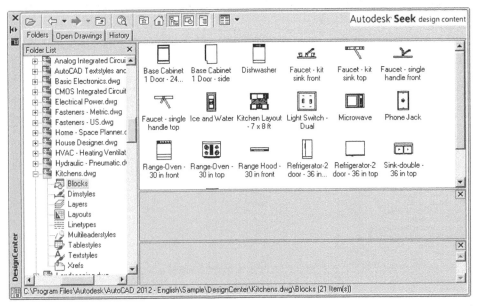

*Figure 6-15 The **DesignCenter** displaying the **Tree pane**, **Palette**, **Preview pane**, and **Description box***

You can drag and drop any of the contents into the current drawing, or add them by double-clicking on them. These are then reused as part of the current drawing. When you double-click on specific Xrefs and blocks, AutoCAD LT displays the **External Reference** dialog box and the **Insert** dialog box, respectively, to help in attaching the external reference and inserting the block, respectively. Right-clicking a block displays the options of **Insert Block**, **Copy**, or **Create Tool Palette** and right-clicking an Xref displays the options of **Attach Xref** or **Copy** in the shortcut menus. Similarly, when you double-click a layer, text style, dimstyle, layout, or linetype style, they also get added to the current drawing. If any of these named objects already exist in the current drawing, duplicate definition is ignored and it is not added again. When you right-click on a specific linetype, layer, textstyle, layout, or dimstyle in the palette, a shortcut menu is displayed that gives you an option to **Add** or **Copy**. The **Add** option directly adds the selected named object to the current drawing. The **Copy** option copies the specific named object to the clipboard from where you can paste it into a particular drawing.

Note
You will learn more about inserting blocks in Chapter 14, Working with Blocks.

Right-clicking a particular folder or file in the **Tree View** displays a shortcut menu. The various options in the shortcut menu, besides those discussed earlier, are **Add to Favorites**, **Organize Favorites**, **Create Tool Palette**, and **Set as Home**. **Add to Favorites** adds the selected file or folder to the **Favorites** folder, which contains the most often accessed files and folders. **Organize Favorites** allows you to reorganize the contents of the **Favorites** folder. When you select **Organize Favorites** from the shortcut menu, the **Autodesk** folder is opened in a window. **Create Tool Palette** adds the blocks of the selected file or folder to the **Tool Palettes** window, which contains the predefined blocks. **Set as Home** sets the selected file or folder as the **Home** folder. You will notice that when the **Design Center** tool is invoked the next time, the file that was last set as the **Home** folder is displayed selected in the **DesignCenter**.

Open Drawings Tab

The **Open Drawings** tab lists all the drawings that are open, including the current drawing which is being worked on. When you select this tab, the **Tree View** (left pane) displays the tree view of all the drawings that are currently open and the **Palette** (right pane) displays the various contents in the selected drawing.

History Tab

The **History** tab lists the locations of the most recently accessed files through the **DesignCenter**. When you select this tab, the **Tree View** (left pane) and the **Palette** (right pane) are replaced by a list box. Right-clicking a particular file displays a shortcut menu. The various options in the shortcut menu are **Explore, Folders, Open Drawings, Delete**, and **Search** etc. The **Explore** option invokes the **Folders** tab of the **DesignCenter** with the file selected in the **Tree View** and the contents in the selected file displayed in the **Palette View**. The **Folders** option invokes the **Folders** tab of the **DesignCenter**. The **Open Drawings** option invokes the **Open Drawings** tab of the **DesignCenter**. The **Delete** option deletes the selected drawing from the History list. The **Search** option allows you to search for drawings or named objects such as blocks, textstyles, dimstyles, layers, layouts, external references, or linetypes.

Autodesk Seek design content Link

The **Autodesk Seek design content** link allows you to download the *.dwg, .dwf, .pdf, .dgn* files of various products from the Autodesk online source for product specification and design files. To access the online source, click on the **Autodesk seek design content** in the **DesignCenter**; a new web page will be displayed. In this page, you can search for the required file type using the **Search** option. Once you get the required files, you can download them to your system.

Choosing the **Back** button in the **DesignCenter** toolbar displays the last item selected in the **DesignCenter**. If you pick the down arrow on the **Back** button, a list of the recently visited items is displayed. You can view the desired item in the **DesignCenter** by selecting it from the list. The **Forward** button is available only if you have chosen the **Back** button once. This button displays the same page as the current page before you choose the **Back** button. The **Up** button moves one level up in the tree structure from the current location. Choosing the **Favorites** button displays shortcuts to files and folders that are accessed frequently by you and are stored in the **Favorites** folder. This reduces the time you take to access these files or folders from their normal location. Choosing the **Tree View Toggle** button in the **DesignCenter** toolbar displays or hides the tree pane with the tree view of the contents in a hierarchical form. Choosing the **Load** button displays the **Load** dialog box, whose options are similar to those of the standard **Select file** dialog box. When you select a file here and choose the **Open** button, AutoCAD LT displays the selected file and its contents in the **DesignCenter**.

The **Views** button gives four display format options for the contents of the palette: **Large icons**, **Small icons**, **List**, and **Details**. The **List** option lists the contents in the palette, while the **Details** option gives a detailed list of the contents in the palette with the name, file size, and type.

Right-clicking in the palette displays a shortcut menu with all the options provided in the **DesignCenter** in addition to the **Add to Favorites, Organize favorites, Refresh,** and **Create Tool Palette of Blocks** options. The **Refresh** option refreshes the palette display if you have made any changes to it. The **Create Tool Palette of Blocks** option adds the drawings of the selected file or folder to the **Tool Palettes**, which contains the predefined blocks. The following example will illustrate how to use the **DesignCenter** to locate a drawing and then use its contents in the current drawing.

EXAMPLE 1   *DesignCenter*

Use the **DesignCenter** to locate and view the contents of the drawing *Kitchens.dwg*. Also, use the **DesignCenter** to insert a block from this drawing and import a layer and a textstyle from the *Blocks and Tables - Imperial.dwg* file located in the **Sample** folder. Use these to make a drawing of a Kitchen plan (*MyKitchen.dwg*) and then add text to it, as shown in Figure 6-16.

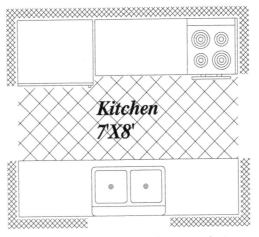

Figure 6-16 Drawing for Example 1

1. Open a new drawing using the **Start from Scratch** option. Make sure the **Imperial (feet and inches)** radio button is selected in the **Create New Drawing** dialog box.

2. Change the units to **Architectural** using the **Drawing Units** dialog box. Increase the limits to 10',10'. Use the **Zoom All** tool to increase the drawing display area.

3. Choose the **DesignCenter** tool from the **Palettes** panel in the **View** tab; the **DesignCenter** window is displayed at its default location.

4. In the **DesignCenter** toolbar, choose the **Tree View Toggle** button to display the **Tree View** and the **Palette** (if is not already displayed). Also, choose the **Preview** button, if it is not displayed already. You can resize the window, if needed, to view both the **Tree View** and the **Palette**, conveniently.

5. Choose the **Search** button in the **DesignCenter** to display the **Search** dialog box. Here, select **Drawings** from the **Look for** drop-down list and **C:** (or the drive in which AutoCAD LT 2012 is installed) from the **In** drop-down list. Select the **Search subfolders** check box. In the **Drawings** tab, type **Kitchens** in the **Search for the word(s)** edit box and select **File Name** from the **In the field(s)** drop-down list. Now, choose the **Search Now** button to commence the search. After the drawing has been located, its details and path are displayed in a list box at the bottom of the dialog box.

6. Now, right-click on *Kitchens.dwg* in the list box of the **Search** dialog box and choose **Load into Content Area** from the shortcut menu. You will notice that the drawing and its contents are displayed in the Tree view.

7. Close the **Search** dialog box, if it is still open.

8. Double-click on *Kitchens.dwg* in the Tree View to expand the tree view and display its contents, in case they are not displayed. You can also expand the contents by clicking on the + sign located on the left of the file name in the Tree view.

9. Select **Blocks** in the Tree View to display the list of blocks in the drawing in the **Palette**. Using the left mouse button, drag and drop the block **Kitchen Layout-7x8 ft** in the current drawing.

10. Now, double-click on the *AutoCAD Textstyles and Linetypes.dwg* file located in the **DesignCenter** folder in the same directory to display its contents in the **Palette**.

11. Double-click on **Textstyles** to display the list of text styles in the **Palette**. Select **Dutch Bold Italic** in the **Palette** and drag and drop it in the current drawing. You can use this textstyle for adding text to the current drawing.

12. Invoke the **Multiline Text** tool and use the imported textstyle to add the text to the current drawing.

   Note
   1. To create the text, you need to change the text height.
   2. You can import Blocks, Dimstyles, Layers, and so on to the current drawing from any existing drawing.

13. Save the current drawing with the name *MyKitchen.dwg*.

Displaying Drawing Properties

Application Menu: Drawing Utilities > Drawing Properties	**Command:** DWGPROPS

The **DWGPROPS** command is used to display information about drawing properties. Choose **Drawing Utilities > Drawing Properties** from the **Application Menu**; the **Drawing Properties** dialog box will be displayed, as shown in Figure 6-17. This dialog box has four tabs under which information about the drawing is displayed. This information helps you look for the drawing more easily. These tabs are discussed next.

General
This tab displays general properties about a drawing like the **Type**, **Size**, and **Location**.

Summary
The **Summary** tab displays predefined properties like the Author, title, and subject. Also this tab is displayed at the last that allows you to specify the information related to the drawing.

Statistics
This tab stores and displays data such as the file size and data such as the dates when the drawing was last saved or modified.

Custom

This tab displays custom file properties including values assigned by you.

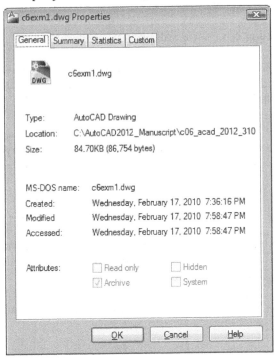

Figure 6-17 The **Drawing Properties** *dialog box*

BASIC DISPLAY OPTIONS

Drawing in AutoCAD LT is much simpler than manual drafting in many ways. Sometimes while drawing manually, it is very difficult to see and alter minute details. In AutoCAD LT, you can overcome this problem by viewing only a specific portion of the drawing. For example, to display a part of the drawing on a larger area use the **ZOOM** command to enlarge or reduce the size of the drawing displayed. Similarly, use the **REGEN** command to regenerate the drawing and **REDRAW** to refresh the screen. In this chapter, you will learn some of the drawing display commands, such as **REDRAW**, **REGEN**, **PAN**, **ZOOM**, and **VIEW**. These commands can also be used in the transparent mode. It means you can use these commands while another command is in progress.

REDRAWING THE SCREEN

Menu Bar: View > Redraw   **Command:** REDRAW

The **REDRAW** command is used to redraw the drawing area. It is used to remove the temporary graphics from the drawing area which are left after using the **VSLIDE** command and some other operations. The **REDRAW** command also redraws the objects that do not display on the screen as a result of editing some other object. In AutoCAD LT, several commands redraw the screen automatically (for example, when a grid is turned off), but sometimes it is useful to redraw the screen explicitly.

To use the **REDRAW** command in transparent mode, add apostrophe as a prefix. For example, if you are drawing a line after specifying few points, type '**Redraw** at the Command prompt as given below.

Specify next point or [Close/Undo]: *Specify a point.*
Specify next point or [Close/Undo]: *'REDRAW*
Resuming LINE command.
Specify next point or [Close/Undo]: *Specify a point.*

In this case, the redrawing process takes place without any prompting for information.

The **REDRAW** command affects only the current viewport. If you have more than one viewport, use the **REDRAWALL** command to redraw all the viewports. **Redraw** in the **View** menu is the **REDRAWALL** command.

REGENERATING DRAWINGS

Menu Bar: View > Regen **Command:** REGEN

The **REGEN** command is used to regenerate the entire drawing to update it. The need for regeneration usually occurs when you change certain aspects of the drawing. All objects in the drawing are recalculated and redrawn in the current viewport. One of the advantages of this command is that the drawing is refined by smoothing out circles and arcs. To use this command, type **REGEN** at the Command prompt and press enter; the message **Regenerating model** will be displayed while the system regenerates the drawing. The **REGEN** command affects only the current viewport. If you have more than one viewport, use the **REGENALL** command to regenerate all of them. The **REGEN** command can be aborted by pressing ESC. This saves time if you are going to use another command that causes automatic regeneration.

Note
Under certain conditions, the ZOOM and PAN commands automatically regenerate the drawing. Some other commands also perform regenerations under certain conditions.

ZOOMING DRAWINGS

Ribbon: View > Navigate 2D > Extents   **Command:** ZOOM
Menu bar: View > Zoom   **Toolbar:** Navigation Bar > Zoom Extents

Creating drawings in AutoCAD LT would not be of much use, if you cannot magnify the drawing view to work on the minute details. The ability to zoom in, or magnify, has been helpful in creating the minuscule circuits used in the electronics and computer industries. This is performed using the **ZOOM** command. This is one of the most frequently used commands. Getting close to or away from the drawing is the function of the **ZOOM** command. In other words, this command enlarges or reduces the view of the drawing on the screen, but it does not affect the actual size of the objects. In this way, the **ZOOM** command functions like the zoom lens of a camera. When you magnify the apparent size of a section of the drawing, you see that area in greater detail. On the other hand, if you reduce the apparent size of the drawing, you see a larger area.

The **ZOOM** command can also be used in transparent mode. This means that this command can be used while working with other commands. Various options of the **ZOOM** command are grouped as tools in the **Zoom** drop-down, as shown in Figure 6-18. You can also right-click in the drawing area and choose the **Zoom** option from the shortcut menu even when you are working with some other command, refer to Figure 6-19. Various options of the **ZOOM** command have been made available in the **Navigation bar** in the drawing area, as shown in Figure 6-20.

This command has several options and can be used in a number of ways. The following is the prompt sequence that is displayed when you invoke this command.

Command: **ZOOM** [Enter]
Specify corner of window, enter a scale factor (nX or nXP), or
[All/Center/Dynamic/Extents/Previous/Scale/Window/Object] <real time>:

Realtime Zooming

To zoom in and zoom out interactively, invoke the **Realtime Zoom** option by choosing the **Zoom Realtime** tool from the **Navigation Bar** in the drawing area. To zoom in, invoke the command, then hold the pick button down and move the cursor up. If you want to zoom in further, release the pick button and bring the cursor down. Specify a point and move the cursor up again. Similarly, to zoom out, hold the pick button down and move the cursor down. If you move the cursor vertically up from the midpoint of the screen to the top of the window, the drawing will be magnified by 100% (zoom in 2x magnification). Similarly, if you move the cursor vertically down from the midpoint of the screen to the bottom of the window, the drawing display will be reduced to 100% (zoom out 0.5x magnification). Realtime zoom is the default setting for the **ZOOM** command. Pressing ENTER after entering the **ZOOM** command automatically invokes the realtime zoom.

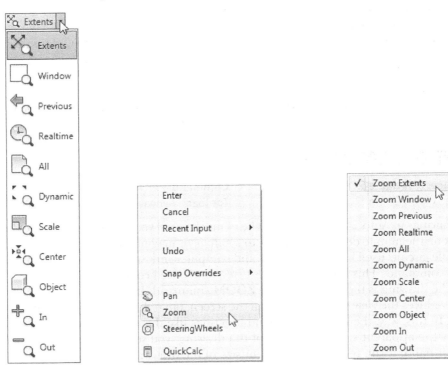

Figure 6-18 Tools in the **Zoom** drop-down

Figure 6-19 The **Zoom** option in the shortcut menu

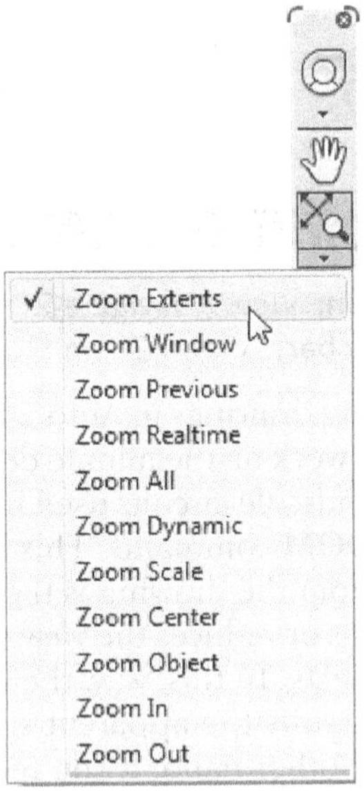

Figure 6-20 The **Zoom** tools in the **Navigation Bar**

When you use the realtime zoom, the cursor becomes a magnifying glass and displays a plus sign (+) and a minus sign (–). When you reach the zoom out limit, AutoCAD LT does not display the minus sign (–) while dragging the cursor. Similarly, when you reach the zoom in limit, AutoCAD LT does not display the plus sign (+) while dragging the cursor. To exit the realtime zoom, press ENTER or ESC, or select **Exit** from the shortcut menu.

All Option

This option of the **ZOOM** command is used to adjust the display area on the basis of the drawing limits (Figure 6-21) or extents of an object, whichever is greater. Even if the objects are not within the limits, they are still included in the display. Therefore, with the **All** option, you can view the entire drawing in the current viewport (Figure 6-22).

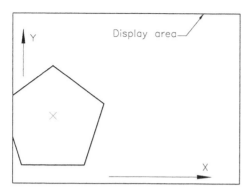

Figure 6-21 Drawing showing the limits

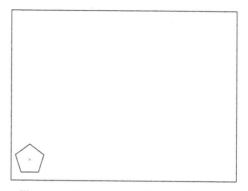

*Figure 6-22 Using the **Zoom All** option*

Center Option

This option is used to define a new display window by specifying its center point (Figures 6-23 and 6-24) and magnification or height. Here, you are required to enter the center and the height of the subsequent screen display. If you press ENTER instead of entering a new center point, the center of the view will remain unchanged. Instead of entering a height, you can enter the **magnification factor** by typing a number. If you press ENTER at the height prompt, or if the height you enter is the same as the current height, magnification does not take place. For example, if the current height is 2.7645 and you press ENTER at the **magnification or height <current>** prompt, magnification will not take place. The smaller the value, the greater is the enlargement of the image. You can also enter a number followed by **X**. This indicates the change in magnification, not as an absolute value, but as a value relative to the current screen.

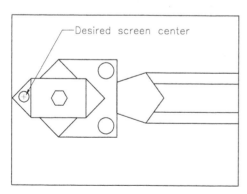

*Figure 6-23 Drawing before using the **ZOOM** Center option*

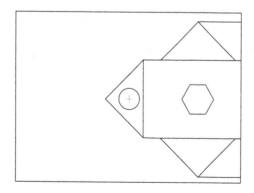

*Figure 6-24 Drawing after using the **ZOOM** Center option*

In Figure 6-22, the current magnification height is 5X, which magnifies the display five times. If you enter the value **2**, the size (height and width) of the zoom area changes to 2 X 2 around the specified center. In Figure 6-25, if you enter 0.12 as the height after specifying the center point as the circle's center, the circle will zoom to fit in the display area since its diameter is 0.12.

Extents Option

As the name indicates, this option is used to zoom to the extents of the biggest object in the drawing. The extents of the drawing comprise the area that has the drawings in it. The rest of the empty area is neglected. With this option, all objects in the drawing are magnified to the largest possible display, see Figure 6-26.

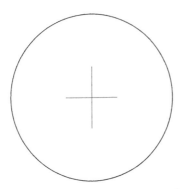

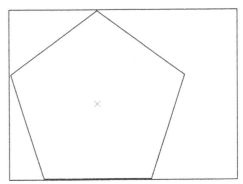

Figure 6-25 *Drawing after using the* **ZOOM** *Center option*

Figure 6-26 *Drawing after using the* **ZOOM** *Extents option*

Dynamic Option

This option displays the portion of the drawing that you have already specified. You can then specify the area to be displayed by manipulating a view box representing the viewport. This option lets you enlarge or shrink the view box and move it around. When the view box is in the proper position and size, the current viewport is cleared and a special view selection screen will be displayed. This special screen comprises information regarding the current view as well as the available views. In a color display, the different viewing windows are very easy to distinguish because of their different colors, but in a monochrome monitor, they can be distinguished by their shape.

Blue dashed box representing drawing extents

Drawing extents are represented by a dashed blue box (Figure 6-27), which constitutes the drawing limits or the actual area occupied by the drawing.

Green dashed box representing the current view

A green dashed box is formed to represent the area of the current viewport (Figure 6-28).

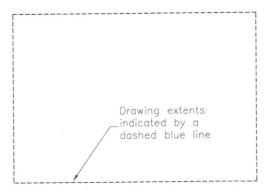

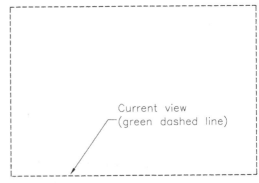

Figure 6-27 *Box representing drawing extents*

Figure 6-28 *Representation of the current view*

Panning view box (X in the center)

A view box initially of the same size as the current view box is displayed with an X in the center (Figure 6-29). You can move this box with the help of your pointing device. This box is known as the panning view box and it helps you to find the center point of the zoomed display you want. When you have found the center, press the pick button to display the zooming view box.

Zooming view box (arrow on the right side)

On pressing the pick button at the center of the panning view box, the X at the center of the view box is replaced by an arrow pointing to the right edge of the box. This zooming view box (Figure 6-30) indicates the ZOOM mode. You can now increase or decrease the area of this box according to the area you want to zoom into. To shrink the box, move the pointer to the left; to increase it, move the pointer to the right. The top, right, and bottom sides of the zooming view box move as you move the pointer, but the left side remains fixed, with the zoom base point at the midpoint of the left side. You can slide it up or down along the left side. When you have the zooming view box in the desired size for your zoom display, press ENTER to complete the command and zoom into the desired area of the drawing. Before pressing ENTER, if you want to change the position of the zooming view box, click the pick button of your pointing device to redisplay the panning view box. After repositioning, press ENTER.

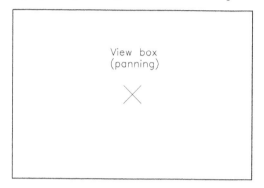

Figure 6-29 *The panning view box*

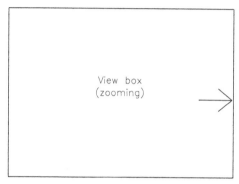

Figure 6-30 *The zooming view box*

Previous Option

While working on a complex drawing, you may need to zoom in on a portion of the drawing to edit some minute details. Once the editing is over you may want to return to the previous view. This can be done by choosing the **Zoom Previous** tool from the **Zoom** drop-down in the **Navigation Bar**. Without this command, it would be very tedious to zoom back to the previous views. AutoCAD LT saves the view specification of the current viewport whenever it is being altered by any of the ZOOM options or by the **PAN**, **VIEW Restore**, **DVIEW**, or **PLAN** commands (which are discussed later). Up to ten views are saved for each viewport. The prompt sequence for this option is given next.

Successive **ZOOM > P** commands can restore up to ten previous views. **VIEW** here refers to the area of the drawing defined by its display extents. If you erase some objects and then issue the **ZOOM > Previous** command, the previous view is restored, but the erased objects are not.

Window Option

This is the most commonly used option of the **ZOOM** command. After invoking this command, you need to specify the area you want to zoom in by specifying two opposite corners of a rectangular window. The center of the specified window becomes the center of the zoomed area. The area inside the window is magnified or reduced in size to fill the display as completely as possible. The points can be specified either by selecting them with the help of the pointing device or by entering their coordinates. The prompt sequence is given next.

Whenever the **ZOOM** command is invoked, the window method is one of two default options. This is illustrated by the previous prompt sequence where you can specify the two corner points of the window without invoking any option of the **ZOOM** command. The **Window** option can also be used by entering **W**. In this case, the prompt sequence is given next.

Scale Option

The **Scale** option of the **ZOOM** command is a very versatile option. It can be used in the following ways:

Scale: Relative to full view

This option of the **ZOOM** command is used to magnify or reduce the size of a drawing according to a scale factor (Figure 6-31). A scale factor equal to 1 displays an area equal in size to the area defined by the established limits. This may not display the entire drawing if the previous view was not centered on the limits or if you have drawn outside the limits. To get a magnification relative to the full view, you can enter any other number. For example, you can type 4 if you want the displayed image to be enlarged four times. If you want to decrease the magnification relative to the full view, you need to enter a number that is less than 1. In Figure 6-32, the image size is decreased because the scale factor is less than 1. In other words, the image size is half of the full view because the scale factor is 0.5.

Figure 6-31 Drawing before the ZOOM Scale option selected

Figure 6-32 Drawing after the ZOOM Scale option selected

Scale: Relative to current view

The second way to scale is with respect to the current view (Figure 6-33). In this case, instead of entering only a number, enter a number followed by an **X**. The scale is calculated with reference to the current view. For example, if you enter **0.25X**, each object in the drawing will be displayed at one-fourth (¼) of its current size. The following example shows how to increase the display magnification by a factor of **0.25** relative to its current value (Figure 6-34).

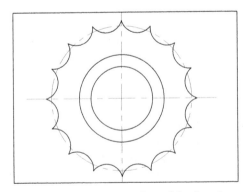

Figure 6-33 Current view of the drawing

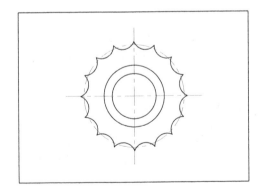

Figure 6-34 Drawing after applying magnification factor of 0.25X

Scale: Relative to paper space units

The third method of scaling is with respect to paper space. You can use paper space in a variety of ways and for various reasons. For example, you can array and plot various views of your model in the paper space. To scale each view relative to paper space units, you can use the **ZOOM XP** option. Each view can have an individual scale. The drawing view can be at any scale of your choice in a model space viewport. For example, to display a model space at one-fourth (¼) the size of the paper space units, the prompt sequence is given next.

Command: **ZOOM** [Enter]
Specify corner of window, enter a scale factor (nX or nXP), or
[All/Center/Dynamic/Extents/Previous/Scale/Window/Object]<real time>: **1/4XP** [Enter]

Note
For a better understanding of this topic, refer to "Model Space Viewports, Paper Space Viewports and Layouts" in Chapter 11.

Object Option

The **Object** option of the **ZOOM** command is used to select one or more than one objects and display them at the center of the screen in the largest possible size.

Zoom In and Out

You can also zoom into the drawing by using the **In** option, which doubles an image size. Similarly, you can use the **Out** option to decrease the size of the image by half. To invoke these options from the command line, enter **ZOOM 2X** for the **In** option or **ZOOM .5X** for the **Out** option at the Command prompt. The center of the screen is taken as the reference point for enlarging or reducing the view of a drawing.

EXERCISE 1   *Zoom*

Draw the profile shown in Figure 6-35 based on the given dimensions. Use the **ZOOM** command to get a bigger view of the drawing. Do not dimension the drawing.

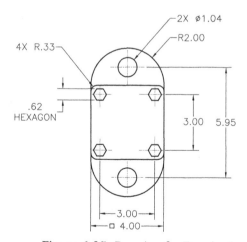

Figure 6-35 Drawing for Exercise 1

PANNING DRAWINGS

Ribbon:	View > Navigate 2D > Pan	**Command:** PAN
Menu Bar:	View > Pan > Realtime	

You may want to view or draw on a particular area outside the current display. You can do this using the **Pan** tool. If done manually, this would be like holding one corner of the drawing and dragging it across the screen. The **Pan** tool allows you to bring into view the portion of the drawing that is outside the current display area. This is done without changing the magnification of the drawing. The effect of this command can be illustrated by imagining that you are looking at a big drawing through a window (**display window**) that allows you to slide the drawing right, left, up, and down to bring the part you want to view inside this window. You can invoke the **Pan** tool from the shortcut menu also.

Panning in Realtime

You can use the **Realtime Pan** to pan the drawing interactively. To pan a drawing, invoke the tool and then hold the pick button down and move the cursor in any direction. When you select the realtime pan, an image of a hand will be displayed indicating that you are in the **Realtime Pan**. This is the default setting for the **Pan** tool. Choosing the **Pan Realtime** tool in the toolbar and entering **PAN** at the Command prompt automatically invokes the realtime pan. To exit the realtime pan, press ENTER or ESC, or choose **Exit** from the shortcut menu.

The **Pan** tool has various options to pan a drawing in a particular direction. These options can be invoked only from the menu bar, as shown in Figure 6-36.

Point

This option is used to specify the actual displacement. To do this, you need to specify in what direction to move the drawing and by what distance. You can give the displacement either by entering the coordinates of the points or by specifying the coordinates by using a pointing device. The coordinates can be entered in two ways. One way is to specify a single coordinate pair. In this case, AutoCAD LT takes it as a relative displacement of the drawing with respect to the screen. For example, in the following case, the **Pan** tool would shift the displayed portion of the drawing 2 units to the right and 2 units up.

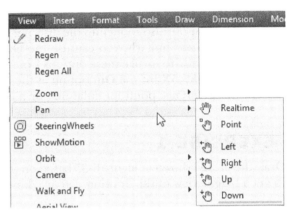

Figure 6-36 The **PAN** command options in the **View** menu

In the second case, you can specify two coordinate pairs. AutoCAD LT computes the displacement from the first point to the second. Here, the displacement is calculated between point (3,3) and point (5,5).

Left

Moves the drawing left so that some of the right portion of the drawing is brought into view.

Right

Moves the drawing right so that some of the left portion of the drawing is brought into view.

Up

Moves the drawing up so that some of the bottom portion of the drawing is brought into view.

Down

Moves the drawing down so that some of the top portion of the drawing is brought into view.

Tip
*You can use the scroll bars to pan the drawing vertically or horizontally. The scroll bars are located at the right side and the bottom of the drawing area. You can control the display of the scroll bars in the **Display** tab of the **Options** dialog box.*

Self-Evaluation Test

Answer the following questions and then compare them to those given at the end of this chapter:

1. The number of grips that will be displayed on an object depends on the object itself. (T/F)

2. You need at least one source object while using the **Match Properties** tool. (T/F)

3. You cannot drag and drop entities from the **DesignCenter** window. (T/F)

4. The **Zoom All** tool displays drawing limits or extents, whichever is greater. (T/F)

5. While using the **Zoom Scale** tool with respect to the current view, you need to enter a number followed by **X**. (T/F)

6. After selecting a polyline, if you place the cursor on the _____ grip, the **Convert to Arc** option will be displayed in the tooltip.

7. The _____ drop-down list will not be available if you select **Select All** from the **Operator** drop-down list of the **Quick Select** dialog box.

Review Questions

Answer the following questions:

1. How many views are saved with the **Zoom Previous** tool?

    (a) 6   (b) 8
    (c) 10   (d) 12

2. Which of the following commands recalculates all objects in a drawing and redraws the current viewport only?

    (a) **REDRAW**   (b) **REDRAWALL**
    (c) **REGEN**   (d) **REGENALL**

3. If you select a grip of an object, the grip becomes a hot grip. (T/F)

4. The **ZOOM** command is used to change the actual size of an object. (T/F)

5. The **REDRAW** command can be used as a transparent command. (T/F)

6. You can view the entire drawing (even if it is beyond limits) with the help of the _____ option.

7. The **VIEW** command does not save any drawing object data. Only the _____ parameters required to redisplay that portion of the drawing are saved.

EXERCISE 2

1. Use the **Line** tool to draw the shape shown in Figure 6-37(a).

2. Use grips (**Stretch** mode) to get the shape shown in Figure 6-37(b).

3. Use the **Rotate** and **Stretch** modes to get the copies shown in Figure 6-37(c).

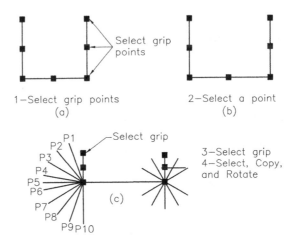

Figure 6-37 Drawing for Exercise 2

EXERCISE 3

Use the drawing and editing tools to create the sketch shown in Figure 6-38. Use the display tools to facilitate the process.

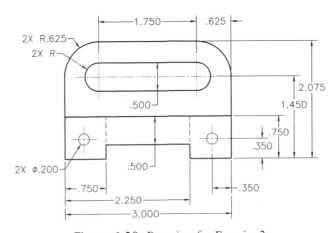

Figure 6-38 Drawing for Exercise 3

EXERCISE 4

Use the drawing and editing tools to create the sketch shown in Figure 6-39. Use the display tools to facilitate the process.

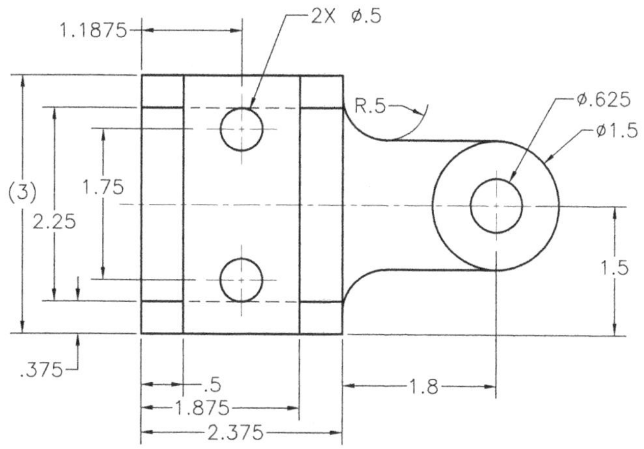

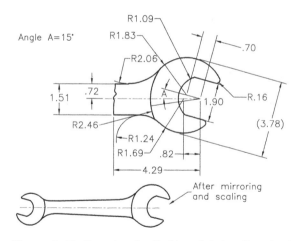

Figure 6-39 *Drawing for Exercise 4*

Problem-Solving Exercise 1

Draw the sketch shown in Figure 6-40 using the draw and edit tools. Use the **Mirror** tool to mirror the shape 9 units across the *Y* axis so that the distance between the two center points is 9 units. Mirror the shape across the *X* axis and then reduce the mirrored shape by 75 percent. Join the two ends to complete the shape of the open end spanner. Save the file. Assume the missing dimensions. Note that this is not a standard size spanner.

Figure 6-40 *Drawing for Problem-Solving Exercise 1*

Problem-Solving Exercise 2

Use the drawing and editing tools to create the drawing shown in Figure 6-41. Use the display tools to facilitate the process.

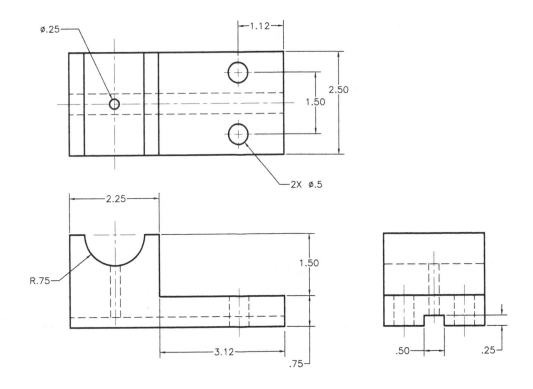

Figure 6-41 Drawing for Problem-Solving Exercise 2

Problem-Solving Exercise 3

Use the drawing and editing tools to create the drawing shown in Figure 6-42. Use the display tools to facilitate the process. Assume the missing dimensions.

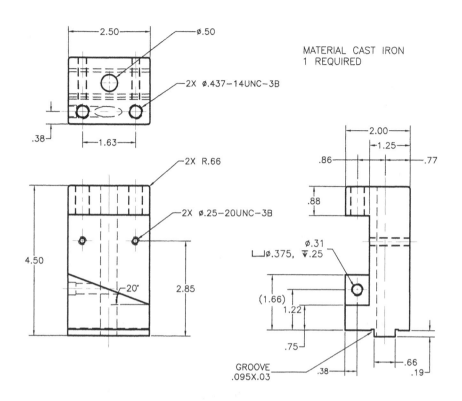

Figure 6-42 *Drawing for Problem-Solving Exercise 3*

Problem-Solving Exercise 4

Draw the reception desk shown in Figure 6-43. To get the dimensions of the chairs, refer to Problem-Solving Exercise 3 of Chapter 5.

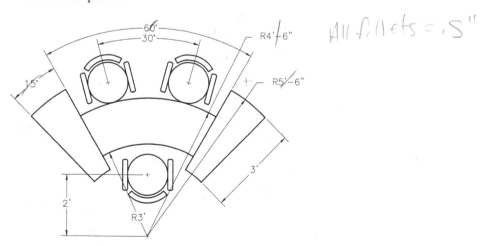

Figure 6-43 *Drawing for Problem-Solving Exercise 4*

Problem-Solving Exercise 5

Draw the views of Vice Body shown in Figure 6-44. The dimensions given in the figure are only for your reference.

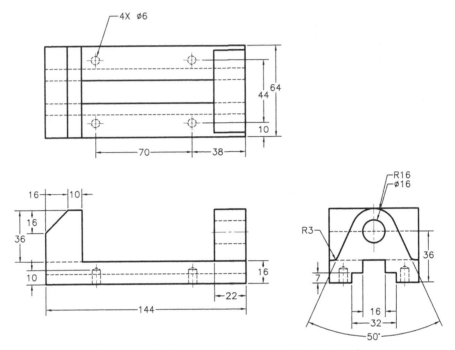

Figure 6-44 *Views and dimensions of the Vice Body*

Answers to Self-Evaluation Test

1. T, **2.** T, **3.** F, **4.** T, **5.** T, **6.** middle, **7.** Value

Chapter 7

Creating Texts and Tables

CHAPTER OBJECTIVES

In this chapter, you will learn:
* *About annotative objects.*
* *To write text using the Single Line and Multi Line Text tools.*
* *To edit text using the Edit tool.*
* *To create text styles using the STYLE command.*
* *To draw tables using the Table tool.*
* *To create and modify a table style.*
* *To use the Properties palette to change properties.*

KEY TERMS

* *Annotative Objects*
* *Annotation Scale*
* *Text*
* *DDEDIT*
* *Table*
* *Data Link*
* *Text Style*
* *Annotative Text*

ANNOTATIVE OBJECTS

One of the recent enhancements in AutoCAD LT is the improved functionality of the drawing annotation that enables you to annotate your drawing easily and efficiently. Annotations are the notes and objects that are inserted into a drawing to add important information to it. The list of annotative objects is given next.

Text	Mtext	Dimensions	Leaders	Blocks
Multileaders	Hatches	Tolerances	Attributes	

All the above mentioned annotative objects have an annotative property. This annotative property allows you to automate the process of display of the drawings at the correct desired scale on the paper.

ANNOTATION SCALE

Annotation Scale is a feature that allows you to control the size of the annotative objects in model space. In the older releases of AutoCAD LT, you had to specify the height of the annotative object in model space, keeping in mind the extent up to which the factor would be scaled down while printing the drawing. But the **Annotation scale** option allows you to set the height of the printed text while annotating, and then allows you to control the height of the object in model space.

Generally, the formula used to calculate the height of the annotative objects in model space is:

Height of the annotative object in model space = Annotation scale X Height of the annotative object in paper space.

For example, if you need to create an annotative object with a height of 1/4" on paper, and assume that annotation scale is set to 1/2" = 1' (implies 1" = 2', or 1" = 24"). Then, the height of the object in model space will be 1/4" x 24"= 6" and the object will be displayed in model space with its height equal to 6".

Note
The above calculation is performed automatically by AutoCAD LT and has been explained to make the concept clear.

Assigning Annotative Property and Annotation Scales

You can apply the annotative properties to objects in many ways. The objects (Mtext, Hatches, Blocks, and Attributes) that are drawn with the help of dialog boxes have the **Annotative** check boxes in their respective dialog box. You can also create the annotative styles, and all the objects created using that style will have the annotative property automatically. The objects that are created using the Command prompt can be converted into annotative after creating them through the **Properties** palette. You can also override the annotative property of an individual object through the **Properties** palette, see Figure 7-1.

All annotative objects are indicated with an annotative symbol attached to the cursor. When you move the cursor over an annotative object, the annotative symbol starts rolling on, see Figure 7-2. All annotative styles are indicated with the same annotative symbol displayed next to the cursor.

To assign the annotation scale while working in model space, choose the **Annotation Scale** button displayed on the right of the status bar; a flyout will be displayed. Select the desired annotation scale from the flyout. This flyout displays 33 commonly used imperial and metric scales, and this list can also be customized. Among these scales, 1:1 annotation scale is selected by default. To change the default annotation scale, enter **CANNOSCALE** in the Command prompt and specify the new annotation scale. To assign the annotation scale while working in viewport, select a viewport first and then assign the annotation scale.

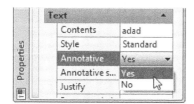

Figure 7-1 *Assigning annotative property through the **Properties** palette*

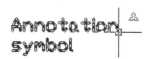

Figure 7-2 *Annotation symbol attached to the cursor*

Customizing Annotation Scale

In any drawing, only few annotation scales are used. Therefore, you can delete unwanted scales from the list according to your requirement. To customize the **Annotation Scale** list, choose the **Custom** option from the flyout that is displayed when you click on the **Annotation Scale** button; the **Edit Drawing Scales** dialog box will be displayed, as shown in Figure 7-3. With this dialog box, you can add, modify, delete, change the sequence of scales displayed, and restore the default list of scales.

Figure 7-3 *The **Edit Drawing Scales** dialog box*

Note
You cannot delete the annotation scales that have been used to draw any annotative object in the drawing.

MULTIPLE ANNOTATION SCALES

Ribbon: Annotate > Annotation Scaling > Add/Delete Scales	**Command:** OBJECTSCALE
Menu Bar: Modify > Annotative Object Scale > Add/Delete Scales	

You can assign more than one annotation scale to an annotative object. This enables you to display or print the same annotative object in different sizes. The annotative object is displayed or printed based on the current annotation scale. Assigning multiple annotation scales to annotative objects saves a considerable amount of time that is lost while creating a set of objects with different scales in different layers. You can add multiple annotation scales to objects manually and automatically. Both these methods are discussed next.

Assigning Multiple Annotation Scales Manually

To assign multiple annotation scales manually to an annotative object, invoke the **Add/Delete Scales** tool; you will be prompted to select an annotative object to which you want to add another annotation scale. Select one or more annotation objects and then press ENTER; the **Annotation Object Scale** dialog box will be displayed, see Figure 7-4. Alternatively, select an annotative object and right-click to display the shortcut menu. Now, choose **Annotative Object Scale > Add / Delete Scales** from the shortcut menu to display the **Annotation Object Scale** dialog box. Using this dialog box, you can add annotation scale to an annotative object or delete the annotation scale assigned to the selected annotative object. However, you cannot delete the current annotation scale by using this dialog box. When you place the cursor over an annotative object, all annotative objects with multiple annotation scales will be indicated with a double-annotation symbol attached to the cursor, see Figure 7-5. You can also control the assignment of multiple annotation scales to annotative objects by using the **Annotation Scaling** panel in the **Annotate** tab, see Figure 7-6.

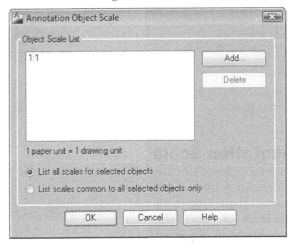

*Figure 7-4 The **Annotation Object Scale** dialog box*

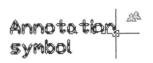

Figure 7-5 Multiple annotation scale symbol attached to the cursor

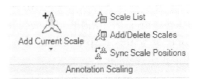

*Figure 7-6 The **Annotation Scaling** panel in the **Ribbon***

Assigning Multiple Annotation Scales Automatically

The annotation scales that have been set as current can be assigned to annotative objects without invoking the **Annotation Object Scale** dialog box. To do so, choose the **Automatically add scales to annotative objects when the annotation scale changes** button located at the right corner of the Status Bar to activate it. Now onward, all annotation scales that are set as current will be automatically added to the annotation objects.

By default, the annotation scale will be applied to all objects irrespective of their layers. However, you can control the assignment of annotation scale depending upon the layer of the object by using the **ANNOAUTOSCALE** system variable. This system variable can have values ranging from -4 to 4 except 0. The description of these values is given next.

1 = This value assigns the current annotation scale to all annotative objects, except the annotative objects that are in the locked, turned off, frozen, and viewport frozen layers.
2 = This value assigns the current annotation scale to all annotative objects, except the annotative objects that are in the turned off, frozen, and viewport frozen layers.
3 = This value assigns the current annotation scale to all annotative objects, except the ones that are in the locked layers.
4 = This value assigns the current annotation scale to all objects.
-1 = On assigning this value, the **ANNOAUTOSCALE** gets turned off, but when turned on again, it regains the value 1.

-2 = On assigning this value, the **ANNOAUTOSCALE** gets turned off, but when turned on again, it regains the value 2.

-3 = On assigning this value, the **ANNOAUTOSCALE** gets turned off, but when turned on again, it regains the value 3.

-4 = On assigning this value, the **ANNOAUTOSCALE** gets turned off, but when turned on again, it regains the value 4.

CONTROLLING THE DISPLAY OF ANNOTATIVE OBJECTS

After assigning annotation scale to objects, the paper height display scale (in case of plotting) or the viewport scale (in case of viewports) is automatically applied to annotative objects and they are displayed accordingly in the model space or viewport. The annotative objects that do not support the current annotation scale will not be scaled and will be displayed according to the previous annotation scale applied to them.

You can control the display of annotative objects by using the **Annotation Visibility** button on the right of the **Annotation Scale** flyout in the Status Bar. If this button is turned on, all annotative objects will be displayed in the model space or viewport regardless of the current annotation scale. If this button is turned off, only the annotative objects that have annotation scale equal to that of the current annotation scale will be displayed. Note that the **Annotation Visibility** buttons in the model and layout tabs are independent of each other.

When you select an annotative object, you can observe that the selected annotative object is displayed in all annotative scales assigned to it. The annotation scale that is equal to the current scale is displayed in dark dashed lines, whereas the other scales of the object are displayed in faded dashed lines. You can position the annotation object of different scales at different locations with the help of grips. However, if you need to synchronize the start point of annotative objects of different scale factors with current annotative objects, select the annotative object and then right-click in the drawing area; a shortcut menu will be displayed. Choose **Annotative Object Scale > Synchronize Multiple-Scale positions** from the shortcut menu; the start point of annotative objects will be synchronized. Alternatively, you can also use the **ANNORESET** command to synchronize the start point.

SELECTIONANNODISPLAY system variable is used to control the display of the supported scale representations. If you assign 0 to the system variable, it will stop displaying all the supported scale representations selected; only the representations with the current annotation scale will be displayed. If you assign 1 to this system variable, it will display all the supported scale representations selected.

Note
Whenever you create a drawing that involves annotative objects in it, use the newly introduced **Drafting & Annotation** *workspace. This workspace displays the* **Ribbon** *with drafting and annotation panels visible by default and hides many of the tools. This also makes the drawing and annotating work much more easy. For all examples and exercises given onward and involving annotative objects, you can use this workspace.*

CREATING TEXT
In manual drafting, lettering is accomplished by hand using a lettering device, pen, or pencil. This is a very time-consuming and tedious job. Computer-aided drafting has made this process extremely easy. Engineering drawings invoke certain standards to be followed in connection with the placement of a text in a drawing. In this section, you will learn how a text can be added in a drawing by using the **TEXT** and **MTEXT** commands.

Writing Single Line Text

Ribbon:	Home > Annotation > Text drop-down > Single Line Or		
	Annotate > Text > Text drop-down > Single Line	**Command:** TEXT or DTEXT	
Menu Bar:	Draw > Text > Single Line Text	**Toolbar:** Text > Single Line Text	

The **Single Line** tool is used to write text on a drawing. While writing you can delete what has been typed by using the BACKSPACE key. On invoking the **Single Line** tool, you will be prompted to specify the start point. The default and the most commonly used option in the **Single Line** tool is the **Start Point** option. By specifying a start point, the text is left-justified along its baseline. Baseline refers to the line along which their bases lies. After specifying the start point, you need to set the height and the rotation angle of the text.

The **Specify height** prompt determines the distance by which the text extends above the baseline, measured by the capital letters. This distance is specified in drawing units. You can specify the text height by specifying two points or by entering a value. In the case of a null response, the default height, that is, the height used for the previous text drawn in the same style, will be used.

The **Specify rotation angle of text** prompt determines the angle at which the text line will be drawn. The default value of the rotation angle is 0-degree (along east); and in this case, the text is drawn horizontally from the specified start point. The rotation angle is measured in counterclockwise direction. The last angle specified becomes the current rotation angle, and if you give a null response, the last angle specified will be used as default rotation angle. You can also specify the rotation angle by specifying two points. The text will be drawn upside down if a point is specified at a location to the left of the start point.

You can now enter the text in the **Text Editor**. The characters will be displayed as you type them. After entering the text, click outside the **Text Editor**. The prompt sequence displayed on choosing this tool is given next.

Specify start point of text or [Justify/Style]: *Specify the start point.*
Specify height <0.2000>: **0.15** Enter
Specify rotation angle of text <0>: Enter; *the textbox will be displayed. Start typing in it.*

After completing a line, press ENTER; the cursor will automatically be placed at the start of the next line and you can enter the next line of the text. However, if you place the cursor at a new location, a new textbox will be displayed, and you can start typing text at this location with new start point and the same text parameters. You can enter multiple lines of text at any desired location in the drawing area on invoking the **Single Line** tool once. By pressing BACKSPACE, you can delete one character to the left of the current position of the cursor box. Even if you have entered several lines of text, you can use BACKSPACE to delete the text, until you reach the start point of the first line. To exit the tool, press the ESC key or click outside the text box.

This tool can be used with most of the text alignment modes, although it is most useful in the case of left-justified texts. In the case of aligned texts, this tool is used to assign a height appropriate for the width of the first line to every line of the text. Even if you select the **Justify** option, the text is first left-aligned at the selected point.

Justify Option

AutoCAD LT offers various options to align text. Alignment refers to the layout of a text. The main text alignment modes are **left**, **center**, and **right**. You can align a text by using a combination of modes, for example, top/middle/bottom and left/center/right (Figure 7-7). **Top** refers to a line along which lie the top points of the capital letters. Letters with descenders (such as p, g, y) dip below the baseline to the bottom. When the **Justify** option is invoked, the user can place the text in one of the fourteen various alignment types by selecting the desired alignment option using the Command prompt or the selection preview (Figure 7-8). The orientation of the text style determines the command interaction for Text Justify. (Text styles and fonts are discussed later in this chapter). For now, assume that the text style orientation is horizontal.

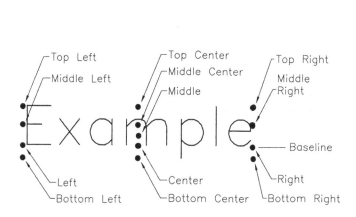

Figure 7-7 *Text alignment positions*

Figure 7-8 *Selection preview for the* ***Justify*** *option*

If the text style is vertically oriented (refer to the "Creating Text Styles" section later in this chapter), only four alignment options are available. If you know what justification you want, you can enter it directly at the **Specify start point of text or [Justify/Style]** prompt instead of first entering **J** to display the justification prompt. If you need to specify a style as well as a justification, you must specify the style first. The various alignment options are as follows.

Align Option. In this option, the text string is written between two points (Figure 7-9). You must specify the two points that act as the endpoints of the baseline. The two points may be specified horizontally or at an angle. AutoCAD LT adjusts the text width (compresses or expands) so that it fits between the two points. The text height is also changed, depending on the distance between points and the number of letters.

Fit Option. This option is very similar to the previous one. The only difference is that in this case, you select the text height, and it does not vary according to the distance between the two points. AutoCAD LT adjusts the letter width to fit the text between the two given points, but the height remains constant (Figure 7-9). The **Fit** option is not accessible for vertically oriented text styles. If you try the **Fit** option on the vertical text style, you will notice that the text string does not appear in the prompt. The prompt sequence is given next.

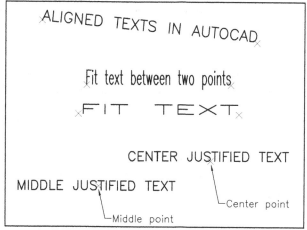

Figure 7-9 *Writing the text using the* ***Align****,* ***Fit****,* ***Center****, and* ***Middle*** *options*

Enter an option [Align/Fit/Center/Middle/Right/TL/TC/TR/ML/MC/MR/BL/BC/BR]: **F**
Specify first endpoint of text baseline: *Specify a point.*
Specify second endpoint of text baseline: *Specify a point.*
Specify height<current>: *Enter the height.*

Note
*You do not need to select the **Justify** option (J) for selecting the text justification. You can enter the text justification by directly entering justification when AutoCAD LT prompts "Specify start point of text or [Justify/Style]:"*

Center Option. You can use this option to select the midpoint of the baseline for the text. This option can be invoked by entering **Justify** and then **Center** or **C**. After you select or specify the center point, you must enter the letter height and the rotation angle (Figure 7-9).

Middle Option. Using this option, you can center text not only horizontally, as with the previous option, but also vertically. In other words, you can specify the middle point of the text string (Figure 7-9). You can alter the text height and the angle of rotation to meet your requirement.

Right Option. This option is similar to the default left-justified start point option. The only difference is that the text string is aligned to the lower right corner (the endpoint you specify), that is, the text is **right-justified** (Figure 7-10). The prompt sequence that will follow when you choose this button is given next.

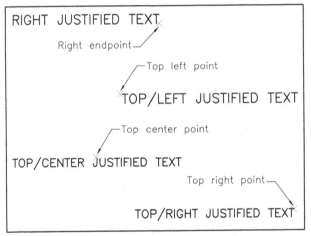

*Figure 7-10 Writing the text using the **Right**, **Top-Left**, **Top-Center**, and **Top-Right** options*

TL Option. In this option, the text string is justified from top left (Figure 7-10).

Note
The rest of the text alignment options are similar to those already discussed, and you can try them on your own. The prompt sequence is almost the same as those given for the previous examples.

Style Option

With this option, you can specify another existing text style. Different text styles can have different text fonts, heights, obliquing angles, and other features. This option can be invoked by entering **TEXT** and then **S** at the next prompt. The prompt sequence that will follow when you choose the **Single Line Text** tool for using this option is given next.

Specify start point of text or [Justify/Style]: **S** [Enter]
Enter style name or [?] <current>: *Specify the desired style or enter* **?** *to list all styles.*

If you want to work in the previous text style, just press ENTER at the last prompt. If you want to activate another text style, enter the name of the style at the last prompt. You can also choose from a list of available text styles, which can be displayed by entering **?**. After you enter **?**, the next prompt is given next.

Enter text style(s) to list <*>: *Specify the text styles to list or enter* *** *to list all styles.*

Press ENTER to display the available text style names and the details of the current styles and commands in the **AutoCAD LT Text Window**.

Note
*With the help of the **Style** option of the **Text** tool, you can select a text style from an existing list. If you want to create a new style, use the **STYLE** command, which is explained later in this chapter.*

ENTERING SPECIAL CHARACTERS

In almost all drafting applications, you need to use special characters (symbols) in the normal text and in the dimension text. For example, you may want to use the degree symbol (°) or the diameter symbol (ø), or you may want to underscore or overscore some text. This can be achieved with the appropriate sequence of control characters (control code). For each symbol, the control sequence starts with a percent sign written twice (%%). The character immediately following the double percent sign depicts the symbol. The control sequences for some of the symbols are given next.

Control sequence	Special character
%%c	Diameter symbol (ø)
%%d	Degree symbol (°)
%%p	Plus/minus tolerance symbol (±)

For example, if you want to write 25° Celsius, you need to enter **25%%dCelsius**. If you want to write 43.0ø, you need to enter **43.0%%c**.

In addition to the control sequences shown earlier, you can use the %%nnn control sequence to draw special characters. The nnn can take a value in the range of 1 to 126. For example, to use the & symbol, enter the text string **%%038**.

To insert a euro symbol, press and hold the ALT key and enter **0128** from the numeric keypad and then release the ALT key. Before entering the numbers, make sure that the NUM LOCK is on.

CREATING MULTILINE TEXT

Ribbon: Home > Annotate > Text drop-down > MultilineText   **Command:** MTEXT
Menu Bar: Draw > Text > Multiline Text
Tool Palette: Draw > MText Or Annotate > Text > Multiline Text
Toolbar: Draw, Text > Multiline Text

The **Multiline Text** tool in the **Text** drop-down in the **Text** panel (see Figure 7-11) is used to write a multiline text whose width is specified by defining two corners of the text boundary or by entering a width, using the coordinate entry. The text created by using the **Multiline Text** tool is a single object, regardless of the number of lines it contains.

On invoking the **Multiline Text** tool, a sample text "abc" is attached to the cursor and you are prompted to specify the first corner. Specify the first corner and move the pointing device so that a box that shows the location and size of the paragraph text is formed. An arrow is displayed within the boundary indicating the direction of the text flow. Specify the other corner to define the boundary. When you define the text boundary, it does not mean that the text paragraph will fit within the defined boundary. AutoCAD LT only uses the width of the defined boundary as the width of the text paragraph. The height of the text boundary has no effect on the text paragraph.

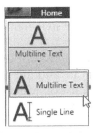

*Figure 7-11 The **Multiline Text** tool in the **Text** drop-down*

Note
*On invoking the **Multiline Text** tool, a sample text "abc" is attached to the cursor. The **MTJIGSTRING** system variable stores the default contents of the sample text. You can specify a string of ten alphanumeric characters as the default sample text.*

The prompt sequence that will be displayed is given next.

Command: **MTEXT** [Enter]
Current text style: "Standard". Text height: 0.2000 Annotative: No
Specify first corner: *Select a point to specify first corner.*
Specify opposite corner or [Height/Justify/Line spacing/Rotation/Style/Width/Columns]: *Select an option or select a point to specify other corner. Now, you can write text in this boundary.*

Note
Although the box boundary that you specify controls the width of the paragraph, a single word is not broken to adjust inside the boundary limits. This means that if you write a single word whose width is more than the box boundary specified, AutoCAD LT will write the word irrespective of the box width and therefore, will exceed the boundary limits.

Once you have defined the boundary of the paragraph text, AutoCAD LT displays the **Text Editor** tab along with a **Text Window**, as shown in Figure 7-12. The window & the tab are discussed next.

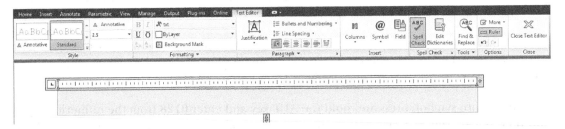

*Figure 7-12 The **Text Editor** tab and the **Text** Window*

Text Window

The **Text** Window is used to enter the multiline text. The width of the active text area is determined by the width of the window that you specify when you invoke the **Multiline Text** tool. You can increase or decrease the size of the text window by dragging the double-headed arrow provided at the top-right and bottom left corner of the text window. You can also move the scroll bar up or down to display the text.

The ruler on the top of the text window is used to specify the indentation of the current paragraph. The top slider of the ruler specifies the indentation of the first line of the paragraph while the bottom slider specifies the indentation of the other lines of the paragraph.

Text Editor Tab

On creating the text window a contextual tab will be added to the **Ribbon**. The options in this tab are discussed next.

Text Style

The list of available text styles are grouped on the left of the **Style** panel in the **Text Editor** tab. Click the down arrow to scroll down the list of text styles. If you choose the double arrow, a flyout containing text styles created in the current drawing will be displayed. You can select the desired text style from this flyout. You can also create a new text style by using the **STYLE** command, which is explained later in this chapter.

Annotative

The **Annotative** button is used to write the annotative text. The annotative text scales itself according to the current annotative setting. The annotative text also keeps on scaling according to the change in the annotative scale. The annotative texts are defined in the drawing area in terms of the paper height and the current annotation scale setting.

Note

*While editing the text, the **Annotative** button is used to convert the non-annotative multiline text into annotative multiline text and vice-versa.*

Text Height

The **Text Height** drop-down list is used to specify the text height of the multiline text. The default value in this drop-down list is 0.2000. Once you modify the height, AutoCAD LT retains that value till you change it. Remember that the multiline text height does not affect the height specified for the **TEXT** command.

Bold, Italic, Underline, Overline

You can use the appropriate buttons in the **Formatting** panel to make the selected text bold, italics, underlined, or create overlined text. Bold and italics are not supported by SHX fonts and hence, they will not be available for the particular fonts. These four buttons toggle between on and off.

Font

The **Font** drop-down list in the **Formatting** panel displays all fonts in AutoCAD LT. You can select the desired font from this drop-down list, see Figure 7-13. Irrespective of the font assigned to a text style, you can assign a different font to that style for the current multiline text by using the **Font** drop-down list.

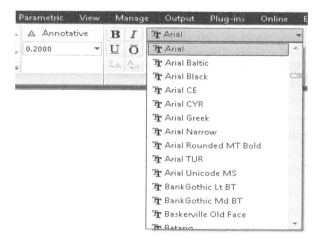

*Figure 7-13 The **Font** drop-down list*

Uppercase

When you select text in the text editor and choose this button, the alphabets written in the lowercase are converted to the uppercase.

Lowercase

On choosing this button, the alphabets written in the uppercase are converted to the lowercase.

Color

The **Color** drop-down list is used to set the color for the multiline text. You can also select the color from the **Select Color** dialog box that is displayed by selecting **Select Colors** in the drop-down list.

Background Mask

This option is used to define a background color for a multiline text. When you choose this option, the **Background Mask** dialog box will be displayed, as shown in Figure 7-14. To add a background mask, select the **Use background mask** check box and select the required color from the drop-down list in the **Fill Color** area. You can set the size of the colored background behind the text using the **Border offset factor** edit box. The previous value of the offset factor is automatically selected in the edit box. The box

Figure 7-14 The Background Mask dialog box

that defines the background color will be offset from the text by the value you define in this edit box. The value in this edit box is based on the height of the text. If you enter **1** as the value, the height of the colored background will be equal to the height of the text and will extend through the length of the window defined to write the multiline text. Similarly, if you enter **2** as the value, the height of the colored box will be twice the height of the text and will be equally offset above and below the text. However, the length of the colored box will still be equal to the length of the window defined to write the multiline text. You can select the **Use drawing background color** check box in the **Fill Color** area to use the color of the background of the drawing area to add the background mask. The previous color used is automatically selected.

Oblique Angle

Expand the **Formatting** panel to view this option. This option is used to specify the slant angle for the text. Enter the angle in the **Oblique Angle** edit box or use spinner to specify the slant angle, which is measured from the positive direction of X-axis in the clockwise direction.

Tracking

Expand the **Formatting** panel to view this option. This option is used to control the spacing between the selected characters. Select the characters and enter the value of the spacing in the **Tracking** edit box. You can also use the **Tracking** spinner to specify this value. The default tracking value is 1.000. You can specify values ranging from 0.7500 to 4.0000.

Width Factor

Expand the **Formatting** panel to view this option. This option is used to control the width of characters. By default, the value is set to 1.000. Select the characters and use the **Width Factor** edit box or the **Width Factor** spinner to specify the width of characters.

Justification

In large complicated technical drawings, the **Justification** option is used to fit the text matter with a specified justification and alignment. For example, if the text justification is bottom-right

(BR), the text paragraph will spill to the left and above the insertion point, regardless of how you define the width of the paragraph. When you choose the **Justification** button in the **Paragraph** panel of the **Text Editor** in the **Ribbon**, a cascading menu appears that displays the predefined text justifications. By default, the text is **Top Left** justified. You can choose the new justification from the cascading menu. The various justifications are TL, ML, BL, TC, MC, BC, TR, MR, and BR. Figure 7-15 shows various text justifications for multiline text.

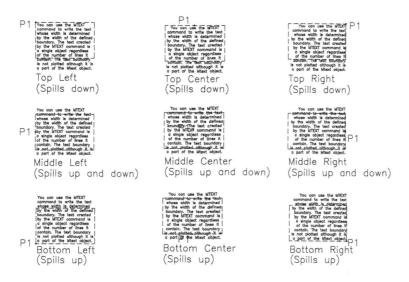

Figure 7-15 Text justifications for multiline text (P1 is the text insertion point)

Paragraph

This button is used to control the setting of a paragraph such as tab, indent, alignment, paragraph spacing, and line spacing. Choose this button to display the **Paragraph** dialog box on the screen, as shown in Figure 7-16. The options in the **Paragraph** dialog box are discussed next.

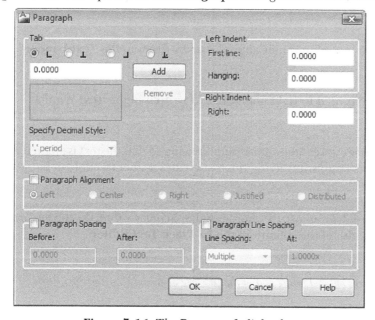

*Figure 7-16 The **Paragraph** dialog box*

Tab. This area is used to specify the tab type by selecting the required radio button. This area is also used to add or remove the additional tab positions up to which the cursor is moved while pressing the TAB key, once at the start of a new paragraph for the left, center, right, and decimal justification. This option can also be set using the mouse by clicking on the ruler of the **In-Place Text** editor.

Left Indent. In this area, you can set the indent of the first line and the following lines of multiline text by entering the values in the **First Line** and the **Hanging** edit boxes.

Right Indent. In this area, you can set the right indent of the paragraph of the multiline text by entering the value in the **Right** edit box.

Paragraph Alignment. Select the **Paragraph Alignment** check box to set the alignment for the current or the selected paragraph.

Paragraph Spacing. Select the **Paragraph Spacing** check box to set the gap before the start of the paragraph and after the end of the paragraph. According to the gap set by you, AutoCAD LT calculates the gap between the two consecutive paragraphs. This gap is equal to the sum of after paragraph gap for the upper paragraph and the before paragraph gap for the lower paragraph.

Paragraph Line Spacing. Select the **Paragraph Line Spacing** check box to set the gap between the two consecutive lines. Select the **Exactly** option from the **Line Spacing** drop-down list to maintain the gap exactly specified by you in the **At** edit box, irrespective of the text height. On selecting the **At least** option, both the user specified arbitrary value as well as the text height will be considered to determine the gap. If the text height is smaller than the specified value, the line space will be determined by the user specified value. If the text height is larger, the line spacing will be equal to the text height value. By selecting the **Multiple** option, you can specify the spacing according to the text height. When the text height is not equal in a line, the line space will be determined by the largest text height value of that line.

Left
This radio button is used to left align the text written in the **Text** Window.

Center
This radio button is used to center align the text written in the **Text** Window.

Right
This radio button is used to right align the text written in the **Text** Window.

Justify
This radio button is used to adjust horizontal spacing so that the text is aligned evenly in between the left and right margins. Justifying the text creates a smooth edge on both sides.

Distribute
This button is used to adjust the horizontal spacing so that the text is evenly distributed throughout the width of the column in the **In-Place Text Editor**.

Note
The spaces entered at the end of the line are also considered while justifying the text.

Line Spacing
Line spacing is the distance between two consecutive lines in a multiline text. Choose **Paragraph > Line Spacing** from the **Ribbon** to display a flyout containing options to select some predefined

line spacing or opening the **Paragraph** dialog box, see Figure 7-17. The **1.0x**, **1.5x**, **2x**, **2.5x** options set the line spacing in the multiples of the largest text height value in the same line. The **More** option is chosen to open the **Paragraph** dialog box that has been discussed earlier. The **Clear Line Space** option removes the space setting for the lines of the selected or the current paragraph. As a result, the line spacing will retrieve the default mtext line space setting.

Bullets and Numbering

This option is used to control the settings to display the bullets and numbering in a multiline text. Choose the **Bullets and Numbering** option; a flyout will be displayed, as shown in Figure 7-18. The options in this flyout are discussed next.

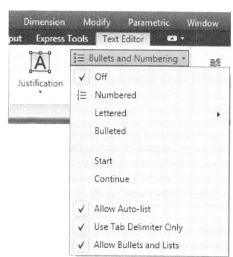

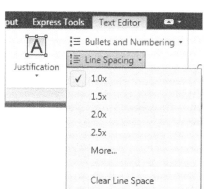

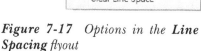

Figure 7-17 Options in the Line Spacing flyout

Figure 7-18 Flyout displayed on choosing the Bullets and Numbering option

Off. Select this option to remove letters, numbers, and bullets from the selected text.

Lettered. This option inserts the letters for list formatting. You can choose the uppercase letters and lower case letters to be used for the list formatting.

Note
If the number of items exceed the number of alphabets, the numbering continues again from the start, but by using the double alphabet.

Numbered. This option inserts numbers for the list formatting.

Bulleted. This option inserts bullets for the list formatting.

Start. This option restarts a new letter or a numbering sequence for the list formatting.

Continue. This option adds the selected paragraphs to the last list and continues the sequence.

Allow Auto-list. Select the **Allow Auto-list** option and follow the procedure given below to start the formatting of list automatically.

1. Start a line of text by entering a number.
2. Use period (.), comma (,), close angle bracket (>), close square bracket (]), close parenthesis ()), or close curly bracket (}) as punctuation after the number.
3. Provide space by pressing the TAB key.

4. Enter the required text.
5. Press the ENTER key to move to the next line; the new line will be automatically listed.
6. Press the SHIFT+ENTER key to add a plain paragraph.
7. To end auto-listing, press the ENTER key twice.

Use Tab Delimiter Only. If this option is checked, list formatting will be applied to the text only when the space after the letter and number is created by the TAB key.

Allow Bullets and Lists. If this option is checked, the list formatting will be applied to the whole text lines in the multiline text area.

Combine Paragraphs

This option is used to combine the selected paragraphs into a single paragraph. AutoCAD LT replaces the returns between all the paragraphs by a space. As a result, the lines in the resultant paragraph will be in continuation.

Columns

This button is chosen to create columns in the multiline text. On choosing this button from the **Insert** panel, a flyout will be displayed that has the options to control the number, height, and gap between the columns. These options are shown in Figure 7-19, and are discussed next.

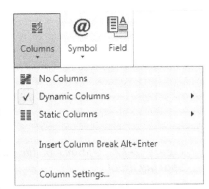

No Columns. This option does not create any column. The whole of the multiline text is written in a single column. When you start a multiline text, this option is selected by default.

Figure 7-19 The options in the **Column** *flyout*

Dynamic Columns. The dynamic columns are the text driven columns that change according to the quantity of the text. According to the quantity of text written, the columns are added or removed automatically. There are two options to control the height of the dynamic columns, **Auto height** and **Manual height**. The **Auto height** option automatically starts a new column when the text exceeds the range that the preset column can accommodate. The default height of the first column is decided by the height of the window that you create while starting the multiline text. All the other new columns generated are equal in height to the first column. If you change the height of the first column, the height of the remaining columns changes accordingly, in order to be in level with the first one. The **Manual height** option, on the other hand, provides the flexibility to control the height of each column individually. A new column will not start if the text exceeds the range that the present column can accommodate. The text will keep on adding to the same column by increasing the height of that column. Later on, you can add extra columns by adjusting the height of the present column. When you decrease the height of the column in which you have entered the text that does not fit the height of the new column, a new column will start automatically. Similarly, you can add more columns by adjusting the height of the last column.

Static Columns. The **Static Columns** option allows you to specify the number of columns before writing the text. All the generated columns are of the same height and width. You can also change the number of columns after writing the text.

Insert Column Break Alt + Enter. This option is used to start writing the text in a new column manually. When you insert a column break, the cursor automatically moves to the start of the next column. You can also press the ALT+ENTER key to insert a column break.

Column Settings. This option controls the setting to create a column. Choose this option to invoke the **Column Settings** dialog box, see Figure 7-20. The **Column Settings** dialog box has four areas: **Column Type**, **Column Number**, **Height**, and **Width**. The **Column Type** area specifies the type of column that you want to create. All options in this area are similar to the options discussed above. In the **Column Number** area, you can specify the number of columns to be generated when you create the manual type of columns. In the **Height** area, you can specify the height of the columns to be generated for **Auto Height Dynamic Columns**, and **Static Column** type. The **Width** area controls the width of the columns and the gap between two consecutive columns.

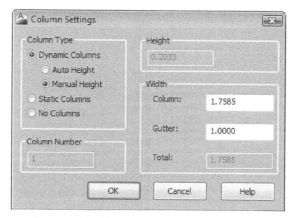

*Figure 7-20 The **Column Settings** dialog box*

Symbol

This option is used to insert the special characters in the text. When you choose the **Symbol** button from the **Insert** panel of the **Text Editor** tab in the **Ribbon**, a flyout will be displayed with some predefined special characters, see Figure 7-21. You can also choose **Other** from the flyout to display the **Character Map** dialog box. This dialog box has a number of other special characters that you can insert in the multiline text. To insert characters from the dialog box, select the character that you want to copy and then choose the **Select** button. Once you have selected all the required special characters, choose the **Copy** button and then close the dialog box. Now in the text window, position the cursor where you want to insert the special characters and right-click to display the shortcut menu. Choose **Paste** to insert the selected special character in the **Text Editor**.

Field

AutoCAD LT allows you to insert a field in the multiline text. A field contains data that is associated with the property that defines the field. For example, you can insert a field having the creator's name of the current drawing. If you have already defined the creator of the current drawing in the **Drawing Properties** dialog box, it will automatically be displayed in the field. If you modify the creator and update the field, the changes will automatically be made in the text. When you choose this option, the **Field** dialog box will be displayed, as shown in Figure 7-22. You can select the field to be added in the **Field names** list box and define the format of the field using the **Format** list box. Choose **OK** after selecting the field and format. If the data in the selected field is already defined, it will be displayed in the **Text** window. If not, the field will display dashes (----).

Note
*To update a field after the text of that field is modified, double-click on the multiline text to display the **In-Place Text Editor**. Click on the field in the **Text** window to select it and then right-click to display the shortcut menu. Choose **Update Field** from this menu; the field will be updated. You can also edit the field or convert it into text using the same shortcut menu.*

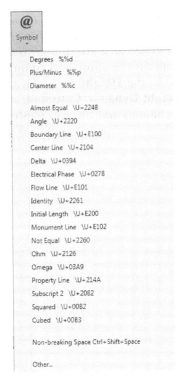

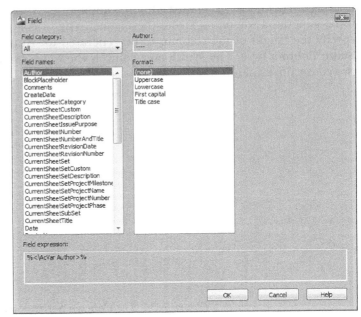

Figure 7-21 *Flyout displayed when you choose the **Symbol** button from the **Insert** panel*

Figure 7-22 *The **Field** dialog box*

Spell Check

To check spelling errors, choose the **Spell Check** button; the misspelt words will appear with a red underline. You can specify settings to check spelling errors as per your requirement. To do so, left-click on the inclined arrow in the **Spell Check** panel; the **Check Spelling Settings** dialog box will be displayed. This dialog box is used to specify what to include for spell check such as the dimension text, block attributes, sub option, and text in external references.

You can also specify what not to include like capitalized words, mixed cases, uppercase, and words with numbers or punctuation.

Edit Dictionaries

This option is used to match the word with the words in dictionaries while a text is run on spell check. On choosing this option, the **Dictionaries** dialog box will be displayed. This dialog box has two areas, **Main dictionary** and **Custom dictionary**. In the **Main dictionary** area, you can select the required dictionary from a list of different language dictionaries. And in the **Custom dictionary** area, you can add the commonly used words to a *.cus* file. You can also import the words from other dictionaries to the current customized *.cus* file.

Find and Replace

When you choose the **Find & Replace** button from the **Tools** panel, the **Find and Replace** dialog box will be displayed, as shown in Figure 7-23. The options that can be chosen from this dialog box are discussed next.

Find what. This edit box is used to enter the text or a part of a word or a complete word that you need to find in the drawing.

Replace with. If you want some text to be replaced, enter new text for replacement in this text box.

Match case. If this check box is selected, AutoCAD LT will find out the word only if the case of all characters in the word are identical to the word mentioned in the **Find what** edit box.

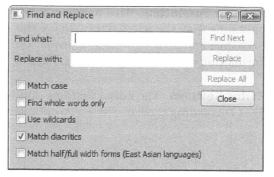

*Figure 7-23 The **Find and Replace** dialog box*

Find whole words only. If this check box is selected, AutoCAD LT will match the word in the text only if it is a single word, identical to the one mentioned in the **Find what** text box. For example, if you enter **and** in the **Find what** edit box and select the **Find whole words only** check box, AutoCAD LT will not match the string **and** in words like sand, land, band, and so on.

Use wildcards. This check box is selected to use the wildcard characters such as * , ?, and so on in the **Find what** edit box and then replace the selected text.

Match diacritics. This check box is selected to match the Latin characters, diacritical marks, or assent in your search.

Match half/full width forms (East Asian languages). If this check box is selected, you can match half or full width characters in your search.

Find Next. Choose this button to continue the search for the text entered in the **Find what** box.

Replace. Choose this button to replace the highlighted text with the text entered in the **Replace with** text box.

Replace All. If you choose this button, all the words in the current multiline text that match the word specified in the **Find what** text box will be replaced with the word entered in the **Replace with** box.

Import Text
Expand the **Tools** panel to view this option. When you choose this option, AutoCAD LT displays the **Select File** dialog box. In this dialog box, select any text file that you want to import as the multiline text; the imported text will be displayed in the text area. Note that only the ASCII or RTF file is interpreted properly.

AutoCAPS
Expand the **Tools** panel to view this option. If you choose this option, the case of all the text written or imported after choosing this option will be changed to uppercase. However, the case of the text written before choosing this option is not changed.

More
To edit text, select it and then choose the **More** button from the **Options** panel in the **Text Editor** tab; a flyout will be displayed. The options in the **More** flyout are discussed next.

Character Set. This option is used to define the character set for the current font. You can select the desired character set from the cascading menu that is displayed when you choose this option.

Remove Formatting. This option is used to remove the formatting such as bold, italics, or underline from the selected text. To use this option, select the text whose formatting you need to change and then right-click to display the shortcut menu. In the menu, choose the **Remove Formatting** option. The formatting of the selected text will be removed.

Editor Settings. The **Editor Settings** option has the sub-options to control the display of the **Text Formatting** toolbar. These sub-options are shown in Figure 7-24 and are discussed next.

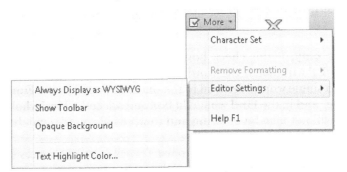

*Figure 7-24 The sub-options of the **Editor Settings** option*

Always Display as WYSIWYG (What you see is what you get). This option controls the display size and orientation of the text in the **Text Editor**. If you choose this sub-option, the text in the **Text Editor** will be displayed in the **In-Place Text Editor** with its original size, position, and orientation. But, if the text is very small, or very large or rotated, then you can deselect this sub-option, so that the displayed text is oriented horizontally and is displayed in the readable size. Thus making it easy to read and edit.

Show Toolbar. This sub-option is used to show or hide the **Text Formatting** toolbar.

Opaque Background. Choose this sub-option to make the background of the **Text** window opaque. By default, the background is transparent. Invoke the text window over the existing objects/entities in the drawing window to see the effect of the opaque background sub-option.

Ruler
The **Ruler** button in the **Options** panel is used to turn on or off the display of ruler in the **Text Window**.

Undo
The **Undo** button allows you to undo the actions in the **In-Place Text Editor**. You can also press the CTRL+Z keys to undo the previous actions.

Redo
The **Redo** button allows you to redo the actions in the **In-Place Text Editor**. You can also press the CTRL+Y keys to redo the previous actions.

The options discussed next are not available in the **Text Editor** tab. However, in the **Text Formatting** toolbar, these options will be displayed on choosing **More > Editor Settings > Show Toolbar** from the **Text Editor** tab.

Stack*
To create a fraction text, you must use the stack option with the special characters /, ^, and #. In AutoCAD LT 2012, this option is available in sleep mode in the **Formatting** panel of the **Text**

Editor tab. When you enter two numbers separated by / or ^ , the stack option becomes active. You can use this option to stack. Alternatively, press ENTER or SPACEBAR after entering two characters separated by / or ^ ; the **AutoStack Properties** dialog box will be displayed, as shown in Figure 7-25. You can use this dialog box to control the stacking properties. The character / stacks the text vertically with a line, and the character ^ stacks the text vertically without a line (tolerance stack). The character # stacks the text with a diagonal line. After you enter the text with the required special character between them, select the text, and then choose the **Stack/Unstack** button. The stacked text is displayed equal to 70 percent of the actual height.

Unstack

This option is also available in the shortcut menu that is displayed on right-clicking on the stack characters from the text editor. The **Unstack** option is used to unstack the selected stacked text.

Stack

This option is available in the shortcut menu if you select the unstacked text. The **Stack** option is used to stack the selected text if there are any stack characters (characters separated by /, #, or ^) available in the multiline text.

Stack Properties

This option is available in the shortcut menu only when you select a stacked text. When you choose this option, the **Stack Properties** dialog box will be displayed, as shown in Figure 7-26. This dialog box is used to edit the text and the appearance of the selected stacked text. The options in this dialog box are discussed next.

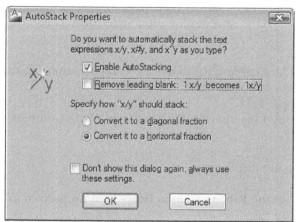

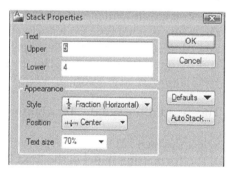

Figure 7-25 *The **AutoStack Properties** dialog box*   *Figure 7-26* *The **Stack Properties** dialog box*

Text Area. You can change the upper and the lower values of the stacked text by entering their values in the **Upper** and **Lower** text boxes, respectively.

Appearance Area. You can change the style, position, and size of the stacked text by entering their values in the **Style**, **Position**, and **Text size** text boxes, respectively.

Defaults. This option allows you to restore the default values or save the new settings as the default settings for the selected stacked text.

AutoStack. When you choose this button, the **AutoStack Properties** dialog box will be displayed, in the same way as shown earlier in Figure 7-25. The options in this dialog box were discussed under the **Stack** heading.

Note
The Cut and Copy sub-options of the Edit option can be used to move or copy the text from the text editor to any other application. Similarly, using the Paste sub-option, you can paste text from any windows text-based application to the Text Editor.

EXAMPLE 1	Multiline Text

In this example, you will use the **Multiline Text** tool to write the following text.

For long, complex entries, create multiline text using the MTEXT option. The angle is 10°, dia = 1/2", and length = 32 1/2".

The font of the text is **Swis721 BT**, text height is 0.20, color is red, and written at an angle of 10-degree with Middle-Left justification. Make the word "multiline" bold, underline the text "multiline text", and make the word "angle" italic. The line spacing type and line spacing between the lines are **At least** and **1.5x**, respectively. Use the symbol for degrees. After writing the text in the **Text window**, replace the word "option" with "command".

1. Choose the **Multiline Text** tool from the **Annotation** panel in the **Home** tab in the **Drafting & Annotation** workspace. After invoking this tool, specify the first corner on the screen to define the first corner of the paragraph text boundary. You need to specify the rotation angle of the text before specifying the second corner of the paragraph text boundary. The prompt sequence is given next.

    Current text style: STANDARD. Text height: 0.2000. Annotative: No
    Specify first corner: *Select a point to specify the first corner.*
    Specify opposite corner or [Height/Justify/Line spacing/Rotation/Style/Width/Columns]: **R** Enter
    Specify rotation angle <0>: 10.
    Specify opposite corner or [Height/Justify/Line spacing/Rotation/Style/Width/Columns]: **L** Enter
    Enter line spacing type [At least/Exactly] <At least>: Enter
    Enter line spacing factor or distance <1x>: **1.5x**
    Specify opposite corner or [Height/Justify/Line spacing/Rotation/Style/Width/Columns]: *Select another point to specify the other corner.*

    The **Text Editor** and the **Text Editor** tab are displayed.

2. Select the **Swis721 BT** true type font from the **Ribbon Combo Box - Font** drop-down list of the **Formatting** panel in the **Text Editor** tab.

3. Enter **0.20** in the **Ribbon Combo Box - Text height** edit box of the **Style** panel, if the value in this edit box is not 0.2.

4. Select **Red** from the **Text Editor Color Gallery** drop-down list in the **Formatting** panel.

5. Now, enter the text in the **Text Editor**, as shown in Figure 7-27. To add the degree symbol, choose the **Symbol** button from the **Insert** panel of the **Text Editor** tab in the **Ribbon**; a flyout is displayed. Choose **Degrees** from the flyout. When you type 1/2 after Dia = and then press the " key, AutoCAD LT displays the **AutoStack Properties** dialog box. Select the **Convert it to a diagonal fraction** radio button, if it is not already selected. Also, make sure the **Enable AutoStacking** check box is selected. Now, close the dialog box.

    Similarly, when you type 1/2 after length = 32 1/2 and then press the " key, AutoCAD LT displays the **AutoStack Properties** dialog box. Select the **Convert it to a diagonal fraction** radio button and then close the dialog box.

6. Double-click on the word "multiline" to select it (or pick and drag to select the text) and then choose the **B** button to make it boldface and underline the words "multiline text" by using the **U** button.

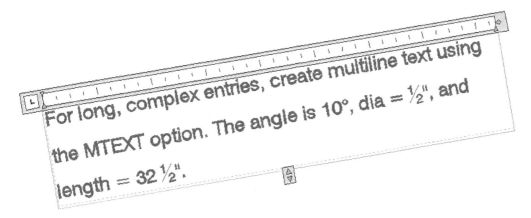

Figure 7-27 *Text entered in the **Text Editor***

7. Highlight the word "angle" by double-clicking on it and then choose the **Italic** button.

8. Choose the **Middle Left** option from the **Justification** drop-down in the **Paragraph** panel.

9. Choose the **Find & Replace** button from the **Tools** panel in the **Text Editor** tab. Alternatively, right-click on the **Text Window** and then choose **Find and Replace** from the shortcut menu. Alternatively, you can use CTRL+R keys. On doing so, the **Find and Replace** dialog box is displayed.

10. In the **Find what** edit box, enter **option** and in the **Replace with** edit box, enter **command**.

11. Choose the **Find Next** button. AutoCAD LT finds the word "option" and highlights it. Choose the **Replace** button to replace **option** by **command**. The **AutoCAD LT** information box is displayed informing you that AutoCAD LT has finished searching for the word. Choose **OK** to close the information box.

Note
To set the width of the multiline text objects, hold and drag the arrowhead on the right side of the ruler. In this example, the text has been accommodated into two lines.

12. Now, choose **Close** to exit the **Find and Replace** dialog box and return to the **In-Place Text Editor**. To exit the editor mode, click outside the **Text Editor**; a text is displayed on the screen, as shown in Figure 7-28.

Figure 7-28 *Multiline text for Example 1*

Tip
The text in the **Text Editor** *can be selected by double-clicking on the word, by holding the left mouse button of the pointing device and then dragging the cursor, or by triple-clicking on the text to select the entire line or paragraph.*

EXERCISE 1	Single Line & Multiline Text

Write the text using the **Single Line** and **Multiline Text** tools, as shown in Figures 7-29 and 7-30. Use the special characters and the text justification options shown in the drawing. The text height is 0.1 and 0.15 respectively in Figures 7-29 and 7-30.

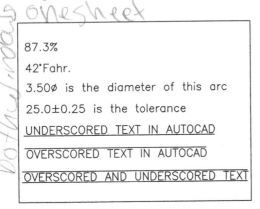

Figure 7-29 *Drawing with special characters*

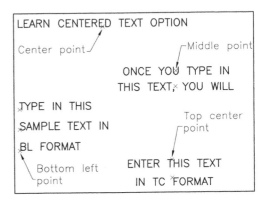

Figure 7-30 *Drawing for Exercise 1*

EDITING TEXT

The contents of **MTEXT** and **TEXT** object can be edited by using the **DDEDIT** and **Properties** commands. You can also use the AutoCAD LT editing commands, such as **MOVE**, **ERASE**, **ROTATE**, **COPY**, **MIRROR**, and **GRIPS** with any text object.

In addition to editing, you can also modify the text in AutoCAD LT. The modification that you can perform on the text include changing its scale and justification. The various editing and modifying operations are discussed next.

Editing Text Using the DDEDIT Command

Menu Bar: Modify > Object > Text > Edit	**Command:** DDEDIT
Toolbar: Text > Edit	

You can use the **DDEDIT** command to edit text. The most convenient way of invoking this command is by double-clicking on the text. If you double-click on a single line text written by using the **Single Line** tool, AutoCAD LT creates an edit box around the text and highlights it. You can modify the text string in this edit box. The size of the bounding box increases or decreases as you add more text or remove the existing text. Note that for the text object, you cannot modify any of its properties in the bounding box. However, if you double-click on a multiline text written by using the **Multiline Text** tool, the text will be displayed in the **Text Editor**. You can make changes using various options in the editor. Apart from changing the text string, you can also change the properties of a paragraph text.

You can also select the text for editing and then right-click in the drawing area; a shortcut menu is displayed. Depending on the text object you have selected, the **Edit** or **Mtext Edit** options will be available in the shortcut menu. On choosing the appropriate option, the **Text Editor** and the **Text Editor** tab will be displayed.

Editing Text Using the Properties Palette

Using the **DDEDIT** command with the text object, you can only change the text string, and not its properties such as height, angle, and so on. In this case, you can use the **Properties** palette for changing the properties. Select the text, right-click to invoke the shortcut menu, and choose the **Properties** option from the shortcut menu; the **Properties** palette with all properties of the selected text will be displayed, as shown in Figure 7-31. In this palette, you can change any value and the text string.

You can edit a single line text in the **Contents** edit box. However, to edit a multiline text, you must choose the **Full editor** button in the **Contents** edit box. On doing so, the **Text Editor** will be displayed and you can make the changes.

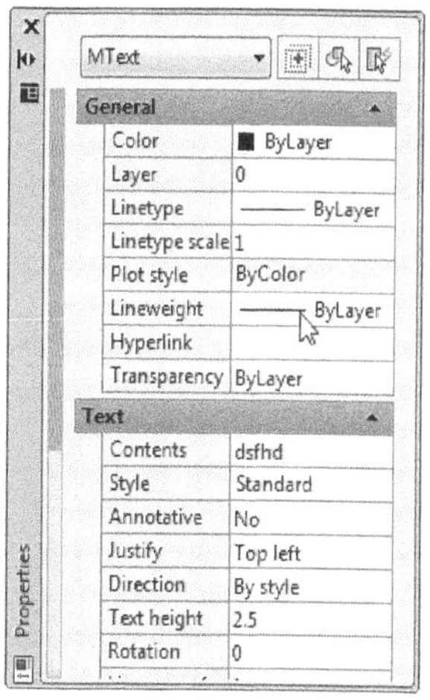

Figure 7-31 The Properties palette

Modifying the Scale of the Text

Ribbon: Annotate > Text > Scale
Menu Bar: Modify > Object > Text > Scale
Toolbar: Text > Scale
Command: SCALETEXT

You can modify the scale factor of a text by using the **Scale** tool in the extended options of the **Text** panel of the **Annotate** tab. On invoking this tool, you can select the text and specify the base point for scaling the text. AutoCAD LT lists the justification options as the base point to scale the text. Specify the appropriate base point and press ENTER; you will be prompted to specify the new model height or select one of the options. All these options are discussed next.

Paper Height

It scales the text height depending on the annotative properties of a drawing. The **Paper height** option can only be applied to the annotative objects.

Match object

You can use the **Match object** option to select an existing text whose height is used to scale a selected text.

Scale factor

You can use the **Scale factor** option to specify a scale factor to scale a text. You can also use the **Reference** option to specify the scale factor for the text.

INSERTING TABLE IN THE DRAWING

Ribbon: Home > Annotation > Table Or Annotate > Tables > Table
Menu Bar: Draw > Table   **Toolbar:** Draw > Table
Tool Palette: Draw > Table   **Command:** JUSTIFYTEXT

A number of mechanical, architectural, electric, or civil drawings require a table in which some information about the drawing is displayed. For example, the drawing of an assembly needs the Bill of Material, which is a table that provides details such as the number of parts in the drawing, their names, their material, and so on. To enter these information, AutoCAD LT allows you to create tables using the **Table** tool, see Figure 7-32. When you invoke this tool, the **Insert Table** dialog box is displayed, as shown in Figure 7-33. The options in this dialog box are discussed next.

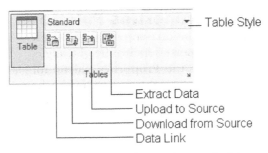

*Figure 7-32 Tools in the **Tables** panel of the **Annotate** tab*

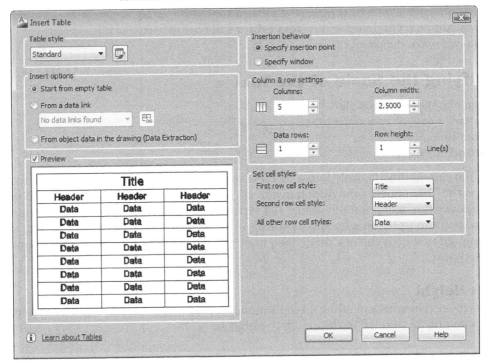

*Figure 7-33 The **Insert Table** dialog box*

Table style Area

The drop-down list in this area displays the names of the various table styles in the current drawing. By default, the **Standard** table style is displayed in the drop-down list. Choose the **Launch the Table Style dialog** button on the right of this drop-down list to display the **Table Style** dialog box. This dialog box can be used to create a new table style, modify, or delete an existing table style. You can also set the selected table style as the current table style. You will learn more about creating a new table style in the next section.

Insert options Area

The options in this area enable you to create tables with different types of data. You can add static data, externally-linked data, or object data to a table. The options in this area are discussed next.

Start from empty table

This option enables you to enter the data manually in the table. An empty table is created in which you have to enter the values manually. This type of table data is known as the static data. This is the default option selected for creating a table.

Tip

*You can copy an existing excel spreadsheet and paste it on the existing drawing as a table with the static data. To do so, use the **PASTESPEC** command and paste the copied data as AutoCAD LT entity. The resulting table will be similar to the table created using the **Start from empty table** option.*

From a data link

This option enables you to create a table automatically in AutoCAD LT from an excel sheet. This excel sheet remains linked with the drawing and any changes made in the excel sheet will reflect in the table. From the drop-down list, you can select an already linked excel sheet or you can also attach a new excel sheet to the drawing. To link a new excel file, choose the **Data Link Manager** button; the **Select a Data Link** dialog box will be displayed, see Figure 7-34. Select the **Create a new Excel Data Link** option; the **Enter Data Link Name** dialog box will be invoked. Enter a name for the new data link that you are creating and choose the **OK** button; the **New Excel Data Link** dialog box will be invoked, see Figure 7-35. Choose the **Browse [...]** button; the **Save As** dialog box will be invoked. Specify the location of the excel file to be linked with the current drawing and choose the **Open** button from the **Save As** dialog box. After choosing the **Open** button, more options will be added in the **New Excel Data Link** dialog box, see Figure 7-36. The options in the modified **New Excel Data Link** dialog box are discussed next.

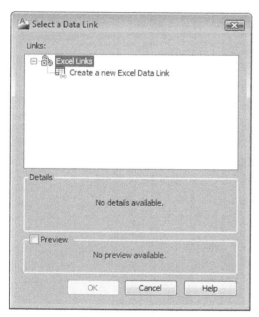

*Figure 7-34 The **Select a Data Link** dialog box*

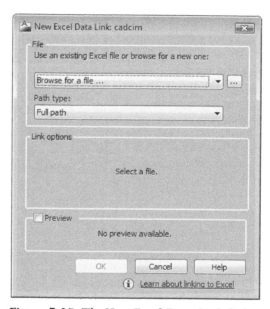

*Figure 7-35 The **New Excel Data Link** dialog box*

Choose an Excel file. This drop-down list displays the excel file attached to the current drawing. Choose the **Browse [...]** button to change the excel file to be linked with the current drawing.

Link options Area. In this area, you can specify the part of the excel file to be linked with the drawing. Select the **Link entire sheet** radio button to link the entire worksheet in the form of a table to the drawing. Select the **Link to a named range** radio button to link the already defined name ranges from the excel sheet to the drawing. Select the **Link to range** radio button to enter the range of cells to be included in the data link. Choose the **Preview** button; the preview of the range of cells included in the data link will be displayed. The preview of the attached data from the excel sheet will be displayed in the preview area. Clear the **Preview** check box to disable the preview of the table.

Cell contents Area. The **Keep data formats and formulas** radio button in this area allows you to link the excel file data along with the supported formulas. The **Keep data formats, solve formulas in Excel** radio button allows you to import data from the excel file, but the calculations made using the formulas are done in Excel. The **Convert data formats to text, solve formulas in Excel** radio button in this area is selected by default and lets you import the data of the excel file as text, and the calculations are done in Excel. The **Allow writing to source file** check box is selected by default. This check box enables you to choose the **Download from Source** button from the **Tables** panel of the **Annotate** tab in the **Ribbon** to update the changes made in the drawing table that is linked to the excel sheet.

Cell formatting Area. Select the **Use Excel formatting** check box to import any formatting settings if specified in the excel sheet. Other options in this area will be available only when the **Use Excel formatting** check box is selected. The **Keep table updated to Excel formatting** radio button allows you to update the drawing table according to the changes made in the excel sheet. If you select the **Start with Excel formatting, do not update** radio button, any formatting changes specified in the excel sheet will be imported to the table, but the changes made in the excel sheet after importing will not be updated in the drawing table. Choose the **OK** button twice to display the **Insert Table** dialog box.

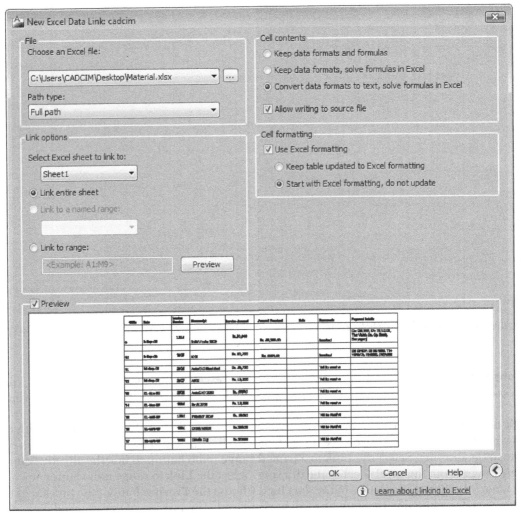

*Figure 7-36 The modified **New Excel Data Link** dialog box*

Tip
*If you have made any changes in the drawing table, choose the **Upload to Source** tool from the **Tables** panel in the **Annotate** tab; the changes made in the drawing file will reflect in the excel sheet that is linked to the drawing table. Similarly, if you have made any changes in the excel file after uploading, choose the **Download from Source** tool from the **Tables** panel in the **Annotate** tab; the changes made in the excel file will reflect in the drawing file.*

From object data in the drawing (Data Extraction)

To create a table by automatically extracting the data related to the objects created in the current drawing file, select the **From object data in the drawing (Data Extraction)** radio button from the **Insert Table** dialog box and choose the **OK** button; AutoCAD LT will start the **Data Extraction** wizard that will guide you step-by-step to insert the desired data into the current drawing.

Insertion behavior Area

The options in this area are used to specify the method of placing the table in the drawing. These options are discussed next.

Specify insertion point

This radio button is selected to place the table using the upper left corner of the table. If this radio button is selected and you choose **OK** from the **Insert Table** dialog box, you will be prompted to select the insertion point, which is by default the upper left corner of the table. By creating a different table style, you can change the point using which the table is inserted.

Specify window

If this radio button is selected and you choose **OK** from the **Insert Table** dialog box, you will be prompted to specify two corners for placing the table. The number of rows and columns in the table will depend on the size of the window you define.

Column and row settings Area

The options in this area are used to specify the number and size of rows and columns. The availability of these options depend on the option selected from the **Insert options** and **Insertion behavior** area. These options are discussed next.

Columns

This spinner is used to specify the number of columns in the table.

Column width

This spinner is used to specify the width of columns in the table.

Data rows

This spinner is used to specify the number of rows in the table.

Row height

This spinner is used to specify the height of rows in the table. The height is defined in terms of lines and the minimum value is one line.

Set cell styles Area

The options in this area are used to assign different cell styles for the rows in the new table. You can assign different cell styles to all the rows of a table. The options in this area are discussed next.

First row cell style

This drop-down list is used to specify a cell style for the first row of the table. By default, the **Title** cell style is selected for the first row of the table.

Second row cell style

This drop-down list is used to specify a cell style for the second row of the table. By default, the **Header** cell style is selected for the second row of the table.

All other row cell styles

This drop-down list is used to specify a cell style for all the other rows of the table. By default, the **Data** cell style is selected for the remaining rows of the table.

After setting the parameters in the **Insert Table** dialog box, choose the **OK** button. Depending on the type of insertion behavior selected, you will be prompted to insert the table. As soon as you complete the insertion procedure, the **In-Place Text editor** is displayed and you are allowed to enter the parameters in the first row of the table. By default, the first row is the title of the table. After entering the data, press ENTER. The first field of the first column is highlighted, which is the column head, and you are allowed to enter the data in it.

AutoCAD LT allows you to use the arrow keys on the keyboard to move to the other cells in the table. You can enter the data in the field and then press the arrow key to move to the other cells in the table. After entering the data in all the fields, press ENTER to exit the **Text Formatting** toolbar.

Tip
You can also right-click while entering the data in the table to display the shortcut menu. This shortcut menu is similar to that shown in the **In-Place Text Editor** *and can be used to insert field, symbols, text, and so on.*

CREATING A NEW TABLE STYLE

Ribbon: Home > Annotation > Table Style	**Toolbar:** Styles > Table Style
Menu Bar: Format > Table Style	**Command:** TABLESTYLE

 To create a new table style, choose **Table Style** from the extended options of the **Annotation** panel in the **Home** tab; the **Table Style** dialog box will be displayed, as shown in Figure 7-37. You can also invoke this dialog box by choosing the inclined arrow of the **Tables** panel in the **Annotate** panel.

To create a new table style, choose the **New** button from the **Table Style** dialog box; the **Create New Table Style** dialog box will be displayed, as shown in Figure 7-38.

Enter the name of the table style in the **New Style Name** edit box. Select the style on which you want to base the new style from the **Start With** drop-down list. By default, this drop-down list shows only the **Standard** table style. After specifying the settings, choose the **Continue** button from the **Create New Table Style** dialog box; the **New Table Style** dialog box will be displayed, see Figure 7-39. The options in this dialog box are discussed next.

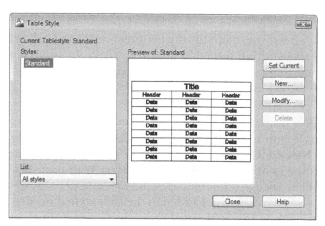

Figure 7-37 *The Table Style dialog box*

Figure 7-38 *The Create New Table Style dialog box*

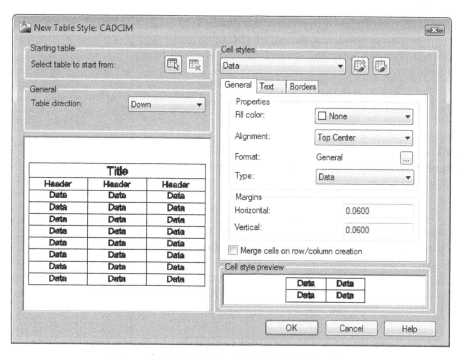

Figure 7-39 *The New Table Style dialog box*

Starting table Area

The options in this area enable you to select a table in your drawing to be used as reference for formatting the current table style. Once the table is selected, the table style associated with that table gets copied to the current table style and then you can modify it according to your requirement. The **Remove Table** button allows you to remove the initial table style from the current table style. This button is highlighted only when a table style is attached to the current one.

General Area

The **Table direction** drop-down list from the **General** area is used to specify the direction of the table. By default, this direction is down. As a result, the title and headers will be at the top and the data fields will be below them. If you select **Up** from the **Table direction** drop-down list, the title and headers will be at the bottom of this table and the data fields will be on the top of the table.

Cell styles Area

This area has the options to define a new cell style or to modify the existing ones. The **Cell style** drop-down list displays the existing cell styles within the table. It also displays the options to create a new cell style or to manage the existing ones. These options are discussed next.

Create new cell style

To create a new cell style, select this option from the **Cell styles** drop-down list. Alternatively, you can choose the **Create a new cell style** button on the right of the **Cell styles** drop-down list. On choosing this button, the **Create New Cell Style** dialog box will be invoked. Next, enter a style name for the new cell style. Select the existing cell style from the **Start With** drop-down list; the settings from the existing style will be used as a reference for the new one to be created. Next, choose the **Continue** button; the new cell style will get added to the **Cell style** drop-down list. Next, you can modify this new cell style by modifying the options in the **General**, **Text**, and **Borders** tab of the **New Table Style** dialog box.

General Tab

The options in this tab are used to control the general appearance, alignment, and formatting of the table cells. These options are shown in Figure 7-40 and are discussed next.

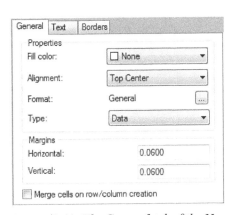

Figure 7-40 The General tab of the New Table Style dialog box

Fill color. This drop-down list is used to specify the fill color for the cells.

Alignment. This drop-down list is used to specify the alignment of the text entered in the cells. The default alignment is top center.

Format. If you choose the **Browse** [...] button available on the right of **Format**, the **Table Cell Format** dialog box will be displayed. This dialog box is used to specify the data type and format of the data type to be entered in the table. While creating the table, once the data type and format are specified, you cannot enter any other type of data or format without changing or modifying the table style. The default data type is **General**. In this data type, you can enter any alphanumeric characters.

Type. This drop-down list is used to specify the cell style either as a **Label** or **Data**.

Horizontal. This edit box is used to specify the minimum spacing between the data entered in the cells and the left and right border lines of the cells.

Vertical. This edit box is used to specify the minimum spacing between the data entered in the cells and the top and bottom border lines of the cells.

Merge cells on row/column creation. This check box is selected to merge all the new rows and columns created by using this cell style into one cell.

Text Tab

The options in this tab are used to control the display of the text to be written in the cells. These options are shown in Figure 7-41 and are discussed next.

Text style. This drop-down list is used to select the text style that is used for entering the text in the cells. By default, it shows only **Standard**, which is the default text style. You will learn to create more text styles later in this chapter.

Text height. This edit box is used to specify the height of the text to be entered in the cells.

Text color. This drop-down list is used to specify the color of the text that will be entered in the cells. If you select the **Select Color** option, the **Select Color** dialog box will be displayed, which can be used to select from index color, true color, or from the color book.

Text angle. This edit box is used to specify the slant angle of the text to be entered in the cell.

Borders Tab
The options in this area are used to set the properties of the border of the table, see Figure 7-42. The line weight and color settings that you specify using this area will be applied to all borders, outside borders, inside borders, bottom border, left border, top border, right border, or without border depending on which button is chosen from this area. Select the **Double line** check box to display the borders with double lines. You can also control the spacing between the double lines by entering the gap value in the **Spacing** edit box.

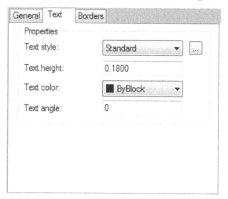

*Figure 7-41 The **Text** tab of the **New Table Style** dialog box*

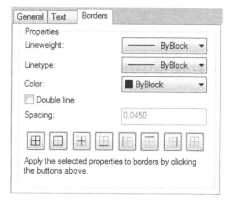

*Figure 7-42 The **Borders** tab of the **New Table Style** dialog box*

Manage Cell Styles
To create a new cell style, select this option from the **Cell style** drop-down list. Alternatively, you can choose the **Manage Cell Style dialog** button on the right of the **Cell styles** drop-down list. On choosing this button, the **Manage Cell Styles** dialog box will be invoked, see Figure 7-43. This dialog box displays all cell styles in the current table. You can also create a new cell style, delete, or rename an existing cell style. Note that the cell styles **Title**, **Header**, and **Data** are the default table styles provided in AutoCAD LT, and they cannot be deleted or renamed.

SETTING A TABLE STYLE AS CURRENT
To set a table style as the current style for creating all the new tables, invoke the **Table Style** dialog box by choosing **Table Style** from the extended options of

*Figure 7-43 The **Manage Cell Styles** dialog box*

the **Annotation** panel in the **Home** tab. Next, select the table style from the **Styles** list box in the **Table Style** dialog box and choose the **Set Current** button. You can also set a table style current by selecting it from the **Table Style** drop-down list in the **Tables** panel. This is a convenient method of setting a table style current.

MODIFYING A TABLE STYLE

To modify a table style, invoke the **Table Style** dialog box by choosing **Table Style** in the extended options of the **Annotation** panel in the **Home** tab. Select the table style from the **Styles** list box in the **Table Style** dialog box and choose the **Modify** button; the **Modify Table Style** dialog box is displayed. This dialog box is similar to the **New Table Style** dialog box. Modify the options in the various tabs and areas of this dialog box and then choose **OK** to exit from the **Modify Table Style** dialog box.

MODIFYING TABLES

Select any cell in the table by double-clicking in it; the **Table Cell** tab will be added to the **Ribbon**, as shown in Figure 7-44. The options in the **Table Cell** tab are used to modify the table, insert block, add formulas, and perform other operations.

*Figure 7-44 The **Table Cell** tab added to the **Ribbon***

Modifying Rows

To insert a row above a cell, select a cell and choose the **Insert Above** tool from the **Rows** panel in the **Table Cell** tab. To insert a row below a cell, select a cell and choose the **Insert Below** tool from the **Rows** panel in the **Table Cell** tab. To delete the selected row, choose the **Delete Row(s)** tool from the **Rows** panel in the **Table Cell** tab. You can also add more than one row by selecting more than one row in the table.

Modifying Columns

To add a column to the left of a cell, select the cell and choose the **Insert Left** tool from the **Columns** panel in the **Table Cell** tab. To add a column to the right of a cell, select a cell and choose the **Insert Right** tool from the **Columns** panel in the **Table Cell** tab. To delete the selected column, choose the **Delete Column(s)** tool from the **Columns** panel in the **Table Cell** tab. You can also add more than one column by selecting more than one row in the table.

Merge Cells

This button is used to merge cells. Choose this button; the **Merge Cells** drop-down is displayed. There are three options available in the drop-down. Select multiple cells using the **SHIFT** key and then choose **Merge All** from the drop-down to merge all the selected cells. To merge all the cells in the row of the selected cell, choose the **Merge By Row** button from the drop-down. Similarly, to merge all cells in the column of the selected cell, choose the **Merge By Column** tool from the drop-down. You can also divide the merged cells by choosing the **Unmerge Cells** button from the **Merge** panel.

Match Cells

This button is used to inherit the properties of one cell into the other. For example, if you have specified **Top Left Cell Alignment** in the source cell, then using the **Match Cells** button, you can inherit this property to the destination cell. This option is useful if you have assigned a number of properties to one cell, and you want to inherit these properties in some specified number of cells. Choose **Match Cell** from the **Cell Styles** panel in the **Table Cell** tab; the cursor is changed to the match properties cursor and you are prompted to choose the destination cell. Choose the cells to which you want the properties to be inherited and then press ENTER.

Table Cell Styles

This drop-down list displays the preexisting cell styles or options to modify the existing ones. Select the desired cell style to be assigned to the selected cell. The **Cell Styles** drop-down list also has the options to create a new cell style or manage the existing ones. These options have been discussed earlier in the **Creating a New Table Style** topic.

Cell Borders

Choose the **Edit Borders** button from the **Table Cell** tab; the **Cell Border Properties** dialog box will be displayed, as shown in Figure 7-45. The options in this dialog box are similar to those in the **Border** tab of the **New Table Style** dialog box.

Text Alignment

The down arrow on the right of the **Middle-Center** button of the **Cell Styles** panel in the **Ribbon** is used to align the text written in cells with respect to the cell boundary. Choose this button; the **Text Alignment** drop-down will be displayed. Select the desired text alignment from this drop-down; the text of the selected cell will get aligned accordingly.

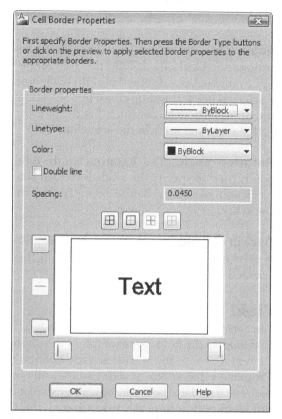

Figure 7-45 The Cell Border Properties dialog box

Cell Locking

This button is used to lock the cells so that they cannot be edited by accident. Select a cell and choose **Cell Locking** from the **Cell Format** panel in the **Table Cell** tab; the **Cell Locking** drop-down list will be displayed. Four options are available in the drop-down list. The **Unlocked** option is chosen by default. Choose the **Content Locked** option to prevent the modification in the content of the text, but you can modify the formatting of the text. Choose the **Format Locked** option to prevent the modification in the formatting of the text, but in this case, you can modify the content of the text. Select the **Content and Format Locked** option to prevent the modification of both formatting and content of the text.

Data Format

The display of the text in the cell depends on the format type selected. Choose **Cell Format** to change the format of the text in the cell. On doing so, the **Data Format** drop-down list is displayed. Choose the required format from it. You can also select the **Custom Table Cell** option and choose the required format from the **Data type** list box in the **Table Cell Format** dialog box and then choose the **OK** button.

Block

This tool is used to insert a block in the selected cell. Choose the **Block** tool from the **Insert** panel; the **Insert a Block in a Table Cell** dialog box will be displayed, as shown in Figure 7-46. Enter the name of the block in the **Name** edit box or choose the **Browse** button to locate the destination file of the block. If you have browsed the file path, it will be displayed in the **Path** area. The options available in the **Insert a Block in a Table Cell** dialog box are discussed next.

Properties Area

The options in this area are discussed next.

Scale. This edit box list is used to specify the scale of the block. By default, this edit box is not available because the **AutoFit** check box is selected below this drop-down list. Selecting the **AutoFit** check box ensures that the block is scaled such that it fits in the selected cell.

Rotation angle. The **Rotation angle** edit box is used to specify the angle by which the block will be rotated before being placed in the cell.

Overall cell alignment. This drop-down list is used to define the block alignment in the selected cell.

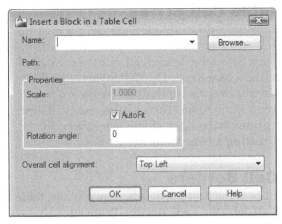

*Figure 7-46 The **Insert a Block in a Table Cell** dialog box*

Field

You can also insert a field in the cell. The field contains the data that is associative to the property that defines the field. For example, you can insert a field that has the name of the author of the current drawing. If you have already defined the author of the current drawing in the **Drawing Properties** dialog box, it will automatically be displayed in the field. If you modify the author name and update the field, the changes will automatically be made in the text. When you choose the **Field** button from the **Insert** panel, the **Field** dialog box will be displayed. You can select the field to be added from the **Field names** list box and select the format of the field from the **Format** list box. Choose **OK** after selecting the field and format. If the data in the selected field is already defined, it will be displayed in the **Text window**. If not, the field will display dashes (----).

Formula

Choose **Formula** from the **Insert** panel; a drop-down list is displayed. This drop-down list contains the formulas that can be applied to a given cell. The formula calculates the values for that cell using the values of other cell. In a table, the columns are named with letters (like A, B, C, ...) and rows are named with numbers (like 1, 2, 3, ...). The **TABLEINDICATOR** system variable controls the display of column letters and row numbers. By default, the **TABLEINDICATOR** system variable is set to 1, which means the row numbers and column letters will be displayed when **Text Editor** is invoked. Set the system variable to zero to turn off the visibility of row numbers and column letters. The nomenclature of cells is done using the column letters and row numbers. For example, the cell corresponding to column A and row 2 is A2. For a better understanding, some of the cells have been labeled accordingly in Figure 7-47.

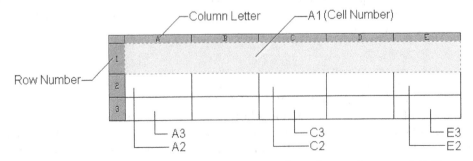

*Figure 7-47 The **Table** showing nomenclature for **Columns**, **Rows**, and **Cells***

Formulas are defined by the range of cells. The range of cells is specified by specifying the name of first and the last cell of the range, separated by a colon (:). The range takes all the cells falling between specified cells. For example, if you write A2 : C3, this means all the cells falling in 2nd and 3rd rows, Column A and B will be taken into account. To insert a formula, double click on the cell; **Text Editor** is invoked. You can now write the syntax of the formula in the cell. The syntax for different formulas are discussed later while explaining different formulas. Formulas can also be inserted by using the **Formula** drop-down list. Different formulas available in the **Formula** drop-down list are discussed next.

Sum

The **Sum** option gives output for a given cell as the sum of the numerical values entered in a specified range of cells. Choose the **Sum** option from the **Table Cell > Insert > Formula** drop-down; you will be prompted to select the first corner of the table cell range and then the second corner. The sum of values of all the cells that fall between the selected range will be displayed as the output. As soon as you specify the second corner, the **Text Editor** is displayed and also the formula is displayed in the cell. In addition to the formula, you can also write multiline text in the cell. Choose **Close Text Editor** from the **Close** panel to exit the editor. When you exit the text editor, the formula is replaced by a hash (#). Now, if you enter numerical values in the cells included in the range, the hash (#) is replaced according to the addition of those numerical values. The prompt sequence, when you select the **Sum** option, is given next.

Select first corner of table cell range: *Specify a point in the first cell of the cell range.*
Select second corner of table cell range: *Specify a point in the last cell of the cell range.*

Note
*The syntax for the **Sum** option is: =Sum{Number of the first cell of cell range (for example: A2): Number of the last cell of the cell range (for example: C5)}*

Average

This option is used to insert a formula that calculates the average of values of the cells falling in the cell range. Prompt sequence is the same as for the **Sum** option.

Note
*The syntax for the **Average** option is: =Average{Number of the first cell of the cell range (for example: A2): Number of the last cell of the cell range (for example: C5)}*

Count

This option is used to insert a formula that calculates the number of cells falling under the cell range. The prompt sequence is the same as for the **Sum** option.

Note
*The syntax for the **Count** option is: =Count{Number of the first cell of cell range (for example: A2): Number of the last cell of cell range (for example: C5)}*

Cell

This option equates the current cell with a selected cell. Whenever there is a change in the value of the selected cell, the change is automatically updated in the other cell. To do so, choose the **Cell** option from **Table Cell > Insert > Formula** drop-down; you will be prompted to select a table cell. Select the cell with which you want to equate the current cell. The prompt sequence for the **Cell** option is given next.

Select table cell: *Select a cell to equate with the current cell.*

Note
*The syntax for the **Cell** option is: =Number of the cell.*

Equation

Using this option, you can manually write equations. The syntax for writing the equations should be the same as explained earlier.

SUBSTITUTING FONTS

AutoCAD LT provides you the facility to designate the fonts that you want to substitute for the other fonts used in the drawing. The information about font mapping is specified in the font mapping file (*acadlt.fmp*). The font mapping has the following advantages:

1. You can specify a font to be used when AutoCAD LT cannot find a font used in the drawing.

2. You can enforce the use of a particular font in the drawings. If you load a drawing that uses different fonts, you can use font mapping to substitute the desired font for the fonts used in the drawing.

3. You can use *.shx* fonts while creating or editing a drawing. When you are done and ready to plot the drawing, you can substitute other fonts for *.shx* fonts.

The font mapping file is an ASCII file with *.fmp* extension containing one font mapping per line. The format on the line is given next.

Base name of the font file; Name of the substitute font with extension (ttf, shx, etc.)

For example, if you want to substitute the ROMANC font for *SWISS.TTF*, the entry is given next.

SWISS;ROMANC.SHX

You can enter this line in the *acadlt.fmp* file or create a new file. To create a new font mapping file, you need to specify this new file. You can use the **Options** dialog box to specify the new font mapping file. Choose the **Options** button available in the **Application Menu**; the **Options** dialog box will be displayed. Choose the **Files** tab and click on the **plus** sign next to **Text Editor**, **Dictionary**, and **Font File Names**. Now, click on the plus sign next to **Font Mapping File** to display the path and the name of the font mapping file. Double-click on the file; the **Select a file** dialog box will be displayed. Next, select the new font mapping file and exit the **Options** dialog box. At the Command prompt, enter **REGEN** to convert the existing text font to the font as specified in the new font mapping file. You can also use the **FONTMAP** system variable to specify the new font map file.

Command: **FONTMAP** `Enter`
Enter new value for FONTMAP, or . for none <"path and name of the current font mapping file">: *Enter the name of the new font mapping file.*

The following file is a partial listing of the *acadlt.fmp* file with the new font mapping line added (swiss;romanc.shx).

swiss;romanc.shx	cibt;CITYB___.TTF	cobt;COUNB___.TTF
eur;EURR____.TTF	euro;EURRO___.TTF	par;PANROMAN.TTF
rom;ROMANTIC.TTF	romb;ROMAB___.TTF	romi;ROMAI___.TTF
sas;SANSS___.TTF	sasb;SANSSB__.TTF	sasbo;SANSSBO_.TTF
saso;SANSSO__.TTF		

Note
The text styles that were created using the PostScript fonts are substituted with an equivalent TrueType font and plotted using the substituted font.

Specifying an Alternate Default Font

When you open a drawing file that specifies a font file that is not on your system or is not specified in the font mapping file, AutoCAD LT by default, substitutes the *simplex.shx* font file. You can specify a different font file in the **Options** dialog box or do so by changing the **FONTALT** system variable.

Command: **FONTALT** [Enter]
Enter new value for FONTALT, or . for none <"simplex.shx">: *Enter the font file name.*

CREATING TEXT STYLES

Ribbon: Annotate > Text > Text Style (*Inclined arrow*)
Menu Bar: Format > Text Style
Toolbar: Text > Text Style or Styles > Text Style
Command: STYLE

By default, the text in AutoCAD LT is written using the default text style which is called **Standard**. This text style is assigned a default text font (*txt.shx*). Another default text style that is available is **Annotative**. This text style is also assigned a default text font (*txt.shx*). If you need to write a text using some other fonts and other parameters, you need to use the **Text Editor**. This is because you can change the formatting and font of the text only by using this command.

However, it is a tedious job to use the **Text Editor** every time to write the text and change its properties. That is why, AutoCAD LT provides you with an option for modifying the default text style or creating a new text style. After creating a new text, you can make it current. All the texts written after making the new style current will use this style.

To create a new text style or modify the default style, left click on the inclined arrow in the **Text** panel of the **Annotate** tab; the **Text Style** dialog box will be displayed, as shown in Figure 7-48.

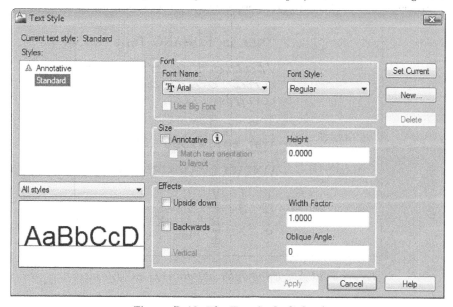

Figure 7-48 *The **Text Style** dialog box*

The **Styles** area displays the styles present in the drawing along with the current style highlighted in blue. An annotative symbol is displayed in front of the annotative text styles. The **Style List Filter** drop-down list below the **Styles** area is used to specify whether all styles will be displayed or only the styles that have been used in the drawing will be displayed. To create a new style, choose the **New** button from the **Text Style** dialog box; the **New Text Style** dialog box will be displayed, as shown in Figure 7-49. Choose the **OK** button from the **Style Name** edit box.

*Figure 7-49 The **New Text Style** dialog box*

A new style having the entered name and the properties present in the **Text Style** dialog box will be created. To modify this style, select the style name from the list box and then change the different settings by entering new values in the appropriate boxes. You can change the font by selecting a new font from the **Font Name** drop-down list. Similarly, you can change the text height, width, and oblique angle.

Remember that if you have already specified the height of the text in the **Text Style** dialog box, AutoCAD LT will not prompt you to enter the text height while writing the text using the **Single Line** tool. The text will be created using the height specified in the text style. If you want AutoCAD LT to prompt you for the text height, specify 0 text height in the dialog box. Select the **Annotative** check box to automate the process of scaling the text height. Annotative texts are defined according to the height of the text to be displayed on the paper. According to the annotation scale set for the spaces, the text will be displayed in the viewports and the model space. Select the **Match text orientation to layout** check box to match the orientation of the text in the paper space viewport with the orientation of the layout.

For **Width Factor**, 1 is the default value. If you want the letters expanded, enter a width factor greater than 1. For compressed letters, enter a width factor less than 1. Similarly, for the **Oblique Angle**, 0 is the default value. If you want the slant of the letters toward the right, the value should be greater than 0; to slant the letters toward the left, the value should be less than 0. You can also force the text to be written upside down, backwards, and vertically by checking their respective check boxes. As you make the changes, you can see their effect in the **Preview** box. After making the desired changes, choose the **Apply** button and then the **Close** button to exit the dialog box. Figure 7-50 shows the text objects with all these settings.

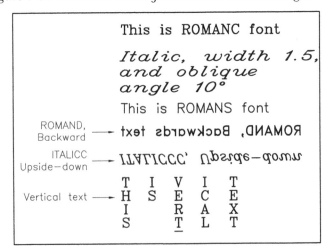

Figure 7-50 Specifying different features to text style files

DETERMINING TEXT HEIGHT

The actual text height is equal to the product of the **scale factor** and the **plotted text height**. Therefore, scale factors are important numbers for plotting the text at the correct height. This factor is a reciprocal of the drawing plot scale. For example, if you plot a drawing at a scale of ¼ = 1, you calculate the scale factor for text height given next.

¼" = 1" (i.e., the scale factor is 4)

The scale factor for an architectural drawing that is to be plotted at a scale of ¼" = 1'0" is calculated as given next

¼" = 1'0", or ¼" = 12", or 1 = 48
Therefore, in this case, the scale factor is 48.

For a civil engineering drawing with a scale 1"= 50', the scale factor is shown next.

1" = 50', or 1" = 50X12", or 1 = 600

Therefore, the scale factor is 600.

Next, calculate the height of the AutoCAD LT text. If it is a full-scale drawing (1=1) and the text is to be plotted at 1/8" (0.125), it should be drawn at that height. However, in a civil engineering drawing, a text drawn 1/8" high will look like a dot. This is because the scale for a civil engineering drawing is 1"= 50', which means that the drawing you are working on is 600 times larger. To draw a normal text height, multiply the text height by 600. Now, the height will be as calculated below.

0.125" x 600 = 75

Similarly, in an architectural drawing, which has a scale factor of 48, a text that is to be 1/8" high on paper must be drawn 6 units high, as shown in the following calculation:

0.125 x 48 = 6.0

It is very important to evaluate scale factors and text heights before you begin a drawing. It would be even better to include the text height in your prototype drawing by assigning the value to the **TEXTSIZE** system variable.

CREATING ANNOTATIVE TEXT

One of the recent inclusions in AutoCAD LT is now you do not need to calculate the text height in advance. While creating the annotative text, if you decide the text height to be displayed on the paper, the current annotation scale will automatically decide the display size of the text in the model space or the paper space viewport. For example, if you want the text to be displayed at a height of 1/4" on the paper, you can define a text style having a **Paper Text Height** of 1/4". When you add text to a viewport having a scale of 1/4"=1'0", the current annotation scale, which is set as the same scale as of the viewport, automatically scales the text to display appropriately at 12". You can create annotative text by assigning the annotative text style that has been explained earlier.

To write a single line annotative text, choose an annotative type text style from the **Text Style** dialog box and set it as the current text style. The annotative type text style will be displayed with an annotative symbol on its side. Next, enter the text in the drawing using the **Single Line** tool in the Command prompt. To write multiline annotative text, enter the **Multiline Text** tool at the Command prompt and specify the two opposite corners of the box denoting the width of the multiline text; the **Text Editor** will be displayed on the screen. You can also select an existing annotative text style from **Text Style** option in the **Text Editor** tab or choose the **Annotative** button in the **Style** panel of the **Text Editor** tab to create the annotative multiline text.

The existing non-annotative texts whether it is single line or multiline can also be converted into the annotative text. To do so, select the text object and right-click on it to choose the **Properties** option from the shortcut menu. In the **Properties** palette below the **Text** area, click on the **Annotative** edit box and select the **Yes** option from the drop-down list.

Self-Evaluation Test

Answer the following questions and then compare them to those given at the end of this chapter:

1. Tables in AutoCAD LT are created using the **TABLET** command. (T/F)

2. An annotative text automatically gets scaled according to the viewport's scale. (T/F)

3. You can insert a block into a table cell. (T/F)

4. The **Standard** text style cannot be used for creating annotative text. (T/F)

5. You can control the height of an individual column separately by choosing the **Manual height** sub-option from **Text Editor > Insert > Columns >Dynamic Columns** of the **Ribbon**. (T/F)

6. Multiple lines of text can be entered at any desired location in the drawing area by using the _____ tool.

7. With the _____ justification option of the **Single Line** tool, AutoCAD LT adjusts the letter width to fit the text between the two given points, but the height remains constant.

8. While writing a text by using the **Multiline Text** tool, the height specified in the **Text Editor** does not affect the _____ system variable.

9. You can change the text string in the edit box by using the _____ tool to edit a single line text. However, to edit a multiline text, you must choose the **Full editor** button in the **Content** edit box of the **Properties** palette.

10. You can use the _____ system variable to specify the new font mapping file.

Review Questions

Answer the following questions:

1. You cannot insert a field by using the **Multiline Text** tool. (T/F)

2. You can add or delete rows and columns from a table by using the **Table** toolbar. (T/F)

3. The **Single Line** tool does not allow you to see the text on the screen as you type it. (T/F)

4. Which of the following text styles is not present in AutoCAD LT by default?

    (a) **Standard**   (b) **Annotative**
    (c) **Auto text**   (d) None of these

5. Which of the following characters in the **Text Editor** tab is used to stack the text with a diagonal line without using the **Autostack Properties** dialog box?

    (a) ^   (b) /
    (c) #   (d) @

6. Which of the following commands can be used to create a new text style and modify the existing ones?

    (a) **TEXT**   (b) **MTEXT**
    (c) **STYLE**   (d) **SPELL**

7. The columns created by the _____ sub-option of the **Dynamic Columns** option of the **Columns** button in the **Insert** panel of the **Text Editor** tab are equal in size. (T/F)

8. The _____ sub-option in the **Formula** flyout of the **Insert** panel in the **Table** tab is used to equate the current cell with the selected cell.

9. When the **Justify** option is invoked, the user can place the text in one of the _____ various types of alignment by choosing the desired alignment option.

10. A text created by using the _____ tool is a single object irrespective of the number of lines it contains.

11. Using the **Multiline Text** tool, the character _____ stacks a text vertically without a line (tolerance stack).

12. If you want to edit text, select it and then right-click such that various editing options _____ in the menu are available.

EXERCISE 2   *Text*

Write the text, shown in Figure 7-51, on the screen. Use the text justification that will produce the text as shown in the drawing. Assume a value for text height. Use the **Properties** palette to change the text, as shown in Figure 7-52.

Figure 7-51 Drawing for Exercise 2

Figure 7-52 Drawing for Exercise 2 (After changing the text)

EXERCISE 3   *Text Style*

Write the text on the screen, as shown in Figure 7-53. First, you must define new text styles by using the **STYLE** command with the attributes, refer to Figure 7-53. The text height is 0.25 units.

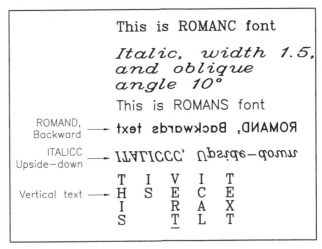

Figure 7-53 Drawing for Exercise 3

EXERCISE 4

Draw the sketch shown in Figure 7-54 using the draw, edit, and display commands. Do not dimension the drawing.

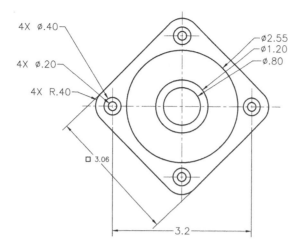

Figure 7-54 *Drawing for Exercise 4*

EXERCISE 5 *Mirror*

Draw the sketches shown in Figures 7-55 and 7-56. Use the **Mirror** tool to duplicate the features that are identical. Do not dimension the drawing.

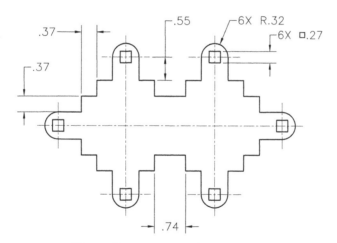

Figure 7-55 *Drawing for Exercise 5*

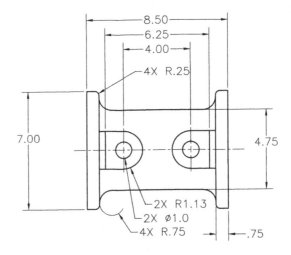

Figure 7-56 *Drawing for Exercise 5*

EXERCISE 6

Draw the sketch shown in Figure 7-57. Do not dimension the drawing.

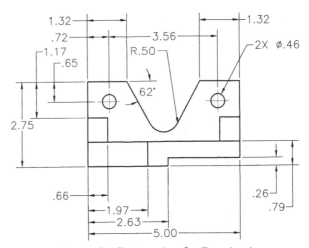

Figure 7-57 *Drawing for Exercise 6*

Problem-Solving Exercise 1

Draw Figure 7-59 using AutoCAD LT's draw, edit, and display commands. Also, add text to the drawing. Assume the missing dimensions. Do not dimension the drawing.

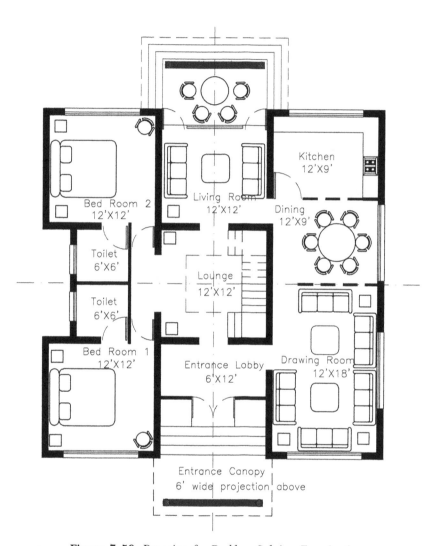

Figure 7-59 Drawing for Problem-Solving Exercise 1

Problem-Solving Exercise 2

Draw the sketch shown in Figure 7-58 using the draw, edit, and display commands. Assume the missing dimensions. Do not dimension the drawing.

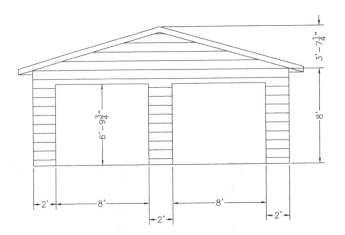

Figure 7-58 *Drawing for Problem-Solving Exercise 2*

Answers to Self-Evaluation Test

1. F, **2.** T, **3.** T, **4.** F, **5.** T, **6. Single Line**, **7. Fit**, **8. TEXTSIZE**, **9. Edit**, **10. FONTMAP**

Chapter 8

Basic Dimensioning,
Geometric Dimensioning,
and Tolerancing

CHAPTER OBJECTIVES

In this chapter, you will learn:
- *About the need for dimensioning in drawings.*
- *About the Fundamental dimensioning terms.*
- *About the associative and annotative dimensioning.*
- *To use the Quick Dimension option for quick dimensioning.*
- *To create various types of dimensions in a drawing.*
- *To create center marks and centerlines.*
- *To attach leaders to objects.*
- *To attach and modify multileaders.*
- *To use geometric tolerancing, feature control frames, and characteristic symbols.*
- *To combine geometric characteristics and create composite position tolerancing.*
- *To use the projected tolerance zone.*
- *To use feature control frames with leaders.*

KEY TERMS

- *Associative Dimensions*
- *Definition Points*
- *Annotative Dimensions*
- *Center Marks and Centerlines*
- *Inspection Dimensions*
- *Leaders*
- *Multileaders*
- *Geometric Tolerance*
- *Complex Feature Control Frames*
- *Projected Tolerance Zone*

NEED FOR DIMENSIONING

To make designs more informative and practical, a drawing must convey more than just the graphic picture of a product. To manufacture an object, the drawing of that object must contain size descriptions such as the length, width, height, angle, radius, diameter, and location of features. These informations are added to the drawing by dimensioning. Some drawings also require information about tolerances with the size of features. The information conveyed through dimensioning are vital and often as important as the drawing itself. With the advances in computer-aided design/drafting and computer-aided manufacturing, it has become mandatory to draw part to actual size so that dimensions reflect the actual size of features. At times, it may not be necessary to draw the object of the same size as the actual object would be, but it is absolutely essential that the dimensions be accurate. Incorrect dimensions will lead to manufacturing errors.

By dimensioning, you not only give the size of a part, but also give a series of instructions to a machinist, an engineer, or an architect. The way the part is positioned in a machine, the sequence of machining operations, and the location of various features of the part depend on how you dimension the part. For example, the number of decimal places in a dimension (2.000) determines the type of machine that will be used to do that machining operation. The machining cost of such an operation is significantly higher than for a dimension that has only one digit after the decimal (2.0). Similarly, whether a part is to be forged or cast, the radii of the edges, and the tolerance you provide to these dimensions determine the cost of the product, the number of defective parts, and the number of parts you get from a single die.

DIMENSIONING IN AutoCAD LT

The objects that can be dimensioned in AutoCAD LT range from straight lines to arcs. The dimensioning commands provided by AutoCAD LT can be classified into four categories:

Dimension Drawing Commands   **Dimension Style Commands**
Dimension Editing Commands   **Dimension Utility Commands**

While dimensioning an object, AutoCAD LT automatically calculates the length of the object or the distance between two specified points. Also, settings such as the gap between the dimension text and the dimension line, the space between two consecutive dimension lines, arrow size, and text size are maintained and used when the dimensions are being generated for a particular drawing. The generation of arrows, lines (dimension lines, extension lines), and other objects that form a dimension is automatically performed by AutoCAD LT to save the user's time. This also results in uniform drawings. However, you can override the default measurements computed by AutoCAD LT and change the settings of various standard values. The modification of dimensioning standards can be achieved through the dimension variables.

The dimensioning functions offered by AutoCAD LT provide you with extreme flexibility in dimensioning by letting you dimension various objects in a variety of ways. This is of great help because different industries, such as architectural, mechanical, civil, or electrical have different standards for the placement of dimensions.

FUNDAMENTAL DIMENSIONING TERMS

Before studying AutoCAD LT's dimensioning commands, it is important to know and understand various dimensioning terms that are common to linear, angular, radius, diameter, and ordinate dimensioning. Figures 8-1 and 8-2 show various dimensioning parameters.

Dimension Line

The dimension line indicates the distance or the angle being measured. Usually, this line has arrows at both ends, and the dimension text is placed along the dimension line. By default, the dimension line is drawn between the extension lines (Figure 8-1 and Figure 8-2). If the dimension line does not fit inside, two short lines with arrows pointing inward are drawn outside the extension lines. The dimension line for angular dimensions (which are used to dimension angles) is an arc. You can control the positioning and various other features of the dimension lines by setting the parameters in the dimension styles. (The dimension styles are discussed in Chapter 10.)

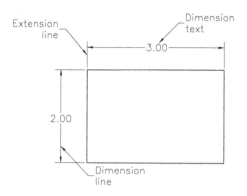

Figure 8-1 *Various dimensioning parameters*

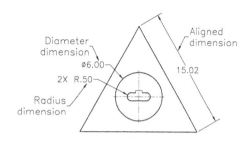

Figure 8-2 *Various dimensioning parameters*

Dimension Text

The dimension text is a text string that reflects the actual measurement (dimension value) between the selected points as calculated by AutoCAD LT. You can accept the value that AutoCAD LT returns or enter your own value. In case you use the default text, AutoCAD LT can be supplied with instructions to append the tolerances to it. Also, you can attach prefixes or suffixes of your choice to the dimension text.

Arrowheads

An arrowhead is a symbol used at the end of a dimension line (where dimension lines meet the extension lines). Arrowheads are also called terminators because they signify the end of the dimension line. Since drafting standards differ from company to company, AutoCAD LT allows you to draw arrows, tick marks, closed arrows, open arrows, dots, right angle arrows, or user-defined blocks (Figure 8-3). The user-defined blocks at the two ends of the dimension line can be customized to your requirements. The size of the arrows, tick marks, user blocks, and so on can be regulated by using the dimension variables.

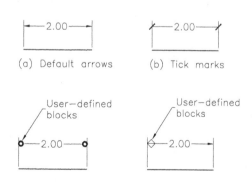

Figure 8-3 *Using arrows, tick marks, and user-defined blocks*

Extension Lines

Extension lines are drawn from the object measured to the dimension line (Figure 8-4). These lines are also called witness lines. Extension lines are used in linear and angular dimensioning. Generally, extension lines are drawn perpendicular to the dimension line. However, you can make extension lines inclined at an angle by choosing the **Oblique** tool from the **Dimensions** panel of the **Annotate** tab. Alternatively, you can choose the **Dimension Edit** tool from the **Dimension** toolbar. AutoCAD LT also allows you to suppress either one or both extension lines in a dimension (Figure 8-5). You can insert breaks in a dimension or an extension line, in case they intersect other geometric objects or dimension entities. You can also control various other features of the extension lines by setting parameters in dimension styles. (Dimension styles are discussed in Chapter 10.)

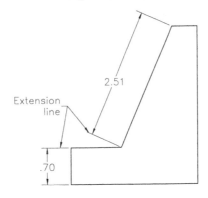

Figure 8-4 Extension lines

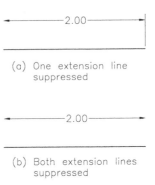

Figure 8-5 Extension line suppressed

Leader

A leader is a line that stretches from the dimension text to the object being dimensioned. Sometimes the text for dimensioning and other annotations do not adjust properly near the object. In such cases, you can use a leader and place the text at the end of the leader line. For example, the circle shown in Figure 8-6 has a keyway slot that is too small to be dimensioned. In this situation, a leader can be drawn from the text to the keyway feature. Also, a leader can be used to attach annotations such as part numbers, notes, and instructions to an object. You can also draw multileaders that are used to connect one note to different places or many notes to one place.

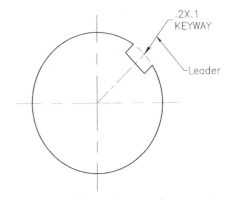

Figure 8-6 Leader used to attach annotation

Center Mark and Centerlines

The center mark is a cross mark that represents the center point of a circle or an arc. Centerlines are mutually perpendicular lines that pass through the center of a circle/arc and intersect the circumference of the circle/arc. A center mark or a centerline is automatically drawn when you dimension a circle or an arc (see Figure 8-7). The length of center mark and the extension of centerline beyond the circumference of circle are determined by the value assigned to the **DIMCEN** dimension variable. You can toggle between the center mark and the centerlines by entering a positive and a negative value respectively for the **DIMCEN** variable. Alternatively you can use the **Dimension Style Manager** dialog box to toggle between the center mark and the centerlines. This will be discussed in detail in Chapter 10.

Alternate Units

With the help of alternate units, you can generate dimensions for two systems of measurement at the same time (Figure 8-8). For example, if the dimensions are in inches, you can use the alternate units dimensioning facility to append metric dimensions to the dimensions (controlling the alternate units through the dimension variables is discussed in Chapter 10).

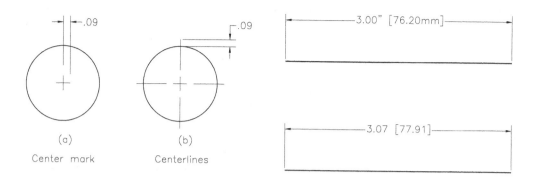

Figure 8-7 *Center mark and centerlines*   **Figure 8-8** *Using alternate units for dimensioning*

Tolerances

Tolerance is the amount by which the actual dimension can vary (Figure 8-9). AutoCAD LT can attach the plus/minus tolerances to the dimension text (actual measurement computed by AutoCAD LT). This is also known as deviation tolerance. The plus and minus tolerances that you specify can be same or different. You can use the dimension variables to control the tolerance feature (these variables are discussed in Chapter 10).

Limits

Instead of appending tolerances to dimension text, you can apply tolerances to the measurement itself (Figure 8-10). Once you define tolerances, AutoCAD LT automatically calculates the upper and lower limit values of the dimension. These values are then displayed as a dimension text.

For example, if the actual dimension as computed by AutoCAD LT is 2.6105 units and the tolerance values are +0.025 and -0.015, the upper and lower limits will be 2.6355 and 2.5955. After calculating the limits, AutoCAD LT will display them as a dimension text, as shown in Figure 8-10. The dimension variables that control the limits are discussed in Chapter 10.

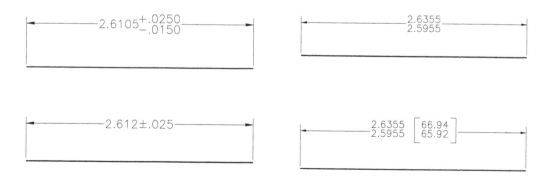

Figure 8-9 *Using tolerances with dimensions*   **Figure 8-10** *Using limits with dimensions*

ASSOCIATIVE DIMENSIONS

The associative dimensioning is a method of dimensioning, in which the dimension is associated with the object that is dimensioned. In other words, the dimension is influenced by the changes in the size of the object. In the earlier releases of AutoCAD LT, the dimensions were not truly associative, but were related to the objects being dimensioned by definition points on the

DEFPOINTS layer. To cause the dimension to be associatively modified, these definition points had to be adjusted along with the object being changed. If, for example, you use the **Scale** tool to change an object's size and select the object, the dimensions will not be modified. If you select the object and its defpoints (using the **Crossing** selection method), then the dimension will be modified. If the dimensions are associated to the object and the object changes its size, the dimensions will also change automatically. With the introduction of the true associative dimensions, there is no need to select the definition points along with the object. This eliminates the use of definition points for updating the dimensions.

The values and location of the associative dimensions are updated automatically if the value or location of the object is modified. For example, if you edit an object using simple editing operations such as breaking an object using the **Break** tool, then the true associative dimension will be modified automatically. The dimensions can be converted into the true associative dimensions using the **Reassociate** tool in the **Dimensions** panel of the **Annotate** tab to reassociate the dimension. The association of the dimensions with the objects can be removed using the **DIMDISASSOCIATE** command. Both these commands will be discussed later in this chapter.

The dimensioning variable **DIMASSOC** controls the associativity of dimensions. The default value of this variable is **2**, which means the dimensions are associative. When the value is **1**, the dimensions placed are non-associative. When the **DIMASSOC** is turned off (value of this variable is **0**), then the dimension will be placed in the exploded format. This means that the dimensions will now be placed as a combination of individual arrowheads, dimension lines, extension lines, and text. Also, note that the exploded dimensions cannot be associated to any object.

DEFINITION POINTS

Definition points are the points drawn at the positions used to generate a dimension object. The definition points are used by the dimensions to control their updating and rescaling. AutoCAD LT draws these points on a special layer called **DEFPOINTS**. These points are not plotted by the plotter because AutoCAD LT does not plot any object on the **DEFPOINTS** layer. If you explode a dimension (which is as good as turning **DIMASSOC** off), the definition points are converted to point objects on the **DEFPOINTS** layer. In Figure 8-11, the small circles indicate the definition points for different objects.

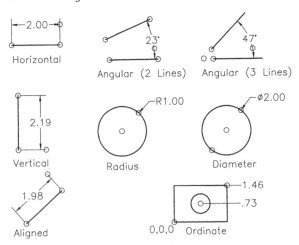

Figure 8-11 *Definition points of linear, radial, angular, and ordinate dimensions*

The definition points for linear dimensions are the points used to specify the extension lines and the point of intersection of the first extension line and the dimension line. The definition points for the angular dimension are the endpoints of the lines used to specify the dimension and the point used to specify the dimension line arc. For example, for a three-point angular dimension, the definition points are the extension line endpoints, angle vertex, and the point used to specify the dimension line arc.

The definition points for the radius dimension are the center points of the circle or arc, and the point where the arrow touches the object. The definition points for the diameter dimension are the points where the arrows touch the circle. The definition points for the ordinate dimension are the UCS origin, feature location, and leader endpoint.

Note
In addition to the definition points just mentioned, the middle point of the dimension text serves as the definition point for all types of dimensions.

ANNOTATIVE DIMENSIONS

When all the elements of a dimension such as text, spacing, and arrows get scaled according to the specified annotation scale, it is known as Annotative Dimension. They are created in the drawing by assigning annotative dimension styles to them. You can also change the non-annotative dimensions to annotative by changing their **Annotative** property to **Yes** in the **Properties** palette.

SELECTING DIMENSIONING COMMANDS

AutoCAD LT provides the following fundamental dimensioning types:

Quick dimensioning	**Linear dimensioning**	**Diameter dimensioning**
Radius dimensioning	**Angular dimensioning**	**Ordinate dimensioning**
Arc Length dimensioning	**Aligned dimensioning**	**Jogged dimensioning**

Figures 8-12 and 8-13 show various fundamental dimension types.

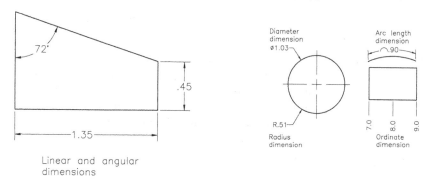

Figure 8-12 *Linear and angular dimensions*   **Figure 8-13** *Radius, diameter, and ordinate dimensions*

You can select the requisite command from the menu bar, toolbar, and **Ribbon** to apply dimensions. You can also use the command bar to work with the dimensioning. The procedure to select the dimensioning command is discussed next.

Using the Ribbon and the Toolbar

You can select the dimensioning tools from the **Dimensions** panel of the **Annotate** tab (Figure 8-14) or from the **Dimension** toolbar (Figure 8-15). The **Dimension** toolbar can be displayed by choosing **Tools > Toolbars > AutoCAD LT > Dimension** from the menu bar, if the menu bar is displayed.

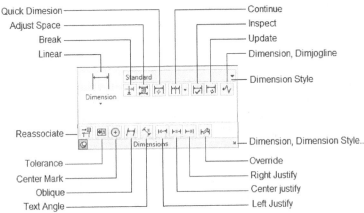

Figure 8-14 The **Dimensions** panel

Figure 8-15 The **Dimension** toolbar

Using the Command Line

You can directly enter a dimensioning command in the Command line or use the **DIM** or the **DIM1** commands to invoke the dimensioning commands.

> **Note**
> The **DIMDEC** variable sets the number of decimal places for the value of primary dimension and the **DIMADEC** variable for angular dimensions. For example, if **DIMDEC** is set to **3**, AutoCAD LT will display the decimal dimension up to three decimal places (2.037).

DIMENSIONING A NUMBER OF OBJECTS TOGETHER

Ribbon:	Annotate > Dimensions > Quick Dimension	Command: QDIM
Menu Bar:	Dimension > Quick Dimension	Toolbar: Dimension > Quick Dimension

 The **Quick Dimension** tool is used to dimension a number of objects at the same time. It also helps you to quickly edit dimension arrangements already existing in the drawing and also create new dimension arrangements. It is especially useful when creating a series of baseline or continuous dimensions. It also allows you to dimension multiple arcs and circles at the same time. When you are using the **Quick Dimension** tool, you can relocate the datum base point for baseline and ordinate dimensions. The prompt sequence that will follow when you choose this tool is given next.

Select geometry to dimension: *Select the objects to be dimensioned and press ENTER.*
Select geometry to dimension: Enter
Specify dimension line position, or [Continuous/Staggered/Baseline/Ordinate/Radius/Diameter/datumPoint/Edit/seTtings] <Continuous>: *Press ENTER to accept the default dimension arrangement and specify dimension line location or enter new dimension arrangement or edit the existing dimension arrangement.*

For example, you can dimension all circles in a drawing (Figure 8-16) by using the quick dimensioning as follows:

Associative dimension priority = Endpoint.
Select geometry to dimension: *Select all circles.*

Select geometry to dimension: [Enter]
Specify dimension line position, or
[Continuous/Staggered/Baseline/Ordinate/Radius/Diameter/datumPoint/Edit/
seTtings] <Continuous>: *Press D for diameter dimensioning and select a point where you want
to position the radial dimension.*

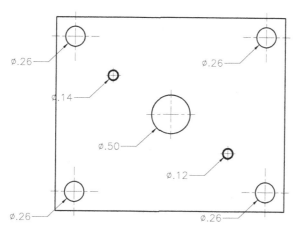

Figure 8-16 *Using the* **QDIM** *command to dimension multiple circles*

CREATING LINEAR DIMENSIONS

Ribbon: Annotate > Dimensions > Dimension drop-down > Linear
Menu Bar: Dimension > Linear   **Toolbar:** Dimension > Linear
Command: DIMLIN or DIMLINEAR

Linear dimensioning is used to measure the shortest distance between two points. You can directly select the object to dimension or select two points. The points can be any two points in the space, endpoints of an arc or line, or any set of points that can be identified. To achieve accuracy, points must be selected with the help of object snaps or by selecting an object to dimension. In case, the object selected is aligned, then the linear dimensions will add the **Horizontal** or **Vertical** dimension to the object. The prompt sequence that will follow when you choose the **Linear** tool is given next.

Specify first extension line origin or <select object>: [Enter]
Select object to dimension: *Select the object.*
Specify dimension line location or
[Mtext/Text/Angle/Horizontal/Vertical/Rotated]: *Select a point to locate the position of the dimension.*

Instead of selecting the object, you can also select the two endpoints of the line that you want to dimension (Figure 8-17). Usually the points on the object are selected by using the **object snaps** (endpoints, intersection, center, etc.). The prompt sequence is as follows.

Specify first extension line origin or <select object>: *Select a point.*
Specify second extension line origin: *Select second point.*

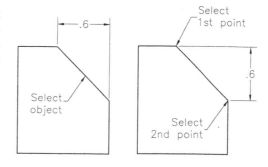

Figure 8-17 *Drawing linear dimensions*

Specify dimension line location or
[Mtext/Text/Angle/Horizontal/Vertical/Rotated]: *Select a point to locate the position of the dimension.*

Using the **Linear** tool, you can obtain the horizontal or vertical dimension by simply defining the appropriate dimension location point. If you select a point above or below the dimension, AutoCAD LT creates a horizontal dimension. If you select a point that is on the left or right of the dimension, AutoCAD LT creates a vertical dimension through that point.

DIMLINEAR Command Options
The options under this command are discussed next.

Mtext Option
The **Mtext** option is used to override the default dimension text and also change the font, height, and so on, by using the **Text Editor**. When you enter **M** at the **Specify dimension line location or [Mtext/Text/Angle/Horizontal/Vertical/Rotated]** prompt, the **Text Editor** is displayed. You can change the text by entering a new text. You can also use various options of the **Text Editor** (explained in Chapter 7). Choose the **OK** button. However, if you override the default dimensions, the dimensional associativity of the dimension text is lost. This means that if you modify the object using the definition points, AutoCAD LT will not recalculate the dimension text. Even if the dimension is a true associative dimension, the text will not be recalculated when the object is modified. The prompt sequence to invoke this option is given next.

Specify first extension line origin or <select object>: *Specify a point.*
Specify second extension line origin: *Specify the second point.*
Specify dimension line location or
[Mtext/Text/Angle/Horizontal/Vertical/Rotated]: **M** *(Enter the dimension text in the **Text Editor** and then click outside the text editor to accept the changes.)*
Specify dimension line location or
[Mtext/Text/Angle/Horizontal/Vertical/Rotated]: *Specify the dimension location.*

Text Option
This option also allows you to override the default dimension. However, this option will prompt you to specify the new text value in the Command prompt itself, see Figure 8-18. The prompt sequence to invoke this option is given next.

Specify first extension line origin or <select object>: *Select a point.*
Specify second extension line origin: *Select second point.*
Specify dimension line location or
[Mtext/Text/Angle/Horizontal/Vertical/Rotated]: **T**
Enter dimension text <Current>: *Enter new text.*
Specify dimension line location or
[Mtext/Text/Angle/Horizontal/Vertical/Rotated]: *Specify the dimension location.*

Angle Option
This option lets you change the angle of the dimension text, see Figure 8-18.

Rotated Option
This option lets you create a dimension that is rotated at a specified angle, see Figure 8-18.

Horizontal Option
This option lets you create a horizontal dimension regardless of where you specify the dimension location, see Figure 8-19.

Vertical Option

This option lets you create a vertical dimension regardless of where you specify the dimension location, see Figure 8-19.

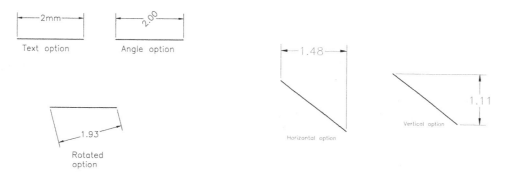

Figure 8-18 *The **Text**, **Angle**, and **Rotated** options*

Figure 8-19 *The **Horizontal** and **Vertical** options*

Note
If you override the default dimensions, the dimensional associativity of the dimension text is lost and AutoCAD LT will not recalculate the dimension when the object is scaled.

EXAMPLE 1   *Horizontal Dimension*

In this example, you will use linear dimensioning to dimension a horizontal line of 4 units length. The dimensioning will be done first by selecting the object and later on by specifying the first and second extension line origins. Using the **Text Editor**, modify the default text such that the dimension is underlined.

Selecting the Object

1. Start a new file in the **Drafting & Annotation** workspace and draw a line of 4 units length.

2. Choose the **Linear** tool from **Annotate > Dimensions > Dimension** drop-down; you will be prompted to specify the extension line origin or the object. The prompt sequence to apply the linear dimension is as follows:

    Specify first extension line origin or <select object>: [Enter]
    Select object to dimension: *Select the line.*
    Specify dimension line location or
    [Mtext/Text/Angle/Horizontal/Vertical/Rotated]: **M** [Enter]
    *The **Text Editor** will be displayed, as shown in Figure 8-20. Select the default dimension value and then choose the **Underline** button from the **Formatting** panel of the **Text Editor** tab of the **Ribbon** to underline the text. Click anywhere in the drawing area to exit the **Text Editor** tab.*
    Specify dimension line location or
    [Mtext/Text/Angle/Horizontal/Vertical/Rotated]: *Place the dimension.*
    Dimension text = 4.0000

Figure 8-20 *The **Text Editor** tab*

Specifying Extension Line Origins

1. Choose the **Linear** tool from **Annotate > Dimensions > Dimension** drop-down. The prompt sequence is as follows:

Specify first extension line origin or <select object>: *Select the first endpoint of the line using the **Endpoint** object snap, see Figure 8-21.*

Specify second extension line origin: *Select the second endpoint of the line using the **Endpoint** object snap, see Figure 8-21.*
Specify dimension line location or
[Mtext/Text/Angle/Horizontal/Vertical/Rotated]: **M**
*Select the text and then choose the **Underline** button from the **Ribbon** to underline the text in the **Text Editor**.*
Specify dimension line location or
[Mtext/Text/Angle/Horizontal/Vertical/Rotated]: *Place the dimension.*
Dimension text = 4.00

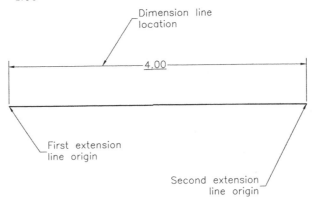

Figure 8-21 *Line for Example 1*

CREATING ALIGNED DIMENSIONS

Ribbon: Annotate > Dimensions > Dimension drop-down > Aligned	
Menu Bar: Dimension > Aligned	**Toolbar:** Dimension > Aligned
Command: DIMALIGNED	

Generally, the drawing consists of various objects that are neither parallel to the *X* axis nor to the *Y* axis. Dimensioning of such objects can be done using aligned dimensioning. In horizontal or vertical dimensioning, you can only measure the shortest distance from the first extension line origin to the second extension line origin along the horizontal or vertical axis, respectively, whereas with the help of aligned dimensioning, you can measure the true aligned distance between the two points. The function of the **Aligned** tool is similar to that of the other linear dimensioning commands. The dimension created with the **Aligned** tool is parallel to the object being dimensioned. The prompt sequence that will follow when you choose this tool is given next.

Specify first extension line origin or <select object>: *Specify the first point or press ENTER.*
Specify second extension line origin: *Specify second point.*
Specify dimension line location or [Mtext/Text/Angle]: *Specify the location for the dimension line.*
Dimension text = Current

The options in this tool are similar to those of the **Linear** tool. Figure 8-22 illustrates the aligned dimensioning.

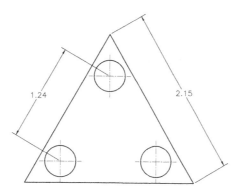

Figure 8-22 *The aligned dimensioning*

EXERCISE 1   *Aligned Dimension*

Draw the object shown in Figure 8-23 and then use linear and aligned dimensioning to dimension the part. The distance between the dotted lines is 0.5 units. The dimensions should be up to 2 decimal places. To get dimensions up to 2 decimal places, enter DIMDEC at the Command prompt and then enter 2. (There will be more information about dimension variable in Chapter 10.)

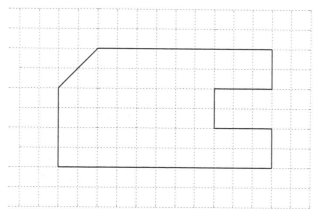

Figure 8-23 *Drawing for Exercise 1*

CREATING ARC LENGTH DIMENSIONS

Ribbon: Annotate > Dimensions > Dimension drop-down > Arc Length
Menu Bar: Dimension > Arc Length   **Toolbar:** Dimension > Arc Length
Command: DIMARC

The Arc Length dimensioning is used to dimension the length of an arc or the polyline arc segment. You are required to select an arc or a polyline arc segment and the dimension location. Figure 8-24 shows the Arc Length dimensioning of an arc. You can invoke this command by choosing the **Arc Length** tool in the **Dimensions** panel. The prompt sequence that will follow is given next.

Select arc or polyline arc segment: *Select arc or polyline arc segment to dimension.*
Specify arc length dimension location, or [Mtext/Text/Angle/Partial/Leader]: *Specify the location for the dimension line.*
Dimension text = *Current.*

Using the **Partial** option, you can dimension a selected portion of the arc, as shown in Figure 8-25. The prompt sequence for the **Partial** option is given next.

Select arc or polyline arc segment: *Select arc or polyline arc segment to dimension.*
Specify arc length dimension location, or [Mtext/Text/Angle/Partial]: **P** Enter
Specify first point for arc length dimension: *Specify the first point on arc.*
Specify second point for arc length dimension: *Specify the second point on arc.*
Specify arc length dimension location, or [Mtext/Text/Angle/Partial]: *Specify the location for the dimension line.*
Dimension text = *Current*

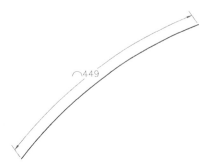 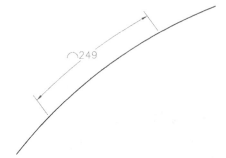

Figure 8-24 *Arc Length dimensioning*   **Figure 8-25** *Partial Arc Length dimensioning*

Using the **Leader** option, you can attach a leader to the dimension text, starting from its circumference. This leader is drawn radial to the arc, as shown in Figure 8-26.

 Note
*The **Leader** option is displayed only when the arc subtends an included angle greater than 90 degrees at its centre.*

CREATING ROTATED DIMENSIONS

Rotated dimensioning is used when you want to place the dimension line at an angle (if you do not want to align the dimension line with the selected extension line origins), as shown in Figure 8-27. You can invoke this option by entering **ROTATED** at the command line after choosing the **Linear** tool from the **Dimensions** panel. The **ROTATED** dimension option will prompt you to specify the dimension line angle. The prompt sequence is given next.

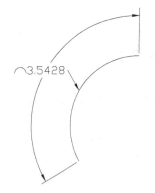 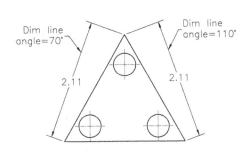

Figure 8-26 *Leader Arc Length dimensioning*   **Figure 8-27** *Rotated dimensioning*

Specify first extension line origin or <select object>: *Select the origin of the first extension line.*
Specify second extension line origin: *Select the origin of the second extension line.*
Non-associative dimension created.
Specify dimension line location or
[Mtext/Text/Angle/Horizontal/Vertical/Rotated]: **R**

Specify angle of dimension line <0>: **110**
Specify dimension line location or [Mtext/Text/Angle/Horizontal/Vertical/Rotated]: *Select the location for the dimension line.*
Dimension text = current

Note
You can draw horizontal and vertical dimensioning by specifying the rotation angle of 0° for horizontal dimensioning and 90° for vertical dimensioning.

CREATING BASELINE DIMENSIONS

Ribbon: Annotate > Dimensions > Continue drop-down > Baseline
Menu Bar: Dimension > Baseline   **Toolbar:** Dimension > Baseline
Command: DIMBASE or DIMBASELINE

Sometimes in manufacturing, you may want to locate different points and features of a part with reference to a fixed point (base point or reference point). This can be accomplished by using the Baseline dimensioning (Figure 8-28). To invoke the baseline dimension, choose the **Baseline** tool from the **Dimensions** panel. Using this tool, you can continue a linear dimension from the first extension line origin of the first dimension to the dimension point. The new dimension line is automatically offset by a fixed amount to avoid overlapping of the dimension lines. This has to be kept in mind that there must already exist a linear, ordinate, or angular associative dimension to use the Baseline dimensions. When you choose the **Baseline** tool, the last linear, ordinate, or angular dimension created will be selected and used as the baseline. The prompt sequence that will follow when you choose this tool is given next.

Specify a second extension line origin or [Undo/Select] <Select>: *Select the origin of the second extension line.*
Dimension text = current
Specify a second extension line origin or [Undo/Select] <Select>: *Select the origin of the second extension line.*
Dimension text = current
Specify a second extension line origin or [Undo/Select] <Select>: *Select the origin of the second extension line or press ENTER.*
Select base dimension: [Enter]

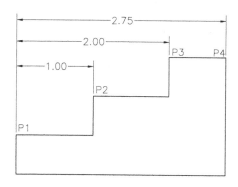

Figure 8-28 Baseline dimensioning

When you use the **Baseline** tool, you cannot change the default dimension text. However, the **DIM** command allows you to override the default dimension text.

Command: **DIM**
Dim: **HOR**
Specify first extension line origin or <select object>: *Select left corner (P1, Figure 8-28). (Use Endpoint object snap.)*
Specify second extension line origin: *Select the origin of the second extension line (P2).*
Specify dimension line location or [MText/Text/Angle]: **T**
Enter dimension text <1.0000>: **1.0**
Specify dimension line location or [MText/Text/Angle]: *Select the dimension line location.*
Dim: **BASELINE (or BAS)**

Specify a second extension line origin or [Select] <Select>: *Select the origin of the next extension line (P3).*
Enter dimension text <2.0000>: **2.0**
Dim: **BAS**
Specify a second extension line origin or [Select] <Select>: *Select the origin of the next extension line (P4).*
Enter dimension text <3.000>: **2.75**

The next dimension line is automatically spaced and drawn by AutoCAD LT.

CREATING CONTINUED DIMENSIONS

Ribbon: Annotate > Dimensions > Continue drop-down > Continue	
Menu Bar: Dimension > Continue	**Toolbar:** Dimension > Continue
Command: DIMCONT or DIMCONTINUE	

Using the **Continue** tool, you can continue a linear dimension from the second extension line of the previous dimension. This is also called as Chained or Incremental dimensioning. Note that there must exist linear, ordinate, or angular associative dimension to use the Continue dimensions. The prompt sequence that will follow when you choose this tool is given next.

Specify a second extension line origin or [Undo/Select] <Select>: *Specify the point on the origin of the second extension line.*
Dimension text = current
Specify a second extension line origin or [Undo/Select] <Select>: *Specify the point on the origin of the second extension line.*
Dimension text = current
Specify a second extension line origin or [Undo/Select] <Select>: Enter
Select continued dimension: Enter

Also, in this case, the **DIM** command should be used if you want to change the default dimension text.

Command: **DIM**
Dim: **HOR**
Specify first extension line origin or <select object>: *Select left corner (P1, see Figure 8-29).* *(Use Endpoint object snap.)*
Specify second extension line origin: *Select the origin of the second extension line (P2, see Figure 8-29).*

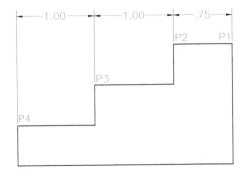

***Figure 8-29** Continue dimensioning*

Specify dimension line location or [MText/Text/Angle]: **T**
Enter dimension text <current>: **0.75**
Specify dimension line location or [MText/Text/Angle]: *Select the dimension line location.*
Dim: **CONTINUE**
Specify a second extension line origin or [Select] <Select>: *Select the origin of the next extension line (P3, see Figure 8-29).*
Enter dimension text <current>: [Enter]
Dim: **CONTINUE**
Specify a second extension line origin or [Select] <Select>: *Select the origin of next extension line (P4, see Figure 8-29).*
Enter dimension text <current>: [Enter]

The default base (first extension line) for the dimensions created with the **CONTINUE** command is the previous dimension's second extension line. You can override the default extension by pressing ENTER at the **Specify a second extension line origin or [Select] <Select>** prompt, and then specifying the other dimension. The extension line origin nearest to the selection point is used as the origin for the first extension line.

Tip
*You can use the **Select** option of the **DIMBASELINE** or the **DIMCONTINUE** command to select any other existing dimension to be used as the baseline or continuous dimension.*

EXERCISE 2   Baseline Dimension

Draw the object shown in Figure 8-30 and then use baseline dimensioning to dimension the top half and continue dimensioning to dimension the bottom half. The distance between the dotted lines is 0.5 unit.

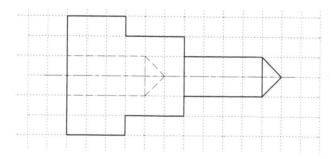

Figure 8-30 Drawing for Exercise 2

CREATING ANGULAR DIMENSIONS

Ribbon: Annotate > Dimensions > Dimension drop-down > Angular
Menu Bar: Dimension > Angular   **Toolbar:** Dimension > Angular
Command: DIMANG or DIMANGULAR

The Angular dimensioning is used for applying angular dimension to an entity. The **Angular** tool is used to generate a dimension arc (dimension line in the shape of an arc with arrowheads at both ends) to indicate the angle between two nonparallel lines. This tool can also be used to dimension the vertex and two other points, a circle with another point, or the angle of an arc. For every set of points, there exists one acute angle and one obtuse angle (inner and outer angles). If you specify the dimension arc location between the two points, you will get the acute angle; if you specify it outside the two points, you will get the obtuse angle. Figure 8-31 shows the four ways to dimension two nonparallel lines. The prompt sequence that will follow when you choose this tool is given next.

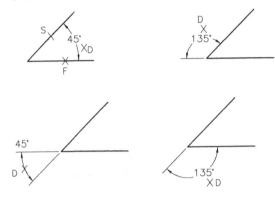

F=First object
S=Second object
D=Dimension location

Figure 8-31 *Angular dimensioning between two nonparallel lines*

Select arc, circle, line, or <specify vertex>: *Select the object or press ENTER to select a vertex point where two segments meet.*
Select second line: *Select the second object.*
Specify dimension arc line location or [Mtext/Text/Angle/Quadrant]: *Place the dimension or select an option.*
Dimension text = current

If you want to override the default angular value, use the **Mtext** or **Text** option. Use the %%d control sequence after the number at the text prompt. For example, for 45°, type 45%%d and then press ENTER.

The methods of dimensioning various entities using this command are discussed next.

Dimensioning the Angle between Two Nonparallel Lines

The angle between two nonparallel lines or two straight line segments of a polyline can be dimensioned using the **DIMANGULAR** dimensioning command. The vertex of the angle is taken as the point of intersection of the two lines.

The following example illustrates the dimensioning of two nonparallel lines by using the **DIMANGULAR** command. Alternatively, you can apply the angular dimension by choosing the **Angular** tool from the **Dimension** drop-down in the **Dimensions** panel.

Select arc, circle, line, or <specify vertex>: *Select the first line.*
Select second line: *Select the second line.*
Specify dimension arc line location or [Mtext/Text/Angle/Quadrant]: **M** (*Enter the new value in the* **Text Editor**. *Specify dimension arc line location or [Mtext/Text/Angle/Quadrant]: Specify the dimension arc location or select an option.*

The location of the extension lines and the dimension arc is determined by the placement of the dimension arc. In AutoCAD LT, you can place the dimension text outside the quadrant in which you measure the angle by extending the dimension arc. Choose the **Quadrant** option from the shortcut menu or from the **Specify dimension arc line location or [Mtext/Text/Angle/Quadrant]** prompt. Next, you will be prompted to specify the quadrant in which you want to measure the angle. Then, specify the quadrant using mouse. If the dimension arc line is lying outside the quadrant that is being measured, the dimension arc will be extended up to that location with the help of extension line. Figure 8-32(a) shows a dimension created without using the Quadrant option and Figure 8-32(b) shows the same dimension created by using the Quadrant option.

Dimensioning the Angle of an Arc

Angular dimensioning can also be used to dimension the angle of an arc. In this case, the center point of the arc is taken as the vertex and the two endpoints of the arc are used as the extension line origin points for the extension lines (Figure 8-33). The following example illustrates the dimensioning of an arc by using the **Angular** tool:

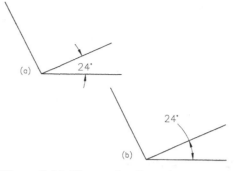

Select arc, circle, line, or <specify vertex>: *Select the arc.*

Specify dimension arc line location or [Mtext/Text/Angle/Quadrant]: *Specify a location for the arc line or select an option.*

*Figure 8-32 The angular dimension created with and without choosing the **Quadrant** option*

Angular Dimensioning of Circles

The angular feature associated with the circle can be dimensioned by selecting a circular object at the **Select arc, circle, line, or <specify vertex>** prompt. The center of the selected circle is used as the vertex of the angle. The first point selected (when the circle is selected for angular dimensioning) is used as the origin of the first extension line. In the similar manner, the second point selected is taken as the origin of the second extension line (Figure 8-34). The following is the prompt sequence for dimensioning a circle:

Select arc, circle, line, or <specify vertex>: *Select the circle at the point where you want the first extension line.*

Specify second angle endpoint: *Select the second point on or away from the circle.*

Specify dimension arc line location or [Mtext/Text/Angle/Quadrant]: *Select the location for the dimension line.*

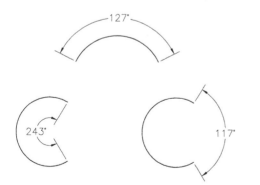

Figure 8-33 Angular dimensioning of arcs

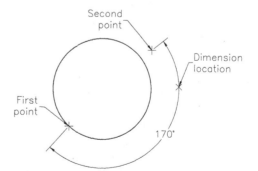

Figure 8-34 Angular dimensioning of a circle

Angular Dimensioning based on Three Points

If you press ENTER at the **Select arc, circle, line, or <specify vertex>** prompt, AutoCAD LT allows you to select three points to create an angular dimension. The first point is the vertex point, and the other two points are the first and second angle endpoints of the angle (Figure 8-35). The coordinate specifications of the first and the second angle endpoints must not be identical. However, the angle vertex coordinates and one of the angle endpoint coordinates can be identical.

The following example illustrates angular dimensioning by defining three points:

Select arc, circle, line, or <specify vertex>: [Enter]
Specify angle vertex: *Specify the first point, vertex. This is the point where two segments meet. If the two segments do not meet, use the **Apparent Intersection** object snap.*
Specify first angle endpoint: *Specify the second point. This point will be the origin of the first extension line.*
Specify second angle endpoint: *Specify the third point. This point will be the origin of the second extension line.*
Specify dimension arc line location or [Mtext/Text/Angle/Quadrant]: *Select the location for the dimension line.*
Dimension text = current

EXERCISE 3   *Angular Dimension*

Draw the profile as shown in Figure 8-36 and then use angular dimensioning to dimension all angles of the part. The distance between the dotted lines is 0.5 unit.

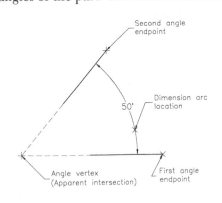

Figure 8-35 *Angular dimensioning using 3 points*

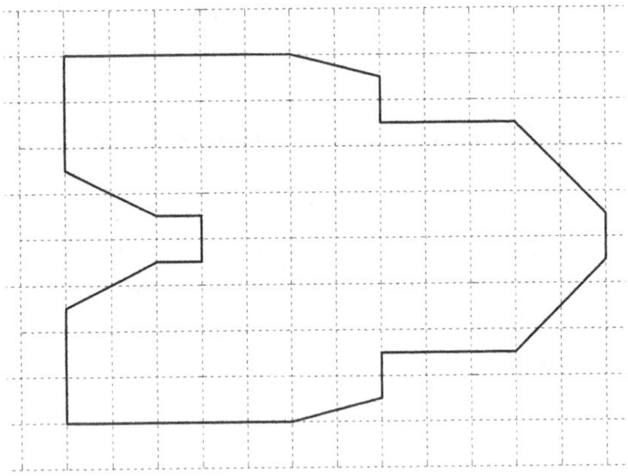

Figure 8-36 *Drawing for Exercise 3*

CREATING DIAMETER DIMENSIONS

Ribbon: Annotate > Dimensions > Dimension drop-down > Diameter
Menu Bar: Dimension > Diameter   **Toolbar:** Dimension > Diameter
Command: DIMDIA

Diameter dimensioning is used to dimension a circle or an arc. Here, the measurement is done between two diametrically opposite points on the circumference of the circle or the arc (Figure 8-37). The dimension text generated by AutoCAD LT begins with the ø symbol to indicate a diameter dimension. The prompt sequence that will follow when you choose the **Diameter** tool in the **Dimensions** panel is given next.

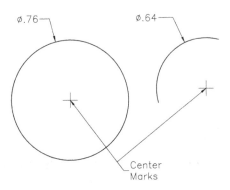

Figure 8-37 *Diameter dimensioning*

Select arc or circle: *Select an arc or circle by selecting a point anywhere on its circumference.*
Dimension text = Current
Specify dimension line location or [Mtext/Text/Angle]: *Specify a point to position the dimension.*

If you want to override the default value of the dimension text, use the **Mtext** or the **Text** option. The control sequence %%C is used to obtain the diameter symbol ø. It is followed by the dimension text that should appear in the diameter dimension. For example, if you want to write a text that displays a value ø20, then enter %%c20 at the text prompt.

CREATING RADIUS DIMENSIONS

Ribbon: Annotate > Dimensions > Dimension drop-down > Radius
Menu Bar: Dimension > Radius   **Toolbar:** Dimension > Radius
Command: DIMRAD

The Radius dimensioning is used to dimension a circle or an arc (Figure 8-38). Radius and diameter dimensioning are similar; the only difference is that instead of the diameter line, a radius line is drawn (half of the diameter line), which is measured from the center to any point on the circumference. The dimension text generated by AutoCAD LT is preceded by the letter **R** to indicate a radius dimension. If you want to use the default dimension text (dimension text generated automatically by AutoCAD LT), simply specify a point to position the dimension at the **Specify dimension line location or [Mtext/Text/Angle]** prompt. You can also enter a new value or specify a prefix or suffix, or suppress the entire text by entering a blank space following the **Enter dimension text <current>** prompt. A center mark for the circle/arc is drawn automatically, provided the center mark value controlled by the **DIMCEN** variable is not 0. The prompt sequence that will follow when you choose this button is given next.

Select arc or circle: *Select the object that you want to dimension.*
Dimension text = Current
Specify dimension line location or [Mtext/Text/Angle]: *Specify the dimension location.*

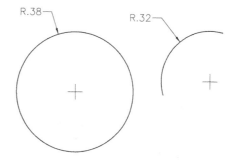

If you want to override the default value of the dimension text, use the **Text** or the **Mtext** option. You can also enter the required value at the text prompt.

Figure 8-38 Radius dimensioning

Note
*In case of diametric, radial, and jogged radial dimensions, you can extend the dimension line beyond the endpoints of the arc by creating the arc extension line beyond the endpoints. These arc extension lines are similar to the other extension lines. The system variables **DIMSE1** and **DIMSE2** allow the display of the first and the second extension lines, respectively. These variables should be **ON** in order to suppress the respective extension line.*

CREATING JOGGED LINEAR DIMENSIONS

Ribbon: Annotate > Dimensions > Dimension, Dimjogline   **Toolbar:** Dimension > Jogged Linear
Menu Bar: Dimension > Jogged Linear   **Command:** DIMJOGLINE

The **Dimension, Dimjogline** tool is used to add or remove a jog in the existing dimensions. This kind of dimensioning technique is generally used to dimension the components that have a high length to width ratio, see Figure 8-39. To add a jog to a linear dimension, choose the **Dimjogline** tool from the **Dimensions** panel and select the dimension to which you want to add a jog. Next, pick a point along the dimension line to specify the location of the jog placement. Alternatively, you can press the ENTER key to place the jog automatically. To remove a jog, invoke the **DIMJOGLINE** command and choose **Remove** from the shortcut menu. Next, specify the dimension line from which you want to remove the jog. You can modify the location of the jog symbol with the help of grips. Note that you can add a jog only to the linear or aligned dimensions with this command.

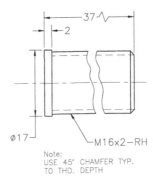

***Figure 8-39** Jogged linear dimensioning*

Note
*The height of jog symbol can be changed by varying the **Jog height factor** in the **Lines** & **Arrows** rollout of the **Properties** palette.*

GENERATING CENTER MARKS AND CENTERLINES

Ribbon: Annotate > Dimensions > Center Mark	**Toolbar:** Dimension > Center Mark
Menu bar: Dimension > Center Mark	**Command:** DIMCENTER

When circles or arcs are dimensioned with the **DIMRADIUS** or **DIMDIAMETER** command, a small mark known as center mark, or a line known as centerline, may be drawn at the center of the circle/arc. Sometimes, you need to mark the center of a circle or an arc without using these dimensioning commands. This can be achieved with the help of the **Center Mark** tool. You can invoke this tool by choosing the **Center Mark** tool from the **Dimensions** panel or by entering **CENTER** (or **CEN**) at the **Dim:** prompt. When you invoke this tool, you are prompted to select the arc or the circle. The result of this command will depend upon the value of the **DIMCEN** variable. If the value of this variable is positive, center marks are drawn, see Figure 8-40 and if the value is negative, centerlines are drawn, see Figure 8-41.

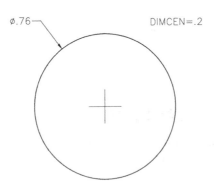

***Figure 8-40** Using a positive value for the **DIMCEN** variable*

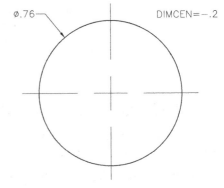

***Figure 8-41** Using a negative value for the **DIMCEN** variable*

Note
*The center marks created by **DIMCENTER** or **DIM CENTER** are lines, but not associative dimensioning objects, and they have an explicit linetype.*

CREATING ORDINATE DIMENSIONS

Ribbon: Annotate > Dimensions > Dimension drop-down > Ordinate
Menu Bar: Dimension > Ordinate   **Toolbar:** Dimension > Ordinate
Command: DIMORD

Ordinate dimensioning is used to dimension the X and Y coordinates of the selected point. This type of dimensioning is also known as arrowless dimensioning because no arrowheads are drawn in it. Ordinate dimensioning is also called datum dimensioning because all dimensions are related to a common base point. The current UCS (user coordinate system) origin becomes the reference or the base point for ordinate dimensioning. With ordinate dimensioning, you can determine the X or Y displacement of a selected point from the current UCS origin.

Dimension text (X or Y coordinate value) and the leader line along the X or Y axis are automatically placed using Ordinate dimensioning (Figure 8-42). Since ordinate dimensioning pertains to either the X coordinate or the Y coordinate, you should keep ORTHO on. When ORTHO is off, the leader line is automatically given a bend when you select the second leader line point that is offset from the first point. This allows you to generate offsets and avoid overlapping text on closely spaced dimensions. In ordinate dimensioning, only one extension line (leader line) is drawn.

The leader line for an X coordinate value will be drawn perpendicular to the X axis, and the leader line for a Y coordinate value will be drawn perpendicular to the Y axis. Since you cannot override this, the leader line drawn perpendicular to the X axis will have the dimension text aligned with the leader line. The dimension text is the X datum of the selected point. The leader line drawn perpendicular to the Y axis will have the dimension text, which is the Y datum of the selected point, aligned with the leader line. Any other alignment specification for the dimension text is nullified. Hence, changes in the Text Alignment in the **Dimension Style Manager** dialog box (**DIMTIH** and **DIMTOH** variables) have no effect on the alignment of the dimension text. You can specify the coordinate value that you want to dimension at the **Specify leader endpoint or [Xdatum/Ydatum/MText/Text/Angle]** prompt.

If you select or enter a point, AutoCAD LT checks the difference between the feature location and the leader endpoint. If the difference between the X coordinates is greater, the dimension measures the Y coordinate; otherwise, the X coordinate is measured. In this manner, AutoCAD LT determines whether it is an X or Y type of ordinate dimension. However, if you enter Y instead of specifying a point, AutoCAD LT will dimension the Y coordinate of the selected feature. Similarly, if you enter X, AutoCAD LT will dimension the X coordinate of the selected point. The prompt sequence that follows when you choose this tool is given next.

Specify feature location: *Select a point on an object.*
Specify leader endpoint or [Xdatum/Ydatum/Mtext/Text/Angle]: *Enter the endpoint of the leader.*

You can override the default text with the help of the **Mtext** or **Text** option. If you use the **Mtext** option, the **Text Editor** will be displayed. If you use the **Text** option, you will be prompted to specify the new text in the Command line itself.

EXERCISE 4   *Ordinate Dimension*

Draw the model shown in Figure 8-43 and then use ordinate dimensioning to dimension the part. The distance between the dotted lines is 0.5 unit.

(A)= X coordinate value
(B)= Y coordinate value

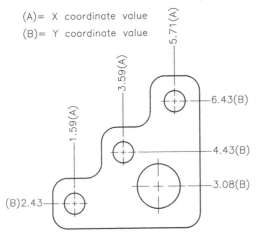

Figure 8-42 Ordinate dimensioning

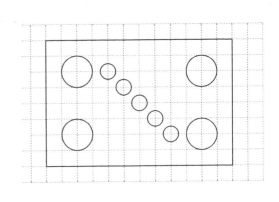

Figure 8-43 Drawing for Exercise 4

MAINTAINING EQUAL SPACING BETWEEN DIMENSIONS

Ribbon: Annotate > Dimensions > Adjust Space	**Toolbar:** Dimension > Dimension Space
Menu Bar: Dimension > Dimension Space	**Command:** DIMSPACE

This command is used to equally space the overlapping or the unequally spaced linear and angular dimensions. Maintaining equal spacing between the dimension lines increases the clarity of the drawing display. Figure 8-44 shows a drawing with unequally spaced dimensions, and Figure 8-45 shows the same drawing with equally spaced dimensions after the use of the **Adjust Space** tool. Figure 8-46 shows a drawing with its angular dimensions equally spaced.

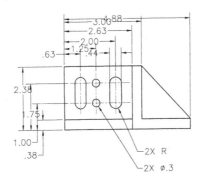

Figure 8-44 Drawing with its linear dimensions unequally spaced

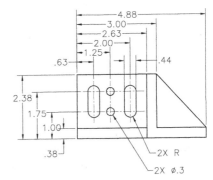

Figure 8-45 Drawing with its linear dimensions equally spaced

The prompt sequence that will follow when you choose the **Adjust Space** tool is given next.

Command: **_DIMSPACE**
Select base dimension: *Select a linear or an angular dimension with respect to which all other dimensions will get spaced.*
Select dimensions to space: *Select the dimensions that you want to be equally spaced from the specified base dimension.*

Select dimensions to space: *Select more similar dimensions or press* ⏎
Enter value or [Auto] <Auto>: *Enter a value to specify the spacing between the selected dimensions or enter **A** to calculate automatically the gap between the dimensions.*

Enter **0** in the above prompt to align all the selected dimensions in a single line. With the **Auto** option selected, AutoCAD LT will calculate the space value on the basis of the dimension text height. The spacing is automatically maintained to a value that is double of the dimension text height.

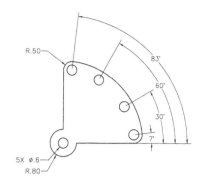

Figure 8-46 *Drawing with its angular dimensions equally spaced*

CREATING INSPECTION DIMENSIONS

Ribbon: Annotate > Dimensions > Inspect	**Toolbar:** Dimensions > Inspect
Menu Bar: Dimension > Inspection	**Command:** DIMINSPECT

A drawing sheet provides every minute information about the dimension of the product, including the inspection rate. The **Inspect** tool in AutoCAD LT is used to describe Inspection Rate of critical dimension of the product to ensure its quality. The inspection rate is used to specify how frequently the dimensions are to be checked to ensure the variations in the dimensions are within the range. Select a dimension from the drawing and choose the **Inspect** tool from the **Dimensions** panel; the **Inspection Dimension** dialog box will be displayed, as shown in Figure 8-47. Choose the **OK** button; the selected dimension will change into the inspection dimension that consists of three fields (see Figure 8-48), which are discussed next.

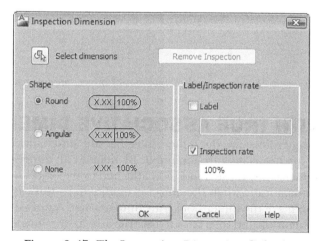

Figure 8-47 *The **Inspection Dimension** dialog box*

Inspection Label
The inspection label is located at the extreme left of the inspection dimension and is used to specify the particular inspection dimension, see Figure 8-48.

Dimension Value
The dimension value is located in the middle of the inspection dimension and is used to display the value of the dimension to be maintained, see Figure 8-48.

Inspection Rate

The inspection rate is located at the right-end of the inspection dimension. It is used to specify the frequency of carrying out inspections, see Figure 8-48. The frequency of inspection is specified in terms of percentage value. The value 100% signifies that you need to check the dimension each time you inspect a component. Similarly, if the value is 50 % then you need to check the dimension for every second component.

If you have not selected the dimension before invoking the **Inspect** tool, choose the **Select dimensions** button from the **Inspection Dimension** dialog box (Refer to Figure 8-48); the dialog box will temporarily disappear from the screen, thereby enabling you to select the dimension that you want to convert into the inspection dimension. Select the dimensions and press the ENTER key; the **Inspection Dimension** dialog box will be displayed again. All the selected dimensions will display the same value of the label and inspection dimension. Next, specify the shape of the boundary around the inspection dimension from the **Shape** area. Figure 8-48 displays the shapes available in the **Inspection Dimension** dialog box. Next, enter the values for the label and inspection rate in their respective edit boxes in the **Label/Inspection rate** area and choose the **OK** button. You can also control the display of label and inspection rate in the inspection dimension by clearing or selecting the **Label** and **Inspection rate** check boxes respectively. To remove the inspection dimension of the selected dimension, choose the **Remove Inspection** button from the **Inspection Dimension** dialog box and then choose the **OK** button.

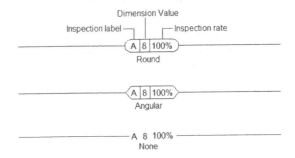

Figure 8-48 Shapes and components of inspection dimension

WORKING WITH TRUE ASSOCIATIVE DIMENSIONS

The true associative dimensions are the dimensions that are automatically modified when the objects to which they are associated are modified. By default, all dimensions in AutoCAD LT are true associative dimensions. If the dimension attached to the object is true associative, then it will be modified automatically when the object is modified. In this case, you do not have to select the definition points of the dimensions. Any dimension in AutoCAD LT can be converted into a disassociated dimension and then back to the true associative dimension. This is discussed next.

Removing the Dimension Associativity

Command: DIMDISASSOCIATE

The **DIMDISASSOCIATE** command is used to remove the associativity of the dimensions from the object to which they are associated. When you invoke this command, you will be prompted to select the dimensions to be disassociated. The true association of the selected dimensions is automatically removed once you exit this command. The number of dimensions disassociated is displayed at the Command prompt.

Converting a Dimension into a True Associative Dimension

Ribbon: Annotate > Dimensions > Reassociate	**Command:** DIMREASSOCIATE
Menu bar: Dimension > Reassociate Dimension	

 The **Reassociate** tool is used to create a true associative dimension by associating the selected dimension to the specified object. When you invoke this command, you will be prompted to select the objects. These objects are the dimensions to be associated. Select the dimensions to be associated and press ENTER; a cross is displayed and you are prompted to select the feature location. This cross implies that the dimension is not associated. You can define a new association point for the dimensions by selecting the objects or by using the object snaps. If you select a dimension that has already been associated to an object, the cross will be displayed inside a box. The prompt sequence that is displayed varies depending upon the type of dimension selected. In case of linear, aligned, radius, and diameter dimensions, you can directly select the object to associate the dimension. If the arcs or circles are assigned angular dimensions using three points, then also you can select these arcs or circles directly for associating the dimensions. For rest of the dimension types, you can use the object snaps to specify the point to associate the dimensions.

Note

*If you have edited a dimension by using the **Mtext** or **Text** option, then on using the **DIMREASSOCIATE** command, the overridden value will be replaced by the original value.*

EXERCISE 5

Draw and dimension the object, as shown in Figure 8-49.

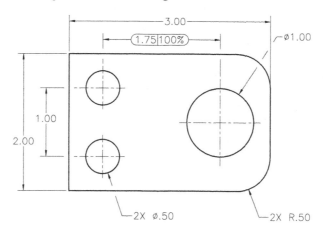

Figure 8-49 *Drawing for Exercise 5*

DRAWING LEADERS

Command: QLEADER

The leader line is used to attach annotations to an object or when the user wants to show a dimension without using another dimensioning command. Sometimes, leaders of the dimensions of circles or arcs are so complicated that you need to construct a leader of your own. The leaders can be created using the **QLEADER** command. The leaders drawn by using this command create the arrow and the leader lines as a single object. The text is created as a separate object. This command can create multiline annotations and offer several options such as copying existing annotations and so on. You can customize the leader and annotation by selecting the **Settings** option at the **Specify first leader point, or [Settings] <Settings>** prompt. The prompt sequence that will follow when you use this command is given next.

> Specify first leader point, or [Settings] <Settings>: *Specify the start point of the leader.*
> Specify next point: *Specify the endpoint of the leader.*
> Specify next point: *Specify the next point.*
> Specify text width <current>: *Enter the text width of multiline text.*
> Enter first line of annotation text <Mtext>: *Press ENTER; AutoCAD LT displays the* **Text Editor**. *Enter text in the dialog box and then choose* **Close Text Editor** *to exit from the* **Ribbon**.

If you press ENTER at the **Specify first leader point, or [Settings] <Settings>** prompt, then the **Leader Settings** dialog box is displayed. The **Leader Settings** dialog box gives you a number of options for the leader line and the text attached to it. It has the following tabs:

Annotation Tab

This tab provides you with various options to control annotation features, see Figure 8-50.

Annotation Type Area

The options in **Annotation Type** area and their usage are discussed next.

MText. When this radio button is selected, AutoCAD LT uses the **Text Editor** to create an annotation. Therefore, on selecting this radio button, the options in the **MText options** area become available.

Copy an Object. This option allows you to copy an existing annotation object (like multiline text, single line text, tolerance, or block) and attach it at the end of the leader. For example, if you have a text string in the drawing that you want to place at the end of the leader, you can use the **Copy an Object** option to place it at the end of the leader.

Tolerance. Select the **Tolerance** radio button and choose the **OK** button to exit from the **Leader Settings** dialog box. Then, specify the next point to complete the leader line; AutoCAD LT will display the **Geometric Tolerance** dialog box. In this dialog box, specify the tolerance and choose **OK** to exit it. AutoCAD LT will place the specified geometric tolerance with the feature control frame at the end of the leader (Figure 8-51).

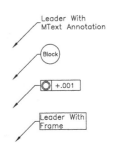

*Figure 8-50 The **Annotation** tab of the **Leader Settings** dialog box*

Figure 8-51 Leaders with different annotation types

Block Reference. The **Block Reference** radio button allows you to insert a predefined block at the end of the leader. When you select this option, AutoCAD LT will prompt you to enter the block name and insertion point.

None. This option creates a leader without placing any annotation at the end of the leader.

MText options Area
The options under this area will be available only if the **MText** radio button is selected from the **Annotation Type** area. This area provides you with the following options.

Prompt for width. Selecting this check box allows you to specify the width of the multiline text annotation.

Always left justify. Select this check box to left justify the multiline text annotation in all situations. Selecting this check box makes the Prompt for the width option unavailable.

Frame text. Selecting this check box draws a box around the multiline text annotation.

Annotation Reuse Area
The options under this area allow you to reuse the annotation.

None. When selected, AutoCAD LT does not reuse the leader annotation.

Reuse Next. This radio button is used to reuse the annotation that you are going to create next for all subsequent leaders.

Reuse Current. This option allows you to reuse the current annotation for all subsequent leaders.

Leader Line & Arrow Tab
The options in the **Leader Line & Arrow** tab are related to the leader parameters, see Figure 8-52.

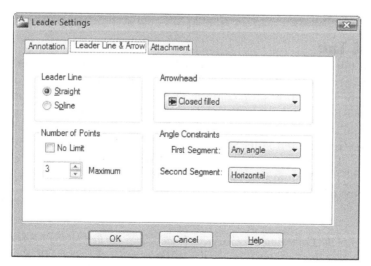

*Figure 8-52 The **Leader Line** & **Arrow** tab of the **Leader Settings** dialog box*

Leader Line Area
This area has the options for the leader line type such as straight or spline. The **Spline** option draws a spline through the specified leader points and the **Straight** option draws straight lines. Figure 8-53 shows the straight and spline leader lines.

Number of Points Area

The options provided under this area are used to specify the number of points in the leader.

No Limit. If this check box is selected, you can define as many number of points as you want in the leader line. AutoCAD LT will keep prompting you for the next point, until you press ENTER at this prompt.

Maximum. This spinner is used to specify the maximum number of points on the leader line. The default value in this spinner is 3; as a result, there will be only three points in the leader line. You can specify the number of points by using this spinner to control the shape of the leader. This has to be kept in mind that the start point of the leader is the first leader point. This spinner will be available only if the **No Limit** check box is clear. Figure 8-53 shows a leader line with five points.

Arrowhead Area

The drop-down list under this area allows you to define a leader arrowhead. The arrowhead is the same as the one for dimensioning. You can also use the user-defined arrows by selecting **User Arrow** from the drop-down list.

Angle Constraints Area

The options provided under this area are used to define the angle for the segments of the leader lines.

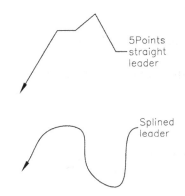

First Segment. This drop-down list is used to specify the angle at which the first leader line segment will be drawn. You can select the predefined values from this drop-down list.

Figure 8-53   Straight and splined leaders

Second Segment. This drop-down list is used to specify the angle at which the second leader line segment will be drawn.

Attachment Tab

The **Attachment** tab (Figure 8-54) will be available only if you have selected **MText** from the **Annotation Type** area of the **Annotation** tab. The options in this tab are used to attach the multiline text to the leader. It has two columns: **Text on left side** and **Text on right side**. Both these columns have five radio buttons below them. Each radio button corresponds to the option of attaching the multiline text. If you draw a leader from the right to the left, AutoCAD LT uses the settings under **Text on left side**. Similarly, if you draw a leader from the left to the right, AutoCAD LT uses the settings as specified under **Text on right side**. This area also provides you with the **Underline bottom line** check box. If this check box is selected, then the last line of the multiline text will be underlined.

Note
*You can use the Command Line to create leaders with the help of the **LEADER** command. The options under this command are similar to those under the **QLEADER** command. The only difference is that the **LEADER** command uses the Command Line.*

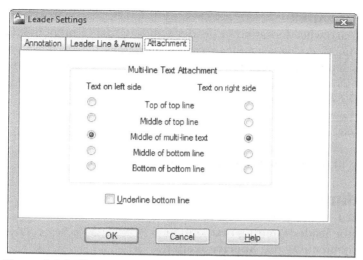

*Figure 8-54 The **Attachment** tab of the **Leader Settings** dialog box*

EXERCISE 6   *Qleader*

Make the drawing shown in Figure 8-55 and then use the **QLEADER** command to dimension the part accordingly. The distance between the dotted lines is 0.5 units.

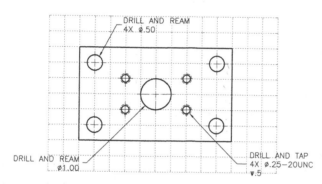

Figure 8-55 Drawing for Exercise 6

MULTILEADERS

Ribbon: Annotate > Leaders > Multileader	**Toolbar:** Multileader > Multileader
Command: MLEADER	

Multileaders are the enhanced leaders, wherein the leader and its content is part of the same object. A Multileader provides you enough flexibility so that you can create either the arrowhead or the tail end first. Alternatively, you can specify the content of the leader first and then draw the leader. Multileaders can have more than one leader so that a single comment can be pointed at more than one location. Besides this, multiple notes can be attached to a single leader so that more than one comment can be pointed at a single location. You can add or remove leaders from the previously created multileaders. You can also control and modify the appearance of the multileaders.

DRAWING MULTILEADERS

To draw a multileader, choose the **Multileader** tool from the **Leaders** panel. The prompt sequence that follows is given next.

Command: _**MLEADER**
Specify leader arrowhead location or [leader Landing first/Content first/Options]
<Options>: *Specify the location for the arrowhead from where the leader will start.*
Specify leader landing location: *Specify the leader landing location, see Figure 8-56.*

AutoCAD LT displays the **Text Editor**. *Enter the text in the dialog box and click outside the editor to accept and exit the command. If you click outside the editor without entering any text and exit the command, no text will be attached to the multileader.*

The other options in the **MLEADER** command are discussed next.

leader Landing first

This option is used to locate the leader landing line first. Choose the **leader Landing first** option from the shortcut menu at the **Specify leader arrowhead location or [leader Landing first/ Content first/Options] <Options>** prompt to invoke this option. Alternatively, if the **Dynamic Input** button is turned on in the Status Bar, then you can choose this option from the dynamic input box associated with the cursor. On doing so, you will be prompted to specify a point where the leader landing should be placed. Specify the leader landing location; you will be prompted to specify the leader arrowhead location. The leader landing will automatically adjust itself to the leader

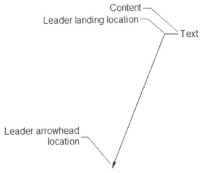

Figure 8-56 *Image displaying the options to locate the leader start point*

landing point, depending upon the direction in which you create the leader. For example, if you create the leader to the left of the leader landing location, the landing will automatically be created to the right of the leader landing location.

Content first

This option is used to specify the content (multiline text or block) of the leader first. Choose the **Content first** option from the shortcut menu or from the **Specify leader arrowhead location or [leader Landing first/Content first/Options] <Options>** prompt to invoke this option. Alternatively, if the **Dynamic Input** button is turned on in the Status Bar, you can choose this option from the dynamic input box associated with the cursor. After specifying the content to be attached with the leader, a horizontal leader landing will automatically be attached to the content and then you can specify the leader arrowhead location.

Note
If you have previously drawn a multileader by using any one of the above-mentioned options, then the succeeding multileaders will be created by using that option only, until otherwise modified.

Options

The suboptions within this option are used to control the leader type, content to be attached with the leader, size of the leader landing, and so on. These suboptions are discussed next.

Leader type

This option provides the suboptions for the leader line type such as straight, spline, or none. The **sPline** suboption draws a spline through the specified leader points and the **Straight** option draws the straight lines. Figure 8-53 shows the straight and spline leader lines. The **None** option enables you to draw the content of the leader without drawing the leader itself.

leader lAnding

This option provides you the suboptions to control the display of the horizontal landing line. The **No** suboption will create a leader with no horizontal landing and the **Yes** suboption will create a leader with the horizontal landing. If you choose the **Yes** suboption, then you will be prompted to specify the length of the horizontal landing. The new leader will be created with the specified landing length. Figure 8-57 shows the leaders created by using various suboptions of the **leader lAnding**.

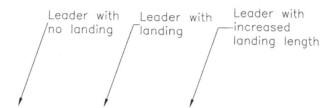

Figure 8-57 Leaders drawn by using various types of landing suboptions

Content type

This option is used to specify the type of content to be attached with the leader. The **Mtext** suboption uses the AutoCAD LT **Text Editor** to create the content. The **Block** suboption allows you to insert a predefined block at the end of the leader. When you select this option, AutoCAD LT will prompt you to enter the block name and the specified block will be attached to the new leader. The **None** suboption creates a leader without placing any content at the end of the leader.

Maxpoints

This option is used to specify the maximum number of points on the leader line. The default value is 2, which means there will be only two points on the leader line. You can specify the maximum number of points by entering the new value. This has to be kept in mind that the start point of the leader is the first leader point.

First angle

This option is used to specify the angle that the first leader line will measure from the horizontal at the start point. You can also specify a value which is the natural number multiple of 15°.

Second angle

This option is used to specify the angle that the second leader line will measure from the horizontal at the second point. You can only specify a value which is the natural number multiple of 15°.

eXit options

This option will return you back to the main options of the multileader.

Note

*All settings specified in the **Options** heading of the multileader will last only for that particular leader, and the next leader will be created with the default settings. You can also change the default settings of the multileader from the **Multileader Style Manager** dialog box that will be discussed in detail in Chapter 10.*

ADDING LEADERS TO EXISTING MULTILEADER

Ribbon: Annotate > Leaders > Add Leaders **Toolbar:** Multileaders > Add Leaders
Command: MLEADEREDIT

The **Add Leaders** tool is used to add leaders to an existing multileader, so that you can point a single content to more than one location. To do so, choose the **Add Leaders** tool in the **Leaders** panel; you will be prompted to select the multileader to which you want to attach the new leader. After selecting the desired multileader, a new leader will branch out from the landing location of the existing multileader. Next, you will be prompted to specify the location of the arrowhead of the new leader. Next, you can attach any number of leaders to the selected multileader. To finish this command, press the ENTER key.

REMOVING LEADERS FROM EXISTING MULTILEADER

Ribbon: Annotate > Leaders > Remove Leader **Toolbar:** Multileaders > Remove Leader
Command: MLEADEREDIT

The **Remove Leader** tool is used to remove leaders from an existing multileader. To remove a leader, choose the **Remove Leader** tool from the **Leaders** panel; you will be prompted to select the multileader from which you want to remove leaders. Select the multileader; you will be prompted to select the leaders to be removed from the selected multileader. Select the leaders and then press the ENTER key. You can also select all the leaders of the specified multileader. But, in such cases, all multileaders will get deleted from the drawing area.

ALIGNING MULTILEADERS

Ribbon: Annotate > Leaders > Align **Toolbar:** Multileaders > Align Multileaders
Command: MLEADERALIGN

The **Align** tool is used to arrange the selected multileaders by aligning them about a line or making them parallel or by maintaining the spacing between the horizontal landing of the leaders. To do so, choose the **Align** tool from the **Leaders** panel; you will be prompted to select the multileaders to be aligned. After selecting the multileaders, press the ENTER key. Next, you will be prompted to select one of the multileaders with respect to which all other multileaders will get aligned. Also, you can choose the alignment type from the different options available at the Command prompt. The prompt sequence for the **Align** tool is given next.

Command: **MLEADERALIGN**
Select multileaders: *Select the multileaders to be aligned and* [Enter].
Current mode: *Use current spacing.*

All further prompt sequences will vary with the alignment type used in aligning the leaders. The alignment type used previously will become the default alignment type for the current command.

Select multileader to align to or [Options]: *Enter* ***O*** *to choose the type of alignment.*
Enter an option [Distribute/make leader segments Parallel/specify Spacing/Use current spacing] <Use current spacing>: *Specify an option and* [Enter].

The options in the above prompt sequence are discussed next.

Distribute

This option is used to accommodate all the selected multileaders at constant spacing between the two specified points. The prompt sequence that will be followed is given next.

Enter an option [Distribute/make leader segments Parallel/specify Spacing/Use current spacing] <Distribute>: **D** Enter.
Specify first point or [Options]: *Specify the location of the first point.*
Specify second point: *Specify the location of the second point and its orientation with respect to the first point.*

The tail end of all the selected leaders landing will get aligned with equal spacing along the line joining the first and the second specified point. Figure 8-58 shows a drawing with its multileaders nonaligned. Figure 8-59 displays the same drawing with its multileaders aligned along an imaginary vertical line by using the **Distribute** option.

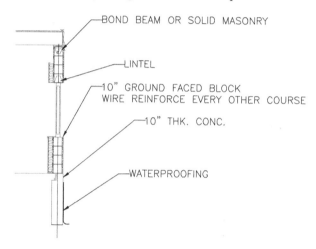

Figure 8-58 Drawing with multileaders not aligned

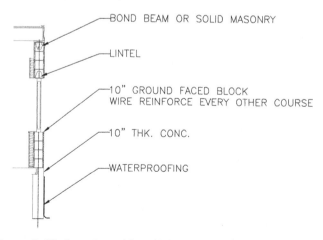

Figure 8-59 Drawing with multileaders aligned using the **Distribute** *option*

make leader segments Parallel

This option is used to make all the selected multileaders parallel to one of the leaders selected as reference. The prompt sequence to be followed is given next.

Enter an option [Distribute/make leader segments Parallel/specify Spacing/Use current spacing] <current>: **P** Enter.
Select multileader to align to or [Options]: *Select the leader with which you want to make all other selected multileaders parallel.*

Figure 8-60 shows the drawing with its leader aligned parallel to the lowest leader of the drawing.

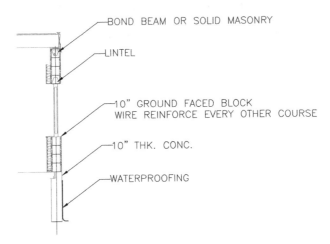

Figure 8-60 Drawing with multileaders aligned using the **make leader segments Parallel** *option*

specify Spacing

This option is used to align the selected multileaders in the specified direction, and also maintains a constant spacing between the landing lines. You need to specify one reference leader, with respect to which the specified interval and direction will be measured. The prompt sequence that will be followed is given next.

Enter an option [Distribute/make leader segments Parallel/specify Spacing/Use current spacing] <current>: **S** Enter.
Specify spacing <current>: *Enter the distance value to be maintained between the two consecutive leader landing lines.*
Select multileader to align to or [Options]: *Select one of the leaders with respect to which the specified distance will be measured.*
Specify direction: *Specify the desired direction in the drawing area for the alignment of multileaders.*

When you select a multileader to align with other multileaders, an imaginary line will be displayed in the drawing area. This line allows you to specify the direction of alignment. All the multileaders will get aligned to the selected multileader at the specified distance and direction. Figure 8-61 shows the drawing with its multileaders aligned vertical using the **specify Spacing** option.

Use current spacing

This option is used to align the selected multileaders in the specified direction and also to retain the distance between the landing lines intact. You need to specify one reference leader, with respect to which the distance will be measured in the specified direction. The prompt sequence to be followed is given next.

Enter an option [Distribute/make leader segments Parallel/specify Spacing/Use current spacing] <specify Spacing>: **U** Enter.
Select multileader to align to or [Options]: *Select one of the leaders with respect to which the direction to be specified is maintained.*
Specify direction: *Specify the desired direction in the drawing area for the alignment of the multileaders.*

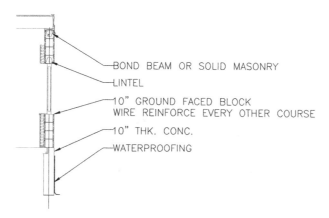

Figure 8-61 *Drawing with multileaders aligned using the* **specify Spacing** *option*

GEOMETRIC DIMENSIONING AND TOLERANCING

One of the most important parts of the design process is assigning the dimensions and tolerances to parts, since every part is manufactured from the dimensions given in the drawing. Therefore, every designer must understand and have a thorough knowledge of the standard practices used in the industry to make sure that the information given on the drawing is correct and can be understood by other people. Tolerancing is equally important, especially in the assembled parts. Tolerances and fits determine how the parts will fit. Incorrect tolerances could result in a product that is not usable. In addition to dimensioning and tolerancing, the function and the relationship that exists between the mating parts is important if the part is to perform the way it was designed. This aspect of the design process is addressed by geometric dimensioning and tolerancing, generally known as GDT.

Geometric dimensioning and tolerancing is a means to design and manufacture parts with respect to the actual function and relationship that exists between different features of the same part or the features of the mating parts. Therefore, a good design is not achieved by just giving dimensions and tolerances. The designer has to go beyond dimensioning and think of the intended function of the part and how the features of the part are going to affect its function. For example, Figure 8-62 shows a part with the required dimensions and tolerances. In this drawing, there is no mention of the relationship between the pin and the plate. Is the pin perpendicular to the plate? If it is, to what degree should it be perpendicular? Also, it does not mention on which surface the perpendicularity of the pin is to be measured. A design like this is open to individual interpretation based on intuition and experience. This is where geometric dimensioning and tolerancing play an important part in the product design process.

Figure 8-63 has been dimensioned using geometric dimensioning and tolerancing. The feature symbols define the datum (reference plane) and the permissible deviation in the perpendicularity of the pin with respect to the bottom surface. From a drawing like this, chances of making a mistake are minimized.

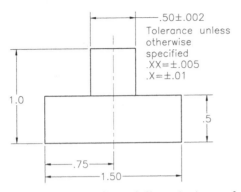

Figure 8-62 *Traditional dimensioning and tolerancing technique*

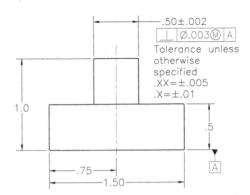

Figure 8-63 *Geometric dimensioning and tolerancing*

GEOMETRIC CHARACTERISTICS AND SYMBOLS

Before discussing the application of AutoCAD LT commands in geometric dimensioning and tolerancing, you need to understand the following feature symbols and tolerancing components. Figure 8-64 shows the geometric characteristics and symbols used in geometric dimensioning and tolerancing.

Kind of feature	Type of feature	Characteristics	
Related	Location	Position	⊕
		Concentricity or Coaxiality	◎
		Symmetry	=
	Orientation	Parallelism	//
		Perpendicularity	⊥
		Angularity	∠
Individual	Form	Cylindricity	⌭
		Flatness	▱
		Circularity or Roundness	○
		Straightness	—
Individual or related	Profile	Surface Profile	⌓
		Line Profile	⌒
Related	Runout	Circular Runout	↗
		Total Runout	↗↗

Figure 8-64 *Characteristics and symbols used in Geometric Tolerancing*

Note
Symbols used in geometric dimensioning and tolerancing are the building blocks of geometric dimensioning and tolerancing.

ADDING GEOMETRIC TOLERANCE

Ribbon: Annotate > Dimensions > Tolerance	**Toolbar:** Dimension > Tolerance
Menu Bar: Dimension > Tolerance	**Command:** TOLERANCE

Geometric tolerance displays the deviations of profile, orientation, form, location, and runout of a feature. In AutoCAD LT, geometrical tolerancing is displayed by feature control frames. The frames contain all information about tolerances for a single dimension. To display feature control frames with various tolerancing parameters, you need to enter specifications in the **Geometric Tolerance** dialog box (Figure 8-65). You can invoke the **Geometric Tolerance** dialog box by choosing the **Tolerance** tool from the **Dimensions** panel. Various components that constitute geometric tolerancing (GTOL) are shown in Figures 8-66 and 8-67.

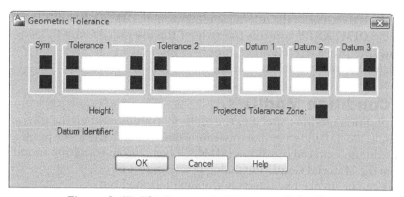

Figure 8-65 *The **Geometric Tolerance** dialog box*

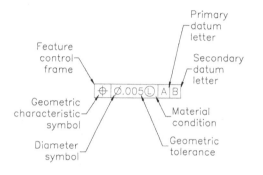

Figure 8-66 *Components of GTOL*

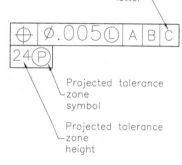

Figure 8-67 *Components of GTOL*

Feature Control Frame

The **feature control frame** is a rectangular box that contains the geometric characteristics symbols and tolerance definition. The box is automatically drawn to standard specifications; you do not need to specify its size. You can copy, move, erase, rotate, and scale the feature control frame. You can also snap to them using various Object snap modes. You can edit feature control frames using the **DDEDIT** command or you can also edit them using **GRIPS**. The system variable **DIMCLRD** controls the color of the feature control frame. The system variable **DIMGAP** controls the gap between the feature control frame and the text.

Geometric Characteristics Symbol

The geometric characteristics symbols indicate the characteristics such as straightness, flatness, perpendicularity, and so on of a feature. You can select the required symbol from the **Symbol** dialog box (Figure 8-68). This dialog box is displayed by selecting the box provided in the **Sym** area of the **Geometric Tolerance** dialog box. To select the required symbol, just pick the symbol using the left mouse button. The symbol will now be displayed in the box under the **Sym** area.

Figure 8-68 *The **Symbol** dialog box*

Tolerance Value and Tolerance Zone Descriptor

The tolerance value specifies the tolerance on the feature as indicated by the tolerance zone descriptor. For example, a value of .003 indicates that the feature must be within a 0.003 tolerance zone. Similarly, .003 indicates that this feature must be located at a true position within a 0.003 diameter. The tolerance value can be entered in the edit box provided under the **Tolerance 1** or the **Tolerance 2** area of the **Geometric Tolerance** dialog box. The tolerance zone descriptor can be invoked by selecting the box located to the left of the edit box. The system variable

DIMCLRT controls the color of the tolerance text, variable **DIMTXT** controls the tolerance text size, and variable **DIMTXSTY** controls the style of the tolerance text. On using the **Projected Tolerance Zone**, the projected tolerance zone symbol, which is an encircled P will be inserted after the projected tolerance zone value.

Material Condition Modifier

The material condition modifier specifies the material condition when the tolerance value takes effect. For example, .003(M) indicates that this feature must be located at a true position within a 0.003 diameter at maximum material condition (MMC). The material condition modifier symbol can be selected from the **Material Condition** dialog box (Figure 8-69). This dialog box can be invoked by selecting the boxes located on the right side of the edit boxes under the **Tolerance 1**, **Tolerance 2**, **Datum 1**, **Datum 2**, and **Datum 3** areas of the **Geometric Tolerance** dialog box.

Figure 8-69 The Material Condition dialog box

Datum

The datum is the origin, surface, or feature from which the measurements are made. The datum is also used to establish the geometric characteristics of a feature. The datum feature symbol consists of a reference character enclosed in a feature control frame. You can create the datum feature symbol by entering characters (like -A-) in the **Datum Identifier** edit box in the **Geometric Tolerance** dialog box and then selecting a point where you want to establish this datum.

You can also combine datum references with geometric characteristics. AutoCAD LT automatically positions the datum references on the right end of the feature control frame.

COMPLEX FEATURE CONTROL FRAMES
Composite Position Tolerancing

Sometimes the accuracy required within a pattern is more important than the location of the pattern with respect to the datum surfaces. To specify such a condition, composite position tolerancing may be used. For example, Figure 8-70 shows four holes (pattern) of diameter 0.15. The design allows a maximum tolerance of 0.025 with respect to datum A, B, and C at the maximum material condition (holes are smallest). The designer wants to maintain a closer positional tolerance (0.010 at MMC) between the holes within the pattern. To specify this requirement, the designer must insert the second frame. This is generally known as composite position tolerancing. AutoCAD LT provides the facility to create two composite position tolerance frames by means of the **Geometric Tolerance** dialog box. The composite tolerance frames can be created as follows:

1. Invoke the **Tolerance** tool to display the **Geometric Tolerance** dialog box. Select the box under the **Sym** area to display the **Symbol** dialog box. Select the **position** symbol. AutoCAD LT will display the selected symbol in the first row of the **Sym** area.

2. In the first row of the **Geometric Tolerance** dialog box, enter the geometric characteristics and the datum references required for the first position tolerance frame.

3. Next, select the box under the **Sym** area from the second row to display the **Symbol** dialog box. Select the position symbol; AutoCAD LT will display the selected symbol in the second row of the **Sym** area.

4. In the second row of the **Geometric Tolerance** dialog box, enter the geometric characteristics and the datum references required for the second position tolerance frame.

5. When you have finished entering the values, choose the **OK** button in the **Geometric Tolerance** dialog box, and then select the point where you want to insert the frames. AutoCAD LT will create two frames and automatically align them with the common position symbol, as shown in Figure 8-70.

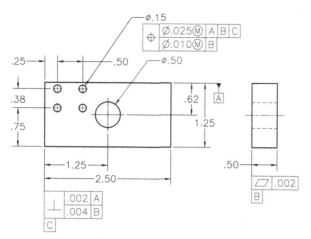

Figure 8-70 *Composite position tolerancing*

PROJECTED TOLERANCE ZONE

Figure 8-71 shows two parts joined with a bolt. The lower part is threaded, and the top part has a drilled hole. When these two parts are joined, the bolt that is threaded in the lower part will have the orientation error that exists in the threaded hole. In other words, the error in the threaded hole will extend beyond the part thickness, which might cause interference, and the parts may not assemble. To avoid this problem, projected tolerance is used. The projected tolerance establishes a tolerance zone that extends above the surface. In Figure 8-71, the position tolerance for the threaded hole is 0.010, which extends 0.1 above the surface (datum A). By using the projected tolerance, you can ensure that the bolt is within the tolerance zone up to the specified distance.

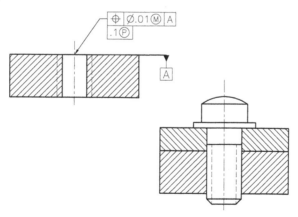

Figure 8-71 *Projected tolerance zone*

You can use the AutoCAD LT GDT feature to create feature control frames for the projected tolerance zone as discussed next.

1. Invoke the **QLEADER** command and then press ENTER at the **Specify first leader point, or [Settings] <Settings>** prompt to display the **Leader Settings** dialog box.

2. Choose the **Annotation** tab and then select the **Tolerance** radio button from the **Annotation Type** area. Choose **OK** to return to the command line. Specify the first, the second, and the third leader points, refer to Figure 8-71. On specifying the third point, the **Geometric Tolerance** dialog box will be displayed. Click once in the **Sym** area in the first row; the **Symbol** dialog box will be displayed. Choose the position symbol from the **Symbol** dialog box.

3. In the first row of the **Geometric Tolerance** dialog box, enter the geometric characteristics and the datum references required for the first position tolerance frame.

4. In the **Height** edit box, enter the height of the tolerance zone (.1 for the given drawing) and select the box on the right of **Projected Tolerance Zone**. The projected tolerance zone symbol will be displayed in the box.

5. Choose the **OK** button in the **Geometric Tolerance** dialog box. AutoCAD LT will create two frames and automatically align them, refer to Figure 8-71.

EXAMPLE 2   *Tolerance*

In this example, you will create a feature control frame to define the perpendicularity specification, see Figure 8-72.

1. Choose the **Tolerance** tool from the **Dimensions** panel of the **Annotate** tab to display the **Geometric Tolerance** dialog box. Choose the upper box from the **Sym** area to display the **Symbol** dialog box. Select the **perpendicularity** symbol. This symbol will be displayed in the **Sym** area.

2. Select the box on the left of the upper edit box under the **Tolerance 1** area; the diameter symbol will appear to denote a cylindrical tolerance zone.

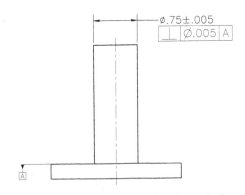

Figure 8-72 Drawing for Example 2

3. Enter **.005** in the upper edit box under the **Tolerance 1** area.

4. Enter **A** in the edit box under the **Datum 1** area. Choose the **OK** button to accept the changes made in the **Geometric Tolerance** dialog box.

5. The **Enter tolerance location** is displayed at the Command prompt and the **Feature Control Frame** is attached to the cursor at its middle left point. Select a point to insert the frame.

6. To attach the datum symbol, invoke the **Leader Settings** dialog box and select the **Tolerance** radio button as explained in step 1.

7. Choose the **Leader Line & Arrowhead** tab and select the **Datum triangle filled** option from the drop-down list in the **Arrowhead** area.

8. Set the number of points in the leader to **2** in the **Number of Points** spinner.

9. Choose **OK** to return to the Command line. Specify the first and second leader points, refer to Figure 8-72. On specifying the second point, the **Geometric Tolerance** dialog box will be displayed.

10. Enter **A** in the **Datum Identifier** edit box. Choose **OK** to exit the **Geometric Tolerance** dialog box. On doing so, the datum symbol will be displayed, refer to Figure 8-72.

EXAMPLE 3   *Tolerance*

In this example, you will create a leader with combination feature control frames to control runout and cylindricity, see Figure 8-73.

1. Enter the **QLEADER** command and follow the prompt sequence given below.

   Specify first leader point, or [Settings] <Settings>: *Press ENTER to display the **Leader Settings** dialog box. Choose the **Annotation** tab. Select the **Tolerance** radio button from the **Annotation Type** area. Choose **OK**.*
   Specify first leader point, or [Settings] <Settings>: *Specify the leader start point, as shown in Figure 8-73.*
   Specify next point: *Specify the second point of the leader.*
   Specify next point: *Specify the third point of the leader line to display the **Tolerance** dialog box.*

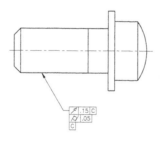

Figure 8-73 Drawing for Example 3

2. Choose the runout symbol from the **Symbol** dialog box; the **runout** symbol will be displayed on the first row of the **Sym** area. Enter **.15** in the first row edit box under the **Tolerance 1** area.

3. Enter **C** in the edit box under the **Datum 1** area.

4. Select the edit box on the second row of the **Sym** area and select the **cylindricity** symbol; the **cylindricity** symbol will be displayed in the second row of the **Sym** area.

5. Enter **.05** in the second row edit box of the **Tolerance 1** area.

6. Enter **C** in the **Datum Identifier** edit box.

7. Choose the **OK** button to accept the changes in the **Geometric Tolerance** dialog box; the control frames will be automatically attached at the end of the leader.

CREATING ANNOTATIVE DIMENSIONS, TOLERANCES, LEADERS, AND MULTILEADERS

Annotative dimensions are drawn in the drawing by assigning annotative dimension style to the current drawing. To assign annotative dimension, select the **Dimension Style** (inclined arrow) from the **Dimensions** panel or from the **Dimension** toolbar. Note that the dimension style selected should have an annotative symbol next to it. You can also change the non-annotative dimensions to annotative by changing the dimension's **Annotative** property to **Yes** in the **Properties** palette.

For drawing the annotative geometric tolerances and leaders, you first need to add the simple tolerances to the drawing and then select all tolerances. Next, you need to modify the **Annotative** property under the **Misc** area of the **Properties** palette to **Yes**.

The annotative leaders are drawn by assigning annotative dimension style, whereas the annotative multileaders are drawn by assigning annotative multileader style. The leaders are created with two components: the leader and its content. Therefore, drawing annotative leaders does not ensure that the content attached to the leader will also be annotative. But, the multileaders are drawn as a single component, so the multileaders drawn with annotative style will have annotative content also.

Note
Creating and modifying dimension styles and multileader styles will be discussed in detail in Chapter 10.

Self-Evaluation Test

Answer the following questions and then compare them to those given at the end of this chapter:

1. You can specify dimension text or accept the measured value computed by AutoCAD LT. (T/F)

2. The **Adjust Space** tool is used to maintain equal spacing between linear dimensions or angular dimensions. (T/F)

3. The leaders drawn by using the **QLEADER** command create arrow, leader lines, and text as a single object. (T/F)

4. You cannot combine GTOL with leaders. (T/F)

5. The _____ tool is used to dimension only the *X* coordinate of a selected object.

6. The _____ symbols are the building blocks of geometric dimensioning and tolerances.

7. In the _____ dimensioning, the dimension text is aligned by default with the object being dimensioned.

8. The _____ dimensions are automatically updated when the object to which they are assigned is modified.

9. The _____ point is taken as the vertex point of the angular dimensions while dimensioning an arc or a circle.

10. Extra leaders can be added or removed from existing multileaders by using the _____ tool.

Review Questions

Answer the following questions:

1. Only inner angles (acute angles) can be dimensioned with angular dimensioning. (T/F)

2. In addition to the most recently drawn dimension (the default base dimension), you can use any other linear dimension as the base dimension. (T/F)

3. In the continued dimensions, the base point for the successive continued dimensions is the base dimension's first extension line. (T/F)

4. You cannot add dimension break to straight multileaders. (T/F)

5. Using the **Multileader** tool, you can specify the content of a multileader before drawing the leader itself. (T/F)

6. Which of the following tools can be used to convert dimensions into true associative dimensions?

    (a) **Reassociate**   (b) **Associate**
    (c) **Disassociate**   (d) None of the above

7. Which of the following tools can be used to dimension more than one object in a single effort?

    (a) **Linear**   (b) **Angluar**
    (c) **Quick Dimension**   (d) None of the above

8. Which of the following tools is used to dimension different points and features of a part with reference to a fixed point?

    (a) **Baseline**   (b) **Angular**
    (c) **Radius**   (d) **Aligned**

9. Which of the following tools can be used to add geometric dimensions and tolerance to the current drawing?

    (a) **GTOL**   (b) **Tolerance**
    (c) **Single Line**   (d) None of the above

10. Which of the following options of the **Align** tool can be used to maintain a constant spacing between the selected multileader landing lines?

   (a) **Distribute**   (b) **make leader segments Parallel**
   (c) **Specify Spacing**   (d) **Use current spacing**

11. Geometric dimensioning and tolerancing is generally known as _____.

12. The three ways to return to the Command prompt from the **Dim:** prompt (dimensioning mode) are _____, _____, and _____.

13. Horizontal dimensions measure displacement along the _____.

EXERCISE 7

Draw the object shown in Figure 8-74 and then dimension it. Save the drawing as *DIMEXR7*.

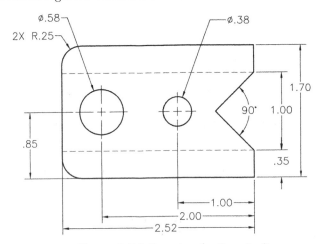

Figure 8-74 Drawing for Exercise 7

EXERCISE 8

Draw and dimension the object shown in Figure 8-75. Save the drawing as *DIMEXR8*.

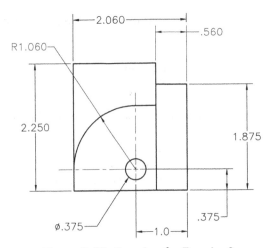

Figure 8-75 Drawing for Exercise 8

EXERCISE 9

Draw the object shown in Figure 8-76 and then dimension it. Save the drawing as *DIMEXR9*.

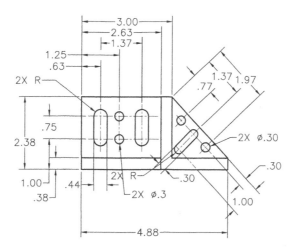

Figure 8-76 *Drawing for Exercise 9*

EXERCISE 10

Draw the object shown in Figure 8-77 and then dimension it. Save the drawing as *DIMEXR10*.

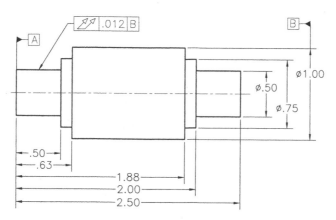

Figure 8-77 *Drawing for Exercise 10*

EXERCISE 11

Draw the object shown in Figure 8-78 and then dimension it. Save the drawing ɛ

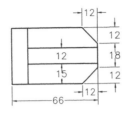

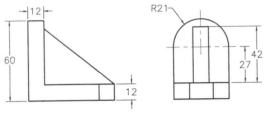

Figure 8-78 Drawing for Exercise 11

EXERCISE 12

Draw the object shown in Figure 8-79 and then dimension it. Save the drawing as *DIMEXR12*.

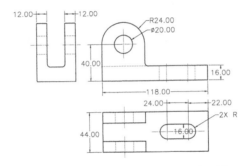

Figure 8-79 Drawing for Exercise 12

EXERCISE 13

Draw the object shown in Figure 8-80 and then dimension it. Save the drawing as *DIMEXR13*.

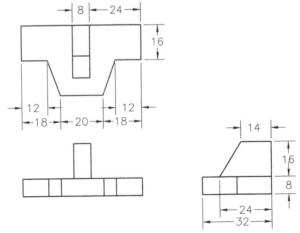

Figure 8-80 Drawing for Exercise 13

Problem-Solving Exercise 1

Draw the object shown in Figure 8-81 and dimension it, as shown in the drawing. Save the drawing as *DIMPSE1*.

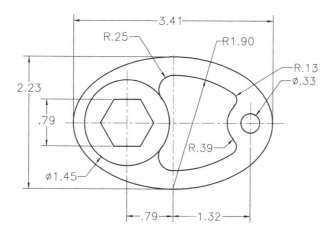

Figure 8-81 Drawing for Problem-Solving Exercise 1

Problem-Solving Exercise 2

Draw Figure 8-82 and then dimension it, as shown in the drawing. Save the drawing as *DIMPSE2*.

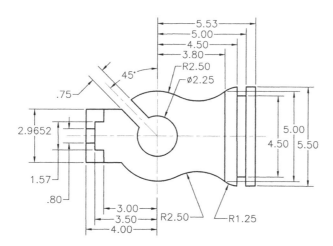

Figure 8-82 Drawing for Problem-Solving Exercise 2

Problem-Solving Exercise 3

Draw Figure 8-83 and then dimension it, as shown in the drawing. Save the drawing as *DIMPSE3*.

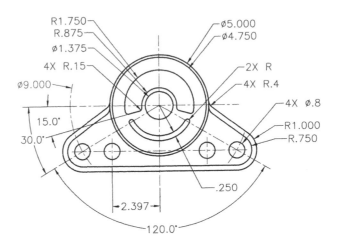

Figure 8-83 Drawing for Problem-Solving Exercise 3

Answers to Self-evaluation Test

1. T, **2.** T, **3.** F, **4.** F, **5. Ordinate**, **6.** geometric characteristics, **7.** aligned, **8.** true associative dimensions, **9.** center, **10. Remove Leader**

Chapter 9

Editing Dimensions

CHAPTER OBJECTIVES

In this chapter, you will learn to:
- *Edit dimensions.*
- *Stretch, extend, and trim dimensions.*
- *Use the Oblique and Text Angle command options to edit dimensions.*
- *Update dimensions using the Update command.*
- *Use the Properties palette to edit dimensions.*
- *Dimension in model space and paper space.*

KEY TERMS

- *Dimension editing tools*
- *Stretch*
- *Trim*
- *Extend*
- *Edit Dimension Text*
- *Update*
- *Dimension Properties Palette*
- *Multileader Properties Palette*
- *Model Space Dimension*
- *Paper Space Dimension*

EDITING DIMENSIONS USING EDITING TOOLS

For editing dimensions, AutoCAD LT has provided some special editing commands that work with dimensions. These editing commands can be used to define a new dimension text, return to the home text, create oblique dimensions, and rotate and update the dimension text. You can also use the Trim, Stretch, and Extend tools to edit the dimensions. In case the dimension assigned to the object is a true associative dimension, it will be automatically updated if the object is modified. However, if the dimension is not true associative dimension, you will have to include the dimension along with the object in the edit selection set. The properties of the dimensioned objects can also be changed using the **Properties** palette or the **Dimension Style Manager**.

Editing Dimensions by Stretching

You can edit a dimension by stretching it. However, to stretch a dimension, appropriate definition points must be included in the selection crossing or window. As the middle point of the dimension text is a definition point for all types of dimensions, you can easily stretch and move the dimension text to any location you want. When you stretch the dimension text, the gap in the dimension line gets filled automatically. While editing, the definition points of the dimension being edited must be included in the selection crossing box. The dimension is automatically calculated when you stretch the dimension.

Note
The dimension type remains the same after stretching. For example, the vertical dimension maintains itself as a vertical dimension and measures only the vertical distance even after the line it dimensions is modified and converted into an inclined line. The following example illustrates the stretching of object lines and dimensions.

EXAMPLE 1	*Edit by Stretching*

In this example, you will stretch the objects and dimensions shown in Figure 9-1 using grips. The new location of the lines and dimensions is at a distance of 0.5 unit in the positive *Y* axis direction, see Figure 9-2.

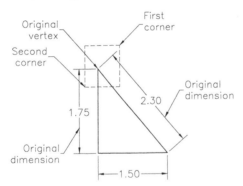

Figure 9-1 *Original location of lines and dimensions*

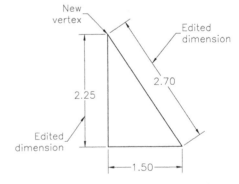

Figure 9-2 *New location of lines and dimensions*

1. Choose the **Stretch** tool from the **Modify** panel of the **Home** tab. The prompt sequence that will follow is given below:

    Select objects to stretch by crossing-window or crossing-polygon
    Select objects: Specify opposite corner: *Define a crossing window using the first and second corners, as shown in Figure 9-1.*
    Select objects: [Enter]
    Specify base point or [Displacement]<Displacement>: *Select original vertex using the osnaps as the base point.*

Specify second point of displacement or <use first point as displacement>: **@0.5<90**

2. The selected entities will be stretched to the new location. The dimension that was initially 1.75 will become 2.25 and the dimension that was initially 2.30 will become 2.70, see Figure 9-2. Press ESC to remove the grip points from the objects.

EXERCISE 1

The two dimensions given in Figure 9-3(a) are too close. Fix the drawing by stretching the dimension, as shown in Figure 9-3(b).

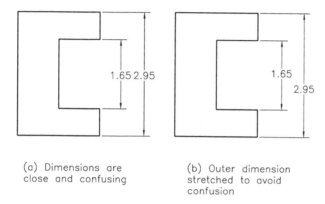

(a) Dimensions are close and confusing

(b) Outer dimension stretched to avoid confusion

Figure 9-3 *Drawing for Exercise 1, stretching dimensions*

1. Stretch the outer dimension to the right so that there is some distance between the two dimensions.
2. Stretch the dimension text of the outer dimension so that the dimension text is staggered (lower than the first dimension).

Editing Dimensions by Trimming and Extending

Trimming and extending operations can be carried out with all types of linear dimensions (horizontal, vertical, aligned and, rotated) and the ordinate dimension. Even if the dimensions are true associative, you can trim and extend them (see Figures 9-4 and 9-5). AutoCAD LT trims or

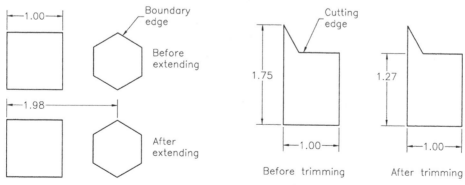

Figure 9-4 *Dimensions edited by extending*   ***Figure 9-5*** *Edgemode extended trimming*

extends a linear dimension between the extension line definition points and the object used as a boundary or trimming edge. To extend or trim an ordinate dimension, AutoCAD LT moves the feature location (location of the dimensioned coordinate) to the boundary edge. To retain the original ordinate value, the boundary edge to which the feature location point is moved should be orthogonal to the measured ordinate. In both cases, the imaginary line drawn between the two extension line definition points is trimmed or extended by AutoCAD LT, and the dimension is adjusted automatically.

EXERCISE 2

Use the **Edge > Extend** option of the **TRIM** command to trim the dimension given in Figure 9-6(a), so that it looks like Figure 9-6(b).

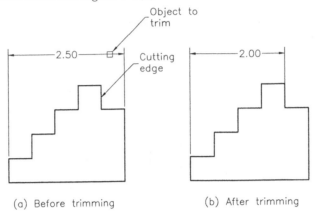

Figure 9-6 Drawing for Exercise 2

1. Make the drawing and dimension it, as shown in Figure 9-6(a). Assume the missing dimensions.
2. Trim the dimensions by using the **Edge > Extend** option of the **TRIM** command.

Flipping Dimension Arrow

You can flip the arrowheads individually. To flip the arrow, select the dimension. Place the cursor on the grip corresponding to the arrowhead that you want to flip. When the color of the grip turns red, invoke the shortcut menu by right-clicking and choose the **Flip Arrow** option from the shortcut menu.

MODIFYING THE DIMENSIONS

Toolbar: Dimension > Dimension Edit   **Command:** DIMEDIT

The dimensions can be modified by choosing the **Dimension Edit** tool from the **Dimension** toolbar (Figure 9-7). Alternatively, you can use the **DIMEDIT** command to modify the dimensions. This command has four options: **New**, **Rotate**, **Home**, and **Oblique**. The prompt sequence that will follow when you choose this tool is given below:

Enter type of dimension editing (Home/New/Rotate/Oblique) <Home>: *Enter an option.*

Figure 9-7 Invoking the DIMEDIT command from the Dimension toolbar

New

The **New** option is used to replace the existing dimension with a new text string. When you invoke this option, the **Text Editor** will be displayed. By default, 0.0000 will be displayed. Using the **Text Editor**, enter the dimension or write the text string with which you want to replace the existing dimension. Once you have entered a new dimension in the editor and exit the **Text Editor**, you will be prompted to select the dimension to be replaced. Select the dimension and press ENTER; it will be replaced with the new dimension.

Rotate

The **Rotate** option is used to position the dimension text at the specified angle. With this option, you can change the orientation (angle) of the dimension text of any number of associative dimensions. The angle can be specified by entering a value at the **Specify angle for dimension text** prompt or by specifying two points at the required angle. Once you have specified the angle, you will be prompted to select the dimension text to be rotated. Select the dimension and press ENTER; the text will rotate about its middle point, see Figure 9-8. You can also invoke this option by choosing the **Text Angle** tool from the **Dimensions** panel.

Home

The **Home** option restores the text of a dimension to its original (home/default) location if the position of the text has been changed by stretching or editing, see Figure 9-8.

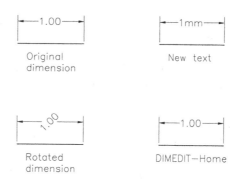

Figure 9-8 *Using the **DIMEDIT** command to edit dimensions*

Oblique

In linear dimensions, extension lines are drawn perpendicular to the dimension line. The **Oblique** option bends the linear dimensions. It draws extension lines at an oblique angle (Figure 9-9). This option is particularly important to create isometric dimensions and can be used to resolve conflicting situations due to the overlapping of extension lines with other objects. Making an existing dimension oblique by specifying an angle oblique to it does not affect the generation of new linear dimensions. The oblique angle is maintained even after performing most editing operations. (See Chapter 8 for details about how to use this option) When you invoke this option, you will be prompted to select the dimension to be edited. After selecting it, you will be prompted to specify the obliquing angle. The extensions lines will be bent at the angle specified. You can also invoke this option by choosing the **Oblique** tool from the **Dimensions** panel.

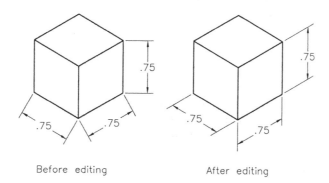

Figure 9-9 *Using the **Oblique** option to edit dimensions*

EDITING THE DIMENSION TEXT

Toolbar: Dimension > Dimension Text Edit **Command:** DIMTEDIT
Menu Bar: Dimension > Align Text

The dimension text can be edited by using the **Dimension Text Edit** tool from the **Dimension** toolbar. This command is used to edit the placement and orientation of a single existing dimension. You can use this tool in cases where dimension texts of two or more dimensions are too close together. In such cases, the **Dimension Text Edit** tool is invoked to move the dimension text to some other location so that there is no confusion. The prompt sequence that will follow when you choose the **Dimension Text Edit** tool is given next.

Select dimension: *Select the dimension to modify.*
Specify new location for dimension text or [Left/Right/Center/Home/Angle]:

Left

With this option, you can left-justify the dimension text along the dimension line. The vertical placement setting determines the position of the dimension text. In this setting, the horizontally aligned text is moved to the left and the vertically aligned text is moved down, see Figure 9-10. This option can be used only with the linear, diameter, or radial dimensions. You can also invoke this option by choosing the **Left** tool from the **Dimensions** panel.

Right

With this option, you can right-justify the dimension text along the dimension line. Similar to the Left option, the vertical placement setting determines the position of the dimension text. The horizontally aligned text is moved to the right, and the vertically aligned text is moved up, see Figure 9-10. This option can be used only with linear diameter and radius dimensions. You can also invoke this option by choosing the **Right** tool from the **Dimensions** panel.

Center

With this option, you can center-justify the dimension text for linear and aligned dimensions, see Figure 9-10. The vertical setting controls the vertical position of the dimension text. You can also invoke this option by choosing the **Center** tool from the **Dimensions** panel.

Home

The **Home** option is used to restore (move) the dimension text of a dimension to its original (home/default) location, if the position of the text has changed, see Figure 9-10.

Angle

With the **Angle** option, you can position the dimension text at the angle you specify, see Figure 9-10. The angle can be specified by entering its value at the **Specify angle for dimension text** prompt or by specifying two points at the required angle. You will notice that the text rotates around its middle point. If the dimension text alignment is set to Orient Text Horizontally, the dimension text is aligned with the dimension line. If information about the dimension style is available on the selected dimension, AutoCAD LT uses it to

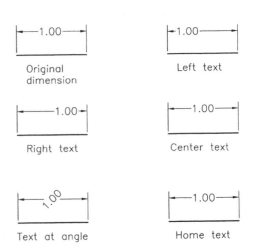

*Figure 9-10 Using the **DIMTEDIT** command to edit dimensions*

redraw the dimension, or the prevailing dimension variable settings are used for the redrawing process. Entering 0-degree angle changes the text to its default orientation.

UPDATING DIMENSIONS

Ribbon: Annotate > Dimensions > Update	**Toolbar:** Dimension > Dimension Update
Menu Bar: Dimension > Update	**Command:** -DIMSTYLE

The **Update** tool is used to regenerate and update the prevailing dimension entities (such as arrows heads and text height) using the current settings for the dimension variables, dimension style, text style, and units. On choosing this tool, you will be prompted to select the dimensions to be updated. You can select all the dimensions or specify those that should be updated.

EDITING DIMENSIONS WITH GRIPS

You can also edit dimensions by using the GRIP editing modes. GRIP editing is the easiest and quickest way to edit dimensions. You can perform the following operations with GRIPS.

1. Position the text anywhere along the dimension line. Note that you cannot move the text and position it above or below the dimension line.
2. Stretch a dimension to change the spacing between the dimension line and the object line.
3. Stretch the dimension along the length. When you stretch a dimension, the dimension text automatically changes.
4. Move, rotate, copy, mirror, or scale the dimensions.
5. Relocate the dimension origin.
6. Change properties such as color, layer, linetype, and linetype scale.
7. Load Web browser (if any *Universal Resource Locator* is associated with the object).

EDITING DIMENSIONS USING THE PROPERTIES PALETTE

Ribbon: View > Palettes > Properties	**Toolbar:** Standard > Properties
Menu Bar: Modify > Properties	**Command:** PROPERTIES

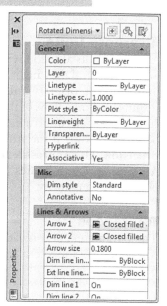

You can also modify a dimension or leader by using the **Properties** palette. The **Properties** palette is displayed when you choose the **Properties** button from the **Palettes** panel. Alternatively, you can invoke the **Properties** palette by choosing the **Properties** option from the **Palettes** cascade in the **Tools** menu. All the properties of the selected object are displayed in the **Properties** palette (see Figure 9-11). Select the dimension before invoking the **Properties** palette, otherwise it would not give the description of the dimension.

Properties Palette (Dimension)

You can use the **Properties** palette (Figure 9-11) to change the properties, the dimension text style, or geometry, format, and annotation-related features of the selected dimension. The changes take place dynamically in the drawing. The **Properties** palette provides the following categories for the modification of dimensions.

*Figure 9-11 The **Properties** palette for dimensions*

General

In the general category, the various parameters displayed are **Color**, **Layer**, **Linetype**, **Linetype scale**, **Plot style**, **Lineweight**, **Hyperlink**, and **Associative** with their current values. To change the color of the selected object, select **Color** property and then select the required color from the drop-down list. Similarly, layer, plot style, linetype, and lineweight can be changed from the respective drop-down lists. The linetype scale can be changed manually in the corresponding cell.

Misc

This category displays the dimension style by name (for the **DIMSTYLE** system variable, use **SETVAR**) and also specifies whether the dimension text will be annotative or not. You can change the dimension style and the annotative property of the text from the respective drop-down lists of the selected dimension.

Lines & Arrows

The various parameters of the lines and arrows in the dimension such as arrowhead size, type, arrow lineweight, and so on can be changed in this category.

Text

The various parameters that control the text in the dimension object such as text color, text height, vertical position text offset, and so on can be changed in this category.

Fit

In the fit category, the parameters available are: **Dim line forced**, **Dim line inside**, **Dim scale overall**, **Fit**, **Text inside**, and **Text movement**.

Primary Units

In the primary units category, the parameters displayed are **Decimal separator**, **Dim prefix**, **Dim suffix**, **Dim roundoff**, **Dim scale linear**, **Dim units**, **Suppress leading zeros**, **Suppress trailing zeros**, **Suppress zero feet**, **Suppress zero inches**, and **Precision**. Among these parameters, **Dim units**, **Suppress leading zeros**, **Suppress trailing zeros**, **Suppress zero feet**, **Suppress zero inches**, and **Precision** can be changed with the help of corresponding drop-down lists. The other parameters can be changed manually.

Alternate Units

Alternate units are required when a drawing is to be read in two different units. For example, if an architectural drawing is to be read in both metric and feet-inches, you can turn the alternate units on. The primary units can be set to metric and the alternate units to architectural. As a result, the dimensions of the drawing will be displayed in metric units as well as in engineering. In the alternate unit category, there are various parameters for the alternate units. They can be changed only if the **Alt enabled** parameter is **on**. The parameters such as **Alt format**, **Alt precision**, **Alt suppress leading zeros**, **Alt suppress trailing zeros**, **Alt suppress zero feet**, and **Alt suppress zero inches** can be changed from the respective drop-down lists and others can be changed manually.

Tolerances

The parameters of this category can be changed only if the **Tolerances** display parameter has some mode of the tolerance selected. The parameters listed in this rollout depend on the mode of tolerance selected.

Properties Palette (Multileader)

The **Properties** palette for **Multileader** can be invoked by selecting a Leader and then choosing the **Properties** option from the **Palettes** panel. You can also invoke the **Properties** palette (Figure 9-12) from the shortcut menu by right-clicking in the drawing area and then choosing **Properties**. This palette can also be invoked by double-clicking in the leader to be edited. The various properties under the **Properties** palette (Multileader) are described next.

General

The parameters in the general category are the same as those discussed in the previous section (**Properties** palette for dimensions).

Misc

This category displays the **Overall scale**, **Multileader style**, **Annotative**, and **Annotative scale** of the **Multileader**. You can change the style, annotative property, and annotation scale of the **Multileader** by using the respective drop-down lists.

Leaders

This category controls the display of certain elements such as lines, arrowheads, landing distance, and so on. The **Multileader** is composed of these elements.

Text

This category displays the properties that are used to control the text appearance and location of the **Multileader** text. These properties can be changed by selecting the desired option from the respective drop-down lists. Now, you can modify the dimension text by double-clicking on the required dimension.

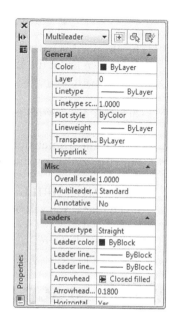

*Figure 9-12 The **Properties** palette for modifying multileaders*

EXAMPLE 2   *Modify Dimensions*

In this example, you will modify the dimensions given in Figure 9-13 so that they match the dimensions given in Figure 9-14. Assume the missing dimensions.

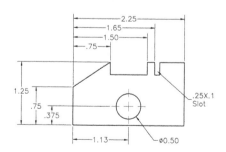

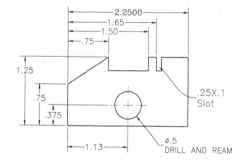

Figure 9-13 Drawing for Example 2   *Figure 9-14 Drawing after editing the dimensions*

1. Choose the **Text Style** (inclined arrow) tool from the **Text** panel of the **Annotate** tab and create a style with the name **ROMANC**. Select **romanc.shx** as the font for the style.

2. Select the dimension **2.25** and enter **PROP** in the command box to display the **Properties** palette.

3. In the **Text** category, select the **Text style** drop-down list and then select the **ROMANC** style from this drop-down list. The changes will take place dynamically.

4. Select **0.0000** from the **Precision** drop-down list in the **Primary Units** area.

5. Once all the required changes are made in the linear dimension, choose the **Select Object** button in the **Properties** palette; you will be prompted to select the object. Select the leader line and then press ENTER.

6. The **Properties** palette will display the leader options. Select **Spline** from the **Leader type** drop-down list in the **Leaders** category; the straight line will be dynamically converted into a spline with an arrow.

7. Close the **Properties** palette.

8. Choose the **Dimension Edit** tool from the **Dimension** toolbar. Enter **N** in the prompt sequence to display the **Text Editor**.

9. Enter **%%C.5 DRILL AND REAM** in the **Text Editor** and then click outside it to accept the changes. You will be prompted to select the object to be changed.

10. Select the diameter dimension and then press ENTER. The diameter dimension will be modified to the new value.

MODEL SPACE AND PAPER SPACE DIMENSIONING

Dimensioning objects can be drawn in the model space or paper space. If the drawings are in model space, associative dimensions should also be created in them. If the drawings are in the model space and the associative dimensions are in the paper space, the dimensions will not change when you perform such editing operations as stretching, trimming, and extending, or such display operations as zoom and pan in the model space viewport. The definition points of a dimension are located in the space where the drawing is drawn. You can select the **Scale dimensions to layout** radio button in the **Fit** tab (see Figure 9-15). This tab is available when you choose the **Modify, New,** or **Override** button from the **Dimension Style Manager** dialog box, depending on whether you want to modify the present style or you want to create a new style. Choose **OK** and then **Close** to exit the dialog boxes. AutoCAD LT calculates a scale factor that is compatible with the model space and the paper space viewports. Now, choose the **Update** tool from the **Dimension** toolbar and select the dimension objects for updating.

The drawing shown in Figure 9-16 uses paper space scaling. The main drawing and detail drawings are located in different floating viewports (paper space). The zoom scale factors for these viewports are different: 0.3XP, 1.0XP, and 0.5XP, respectively. When you use paper scaling, AutoCAD LT automatically calculates the scale factor for dimensioning so that the dimensions are uniform in all the floating viewports (model space viewports).

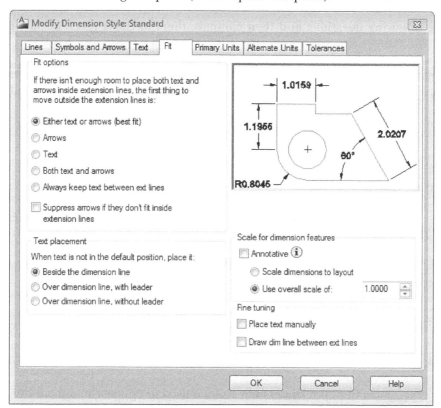

Figure 9-15 *Selecting paper space scaling in the* **Modify Dimension Style** *dialog box*

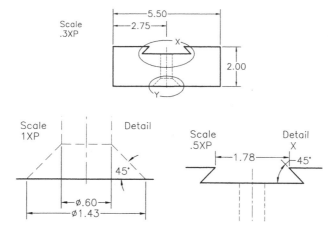

Figure 9-16 *Dimensioning in paper model space viewports using paper space scaling or setting* **DIMSCALE** *to 0*

Self-Evaluation Test

Answer the following questions and then compare them to those given at the end of this chapter:

1. In associative dimensioning, the items constituting a dimension (such as dimension lines, arrows, leaders, extension lines, and dimension text) are drawn as a single object. (T/F)

2. You cannot edit dimensions using grips. (T/F)

3. The true associative dimensions cannot be trimmed or extended. (T/F)

4. You can use the _____ command to break the dimensions into individual entities.

5. The _____ option of the **DIMTEDIT** command is used to justify the dimension text toward the left side.

6. The _____ option of the **DIMTEDIT** command is used to justify the dimension text to the center of the dimension.

7. The _____ option of the **DIMEDIT** command is used to create a new text string.

8. The _____ option of the **DIMEDIT** command is used to bend the extension lines through the specified angle.

9. The _____ tool from the **Dimension** panel is used to update the dimensions.

Review Questions

Answer the following questions:

1. The horizontal, vertical, aligned, and rotated dimensions cannot be edited using grips. (T/F)

2. Trimming and extending operations can be carried out with all types of linear (horizontal, vertical, aligned, and rotated) dimensions and with the ordinate dimension. (T/F)

3. To extend or trim an ordinate dimension, AutoCAD LT moves the feature location (location of the dimensioned coordinate) to the boundary edge. (T/F)

4. Once moved from the original location, the dimension text cannot be restored to its original position. (T/F)

5. With the _____ or _____ commands, you can edit the dimension text.

6. The _____ command is particularly important for creating isometric dimensions and is applicable in resolving conflicting situations due to overlapping of extension lines with other objects.

7. The _____ command is used to edit the placement and orientation of a single existing dimension.

8. The _____ command regenerates (updates) prevailing associative dimension objects (like arrows and text height) using the current settings for the dimension variables, dimension style, text style, and units.

9. Explain when to use the **Extend** tool and how it works with dimensions.

10. Explain the use and working of the **Properties** palette for editing dimensions.

EXERCISE 3   Edit Dimensions

1. Create the drawing shown in Figure 9-17. Assume the dimensions where necessary.
2. Dimension the drawing, as shown in Figure 9-17.
3. Edit the dimensions so that they match the dimensions shown in Figure 9-18.

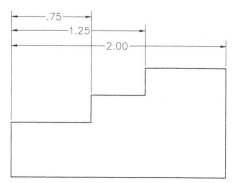 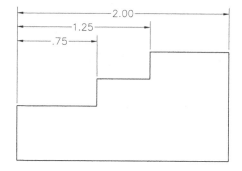

Figure 9-17 *Drawing for Exercise 3 before editing dimensions*

Figure 9-18 *Drawing for Exercise 3 after editing dimensions*

EXERCISE 4   Edit Dimensions

1. Draw the object shown in Figure 9-19(a). Assume the dimensions where necessary.
2. Dimension the drawing, as shown in Figure 9-19(a).
3. Edit the dimensions so that they match the dimensions shown in Figure 9-19(b).

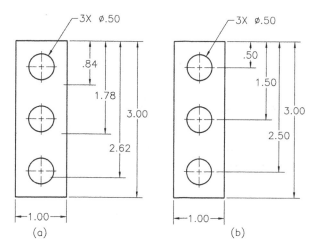

Figure 9-19 *Drawings for Exercise 4*

EXERCISE 5   *Edit Dimensions*

Create the drawing shown in Figure 9-20 and then dimension it. Assume the dimensions wherever necessary. After dimensioning the drawing, edit its dimensions so that they match the dimensions shown in Figure 9-20.

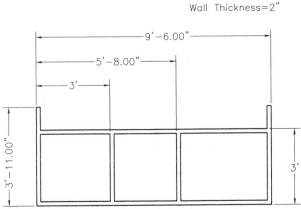

Figure 9-20 Drawing for Exercise 5

Problem-Solving Exercise 1

Create the drawing shown in Figure 9-21 and then dimension it. Edit the dimensions so that they are positioned as shown in the drawing. You can change the dimension text height and arrow size to 0.08 unit.

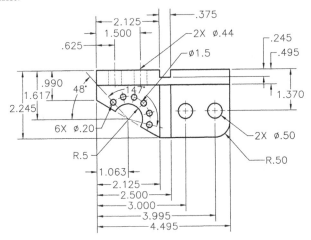

Figure 9-21 Drawing for Problem-Solving Exercise 1

Problem-Solving Exercise 2

Draw the front and side view of an object shown in Figure 9-22 and then dimension the two views. Edit the dimensions so that they are positioned as shown in the drawing. You may change the dimension text height and arrow size to 0.08 units.

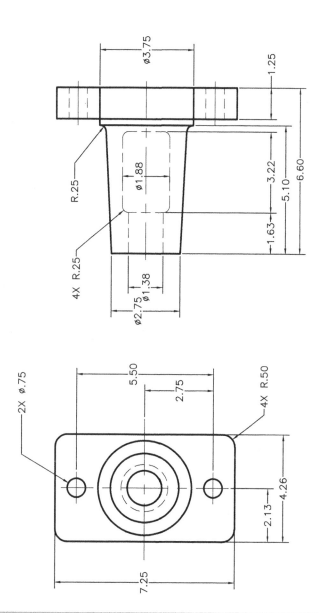

Figure 9-22 *Drawing for Problem-Solving Exercise 2*

Chapter 9

Problem-Solving Exercise 3

Create the drawing of the floor plan shown in Figure 9-23 and then apply dimensions to it. Edit the dimensions, if needed, so that they are positioned as shown in the drawing.

Figure 9-23 Drawing for Problem-Solving Exercise 3

Chapter *10*

Dimension Styles, Multileader Styles, and System Variables

CHAPTER OBJECTIVES

In this chapter, you will learn:
- *To use styles and variables to control dimensions.*
- *To create dimension styles.*
- *To set dimension variables using various tabs of the New, Modify, and Override Dimension Style.*
- *To use dimension style overrides.*
- *To compare and list dimension styles.*
- *To import externally referenced dimension styles.*
- *To create, restore, and modify multileader styles.*

KEY TERMS

- *DIMSTYLE*
- *DIMCEN*
- *Dimension Style Families*
- *Dimension Styles Overrides*
- *MLEADERSTYLE*

USING STYLES AND VARIABLES TO CONTROL DIMENSIONS

In AutoCAD LT, the appearance of dimensions on the drawing area and the manner in which they are saved in the drawing database are controlled by a set of dimension variables. The dimensioning commands use these variables as arguments. The variables that control the appearance of dimensions can be managed using dimension styles. You can use the **Dimension Style Manager** dialog box to control the dimension styles and dimension variables through a set of dialog boxes.

CREATING AND RESTORING DIMENSION STYLES

Ribbon: Annotate > Dimensions > Dimension, Dimension Style (The inclined arrow)
Toolbar: Dimension > Dimension Style or Styles > Dimension Style
Command: DIMSTYLE

The dimension styles control the appearance and positioning of dimensions and leaders in the drawing. If the default dimensioning style (Standard or Annotative) does not meet your requirements, you can select another existing dimensioning style or create a new one. The default names of the dimension style file are **Standard** and **Annotative**. Dimension styles can be created by using the **Dimension Style Manager** dialog box. Left-click on the inclined arrow in the **Dimensions** panel of the **Annotate** tab to invoke the **Dimension Style Manager** dialog box (Figure 10-1).

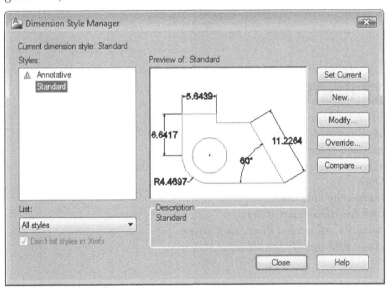

*Figure 10-1 The **Dimension Style Manager** dialog box*

In the **Dimension Style Manager** dialog box, choose the **New** button to display the **Create New Dimension Style** dialog box (Figure 10-2). Enter the dimension style name in the **New Style Name** text box and then select a style that you want to be basis of your style from the **Start With** drop-down list. Select the **Annotative** check box to make the new dimension style annotative. Choose the **i** (information) button to get the help and information about the annotative objects. The **Use for** drop-down list allows you to select the dimension type to which you want to apply the new dimension style. For example, if you wish to use the new style only for the diameter dimension, select **Diameter dimensions** from the **Use for** drop-down list. Choose the **Continue** button to display the **New Dimension Style** dialog box. The parameters of the **New Dimension Style** dialog box will be discussed later. After specifying the parameters of the new dimension style in the **New Dimension Style** dialog box, choose **OK**; the **Dimension Style Manager** dialog box will be displayed again. The options in this dialog box are discussed next.

In the **Dimension Style Manager** dialog box, the current dimension style name is shown in front of **Current dimension style** and is also shown highlighted in the **Styles** list box. A brief description of the current style (its differences from the default settings) is also displayed in the **Description** area. The **Dimension Style Manager** dialog box also has the **Preview of** window that displays the preview of the current dimension style. A style can be made current (restored) by selecting the name of the dimension style you want to make current from the list of defined dimension styles and choosing the

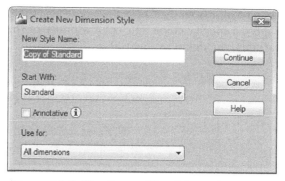

Figure 10-2 The Create New Dimension Style dialog box

Set Current button. You can also make a style current by double-clicking on the style name in the **Styles** list box. The list of dimension styles displayed in the **Styles** list box is dependent on the option selected from the **List** drop down-list. If you select the **Styles in use** option, only the dimension styles in use will be listed in the **Style** list box. If you right-click on a style in the **Styles** list box, a shortcut menu is displayed that provides you with the options to **Set current**, **Rename**, or **Delete** a dimension style. Selecting the **Don't list styles in Xrefs** check box does not list the names of Xref styles in the **Styles** list box. Choosing the **Modify** button displays the **Modify Dimension Style** dialog box where you can modify an existing style. Choosing the **Override** button displays the **Override Current Style** dialog box where you can define overrides to an existing style (discussed later in this chapter). Both these dialog boxes along with the **New Dimension Style** dialog box have identical properties. Choosing the **Compare** button displays the **Compare Dimension Styles** dialog box (also discussed later in this chapter) that allows you to compare two existing dimension styles.

Note
*The **Dimension Style** drop-down list in the **Dimensions** panel under the **Annotate** tab also displays the dimension styles. Selecting a dimension style from this list also sets it current.*

NEW DIMENSION STYLE DIALOG BOX

The **New Dimension Style** dialog box can be used to specify the dimensioning attributes (variables) that affect the various properties of the dimensions. The various tabs provided under the **New Dimension Style** dialog box are discussed next.

Lines Tab

The options in the **Lines** tab (Figure 10-3) of the **New Dimension Style** dialog box are used to specify the dimensioning attributes (variables) that affect the format of the dimension lines. For example, the appearance and behavior of the dimension lines and extension lines can be changed with this tab. If the settings of the dimension variables have not been altered in the current editing session, the settings displayed in the dialog box are the default settings.

Dimension lines Area

This area provides you with the options of controlling the display of the dimension lines and leader lines. These options are discussed next.

Color. This drop-down list is used to set the colors for the dimension lines and arrowheads. Its dimension arrowheads have the same color as the dimension line because arrows constitute a part of the dimension line. The color you set here will also be assigned to the leader lines and arrows. The default color for the dimension lines and arrows is ByBlock. You can specify the color of the dimension line by selecting it from the **Color** drop-down list. You can also select

Select **Color** from the **Color** drop-down list to display the **Select Color** dialog box where you can choose a specific color. The color number or the special color label is stored in the **DIMCLRD** variable, the default value is 0.

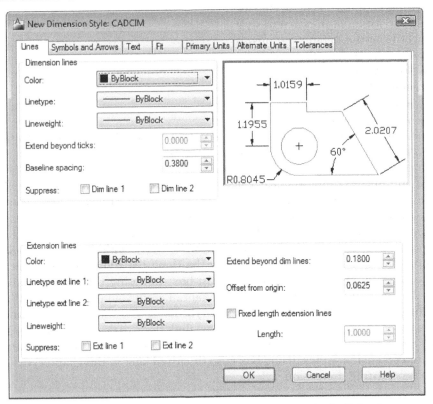

*Figure 10-3 The **Lines** tab of the **New Dimension Style** dialog box*

Linetype. This drop-down list is used to set the linetype for the dimension lines.

Lineweight. This drop-down list is used to specify the lineweight for the dimension line. You can select the required lineweight by selecting it from this drop-down list. This value is also stored in the **DIMLWD** variable. The default value is ByBlock. Remember that you cannot assign the lineweight to the arrowheads using this drop-down list.

Extend beyond ticks. The **Extend beyond ticks** spinner will be available only when you select the oblique, Architectural tick, or any such arrowhead type in the **First** and **Second** drop-down lists in the **Arrowheads** area from the **Symbols and Arrows** tab. This spinner is used to specify the distance by which the dimension line will extend beyond the extension line. The extension value, entered in the **Extend beyond ticks** edit box, gets stored in the **DIMDLE** variable. By default, this edit box is disabled because the oblique arrowhead type is not selected.

Baseline spacing. The **Baseline spacing** (baseline increment) spinner is used to control the spacing between successive dimension lines drawn using the baseline dimensioning, see Figure 10-4. You can specify the dimension line increment to your requirement by specifying the desired value using the **Baseline spacing** spinner. The default value displayed in the **Baseline spacing** spinner is 0.38 units. This spacing value is also stored in the **DIMDLI** variable.

Suppress. The **Suppress** check boxes control the display of the first and second dimension lines. By default, both dimension lines will be drawn. You can suppress one or both the dimension lines by selecting their corresponding check boxes. The values of these check boxes are stored in the **DIMSD1** and **DIMSD2** variables.

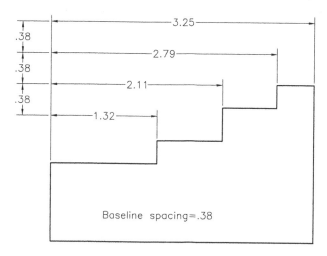

Figure 10-4 *Baseline increment*

 Note
The first and second dimension lines are determined by how you select the extension line origins. If the first extension line origin is on the right, the first dimension line will also be on the right.

Extension lines Area

The options in this area are discussed next.

Color. This drop-down list is used to control the color of the extension lines. The default extension line color is ByBlock. You can assign a new color to the extension lines by selecting it from this drop-down list. The color number or the color label is saved in the **DIMCLRE** variable.

Linetype ext line 1. The options in this drop-down list are used to specify the linetype of extension line 1. By default, the line type for the extension line 1 is set to ByBlock. You can change the linetype by selecting a new value of linetype from the drop-down list.

Linetype ext line 2. The options in this drop-down list are same as for the Linetype ext line 1. The options are used to specify the line type of extension line 2.

 Note
*You can specify different linetypes for the dimensions and the extensions lines. Use the **Linetype** drop-down list in the **Dimension Lines** area to specify the linetype for dimensions. Use the **Linetype ext line 1** and **Linetype ext line 2** drop-down lists to specify the linetype for the extension lines.*

Lineweight. This drop-down list is used to modify the lineweight of the extension lines. The default value is ByBlock. You can change the lineweight value by selecting a new value from this drop-down list. The value for lineweight is stored in the **DIMLWE** variable.

Extend beyond dim lines. It is the distance by which the extension lines extend past the dimension lines, see Figure 10-5. You can change the extension line offset using the **Extend beyond dim lines** spinner. This value is also stored in the **DIMEXE** variable. The default value for the extension distance is 0.1800 units.

Offset from origin. It is the distance by which the extension line is offset from the point you specify as the origin of the extension line, see Figure 10-6. You may need to override this setting for specific dimensions while dimensioning curves and angled lines. You can specify an offset distance of your choice using this spinner. AutoCAD LT stores this value in the **DIMEXO** variable. The default value for this distance is 0.0625.

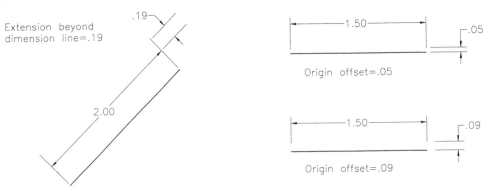

Figure 10-5 Extension beyond dimension lines   *Figure 10-6 The offset from origin*

Fixed length extension lines. With the selection of the **Fixed length extension lines** check box, you can specify a fixed length (starting from the dimension line to the origin) for the extension lines in the **Length** edit box. By default, the check box is cleared and the length spinner is not available. Once the check box is selected, you can specify the length of the extension line either by entering a numerical value in the **Length** edit box or using a spinner. Figure 10-7 displays a drawing with full length extension lines and Figure 10-8 displays the same drawing with fixed length extension lines.

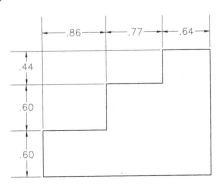

Figure 10-7 Drawings with full length extension lines

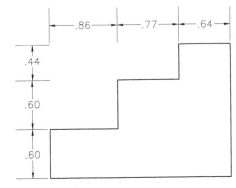

Figure 10-8 Drawing with fixed length extension lines

Suppress. The **Suppress** check boxes are used to control the display of the extension lines. By default, both extension lines will be drawn. You can suppress one or both of them by selecting the corresponding check boxes (Figure 10-9). The values of these check boxes are stored in the **DIMSE1** and **DIMSE2** variables.

Note
The first and second extension lines are determined by how you select the extension line origins. If the first extension line origin is on the right, the first extension line will also be on the right.

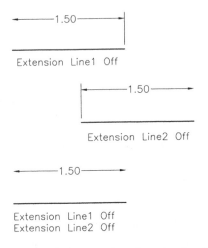

Figure 10-9 Suppressing the extension lines

Symbols and Arrows Tab

The options in the **Symbols and Arrows** tab (Figure 10-10) of the **New Dimension Style** dialog box are used to specify the variables and attributes that affect the format of the symbols and arrows. You can change the appearance of symbols and arrows.

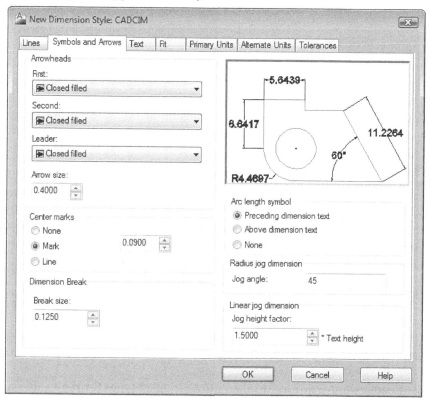

*Figure 10-10 The **Symbols and Arrows** tab of the **New Dimension Style** dialog box*

Arrowheads Area

The options in this area are used to specify the arrowheads and they are discussed next.

First/Second. When you create a dimension, AutoCAD LT draws the terminator symbols at the two ends of the dimension line. These terminator symbols, generally referred to as **arrowheads**, represent the beginning and end of a dimension. AutoCAD LT has provided nineteen standard termination symbols that you can apply at each end of the dimension line. In addition to these, you can create your own arrows or terminator symbols. By default, the same arrowhead type is applied at both ends of the dimension line. If you select the first arrowhead, it is automatically applied to the second end by default. However, if you want to specify a different arrowhead at the second dimension line endpoint, you must select the desired arrowhead type from the **Second** drop-down list. The first endpoint of the dimension line is the intersection point of the first extension line and the dimension line. The first extension line is determined by the first extension line origin. However, in angular dimensioning, the second endpoint is located in a counterclockwise direction from the first point, regardless of how the points were selected when creating the angular dimension. The specified arrowhead types are selected from the **First** and **Second** drop-down lists. The first arrowhead type is saved in the **DIMBLK1** system variable and the second arrowhead type is saved in the **DIMBLK2** system variable.

AutoCAD LT provides you with an option of specifying a user-defined arrowhead. To define a user-defined arrow, you must create one as a block. (See Chapter 14 for information regarding blocks.) Now, from the **First** or **Second** drop-down list, select **User Arrow**; the **Select Custom Arrow Block** dialog box will be displayed, see Figure 10-11.

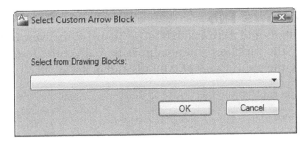

Figure 10-11 *The **Select Custom Arrow Block** dialog box*

All the blocks in the current drawing will be available in the **Select from Drawing Blocks** drop-down list. You can select the desired block and it will become the current arrowhead.

Creating an Arrowhead Block

1. To create a block for an arrowhead, you will use a 1 X 1 box, refer to Figure 10-12. AutoCAD LT automatically scales the X and Y scale factors of the block to the arrowhead size multiplied by the overall scale. You can specify the arrow size in the **Arrow size** spinner. The **DIMASZ** variable controls the length of the arrowhead. For example, if **DIMASZ** is set to 0.25, the length of the arrow will be 0.25 units. Also, if the length of the arrow is not 1 unit, it will leave a gap between the dimension line and the arrowhead block.

2. The arrowhead must be drawn as it would appear on the right side of the dimension line. Choose the **Create** tool from **Block** panel in the **Home** tab to convert it into a block.

3. The insertion point of the arrowhead block must be the point that will coincide with the extension line, see Figure 10-12.

Leader. The **Leader** drop-down list displays the arrowhead types for the Leader arrow. Here, also, you can either select the standard arrowheads from the drop-down list or select **User Arrow** that allows you to define and use a user-defined arrowhead type.

Arrow size. This spinner is used to define the size of the arrowhead, see Figure 10-13. The default value is 0.18 unit, which is stored in the **DIMASZ** system variable.

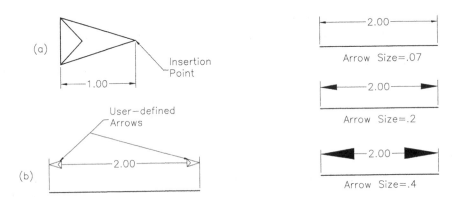

Figure 10-12 *Creating user-defined arrows*

Figure 10-13 *Defining arrow sizes*

Center marks Area

This area deals with the options that control the appearance of the center marks and centerlines in the radius and diameter dimensioning. However, keep in mind that the center marks or the centerlines will be drawn only when dimensions are placed outside the circle.

None. If you select the **None** radio button, no mark or line will be drawn at the center of the circle.

Mark. If you select the **Mark** radio button, a mark will be drawn at the center of the circle.

Line. If you select the **Line** radio button, the centerlines will be drawn at the center of the circles.

The spinner in the **Center marks** area is used to set the size of the center marks or centerlines. This value is stored in the **DIMCEN** variable. The default value of this variable is 0.09.

Note

*If you use the **DIMCEN** command, a positive value will create a center mark, whereas a negative value will create a centerline. If the value is 0, AutoCAD LT does not create center marks or centerlines.*

Dimension Break Area

The **Break size** spinner in this area is used to control the default break length in the dimension while applying the break dimensions. The default value of **Break size** is 0.125. Figure 10-14 shows a drawing with dimensioning breaks.

Arc length symbol Area

The radio buttons in this area are used to specify the position of arc when applying the arc length dimension.

Preceding dimension text. If you select the **Preceding dimension text** radio button, the arc symbol will appear before the dimension text while applying the arc length dimension.

Above dimension text. With the **Above dimension text** radio button selected, the arc symbol in the arc length dimension will appear above the dimension text.

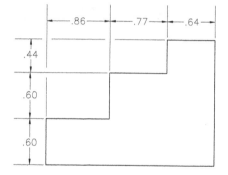

Figure 10-14 Drawing with dimension breaks

None. Select the **None** radio button, if you do not want the arc symbol to appear with the arc length dimension.

Radius jog dimension Area

The **Jog angle** edit box in this area is used to specify the angle of jog that appears while applying the jogged radius dimension. By default, its value is 45°.

Linear jog dimension Area

The option in this area is used to control the height of the jog (vertical height from the vertex of one jog angle to another) that appears while applying the jogged linear dimension. The jog height is always maintained with respect to the text height of the dimension. The **Jog height factor** spinner is used to change the factor that will be multiplied with the text height to calculate the linear jog height.

Note

*Unlike specifying a negative value for the **DIMCEN** variable, you cannot enter a negative value in the **Size** spinner. Selecting **Line** from the **Type** drop-down list automatically treats the value in the **Size** spinner as the size for the centerlines and sets **DIMCEN** to the negative of the value shown.*

EXERCISE 1

Draw and dimension the drawing, as shown in Figure 10-15. Assume the missing dimensions.

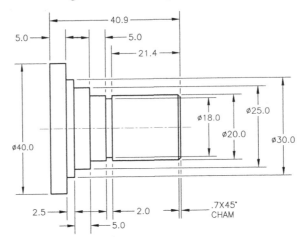

Figure 10-15 Drawing for Exercise 1

CONTROLLING THE DIMENSION TEXT FORMAT

Text Tab

You can control the dimension text format through the **Text** tab of the **New Dimension Style** dialog box (Figure 10-16). In the **Text** tab, you can control the parameters such as the placement, appearance, horizontal and vertical alignment of the dimension text, and so on. For example, you can force AutoCAD LT to align the dimension text along the dimension line. You can also force the dimension text to be displayed at the top of the dimension line. You can save the settings in a

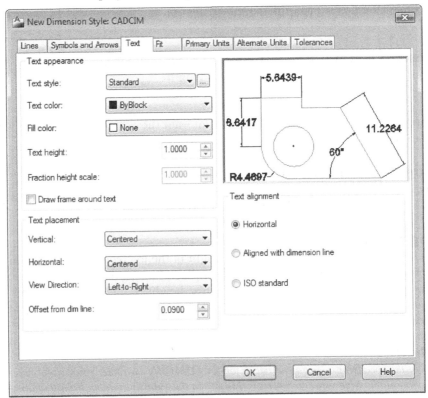

*Figure 10-16 The **Text** tab of the **New Dimension Style** dialog box*

dimension style file for future use. The **New Dimension Style** dialog box has a **Preview** window that updates dynamically to display the text placement as the settings are changed. Individual items of the **Text** tab and the related dimension variables are described next.

Text appearance Area

The options in this area are discussed next.

Text style. The **Text style** drop-down list displays the names of the predefined text styles. From this list, you can select the style name that you want to use for dimensioning. You must define the text style before you can use it in dimensioning (see "**Creating Text Styles**" in Chapter 7). Choosing the [...] button displays the **Text Style** dialog box that allows you to create a new or modify an existing text style. The value of this setting is stored in the **DIMTXSTY** system variable. The change in the dimension text style does not affect the text style you are using to draw the other text in the drawing.

Text color. This drop-down list is used to modify the color of the dimension text. The default color is **ByBlock**. If you choose the **Select Color** option from the **Text color** drop-down list, the **Select Color** dialog box is displayed, where you can choose a specific color. This color or color number is stored in the **DIMCLRT** variable.

Fill color. This drop-down list is used to set the fill color of the dimension text. A box of the selected color will be placed around the dimension text.

Text height. This spinner is used to modify the height of the dimension text, see Figure 10-17. You can change the dimension text height only when the current text style does not have a fixed height. In other words, the text height specified in the **STYLE** command should be zero. This is because a predefined text height (specified in the **STYLE** command) overrides any other setting for the dimension text height. This value is stored in the **DIMTXT** variable. The default text height is 0.1800 units.

Fraction height scale. This spinner is used to set the scale of the fractional units in relation to the dimension text height. This spinner will be available only when you select a format for the primary units, in which you can define the values in fractions, such as architectural or fractional. This value is stored in the **DIMTFAC** variable.

Draw frame around text. Select this check box to draw a frame around the dimension text, see Figure 10-18. This value is stored as a negative value in the **DIMGAP** system variable.

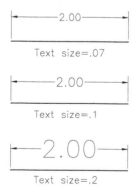

Figure 10-17 Changing the dimension height

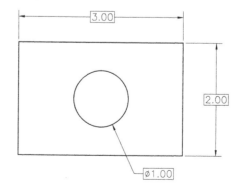

Figure 10-18 Dimension text inside the frame

Text placement Area

The options in this area are discussed next.

Vertical. The **Vertical** drop-down list displays the options that control the vertical placement of the dimension text. The current setting is highlighted. Controlling the vertical placement of the dimension text is possible only when the dimension text is drawn in its normal (default) location. This setting is stored in the **DIMTAD** system variable. The options in this drop-down list are discussed next.

Centered. If this option is selected, the dimension text gets positioned on the dimension line in such a way that the dimension line is split to allow for the placement of the text, see Figure 10-19. If the **1st** or **2nd Extension Line** option is selected in the **Horizontal** drop-down list, this centered setting will position the text on the extension line, not on the dimension line.

Above. If this option is selected, the dimension text is placed above the dimension line, except when the dimension line is not horizontal and the dimension text inside the extension lines is horizontal. The distance of the dimension text from the dimension line is controlled by the **DIMGAP** variable. This results in an unbroken solid dimension line under the dimension text, see Figure 10-19.

Outside. This option places the dimension text on the side of the dimension line.

JIS. This option lets you place the dimension text to conform to the **JIS** (Japanese Industrial Standards) representation.

Below. This option places the dimension text below the dimension line.

Note
*The horizontal and vertical placement options selected are reflected in the dimensions shown in the **Preview** window.*

Horizontal. This drop-down list is used to control the horizontal placement of the dimension text. You can select the required horizontal placement from this list. However, remember that these options will be useful only when the **Place text manually** check box in the **Fine Tuning** area of the **Fit** tab is cleared. The options in this drop-down list are discussed next.

Centered. This option is used to the dimension text between the extension lines. This is the default option.

At Ext Line 1. This option is used to place the text near the first extension line along the dimension line, see Figure 10-20.

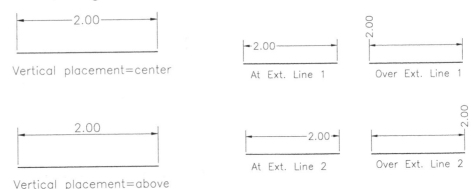

Figure 10-19 Vertical text placement   *Figure 10-20 Horizontal text placement*

At Ext Line 2. This option is selected to place the text near the second extension line along the dimension line, see Figure 10-20.

Over Ext Line 1. This option is selected to place the text over the first extension line and also along the first extension line, see Figure 10-20.

Over Ext Line 2. This option is selected to place the text over the second extension line and also along the second extension line, see Figure 10-20.

Offset from dim line. This spinner is used to specify the distance between the dimension line and the dimension text (Figure 10-21). You can set the text gap you need using this spinner. The text gap value is also used as the measure of minimum length for the segments of the dimension line and in basic tolerance. The default value specified in this box is 0.09 units. The value of this setting is stored in the **DIMGAP** system variable.

Text alignment Area

The options in this area are discussed next.

Horizontal. This is the default option and if selected, the dimension text is drawn horizontally with respect to the current UCS (user coordinate system). The alignment of the dimension line does not affect the text alignment. Selecting this radio button turns both the **DIMTIH** and **DIMTOH** system variables **on**. The text is drawn horizontally even if the dimension line is at an angle.

Aligned with dimension line. If this radio button is selected then the text aligns with the dimension line (Figure 10-22) and both the system variables **DIMTIH** and **DIMTOH** are turned off.

ISO standard. If you select the **ISO Standard** radio button, the dimension text is aligned with the dimension line, only when the dimension text is inside the extension lines. Selecting this option turns the system variable **DIMTOH** on, that is, the dimension text outside the extension line is horizontal, regardless of the angle of the dimension line.

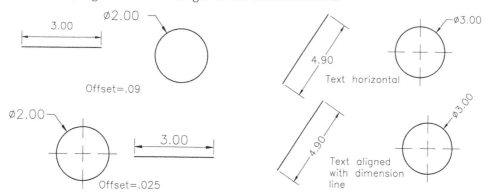

Figure 10-21 Offset from the dimension line   *Figure 10-22 Specifying the text alignment*

EXERCISE 2

Draw Figure 10-23 and then set the values in the **Lines**, **Symbols and Arrows**, and **Text** tabs of the **New Dimension Style** dialog box to dimension the drawing, as shown in the figure. (Baseline spacing = 0.25, Extension beyond dimension lines = 0.10, Offset from origin = 0.05, Arrow size = 0.09, Text height = 0.08.)

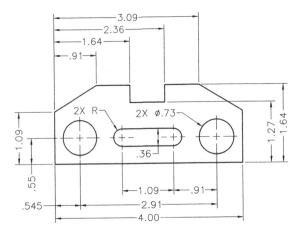

Figure 10-23 *Drawing for Exercise 2*

FITTING DIMENSION TEXT AND ARROWHEADS
Fit Tab
The options in this area are discussed next.

The **Fit** tab provides you with the options that are used to control the placement of dimension lines, arrowheads, leader lines, text, and the overall dimension scale (Figure 10-24).

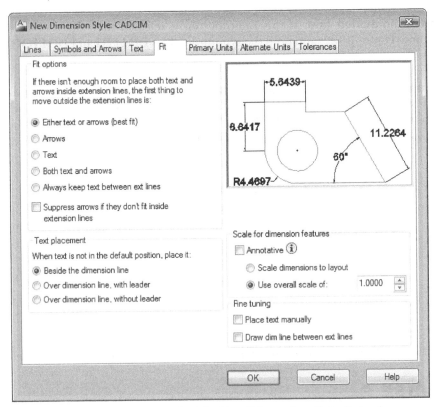

Figure 10-24 *The **Fit** tab of the **New Dimension Style** dialog box*

Fit options Area
The options in this area are used to set the priorities for moving the text and arrowheads outside the extension lines, if the space between the extension lines is not enough to fit both of them.

Either text or arrows (best fit). This is the default option. In this option, AutoCAD LT places the dimension where it fits best between the extension lines.

Arrows. When you select this option, AutoCAD LT places the text and arrowheads inside the extension lines if there is enough space to fit both. If the space is not available, the arrows are moved outside the extension lines. If there is not enough space for text, both text and arrowheads are placed outside the extension lines.

Text. When you select this option, AutoCAD LT places the text and arrowheads inside the extension lines, if there is enough space to fit both. If there is enough space to fit the arrows, the arrows will be placed inside and the dimension text moves outside the extension lines. However, if there is not enough space for either the text or the arrowheads, both are placed outside the extension lines.

Both text and arrows. If you select this option, AutoCAD LT will place the arrows and dimension text between the extension lines, if there is enough space available to fit both. Otherwise, both the text and arrowheads are placed outside the extension lines.

Always keep text between ext lines. This option always keeps the text between the extension lines even in cases where AutoCAD LT would not do so. Selecting this radio button does not affect the radius and diameter dimensions. The value is stored in the **DIMTIX** variable and the default value is off.

Suppress arrows if they don't fit inside extension lines. If you select this check box, the arrowheads are suppressed if the space between the extension lines is not enough to adjust them. The value is stored in the **DIMSOXD** variable and the default value is off.

Text placement Area

This area provides you with the options to position the dimension text when it is moved from the default position. The value is stored in the **DIMTMOVE** variable. The options in this area are as follows:

Beside the dimension line. This option places the dimension text beside the dimension line.

Over dimension line, with leader. Selecting this option places the dimension text away from the dimension line and a leader line is created, which connects the text to the dimension line. But, if the dimension line is too close to the text, a leader is not drawn. The Horizontal placement decides whether the text is placed to the right or left of the leader.

Over dimension line, without leader. In this option, AutoCAD LT does not create a leader line, if there is insufficient space to fit the dimension text between the extension lines. The dimension text can be moved freely, independent of the dimension line.

Scale for dimension features Area

The options under this area are used to set the value for the overall dimension scale or scaling to the paper space.

Annotative. This check box is used to specify that the selected dimension style is annotative. With this option, you can also convert an existing non-annotative dimension style to annotative and vice-versa. If you select the **Annotative** check box from the **Create New Dimension Style** dialog box, then the **Annotative** check box will also be selected by default.

Chapter 10

Use overall scale of. The current general scaling factor that pertains to all of the size-related dimension variables, such as text size, center mark size, and arrowhead size, is displayed in the **Use overall scale of** spinner. You can alter the scaling factor to your requirement by entering the scaling factor of your choice in this spinner. Altering the contents of this box alters the value of the **DIMSCALE** variable, since the current scaling factor is stored in it. The overall scale (**DIMSCALE**) is not applied to the measured lengths, coordinates, angles, or tolerance. The default value for this variable is 1.0. In this condition, the dimensioning variables assume their preset values and the drawing is plotted at full scale. The scale factor is the reciprocal of the drawing size and so the drawing is to be plotted at the half size. The overall scale factor (**DIMSCALE**) will be the reciprocal of ½, which is 2.

Note

*If you are in the middle of the dimensioning process and you change the **DIMSCALE** value and save the changed setting in a dimension style file, the dimensions with that style will be updated.*

Tip

*When you increase the limits of the drawing, you need to increase the overall scale of the drawing using the **Use overall scale of** spinner before dimensioning. This will save the time required in changing the individual scale factors of all the dimension parameters.*

Scale dimensions to layout. If you select the **Scale dimensions to layout** radio button, the scale factor between the current model space viewport and the floating viewport is computed automatically. Also, by selecting this radio button, you disable the **Use overall scale of** spinner (it is disabled in the dialog box) and the overall scale factor is set to 0. When the overall scale factor is assigned a value of 0, AutoCAD LT calculates an acceptable default value based on the scaling between the current model space viewport and the paper space. If you are in the paper space (**TILEMODE=0**), or are not using the **Scale dimensions to layout** feature, AutoCAD LT sets the overall scale factor to 1; otherwise, AutoCAD LT calculates a scale factor that makes it possible to plot text sizes, arrow sizes, and other scaled distances at the values, in which they have been previously set. (For further details regarding model space and layouts, refer to Chapter 11.)

Fine tuning Area

The **Fine tuning** area provides additional options governing placement of the dimension text. The options are as follows.

Place text manually. When you dimension, AutoCAD LT places the dimension text in the middle of the dimension line (if there is enough space). If you select the **Place text manually** check box, you can position the dimension text anywhere along the dimension line. You will also notice that when you select this check box, the **Horizontal Justification** is ignored. This setting is saved in the **DIMUPT** system variable. The default value of this variable is **off**. Selecting this check box enables you to position the dimension text anywhere along the dimension line.

Draw dim line between ext lines. This check box is selected when you want the dimension line to appear between the extension lines, even if the text and dimension lines are placed outside the extension lines. When you select this option in the radius and diameter dimensions (when default text placement is horizontal), the dimension line and arrows are drawn inside the circle or arc, and the text and leader are drawn outside. If you select the **Draw dim line between ext lines** check box, the **DIMTOFL** variable is set to on by AutoCAD LT. Its default setting is off.

FORMATTING PRIMARY DIMENSION UNITS
Primary Units Tab

You can use the **Primary Units** tab of the **New Dimension Style** dialog box to control the dimension text format and precision values (Figure 10-25). You can use the options under this tab to control Units, Dimension Precision, and Zero Suppression for dimension measurements. AutoCAD LT lets you attach a user-defined prefix or suffix to the dimension text. For example, you can define the diameter symbol as a prefix by entering %%C in the **Prefix** edit box; AutoCAD LT will automatically attach the diameter symbol in front of the dimension text. Similarly, you can define a unit type, such as **mm**, as a suffix; AutoCAD LT will then attach **mm** at the end of every dimension text. This tab also enables you to define zero suppression, precision, and dimension text format.

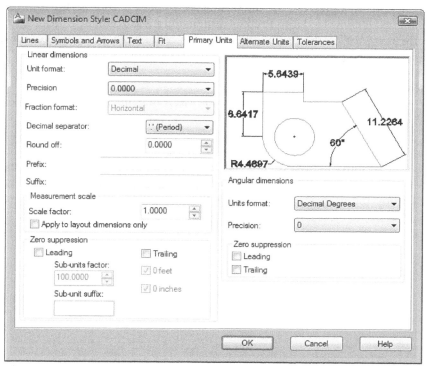

*Figure 10-25 The **Primary Units** tab of the **New Dimension Style** dialog box*

Linear dimensions Area
The options in this area are discussed next.

Unit format. This drop-down list provides you with the options of specifying the units for the primary dimensions. The formats include **Decimal**, **Scientific**, **Architectural**, **Engineering**, **Fraction**, and **Windows Desktop**. Remember that by selecting a dimension unit format, the drawing units (which you might have selected by using the **UNITS** command) are not affected. The unit setting for linear dimensions is stored in the **DIMLUNIT** system variable.

Precision. This drop-down list is used to control the number of decimal places for the primary units. The setting for precision (number of decimal places) is saved in the **DIMDEC** variable.

Fraction format. This drop-down list is used to set the fraction format. The options are Diagonal, Horizontal, and not stacked. This drop-down list will be available only when you select **Architectural** or **Fractional** from the **Unit format** drop-down list. The value is stored in the **DIMFRAC** variable.

Decimal separator. This drop-down list is used to select an option that will be used as the decimal separator. For example, Period [.], Comma [,] or Space [ ]. If you have selected Windows desktop units in the **Unit Format** drop-down list, AutoCAD LT uses the Decimal symbol settings. The value is stored in the **DIMDSEP** variable.

Round off. The **Round off** spinner is used to set the value for rounding off the dimension values. The number of decimal places of the round off value should always be less than or equal to the value in the **Precision** edit box. For example, if the **Round off** spinner is set to 0.05, all dimensions will be rounded off to the nearest 0.05 unit. Therefore, the value 1.06 will round off to 1.05 and the value 1.09 will round off to 1.10, see Figure 10-26. The value is stored in the **DIMRND** variable and the default value in the **Round off** edit box is 0.

Prefix. You can append a prefix to the dimension measurement by entering it in this edit box. The dimension text is converted into **Prefix<dimension measurement>** format. For example, if you enter the text "Abs" in the **Prefix** edit box, "Abs" will be placed in front of the dimension text (Figure 10-27). The prefix string is saved in the **DIMPOST** system variable.

Note
*Once you specify a prefix, default prefixes such as **R** in radius dimensioning and ∅ in diameter dimensioning are cancelled.*

Suffix. Just like appending a prefix, you can append a suffix to the dimension measurement by entering the desired suffix in this edit box. For example, if you enter the text **mm** in the **Suffix** edit box, the dimension text will have <dimension measurement>mm format, see Figure 10-25. AutoCAD LT stores the suffix string in the **DIMPOST** variable.

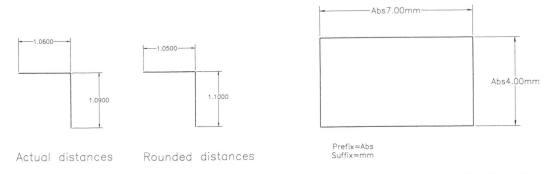

Figure 10-26 Rounding off the dimension measurements

Figure 10-27 Adding prefix and suffix to the dimensions

Tip
*The **DIMPOST** variable is used to append both prefix and suffix to the dimension text. This variable takes a string value as its argument. For example, if you want to have a suffix for centimeters, set **DIMPOST** to cm. To establish a prefix to a dimension text, type the prefix text string and then "<>".*

Measurement scale Area
The options in this area are discussed next.

Scale factor. You can specify a global scale factor for the linear dimension measurements by setting the desired scale factor in the **Scale factor** spinner. All the linear distances measured by dimensions, which include radii, diameters, and coordinates, are multiplied by the existing value in this spinner. For example, if the value of the **Scale factor** spinner is set to 2, two unit segments will be dimensioned as 4 units (2 X 2). However, the angular dimensions are not affected. In this manner, the value of the linear scaling factor affects the contents of the default (original) dimension text (Figure 10-28). The default value for linear scaling is 1. With the default value, the dimension text generated is the actual measurement of the object being dimensioned. The linear scaling value is saved in the **DIMLFAC** variable.

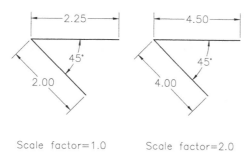

Figure 10-28 *Identical figures dimensioned using different scale factors*

Note
The linear scaling value is not exercised on rounding a value, or on plus or minus tolerance value. Therefore, changing the linear scaling factor will not affect the tolerance values.

Apply to layout dimensions only. When you select the **Apply to layout dimensions only** check box, the scale factor value is applied only to the dimensions in the layout. The value is stored as a negative value in the **DIMLFAC** variable. If you change the **DIMLFAC** variable from the **Dim:** prompt, AutoCAD LT displays the viewport option to calculate the **DIMLFAC** variable. First, set the **TILEMODE** to 0 (paper space), and then invoke the **MVIEW** command to get the **Viewport** option.

Zero suppression Area
The options in this area are used to suppress the leading or trailing zeros in the dimensioning. This area provides you with four check boxes. These check boxes can be selected to suppress the leading or trailing zeros or zeros in the feet and inches. The **0 feet** and the **0 inches** check boxes will be available only when you select **Engineering** or **Architectural** from the **Unit format** drop-down list. When the Architectural units are being used, the **Leading** and **Trailing** check boxes are disabled. For example, if you select the **0 feet** check box, the dimension text 0'-8 ¾" becomes 8 ¾". By default, the 0 feet and 0 inches value is suppressed. If you want to suppress the inches part of a feet-and-inches dimension when the distance in the feet portion is an integer value and the inches portion is zero, select the **0 inches** check box. For example, if you select the **0 inches** check box, the dimension text 3'-0" becomes 3'. Similarly, if you select the **Leading** check box, the dimension that was initially 0.53 will become .53. If you select the **Trailing** check box, the dimension that was initially 2.0 will become 2.

Angular dimensions Area
This area provides you with the options to control the units format, precision, and zero suppression for the Angular units.

Units format. The **Units format** drop-down list displays a list of unit formats for the angular dimensions. The default value, in which the angular dimensions are displayed, is **Decimal Degrees**. The value governing the unit setting for the angular dimensions is stored in the **DIMAUNIT** variable.

Precision. You can select the number of decimal places for the angular dimensions from this drop-down list. This value is stored in the **DIMADEC** variable.

Zero suppression Area. Similar to the linear dimensions, you can suppress the **leading**, **trailing**, neither, or both zeros in the angular dimensions by selecting the respective check boxes in this area. The value is stored in the **DIMAZIN** variable.

FORMATTING ALTERNATE DIMENSION UNITS
Alternate Units Tab

By default, the options in the **Alternate Units** tab of the **New Dimension Style** dialog box is disabled and the value of the **DIMALT** variable is turned off. If you want to perform alternate units dimensioning, select the **Display alternate units** check box. By doing so, AutoCAD LT activates various options in this area (Figure 10-29). This tab sets the format, precision, angles, placement, scale, and so on for the alternate units in use. In this tab, you can specify the values that will be applied to the alternate dimensions.

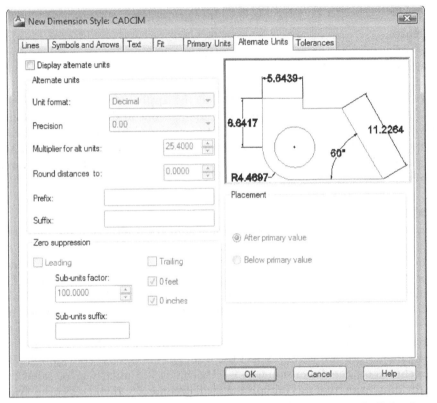

*Figure 10-29 The **Alternate Units** tab of the **New Dimension Style** dialog box*

Alternate units Area

The options in this area are identical to those under the **Linear dimensions** area of the **Primary Units** tab. This area provides you with the options to set the format for all dimension types.

Unit format. You can select a unit format to apply to the alternate dimensions from this drop-down list. The options under this drop-down list include Scientific, Decimal, Engineering, Architectural stacked, Fractional stacked, Architectural, Fractional, and Windows Desktop. The value is stored in the **DIMALTU** variable. The relative size of fractions is governed by the **DIMTFAC** variable.

Precision. You can select the number of decimal places for the alternate units from the **Precision** drop-down list. The value is stored in the **DIMALTD** variable.

Multiplier for alt units. To generate a value in the alternate system of measurement, you need a factor with which all the linear dimensions will be multiplied. The value for this factor can be set using the **Multiplier for alt units** spinner. The default value of 25.4 is for dimensioning in inches with the alternate units in millimeters. This scaling value (contents of the **Multiplier for alt units** spinner) is stored in the **DIMALTF** variable.

Round distances to. This spinner is used to set a value to which you want all your measurements (made in alternate units) to be rounded off. This value is stored in the **DIMALTRND** system variable. For example, if you set the value of the **Round distances to** spinner to 0.25, all the alternate dimensions get rounded off to the nearest .25 unit.

Prefix/Suffix. The **Prefix** and **Suffix** edit boxes are similar to the edit boxes in the **Linear dimensions** area of the **Primary Units** tab. You can enter the text or symbols that you want to precede or follow the alternate dimension text. The value is stored in the **DIMAPOST** variable. You can also use control codes and special characters to display special symbols.

Zero suppression Area

This area allows you to suppress the leading or trailing zeros in decimal unit dimensions by selecting either, both, or none of the **Trailing** and **Leading** check boxes. Similarly, selecting the **0 feet** check box suppresses the zeros in the feet area of the dimension, when the dimension value is less than a foot. Selecting the **0 inches** check box suppresses the zeros in the inches area of the dimension. For example, 1'-0" becomes 1'. The **DIMALTZ** variable controls the suppression of zeros for alternate unit dimension values. The values that are between 0 and 3 affect the feet-and-inch dimensions only.

Placement Area

This area provides the options that control the positioning of the Alternate units. The value is stored in the **DIMAPOST** variable.

After primary value. Selecting the **After primary value** radio button places the alternate units dimension text after the primary units. This is the default option, see Figure 10-30.

Below primary value. Selecting the **Below primary value** radio button places the alternate units dimension text below the primary units, see Figure 10-30.

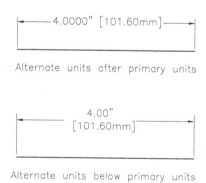

Figure 10-30 Placement of alternate units

FORMATTING THE TOLERANCES
Tolerances Tab

The **Tolerances** tab (Figure 10-31) allows you to set the parameters for options that control the format and display of the tolerance dimension text. These include the alternate unit tolerance dimension text.

Tolerance format Area

The **Tolerance format** area of the **Tolerances** tab (Figure 10-31) is used to specify the tolerance method, tolerance value, position of tolerance text, and precision and height of the tolerance text. For example, if you do not want a dimension to deviate more than plus 0.01 and minus 0.02, you can specify this by selecting **Deviation** from the **Method** drop-down list and then specifying the plus and minus deviation in the **Upper Value** and the **Lower Value** edit boxes. When you

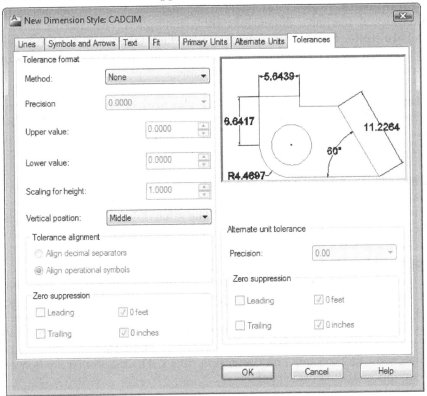

*Figure 10-31 The **Tolerances** tab of the **New Dimension Style** dialog box*

dimension, AutoCAD LT will automatically append the tolerance to it. The **DIMTP** variable sets the maximum (or upper) tolerance limit for the dimension text and **DIMTM** variable sets the minimum (or lower) tolerance limit for the dimension text. Different settings and their effects on relevant dimension variables are explained in the following sections.

Method. The **Method** drop-down list lets you select the tolerance method. The tolerance methods supported by AutoCAD LT are **Symmetrical**, **Deviation**, **Limits**, and **Basic**. These tolerance methods are described next.

None. Selecting the **None** option sets the **DIMTOL** variable to 0 and does not add tolerance values to the dimension text, that is, the **Tolerances** tab is disabled.

Symmetrical. This option is used to specify the symmetrical tolerances. When you select this option, the **Lower Value** spinner is disabled and the value specified in the **Upper Value** spinner is applied to both plus and minus tolerances. For example, if the value specified in the **Upper Value** spinner is 0.05, the tolerance appended to the dimension text is ±0.05, see Figure 10-32. The value of **DIMTOL** is set to 1 and the value of **DIMLIM** is set to 0.

Deviation. If you select the **Deviation** tolerance method, the values in the **Upper Value** and **Lower Value** spinners will be displayed as plus and minus dimension tolerances. If you enter values for the plus and minus tolerances, AutoCAD LT appends a plus sign (+) to the positive values of the tolerance and a negative sign (–) to the negative values of the tolerance. For example, if the upper value of the tolerance is 0.005 and the lower value of the tolerance is 0.002, the resulting dimension text generated will have a positive tolerance of 0.005 and a negative tolerance of 0.002

(Figure 10-32). Even if one of the tolerance values is 0, a sign is appended to it. On specifying the deviation tolerance, AutoCAD LT sets the **DIMTOL** variable value to 1 and the **DIMLIM** variable value to 0. The values in the **Upper Value** and **Lower Value** edit boxes are saved in the **DIMTP** and **DIMTM** system variables, respectively.

Limits. If you select the **Limits** tolerance method from the **Method** drop-down list, AutoCAD LT adds the upper value (contents of the **Upper Value** spinner) to the dimension text (actual measurement) and subtracts the lower value (contents of the **Lower Value** spinner) from the dimension text. The resulting values are displayed as the dimension text, see Figure 10-32. Selecting the **Limits** tolerance method results in setting the **DIMLIM** variable value to 1 and the **DIMTOL** variable value to 0. The numeral values in the **Upper Value** and **Lower Value** edit boxes are saved in the **DIMTP** and **DIMTM** system variables, respectively.

Basic. A basic dimension text is a dimension text with a box drawn around it (Figure 10-32). The basic dimension is also called a reference dimension. Reference dimensions are used primarily in geometric dimensioning and tolerances. The basic dimension can be realized by selecting the basic tolerance method. The distance provided around the dimension text (distance between dimension text and the rectangular box) is stored as a negative value in the **DIMGAP** variable. The negative value signifies the basic dimension. The default setting is off, resulting in the generation of dimensions without the box around the dimension text.

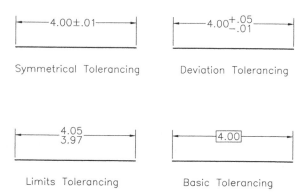

Figure 10-32 Specifying tolerance using various tolerancing methods

Precision. The **Precision** drop-down list is used to select the number of decimal places for the tolerance dimension text. The value is stored in **DIMTDEC** variable.

Upper value/Lower value. In the **Upper value** spinner, the positive upper or maximum value is specified. If the method of tolerances is symmetrical, the same value is used as the lower value also. The value is stored in the **DIMTP** variable. In the **Lower** spinner, the lower or minimum value is specified. The value is stored in the **DIMTM** variable.

Scaling for height. The **Scaling for height** spinner is used to specify the height of the dimension tolerance text relative to the dimension text height. The default value is 1, which means the height of the tolerance text is the same as the dimension text height. If you want the tolerance text to be 75 percent of the dimension height text, enter 0.75 in the **Scaling for height** edit box. The ratio of the tolerance height to the dimension text height is calculated by AutoCAD LT and then stored in the **DIMTFAC** variable. **DIMTFAC = Tolerance Height/Text Height.**

Vertical position. This drop-down list allows you to specify the location of the tolerance text for deviation and symmetrical methods only. The three alignments that are possible are with the **Bottom**, **Middle**, or **Top** of the main dimension text. The settings are saved in the **DIMTOLJ** system variable (Bottom=0, Middle=1, and Top=2).

Chapter 10

Tolerance alignment Area

The options in this area are used to control the alignment of the tolerance value text when they are placed in stacked condition. These options get highlighted only when you select the **Deviation** or **Limit** option from the **Method** drop-down list. Select the **Align decimal separators** radio button to align the tolerance text vertically along the decimal point, see Figure 10-33(a). Select the **Align operational symbols** radio button to align the tolerance text vertically along the plus sign (+) and negative sign(-), see Figure 10-33(b).

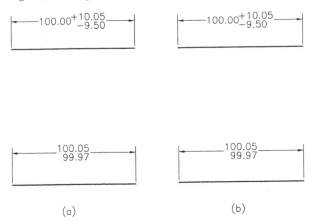

(a)   (b)

Figure 10-33 Various tolerance alignment options

Zero suppression Area

This area controls the zero suppression in the tolerance text depending on which one of the check boxes is selected. Selecting the **Leading** check box suppresses the leading zeros in all the decimal tolerance text. For example, 0.2000 becomes .2000. Selecting the **Trailing** check box suppresses the trailing zeros in all the decimal tolerance text. For example, 0.5000 becomes 0.5. Similarly, selecting both the boxes suppresses both the trailing and leading zeros and selecting none, suppresses none. If you select **0 feet** check box, the zeros in the feet portion of the tolerance dimension text are suppressed if the dimension value is less than one foot. Similarly, selecting the **0 inches** check box suppresses the zeros in the inches portion of the dimension text. The value is stored in the **DIMTZIN** variable.

Alternate unit tolerance Area

The options in this area define the precision and zero suppression settings for the Alternate unit tolerance values. The options under this area will be available only when you display the alternate units along with the primary units.

Precision. This drop-down list is used to set the number of decimal places to be displayed in the tolerance text of the alternate dimensions. This value is stored in the **DIMALTTD** variable.

Zero suppression Area

Selecting the respective check boxes controls the suppression of the **Leading** and **Trailing** zeros in decimal values and the suppression of zeros in the Feet and Inches portions for dimensions in the feet and inches format. The value is stored in the **DIMALTTZ** variable.

EXERCISE 3   *Dimension Style*

Draw Figure 10-34 and then set the values in various tabs of the **New Dimension Style** dialog box to dimension it, as shown. (Baseline spacing = 0.25, Extension beyond dim lines = 0.10, Offset from origin = 0.05, Arrowhead size =0.07, Text height = 0.08.) Assume the missing dimensions.

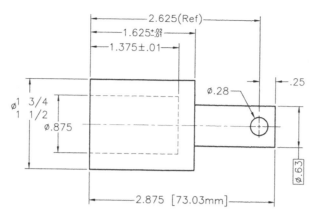

Figure 10-34 *Drawing for Exercise 3*

EXAMPLE 1   *Dimension Style Override*

In this example, you will update the overall dimension (3.00) so that the tolerance is displayed with the dimension. You will also add linear dimensions, as shown in Figure 10-35.

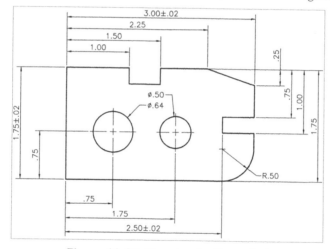

Figure 10-35 *Drawing for Example 1*

This problem can be solved by using dimension style overrides as well as by using the **Properties** palette. However, here only the dimension style overrides method is discussed.

1. Invoke the **Dimension Style Manager** dialog box. Select **MyStyle** from the **Styles** list box and choose the **Override** button to display the **Override Current Style: MyStyle** dialog box. The options in this dialog box are the same as in the **New Dimension Style** dialog box discussed earlier in this chapter.

2. Choose the **Tolerances** tab and select **Symmetrical** from the **Method** drop-down list.

3. Set the value of the **Precision** spinner to two decimal places. Set the value of the **Upper value** spinner to **0.02** and select the **Leading** check box in the **Zero suppression** area. Next, choose the **OK** button to exit the dialog box (this does not save the style). On doing so, you will notice that **<style overrides>** is displayed under **MyStyle** in the **Styles** list box, indicating that the style overrides the **MyStyle** dimension style.

4. The **<style overrides>** is displayed until you save it under a new name or under the style it is displayed in, or until you delete it. Select **<style overrides>** and right-click to display the shortcut menu. Choose the **Save to current style** option from the shortcut menu to save the overrides to the current style. Choosing the **Rename** option allows you to rename the style override and save it as a new style.

5. Choose the **Update** tool from the **Dimension** panel in the **Annotate** tab and select the dimension that measures **3.00**. The dimension now displays the symmetrical tolerance.

6. Draw the remaining two linear dimensions. They will automatically appear with the tolerances, see Figure 10-35.

Tip
*You can also use the **DIMOVERRIDE** command to apply the change to the existing dimensions. Apply the changes to the **DIMTOL**, **DIMTP**, and **DIMTM** variables.*

CREATING AND RESTORING MULTILEADER STYLES

Ribbon: Annotate > Leaders > Multileader Style Manager (*Inclined arrow*)
Toolbar: Multileader > Multileader Style   or   Styles > Multileader Style
Command: MLEADERSTYLE

The multileader styles control the appearance and positioning of multileaders in the drawing. If the default multileader styles (**Standard** and **Annotative**) do not meet your requirement, you can select any other existing multileader style as per your requirement. The default multileader style file names are **Standard** and **Annotative**. Left-click on the inclined arrow in the **Multileaders** panel of the **Annotate** tab; the **Multileader Style Manager** dialog box will be displayed, as shown in Figure 10-36.

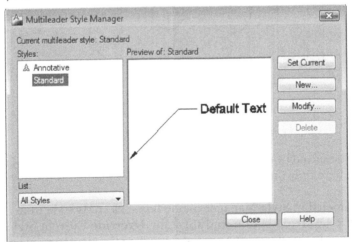

*Figure 10-36 The **Multileader Style Manager** dialog box*

In the **Multileader Style Manager** dialog box, choose the **New** button to display the **Create New Multileader Style** dialog box, see Figure 10-36. Enter the multileader style name in the **New style name** text box and then select a style from the **Start with** drop-down list on which you want to base your current style. Select the **Annotative** check box to specify that the new dimension style should be annotative. Click on the **i** (information) button to get the help and information about the annotative objects. Choose the **Continue** button to display the **Modify Multileader Style** dialog box in which you can define the new style. After defining the new style, choose the **OK** button. The parameters of the **New Dimension Style** dialog box are discussed in the next section.

In the **Multileader Style Manager** dialog box, the current multileader style name is shown in front of the **Current multileader style** option and is also highlighted in the **Styles** list box. The **Multileader Style Manager** dialog box also has a **Preview of** window that displays a preview of the current multileader style. A style can be made current (restored) by selecting the name of the multileader style that you want to make current from the list of defined multileader styles and choosing the **Set Current** button. You can also make a style current by double-clicking on the style name in the **Styles** list box. The **Multileader Style Control** drop-down list in the **Multileaders** panel also displays the multileader styles. Select the required multileader style from this list to set it as current. The list of multileader styles displayed in the **Styles** list box depends on the option selected from the **List** drop down-list. If you select the **Styles in use** option, only the multileader styles in use will be listed in the **Styles** list box. If you right-click on a style in the **Styles** list box, a shortcut menu will be displayed to provide you with the options such as **Set current**, **Modify**, **Rename**, and **Delete**. Choose the **Modify** button to display the **Modify Multileader Style** dialog box in which you can modify an existing style. Choose the **Delete** button to delete the selected multileader style that has not been used in the drawing.

MODIFY MULTILEADER STYLE DIALOG BOX

The **Modify Multileader Style** dialog box can be used to specify the multileader attributes (variables) that affect various properties of the multileader. The various tabs provided under the **Modify Multileader Style** dialog box are discussed next.

Leader Format

The options in the **Leader Format** tab (Figure 10-37) of the **Modify Multileader Style** dialog box are used to specify the multileader attributes that affect the format of the multileader lines. For example, the appearance and behavior of the multileader lines and the arrow head can be changed with this tab.

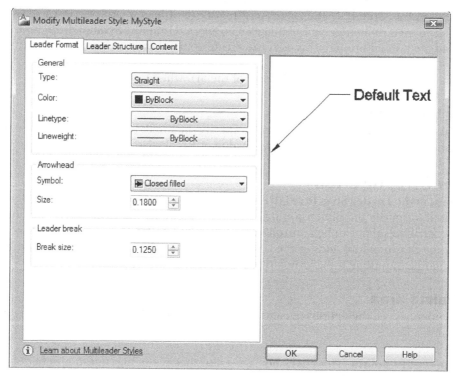

Figure 10-37 The Leader Format tab of the Modify Multileader Style dialog box

General Area
This area provides you the options for controlling the display of the multileader lines. These options are discussed next.

Type. This option is used to specify the type of lines to be used for creating the multileaders. You can select the **Straight**, **Spline**, or **None** option from the **Type** drop-down list. Select the **None** option to create the multileader with no leader lines. You will only be able to draw the content of that multileader. The default line type for the multileaders is **Straight**.

Color. This drop-down list is used to set the colors for the leader lines and arrowheads. The multileader arrowheads have the same color as the multileader lines because the arrows are a part of the multileader lines. The default color for the multileader lines and arrows is **ByBlock**. Select the **Select Color** option from the **Color** drop-down list to display the **Select Color** dialog box from where you can choose a specific color.

Linetype. This drop-down list is used to set the linetype for the multileader lines.

Lineweight. This drop-down list is used to specify the lineweight for the multileader lines. You can select the required lineweight from this drop-down list. The default value is **ByBlock**. Note that you cannot assign the lineweight to the arrowheads using this drop-down list.

Arrowhead Area
This area provides you the options for controlling the shape and size of the arrowhead. The options in this area are discussed next.

Symbol. When you create a multileader, AutoCAD LT draws the terminator symbol at the starting point of the multileader line. This terminator symbol is generally referred to as the arrowhead, and it represents the beginning of the multileader. AutoCAD LT provides you nineteen standard termination symbols that can be selected from the **Symbol** drop-down list of the **Arrowhead** area. In addition to this, you can create your own arrows or terminator symbols.

Size. This spinner is used to specify the size of the arrowhead.

Leader break Area
The **Break size** spinner in this area is used to specify the break length in the multileader while applying the dimension breaks. The default value of **Break size** is 0.125.

Leader Structure Tab
The options in the **Leader Structure** tab (Figure 10-38) of the **Modify Multileader Style** dialog box are used to specify the dimensioning attributes that affect the structure of the multileader lines. The attributes that can be controlled by using the **Leader Structure** tab are the number of lines to be drawn before adding the content, adding landing before the content, length of the landing line, multiline to be annotative or not, and so on.

Constraints Area
This area provides you the options to control the number of multileader points and the direction of the multileader.

Maximum leader points. This check box is used to specify the maximum number of points in the multileader line. The default value is **2**, which means that there will be only two points in the leader line. Select the check box to specify the maximum number of points. You can change the value of the maximum leader points in the spinner in front of this option. Note that the start point of the multileader is the first multileader point and it should also be included in the counting.

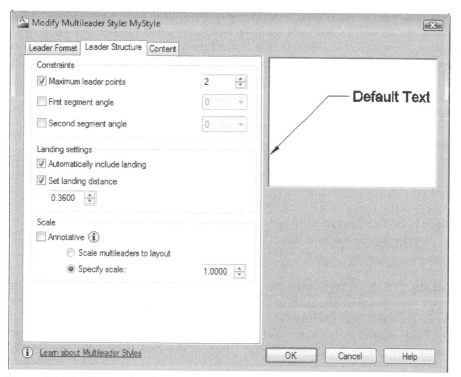

*Figure 10-38 The **Leader Structure** tab of the **Modify Multileader Style** dialog box*

First segment angle. This check box is used to specify the angle of the first multileader line from the horizontal. Select this check box to specify a value in the drop-down list displayed in front of it.

Second segment angle. This check box is used to specify the angle of the second multileader line from the horizontal. Select this check box to specify a value in the drop-down list displayed in front of it.

Note
*The angle values for the **First segment angle** and the **Second segment angle** can be in multiples of the specified angle in the respective spinners.*

Landing settings Area

This area provides you the options to control the inclusion of landing line and its length.

Automatically include landing. Select this check box to attach a landing line to the multileader. By default, this check box is selected and is used to attach the landing line to the multileaders.

Set landing distance. By default, this check box is selected and used to specify the length of the landing line to be attached with the multileader. You can specify the value in the spinner that is below this check box. This spinner gets highlighted only when you select the **Set landing distance** check box. The default value of the landing length is set to 0.36.

Scale Area

The options under this area are used to set the value for the overall multileader scale or the scale of the multileader in the paper space.

Annotative. This check box is used to set the selected multileader style to be annotative. With this option, you can also convert an existing non-annotative multileader style to annotative and vice-versa. If you select the **Annotative** check box from the **Create New Multileader Style** dialog box, then the **Annotative** check box in the **Modify Multileader Style** dialog box will also be selected by default.

Scale multileaders to layout. If you select the **Scale multileaders to layout** radio button, the scale factor between the current model space viewport and the floating viewport (paper space) will be computed automatically. Also, you can disable the **Specify scale** spinner (it is disabled in the dialog box) and the overall scale factor is set to 0 by selecting this radio button. When the overall scale factor is assigned a value of 0, AutoCAD LT calculates an acceptable default value based on the scaling between the current model space viewport and the paper space. AutoCAD LT sets the overall scale factor to 1 if you are in the paper space or not using the **Scale multileaders to layout** feature. Otherwise, AutoCAD LT calculates a scale factor that makes it possible to plot the multileaders at the values in which they have been previously set. For further details regarding the model space and layouts, refer to Chapter 11.

Specify scale. All the current multileaders are scaled with a value specified in the **Specify scale** spinner. You can alter the scaling factor as per your requirement by entering the scaling factor of your choice in this spinner. The default value for this variable is **1.0**. With this value, AutoCAD LT assumes its preset value and the drawing is plotted in a full scale. The scale factor is the reciprocal of the drawing size. So, for plotting the drawing at the one-fourth size, the overall scale factor will be 4.

Content Tab

The options in the **Content** tab (Figure 10-39) of the **Modify Multileader Style** dialog box are used to specify the multileader attributes that affect the content and the format of the text or block to be attached with the multileader.

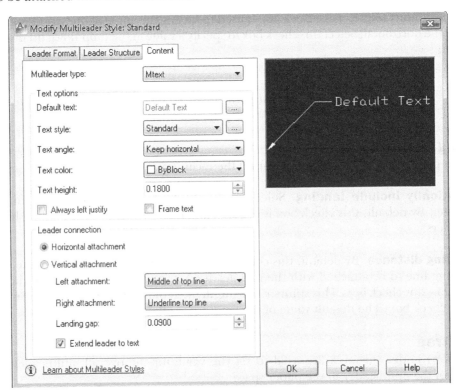

Figure 10-39 The Content tab of the Modify Multileader Style dialog box

You can attach the multiline text or block to the multileader. You can also attach nothing as a content to the multileader. Select the desired multileader type from the **Multileader type** drop-down list; the other options in the **Content** tab of the **Modify Multileader Style** dialog box will vary with the change in the multileader type. Figure 10-39 displays the options in the **Modify Multileader Style** dialog box for the **Mtext** multileader type and these options are discussed next.

Text options Area
The options in this area are discussed next.

Default text. This option is used to specify the default text to be attached with the multileader. Choose the [...] button; the **In-Place Text Editor** will be displayed. Enter the text that you want to display with the multileader by default and then, click outside the text editor window; the preview window in the **Content** tab will display the multileader with the default text attached to it. While creating a new multileader, AutoCAD LT prompts you to specify whether you want to retain the default text specified or overwrite it with the new text.

Text style. This drop-down list is used to select the text style to be used for writing the content of the multileader. Only the predefined and default text styles are displayed in the drop-down list.

Text angle. This drop-down list is used to control the rotation of the multiline text with respect to the landing line.

Text color. This drop-down list is used to select the color to be used for writing the content of the multileader.

Text height. This spinner is used to specify the height of the multiline text to be attached with the multileader.

Always left justify. Select this check box to left justify the text attached to the multileader. On clearing the **Always left justify** check box, a multileader with the multileader style shown in Figure 10-40 (a) is displayed. Whereas, on selecting this check box, a multileader with the multileader style as shown in Figure 10-40 (b) is displayed.

Frame text. Select this check box. Now you can draw a rectangular frame around the multiline text to be attached with the multileader, see Figure 10-41.

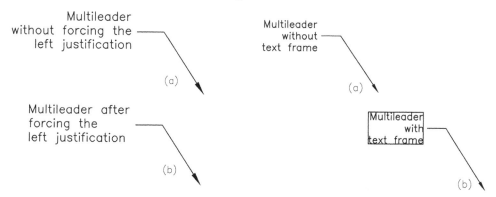

*Figure 10-40 Multileaders displaying the effect of the **Always left justify** option*

*Figure 10-41 Multileaders displaying the effect of the **Frame text** option*

Leader connection Area

The options provided in this area are used for controlling the attachment of the multiline text to the multileader.

Horizontal attachment. Select this radio button to place the leader to the right or left of the text. If you select this radio button, you need to select an appropriate option from the **Left Attachment** and **Right attachment** drop-down lists to attach the multiline text to the landing line.

Vertical attachment. Select this radio button to place the leader at the top or bottom of the text. If you select this radio button, you need to select an appropriate option from the **Top attachment** and **Bottom attachment** drop-down lists to attach the multiline text with the landing line.

If you select **Block** from the **Multileader type** drop-down list, the options will change accordingly. Figure 10-42 displays the options in the **Modify Multileader Style** dialog box for the **Block** option of the **Multileader type** drop-down list and these options are discussed next.

Landing gap. This spinner is used to specify the gap between the landing line and the multiline text at the point of attachment. It is available in both the cases; Horizontal attachment or Vertical attachment. The default value in the spinner is 0.09.

Extend leader to text. Select this check box to extend the leader line to text. If you deselect it then the leader can be extended upto the frame only.

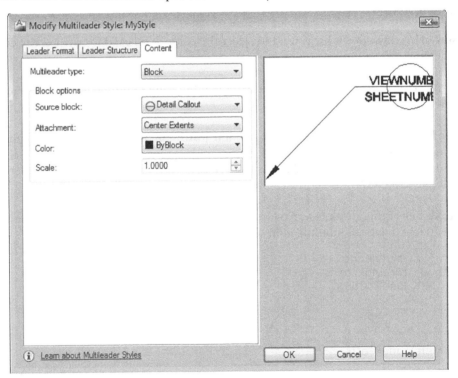

*Figure 10-42 The **Content** tab of the **Modify Multileader Style** dialog box for the **Block** option of the **Multileader type** drop-down list*

Block options Area

Source block. This drop-down list is used to select the block to be attached with the multileader as content. You can attach the standard block listed in the drop-down list or attach the user defined blocks to the multileader by selecting **User Block** from the drop-down list. Six standard shapes of block are available in this drop-down list with their previews on the side of block name. While creating the multileader, if you select the **Detail Callout** option from the **Source block** drop-down list, you will be prompted to specify the **View number** and **Sheet number** to be displayed within the block in stacked form. For the other remaining standard blocks, you will be prompted to specify the **Tag number** only to be displayed within the block. To attach the user-defined block to the multileader, select **User Block** from the **Source block** drop-down list; the **Select Custom Content Block** dialog box will be displayed with the list of all the blocks defined in the current drawing under the **Select from Drawing Blocks** drop-down list. Select the desired block and choose the **OK** button; the selected block will be added to the **Source block** drop-down list for the current drawing. Also, it will be attached to the multileader as content.

Attachment. This drop-down list is used to specify the point of attachment of the block to the leader. Select **Center Extents** from the drop-down list to attach the leader landing line in the middle of the outer boundary of the block. Select **Insertion point** to attach the leader landing line to the insertion point specified while defining the block.

Color. This drop down list is used to specify the color of the block to be attached with the leader landing line.

Self-Evaluation Test

Answer the following questions and then compare them to those given at the end of this chapter:

1. You can invoke the **Dimension Style Manager** dialog box using both the **Annotate** and the **Home** tabs. (T/F)

2. The size of the arrow block is determined by the value specified in the **Arrow size** edit box. (T/F)

3. A block can be set as default content to be attached with the multileader. (T/F)

4. You can define the size of the tolerance text with respect to dimensions. (T/F)

5. The **DIMTVP** variable is used to control the _____ position of the dimension text.

6. When you select the **Arrows** option from the **Fit** tab of the **Dimension Style** dialog box, AutoCAD LT places the text and arrowheads _____.

7. A basic dimension text is the dimension text with a _____ drawn around it.

8. The **Suppress** check boxes in the **Dimension Lines** area are used to control the display of _____ and _____.

9. The _____ button in the **Dimension Style Manager** dialog box is used to override the current dimension style.

Review Questions

Answer the following questions:

1. You cannot replace the default arrowheads at the end of dimension lines. (T/F)

2. When the **DIMTVP** variable has a negative value, the dimension text is placed below the dimension line. (T/F)

3. The length of a multileader landing line cannot be changed. (T/F)

4. The named dimension style associated with the dimension being updated by overriding is not updated. (T/F)

5. Which of the following buttons can be used to make a dimension style active for dimensioning?

   (a) **Set Current**   (b) **New**
   (c) **Override**   (d) **Modify**

6. Which of the following tabs in the **Dimension Style Manager** dialog box is used to add the suffix **mm** to dimensions?

   (a) **Fit**   (b) **Text**
   (c) **Primary Units**   (d) **Alternate Units**

7. Which tab of the **Dimension Style Manager** dialog box will be used, if you want to place the dimension text manually every time you create a dimension?

   (a) **Fit**   (b) **Text**
   (c) **Primary Units**   (d) **Alternate Units**

8. The size of the _____ is determined by the value stored in the **Arrow size** edit box.

9. When **DIMSCALE** is assigned the value _____, AutoCAD LT calculates an acceptable default value based on the scaling between the current model space viewport and the paper space.

10. If you use the **DIMCEN** command, a positive value will create a center mark, whereas a negative value will create a _____.

11. If you select the _____ check box, you can position the dimension text anywhere along the dimension line.

12. You can append a prefix to the dimension measurement by entering the desired prefix in the **Prefix** edit box of the _____ dialog box.

13. If you select the **Limits** tolerance method from the **Method** drop-down list, AutoCAD LT _____ the upper value to the dimension and _____ the lower value from the dimension text.

14. You can also use the _____ command to override a dimension value.

15. What is the dimension style family and how does it help in dimensioning?

EXERCISES 4 Through 9

Create the drawings shown in Figures 10-43 through 10-48. You must create dimension style and multileader style files and specify the values for the different dimension types such as linear, radial, diameter, and ordinate. Assume missing dimensions.

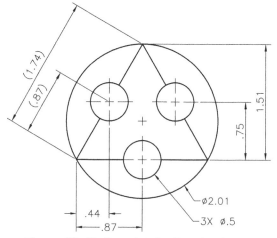

Figure 10-43 *Drawing for Exercise 4*

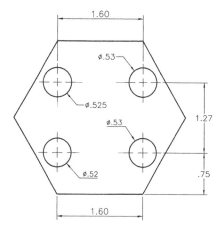

Figure 10-44 *Drawing for Exercise 5*

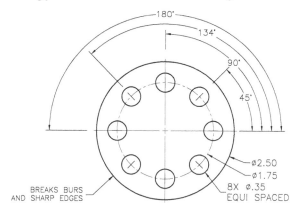

Figure 10-45 *Drawing for Exercise 6*

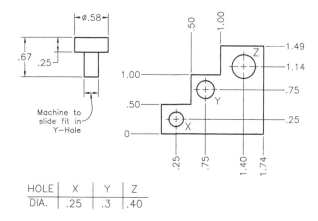

HOLE	X	Y	Z
DIA.	.25	.3	.40

Figure 10-46 *Drawing for Exercise 7*

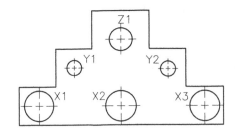

HOLE	X1	X2	X3	Y1	Y2	Z1
DIM.	R.2	R.2	R.2	R.1	R.1	R.15
QTY.	1	1	1	1	1	1
X	.25	1.375	2.50	.75	2.0	1.375
Y	.25	.25	.25	.75	.75	1.125
Z	THRU	THRU	THRU	1.0	1.0	THRU

Figure 10-47 Drawing for Exercise 8

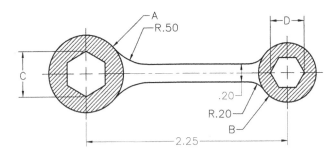

SPANNER NO.	A	B	C	D
S1	.85	.65	.50	.38
S2	1.00	.75	.59	.44
S3	1.15	.88	.67	.52
S4	1.25	.95	.74	.56

Figure 10-48 Drawing for Exercise 9

EXERCISE 10

Draw the sketch shown in Figure 10-49. You must create the dimension style and multileader style. Specify different dimensioning parameters. Also, suppress the leading and trailing zeros in the dimension style. Assume missing dimensions.

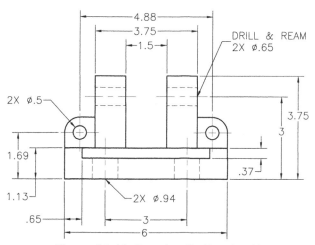

Figure 10-49 *Drawing for Exercise 10*

EXERCISE 11

Draw the sketch shown in Figure 10-50. You must create the dimension style and specify different dimensioning parameters in the dimension style. Assume missing dimensions.

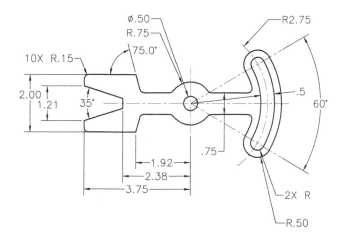

Figure 10-50 *Drawing for Exercise 11*

EXERCISE 12   *Dimension Style*

Draw the sketch shown in Figure 10-51. You must create the dimension style and specify different dimensioning parameters in the dimension style. Assume missing dimensions.

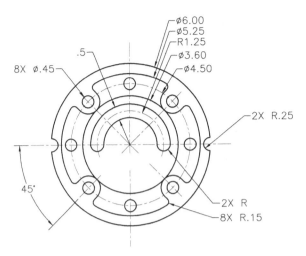

Figure 10-51 Drawing for Exercise 12

Problem-Solving Exercise 1   Dimension Style

Create the drawing shown in Figure 10-52. You must create the dimension style and specify different dimensioning parameters in the dimension style. Also, suppress the leading and trailing zeros in the dimension style. Assume missing dimensions.

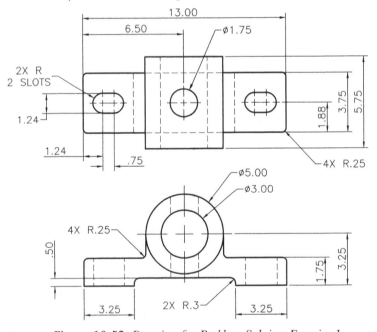

Figure 10-52 Drawing for Problem-Solving Exercise 1

Problem-Solving Exercise 2   Dimension Style

Draw the shaft shown in Figure 10-53. You must create the dimension style and specify the dimensioning parameters based on the given drawing. Assume missing dimensions.

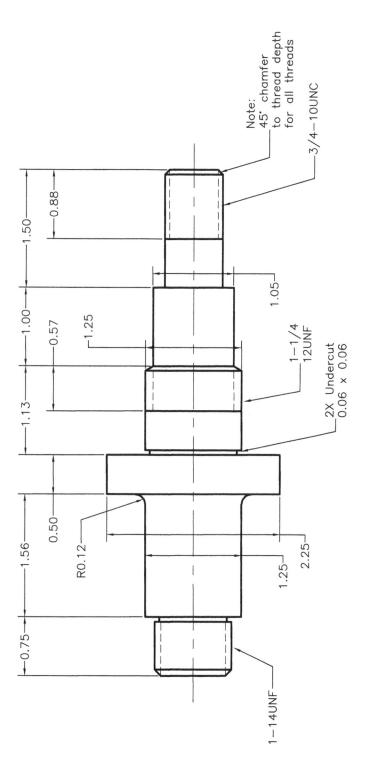

Figure 10-53 *Drawing for Problem-Solving Exercise 2*

Problem-Solving Exercise 3   *Dimension Style*

Draw the connecting rod shown in Figure 10-54. You must create the dimension style and specify the dimensioning parameters based on the given drawing. Assume missing dimensions.

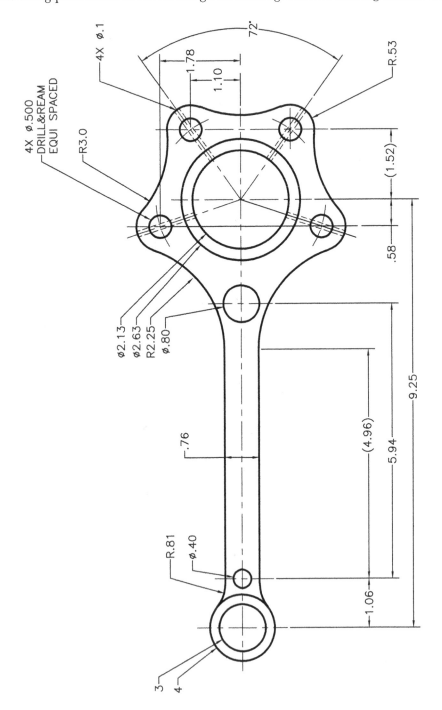

Figure 10-54 Drawing for Problem-Solving Exercise 3

Problem-Solving Exercise 4

Create the drawing shown in Figure 10-55. Assume missing dimensions.

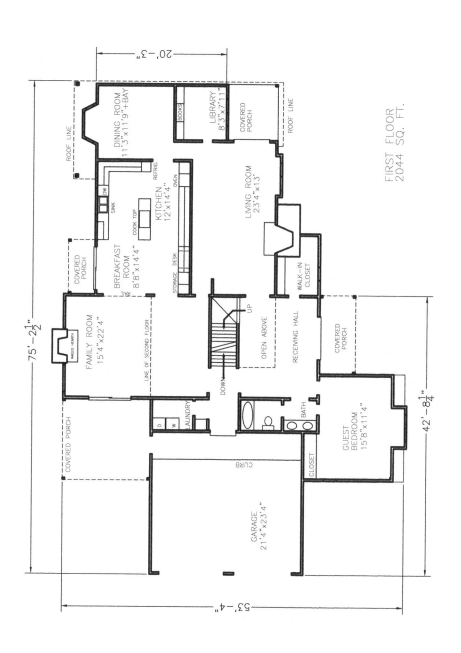

Figure 10-55 Drawing for Problem-Solving Exercise 4

Problem-Solving Exercise 5

Create the drawing shown in Figure 10-56. Assume missing dimensions.

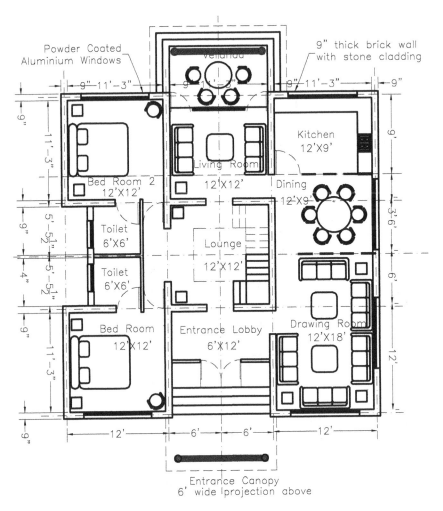

Figure 10-56 *Drawing for Problem-Solving Exercise 5*

Answers to Self-evaluation Test

1. T, **2.** T, **3.** T, **4.** T, **5.** vertical, **6.** inside, **7.** frame, **8.** first, second dimension lines, **9. Override**

Chapter **11**

Model Space Viewports, Paper Space Viewports, and Layouts

CHAPTER OBJECTIVES

In this chapter, you will learn:
- *The concepts of model space and paper space.*
- *To create tiled viewports in the model space.*
- *To create floating viewports.*
- *The use of the MSPACE and PSPACE commands.*
- *To control the visibility of viewport layers.*
- *To set the linetype scaling in paper space.*
- *To control the display of annotative objects in viewports.*

KEY TERMS

- *Viewports*
- *Model Space*
- *Paper Space*
- *Tiled Viewport*
- *Temporary Model Space*
- *Rectangular Viewport*
- *Polygonal Viewport*
- *Maximize Viewport*
- *MVIEW*
- *PAGESETUP*
- *SPACETRANS*

MODEL SPACE AND PAPER SPACE/LAYOUTS

For ease in designing, AutoCAD LT provides two different types of environments, model space, and paper space. The paper space is also called layout. The model space is basically used for designing or drafting work. This is the default environment that is active when you start AutoCAD LT. Almost the entire design is created in the model space. The paper space is used for plotting drawings or generating drawing views for the solid models. By default, the paper space provides you with two layouts. A layout can be considered a sheet of paper on which you can place the design created in the model space and then print it. You can also assign different plotting parameters to these layouts for plotting. Almost all the commands of the model space also work in the layouts. Note that you cannot select the drawing objects created in model space when they are displayed in the viewports in layouts. However, you can snap on to the different points of the drawing objects such as the endpoints, midpoints, center points, and so on, using the **OSNAP** options.

You can shift from one environment to the other by choosing the **Model** tab or the **Layout1/ Layout2** tabs at the bottom of the drawing area. If these tabs are not available by default then, the **Model** and **Layout1** buttons will be available on the Status Bar. Right-click on any of these buttons and choose the **Display Layout and Model Tabs** option from the shortcut menu; the **Model**, **Layout 1**, and **Layout 2** tabs will be displayed at the bottom of the drawing area. You can also invoke the model/layout tabs using the **Quick View Layouts** and **Quick View Drawings** buttons available at the bottom right of the Status Bar. The **Quick View Layouts** button enables a quick display of all the layouts and the model of the current drawing in a series of thumbnails. You can select a thumbnail to view the corresponding layout. Each thumbnail contains two buttons, **Plot** and **Publish**. Using these buttons, you can plot or publish the selected layout. On choosing the **Quick View Layouts** button, a control panel will be displayed along with a series of thumbnails of the existing model and layout tabs. Choose the **New Layout** button in this control panel to create a new layout. On doing so, a new thumbnail is attached to the end of series of thumbnails. The **Publish** button of the control panel enables you to publish all the layouts. You can pin the control panel for frequent use and close when not required. The shortcut menu displayed on right-clicking any thumbnail is the same as that of the **Model** and **Layout** tabs.

The function of the **Quick View Drawings** button is similar to the **Quick View Layouts** button. On choosing this button, all the opened drawings are displayed with their model space and layouts. These opened drawings are displayed in larger thumbnails whereas their layouts are displayed in smaller thumbnails. However, they are enlarged when you move the cursor over them. It allows you to quickly switch between the opened drawings and their layouts. The opened drawing thumbnails contain two buttons; **Save** and **Close**. These buttons enable you to save and close the opened drawings without actually opening them. The control panel displayed on choosing the **Quick View Drawings** button allows you to create a new drawing or open an existing one. In this case also, you can pin the control panel for frequent use, and close it, if no longer required.

You can also shift from one environment to the other using the **TILEMODE** system variable. The default value of this variable is **1**. If the value of this system variable is set to **0**, you will be shifted to the layouts and if its value is set to **1**, you will be shifted to model space. The viewports created in the model space are called tiled viewports and viewports in layouts are called floating viewports.

MODEL SPACE VIEWPORTS (TILED VIEWPORTS)

Menu Bar: View > Viewports > New Viewports
Toolbar: Viewports > Display Viewports Dialog or Layouts > Display Viewports Dialog
Command: VPORTS   **Ribbon:** View > Viewports > Viewport Configurations List

A viewport in the model space is defined as a rectangular area of the drawing window in which you can create the design. When you start AutoCAD LT, only one viewport is displayed in the model space. You can create multiple non-overlapping viewports in the model space to display different views of the same object, see Figure 11-1. Each of these viewports will act as individual drawing area. You can view the same model from different positions by creating the tiled viewports and defining the distinct coordinate system configuration for each viewport. You can also use the **Pan** or **Zoom** tool to display different portions or different levels of the detail of the drawing in each viewport. The tiled viewports can be created using the **Named** tool available in the **Viewports** panel.

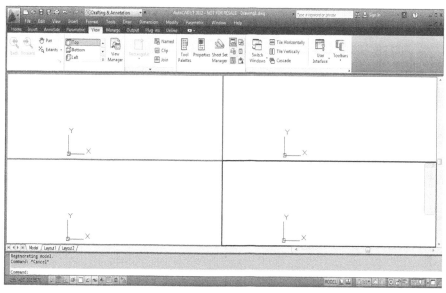

Figure 11-1 *Screen display with multiple tiled viewports*

Creating Tiled Viewports

As mentioned earlier, the display screen in the model space can be divided into multiple non-overlapping tiled viewports. All these viewports are created only in the rectangular shape. This number depends on the equipment and the operating system on which AutoCAD LT is running. Each tiled viewport contains a view of the drawing. The tiled viewports touch each other at the edges without overlapping. While using tiled viewports, you are not allowed to edit, rearrange, or turn individual viewports on or off. These viewports are created using the **New** tool when the system variable **TILEMODE** is set to 1 or the **Model** tab is active. When you choose the **Named** or **New** button from the **Viewports** flyout in the **View** menu, the **Viewports** dialog box is displayed. You can use this dialog box to create new viewport configurations and save them. The options under both the tabs of the **Viewports** dialog box are discussed next.

New Viewports Tab

The **New Viewports** tab of the **Viewports** dialog box (Figure 11-2) provides the options related to standard viewport configurations. You can also save a user-defined configuration using this tab. The name for the new viewport configuration can be specified in the **New name** edit box.

If you do not enter a name in this edit box, the viewport configuration you create is not saved and, therefore, cannot be used later. A list of standard viewport configurations is listed in the **Standard viewports** list box. This list also contains the ***Active Model Configuration***, which is the current viewport configuration. From the **Standard viewports** list, you can select and apply any one of the listed standard viewport configurations. A preview image of the selected configuration is displayed in the **Preview** window. The **Apply to** drop-down list has the **Display** and **Current viewport** options. Selecting the **Display** option applies the selected viewport configuration to the entire display and selecting the **Current viewport** option applies the selected viewport configuration to only the current viewport. With this option, you can create more viewports inside the existing viewports. The changes will be applied to the current viewport and the new viewports will be created inside the current viewport.

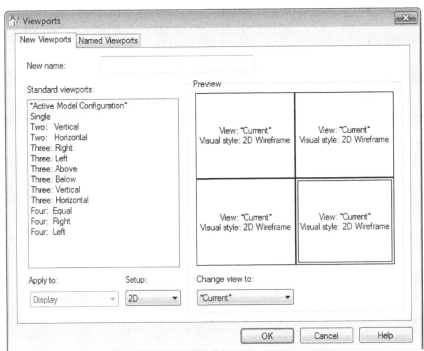

*Figure 11-2 The **New Viewports** tab of the **Viewports** dialog box*

You can modify these standard orthogonal and isometric views by selecting from the **Change view to** drop-down list and replacing the existing view in the selected viewport. For example, you can select the viewport that is assigned to the **Top** view and then choose **Bottom** view from the **Change view to** drop-down list to replace it. The preview image in the **Preview** window reflects the changes you make. If you use the **2D** option, you can select a named viewport configuration to replace the selected one. Choose **OK** to exit the dialog box and apply the created or selected configuration to the current display in the drawing. When you save a new viewport configuration, it saves the information about the number and position of viewports, the viewing direction and zoom factor, and the grid, snap, coordinate system, and UCS icon settings.

Named Viewports Tab

The **Named Viewports** tab of the **Viewports** dialog box (Figure 11-3) displays the name of the current viewport next to **Current name**. The names of all the saved viewport configurations in a drawing are displayed in the **Named viewports** list box. You can select any one of the named viewport configurations and apply it to the current display. A preview image of the selected configuration is displayed in the **Preview** window. Choose **OK** to exit the dialog box and apply the selected viewport configuration to the current display. In the **Named viewports** list box, you can select a name and right-click to display a shortcut menu. Choosing **Delete** deletes the selected viewport configuration and choosing **Rename** allows you to rename the selected viewport configuration.

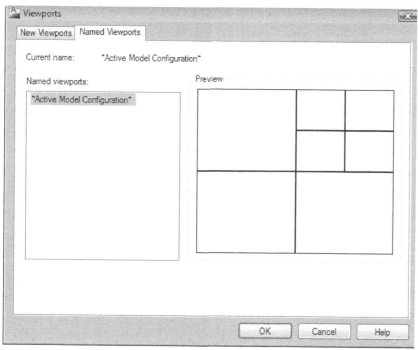

*Figure 11-3 The **Named Viewports** tab of the **Viewports** dialog box*

MAKING A VIEWPORT CURRENT

The viewport you are currently working in is called the current viewport. You can display several model space viewports on the screen, but you can work in only one of them at a time. You can switch from one viewport to another even when you are in the middle of a command. For example, you can specify the start point of the line in one viewport and the endpoint of the line in the other viewport. The current viewport is indicated by a border that is heavy compared to the borders of the other viewports. Also, the graphics cursor appears as a drawing cursor (screen crosshairs) only when it is within the current viewport. Outside the current viewport this cursor appears as an arrow cursor. You can enter points and select objects only from the current viewport. To make a viewport current, you can select it with the pointing device. Another method of making a viewport current is by assigning its identification number to the **CVPORT** system variable. The identification numbers of the named viewport configurations are not listed in the display.

JOINING TWO ADJACENT VIEWPORTS

AutoCAD LT provides you with an option of joining two adjacent viewports. However, remember that the viewports you wish to join should result in a rectangular-shaped viewport only. As mentioned earlier, the viewports in the model space can only be in rectangular shape. Therefore, you will not be able to join two viewports, in case they do not result in a rectangular shape. The viewports can be joined by using the **Join Viewports** tool available in the **Viewports** panel. On invoking this tool, you will be prompted to select the dominant viewport. A dominant viewport is the one whose display is retained after joining. After selecting the dominant viewport, you will be prompted to select the viewport to be joined. Figure 11-4 shows the viewport configuration before joining and Figure 11-5 shows the viewport configuration after joining.

Figure 11-4 *Viewports before joining*

Figure 11-5 *Viewports after joining*

 Note
*You can also use the Command line to create, save, restore, delete, or join the viewport configurations. This is done using the **-VPORTS** command.*

PAPER SPACE VIEWPORTS (FLOATING VIEWPORTS)*

As mentioned earlier, the viewports created in the layouts are called floating viewports. This is because unlike in model space, the viewports in the layouts can be overlapping and of any shape. In layouts, there is no restriction of the shape of the viewports. You can even convert a closed object into a viewport in the layouts. Figure 11-6 shows a layout with floating viewports.

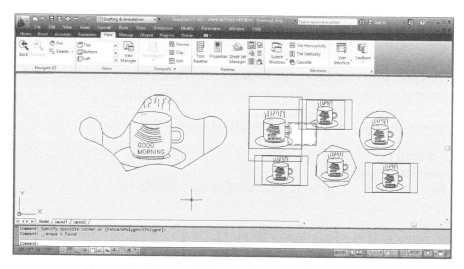

Figure 11-6 *Screen display with multiple floating viewports*

The method of creating floating viewports is discussed next.

Creating Floating Viewports

Ribbon: View > Viewports > Named   **Menu Bar:** View > Viewports > New Viewports
Toolbar: Viewports > Display Viewports Dialog or Layouts > Display Viewports Dialog
Command: VPORTS

 This tool is used to create the floating viewports in layouts. However, when you invoke this tool in the layouts, the dialog box displayed is slightly modified than the one displayed in the Model tab. Instead of the **Apply to** drop-down list in the **New Viewports** tab, the **Viewport Spacing** spinner is displayed, see Figure 11-7. This spinner is used to set the spacing between the adjacent viewports. The rest of the options in both the **New Viewports** and the **Named Viewports** tabs of the **Viewports** dialog box are the same as those discussed under the tiled viewports. When you select a viewport configuration and choose **OK**, you will be prompted to specify the first and the second corner of a box that will act as a reference for placing the viewports. You will also be given an option of **Fit**. This option fits the configuration of viewports such that they fit exactly in the current display.

Note
*You can also use the **+VPORTS** command to display the **Viewports** dialog box. When you invoke this command, you will be prompted to specify the **Tab Index**. Enter **0** to display the **New Viewports** tab and enter **1** to display the **Named Viewports** tab.*

Creating Rectangular Viewports

Ribbon: View > Viewports > Create Viewport drop-down > Create Rectangular
Menu Bar: View > Viewports > New Viewports
Toolbar: Viewports > Polygonal Viewports   **Command:** -VPORTS

To create a rectangular viewport, choose the **Create Rectangular** tool from **View > Viewports > Create Viewports** drop-down (See Figure 11-8) in the **Ribbon**. The prompt sequence that will follow is given next.

Specify corner of viewport or
[ON/OFF/Fit/Shadeplot/Lock/Object/Polygonal/Restore/LAyer/2/3/4] <Fit>: *Specify the start point of the viewport.*

Specify opposite corner: *Specify the end point of the viewport.*
Regenerating model.

You can also create 2, 3 or 4 viewports in one go by entering 2, 3 or 4 at the prompt **Specify corner of viewport or [ON/OFF/Fit/Shadeplot/Lock/Object/Polygonal/Restore/LAyer/2/3/4] <Fit>** . The viewports automatically fit in the drawn rectangular area.

The prompt sequence for the option 2 Viewports is given next.

Command: **-VPORTS**
Specify corner of viewport or
[ON/OFF/Fit/Shadeplot/Lock/Object/Polygonal/Restore/LAyer/2/3/4] <Fit>: 2
Enter viewport arrangement [Horizontal/Vertical] <Vertical>: *Specify the orientation of the viewport.*
Specify first corner or [Fit] <Fit>: *Specify the start point of the viewport.*
Specify opposite corner: *Specify the end point of the viewport.*

The prompt sequence for creating 3 viewports is given next.

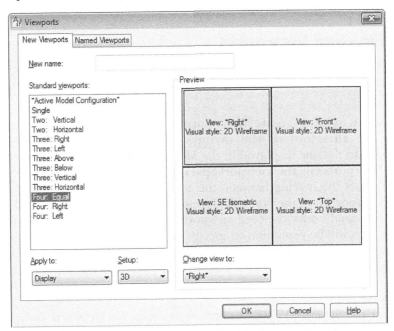

*Figure 11-7 The **New Viewports** tab of the **Viewports** dialog box displayed in layouts*

Command: **-VPORTS**
Specify corner of viewport or
[ON/OFF/Fit/Shadeplot/Lock/Object/Polygonal/Restore/LAyer/2/3/4] <Fit>: 3
Enter viewport arrangement
[Horizontal/Vertical/Above/Below/Left/Right] <Right>: *Specify the orientation of the viewport using Horizontal or Vertical option. You can also specify the position of the largest viewport in the three using Above, Below, Left or Right option.*
Specify first corner or [Fit] <Fit>: *Specify the start point of the viewport.*
Specify opposite corner: *Specify the end point of the viewport.*

The prompt sequence for creating 4 viewports is given next.

Command: **-VPORTS**
Specify corner of viewport or
[ON/OFF/Fit/Shadeplot/Lock/Object/Polygonal/Restore/LAyer/2/3/4] <Fit>: 4
Specify first corner or [Fit] <Fit>: *Specify the start point of the viewport.*
Specify opposite corner:*Specify the end point of the viewport.*

Creating Polygonal Viewports

Ribbon: View > Viewports > Create Viewport drop-down > Create Polygonal
Menu Bar: View > Viewports > New Viewports
Toolbar: Viewports > Polygonal Viewports   **Command:** -VPORTS

As mentioned earlier, you can create floating viewports of any closed shape. The viewports thus created can even be self-intersecting in shape. To create a polygonal viewport, choose the **Create Polygonal** tool from **View > Viewports > Create Viewports** drop-down (See Figure 11-8). The prompt sequence that will follow when you choose this tool is given next.

Command: **-VPORTS**
Specify corner of viewport or
[ON/OFF/Fit/Shadeplot/Lock/Object/Polygonal/Restore/LAyer/2/3/4] <Fit>: Polygonal
Specify start point: *Specify the start point of the viewport.*
Specify next point or [Arc/Length/Undo]: *Specify the next point or select an option.*
Specify next point or [Arc/Close/Length/Undo]: *Specify the next point or select an option.*

Various options in the prompt sequence are discussed next.

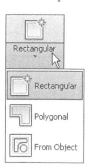

Arc
This option is used to switch to the arc mode for creating the viewports. When you invoke this option, the options for creating the arcs will be displayed. You can switch back to the line mode by choosing the **Line** option.

Length
This option is used to specify the length of the next line of the viewport. The line will be drawn in the direction of the last drawn line segment. In case the last drawn segment was an arc, the line will be drawn tangent to it.

*Figure 11-8 Tools in the **Create Viewports** drop-down*

Undo
This option is used to undo the last drawn segment of the polygonal viewport.

Close
This option is used to close the polygon and create the viewport. The last entity that will be used to close the polygon will depend upon whether you were in the arc mode or in the line mode. If you were in the line mode, the last entity will be a line. If you were in the arc mode, the last entity will be an arc.

Figure 11-9 shows the polygonal viewport created using the combination of lines and arcs.

Chapter 11

Converting an Existing Closed Object into a Viewport

Ribbon: View > Viewports > Create Viewport drop-down > Create From Object
Toolbar: Viewports > Convert Object to Viewport   **Command:** VPORTS

This option allows you to convert an existing closed object into a viewport. However, remember that the object selected should be a single entity. The objects that can be converted into a viewport include polygons drawn using the **Polygon** tool, rectangles drawn using the **Rectangle** tool, polylines (last segment closed using the **Close** option), circles, ellipses, closed splines, or regions. To convert any of these objects into a viewport, choose the **Create from Object** tool from the **Viewports** panel; you will be prompted to select the object that need to be converted into a viewport. Figure 11-10 shows a viewport created using a polygon of nine sides and Figure 11-11 shows a viewport created using a closed spline.

Figure 11-9 A polygonal viewport

Figure 11-10 A viewport created using a polygon of nine sides

Figure 11-11 A viewport created using a closed spline

Note
*When you shift to the layouts, the **Page Setup** dialog box is displayed for printing and a rectangular viewport is created that fits the drawing area. If you want, you can retain or delete this viewport using the **Erase** tool.*

TEMPORARY MODEL SPACE

Sometimes, when you create a floating viewport in the layout, the drawing is not displayed completely inside it, see Figures 11-10 and 11-11. In such cases, you need to zoom or pan the drawings to fit them in the viewport. But when you invoke any of the **Zoom** or the **Pan** tools in the layouts, the display of the entire layout is modified instead of the display inside of the viewport. Now, to change the display of the viewports, you will have to switch to the temporary model space. The temporary model space is defined as a state when the model space is activated in the layouts. The temporary model space is exactly similar to the actual model space and you can make any kind of modifications in the drawing from temporary model space. Therefore, the main reason for invoking the temporary model space is that you can modify the display of the drawing. The temporary model space can be invoked by choosing the **Paper** button from the status bar. You can also switch to the temporary model space by double-clicking inside the viewports. You will see that the model space UCS icon is automatically displayed when you switch to the temporary model space. Also, the extents of the viewport become the extents of the drawing. You can use the **Zoom** and **Pan** tools to fit the model inside the viewport. The temporary model space can also be invoked using the **MSPACE** command.

Once you have modified the display of the drawing in the temporary model space, you have to switch back to the paper space. This is done by choosing the **Model** button from the status bar. You can also switch back to the paper space by double-clicking anywhere in the layout outside the viewport, or by using the **PSPACE** command.

EXAMPLE 1   Create Viewports

In this example, you will draw the object shown in Figure 11-12 and then create a floating viewport of the shape shown in Figure 11-13 to display the object in the layout. The dimensions of the viewport are in the paper space. Do not dimension the object.

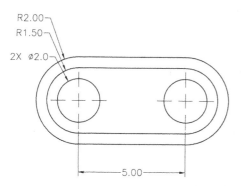

Figure 11-12 *Model for Example 1*   **Figure 11-13** *Shape of the floating viewport*

1. Start a new drawing and then draw the object shown in Figure 11-12.

2. Choose the **Layout1** tab to switch to the layout; a rectangular viewport will be displayed in this layout.

3. Choose the **Erase** tool from the **Modify** panel in the **Home** tab; you will be prompted to select the object. Type **L** in this prompt to delete the last object, that is, the viewport, in this case.

4. Choose the **Polygon** tool from the **Draw** panel in the **Home** tab and create the required hexagon.

5. Choose the **Convert Object to Viewport** tool from **View > Viewports > Create Viewports** drop-down; you will be prompted to select an object. Select the hexagon; it will be converted into a viewport. You will notice that the complete object is not displayed inside the viewport. Therefore, you need to modify its display.

6. Double-click inside the viewport to switch to the temporary model space. On doing so, the border of the viewport will become thick, indicating that you have switched to the temporary model space.

7. Now, using the **Zoom** and the **Pan** tools, fit the drawing inside the viewport.

8. Choose the **Model** button from the status bar to switch back to the paper space. The drawing will be displayed fully inside the viewport, see Figure 11-14.

EDITING VIEWPORTS

You can perform various editing operations on the viewports. For example, you can control the visibility of the objects in the viewports, lock their display, clip the existing viewports using an object, and so on. All these editing operations are discussed next.

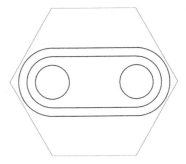

Figure 11-14 Displaying the drawing inside the polygonal viewport

Controlling the Display of Objects in Viewports

The display of the objects in the viewports can be turned on or off. If the display is turned off, the objects will not be displayed in the viewport. However, the object in the model space is not affected by this editing operation. To control the display of the objects, select the viewport entity in the layout and right-click to display the shortcut menu. In this menu, choose **Display Viewport Objects > No**. If there is only one viewport, you will be prompted to confirm whether you really want to turn off all active viewports. Enter **Y** to turn off the display. However, if there are more than one viewports, the visibility of the selected viewports will be automatically turned off when you choose **Display Viewport Objects > No** from the shortcut menu. Similarly, you can again turn on the display of the objects by choosing **Display Viewport Objects > Yes** from the shortcut menu. This shortcut menu is displayed on selecting the viewport and right-clicking. This editing operation can also be done using the **OFF** option of the **MVIEW** or the **-VPORTS** command.

Locking the Display of Objects in Viewports

To avoid accidental modification in the display of objects in the viewports, you can lock their display. If the display of a viewport is locked, the tools such as **Zoom** and **Pan** do not work in it. Also, you cannot modify the view in the locked viewport. For example, if the display of a viewport is locked, you cannot zoom or pan the display or change the view in that viewport even if you switch to the temporary model space. To lock the display of the viewports, select it and right-click on it to display the shortcut menu. In this menu, choose **Display Locked > Yes**. Now, the display of this viewport will not be modified. However, you can draw objects or delete objects in this viewport by switching to the temporary model space. Similarly, you can unlock the display of the objects in the viewports by choosing **Display Locked > No** from the shortcut menu. You can also lock or unlock the display of the viewports using the **Lock** option of the **MVIEW** command or the **-VPORTS** command.

Controlling the Display of Hidden Lines in Viewports

While working with three-dimensional solid or surface models, there are a number of occasions where you have to plot the solid models such that the hidden lines are not displayed. Plotting solid models in the model space (Tilemode=1) can be easily done by selecting the **Hidden** option from the **Shade plot** drop-down list. This drop-down list is available in the **Shaded viewport options** area in **Plot** dialog box. If this area is not available by default, you need to choose the **More Options** button in the dialog box. This option is not available in layouts. In this case, you will have to control the display of the hidden lines in the viewports. To control the display of the hidden lines, select the viewport and right-click to display the shortcut menu. In this menu, choose **Shade plot > Hidden**. Although the hidden lines will be displayed in the viewports, now they will not be displayed in the printouts. The display of the hidden lines can also be controlled using the **Shadeplot** option of the **MVIEW** command or the **-VPORTS** command.

Note
*You can also use the other options in the **Shade plot** drop-down list. These options are explained in detail in Chapter 12 (Plotting Drawings).*

Tip
Apart from the previously mentioned editing operations, you can also move, copy, rotate, stretch, scale, or trim the viewports using the respective commands. You can also use the grips to edit the viewports.

Clipping Existing Viewports

Ribbon: View > Viewports > Clip	**Command:** VCLIP
Toolbar: Viewports > Clip existing Viewport	**Menu Bar:** Modify > Clip > Viewport

You can modify the shape of an existing viewport by clipping it using an object or by defining the clipping boundary. The viewports can be clipped using the **VPCLIP** command. This command can also be invoked by choosing the **Clip** tool from the **Viewports** panel in the **View** tab. The prompt sequence that will follow when you invoke this tool is given next.

Select viewport to clip: *Select the viewport to be clipped.*
Select clipping object or [Polygonal/Delete] <Polygonal>: *Select an object for clipping the viewport or specify an option.*

Select clipping object Option

This option is used to clip the viewport using a selected closed loop. The objects that can be used for clipping the viewports include circles, ellipses, closed polylines, closed splines, and regions. As soon as you select the clipping object, the original viewport will be deleted and the selected object will be converted into a viewport. The portion of the display that was common to both the original viewport and the object selected will be displayed. You can, however, change the display of the viewport using the **Zoom** tool or the **Pan** tool. Figure 11-15 shows a viewport and an object that will be used to clip the viewport and Figure 11-16 shows the new viewport created after clipping.

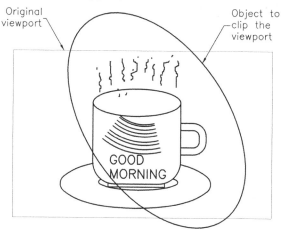

Figure 11-15 *Selecting the object for clipping the viewport*

Figure 11-16 *New viewport created after clipping*

Polygonal

This option is used to create a polygonal boundary for clipping the viewports. When you invoke this option, the options for creating a polygonal boundary will be displayed. You can draw a polygonal boundary for clipping the viewport using these options.

Delete

This option is used to delete the new clipping boundary created using an object or using the **Polygonal** option. The original viewport is restored when you invoke this option, which will be available only if the viewport has been clipped at least once. If the viewport is clipped more than once, you can restore only the last viewport clipping boundary.

Maximizing Viewports

Status Bar: Maximize Viewport

While working with floating viewports, you may need to invoke the temporary model space to modify the drawing. One of the options is that you double-click inside the viewport to invoke the temporary model space and make the changes in the drawing. But in this case, the shape and size of the floating viewport will control the area of the temporary model space. If the viewport is polygonal and small in size, you may have to zoom and pan the drawing a number of times. To avoid this, AutoCAD LT allows you to maximize a viewport on the screen. This provides you all the space in the drawing area to make the changes in the drawing.

To maximize a floating viewport, choose the **Maximize Viewport** button from the Status bar. The viewport is automatically maximized in the drawing area and the **Maximize Viewport** button is replaced by the **Minimize Viewport** button. If there are more than one floating viewports, two arrows will be displayed on either side of the **Minimize Viewport** button. These arrows can be used to switch to the display in the other floating viewports. After making the changes in the drawing, choose the **Minimize Viewport** button to restore the original display of the layout. When you do so, the view and the magnification in all the viewports is the same as that before maximizing them. Also, the visibility of the layers remains the same as that before maximizing the viewport.

CONTROLLING THE LAYERS IN VIEWPORTS USING THE LAYER PROPERTIES MANAGER DIALOG BOX

You can use the **Layer Properties Manager** dialog box to control the layer display properties in viewports. When you invoke the **Layer Properties Manager** dialog box in the layout, some additional properties are added to it, see Figure 11-17. These properties are used to override the global property of the layer in a particular viewport, while retaining the global layer properties in other floating viewports and the model space. To set a property of a viewport double-click inside it to activate the temporary model space and then set the properties. The properties are discussed next.

VP Freeze

When the **TILEMODE** option is turned off, you can freeze or thaw the selected layers in the current floating viewport by selecting the **VP Freeze** option. You can freeze a layer in the current floating viewport if it is thawed in the model space but you cannot thaw a layer in the current viewport if it is frozen in the model space. The frozen layers still remain visible in other viewports.

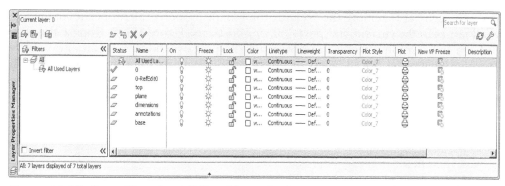

Figure 11-17 *Controlling the visibility of layers in the viewports using the* **Layer Properties Manager** *dialog box*

VP Color

The swatch under the **VP Color** column is used to change the display color of the objects in the selected layer in the current floating viewport. In all other floating viewports and model space, the color of the objects remains unaffected.

VP Linetype

The field under the **VP Linetype** column is used to change the linetype defined for the selected layer in the active floating viewport. In all other floating viewports and model space, the linetype remains unaffected.

VP Lineweight

The field under the **VP Lineweight** column is used to override the lineweight defined for the selected layer in the active floating viewport. In all other floating viewports and the model space, the lineweight remains unaffected.

VP Transparency

The field under the **VP Transparency** column is used to override the transparency defined for the layer selected in the active floating viewport. In all other floating viewports and the model space, the transparency remains unaffected.

VP Plot Style

The field under the **VP Plot Style** column is used to override the plot style settings assigned to the selected layer in the active floating viewport. The plot style for all other floating viewports and model space remains unaffected. You cannot override the plot styles for the color dependent plot styles. The override for the plot style also does not affect the plot if the visual style is set to **Realistic** or **Conceptual**.

Note
By default, all the overrides that you have defined for the current active viewport will get highlighted in light blue color in the **Layer Properties Manager** *dialog box. Also, the icon of the selected layer under the* **Status** *column will change to inform you that some of the properties of the selected layer have been overridden by the new one.*

Removing Viewport Overrides

To remove the viewport overrides defined for the active viewports, open the **Layer Properties Manager** dialog box in the active viewport and right-click on the layer property from which you want to remove the viewport override; a shortcut menu will be displayed. Next, choose the **Remove Viewport Overrides for** option from the shortcut menu to display the cascading menu.

Chapter 11

You can make a choice to remove the override for a single property / all properties of the selected layer / all layers in the current viewport / all viewports, see Figure 11-18. Choose the required option from the cascading menu to remove the viewport overrides. You can also remove the layer property overrides for all layers of the selected viewports from the paper space. To do so, make the paper space current; select the viewports boundaries of the viewports for which you want to remove the override and choose the **Remove Viewport Overrides for All Layers** option from the shortcut menu.

| Remove Viewport Overrides for ▶ | Selected Layers ▶ | In Current Viewport only |
| New Layer VP Frozen in All Viewports | All Layers ▶ | In All Viewports |

*Figure 11-18 Suboptions in the **Remove Viewport Override for** option of the **Layer** shortcut menu*

Note
*For more information about the **Layer Properties Manager** dialog box, see Chapter 4.*

INSERTING LAYOUTS

| **Status Bar:** Quick View Layouts > New Layout | **Command:** LAYOUT |
| **Menu Bar:** Insert > Layout > New Layout | **Toolbar:** Layouts > New Layout |

 The **LAYOUT** command is used to create a new layout. It also allows you to rename, copy, save, and delete existing layouts. A drawing designed in the **Model** tab can be composed for plotting in the **Layout** tab. The prompt sequence is as follows.

Enter layout option [Copy/Delete/New/Template/Rename/SAveas/Set/?]<Set>:

The options in the prompt sequence are discussed next.

New Option

This option is used to create a new layout. On choosing this option, you will be prompted to specify the name of the new layout. A new tab with the new layout name will appear in the drawing. Alternatively, you can right-click on the **Model** or the **Layout** tab and choose **New layout** from the shortcut menu to add a new layout. You can also, choose the **Quick View Layouts** button in the Status Bar and then choose **New Layout** button available below the thumbnails to create a new layout. The new layout tab will be added at the end of the existing layout tabs with the default name **Layout N**, where **N** is a natural number starting from one and acquires an ascending value that has not been used in the layout names of the current drawing.

Copy Option

This option is used to copy a layout. When you invoke this option, you will be prompted to specify the layout that has to be copied. Upon specifying the layout, you will be prompted to specify the name of the new layout. If you do not enter a name, the name of the copied layout is assumed with an incremental number in the brackets next to it. For example, Layout 1 is copied as Layout1 (2). The name of the new layout appears as a new tab next to the copied layout tab. Alternatively, you can right-click on the **Model** or **Layout** tab or on the **Quick View Layouts** tile and then choose **Move or Copy** from the shortcut menu to move or copy the selected layout; the **Move or Copy** dialog box will be displayed, see Figure 11-19. Select the

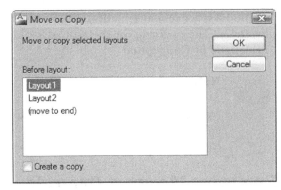

*Figure 11-19 The **Move or Copy** dialog box*

layout from the **Before layout** area to move it above the previous layout and then choose the **OK** button. For example, if you want to move the Layout 2 before Layout 1, then select Layout 2 from the **Move or Copy** dialog box; the Layout 2 will be moved before Layout 1. To create a copy of the selected layout select the **Create a copy** check box.

Tip
You can also drag and drop layouts to move them. To create copies of the selected layouts, press the CTRL key as you drag and drop the layouts.

Delete Option

This option is used to delete an existing layout. On invoking this option, you will be prompted to specify the name of the layout to be deleted. The current layout is the default layout for deleting. Remember that the **Model** tab cannot be deleted. You can also right-click on the **Model** or the **Layout** tab or on the **Quick View Layouts** tiles and choose **Delete** from the shortcut menu; the AutoCAD LT alert window will be displayed. Choose the **OK** button to delete the selected layout.

Template Option

This option is used to create a new template based on the existing layout template in the *.dwg*, *.dwt*, or *.dxf* file. This option invokes the **Select Template From File** dialog box, see Figure 11-20. You can also invoke this dialog box by right-clicking on the **Model**, the **Layout** tab or on the **Quick View Layouts** tiles and choose the **From template** option from the shortcut menu.

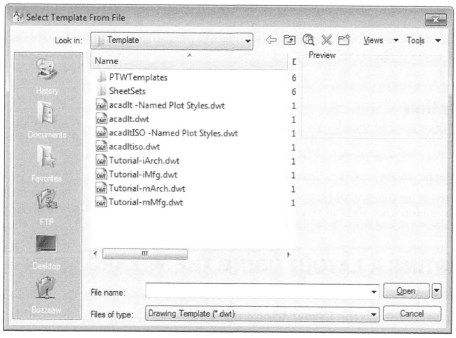

*Figure 11-20 The **Select Template From File** dialog box*

The layout and geometry from the specified template or drawing file is inserted into the current drawing. After the dwt, dwg, or dxf file is selected, the **Insert Layout(s)** dialog box is displayed, as shown in Figure 11-21.

Choose the **Layout from Template** button from the **Layouts** toolbar to create a layout using an existing template or a drawing file.

Note
If you insert a template that has a title block, it will be inserted as a block and all the text in the title block will be inserted as attributes. You will learn more about blocks and attributes in later chapters.

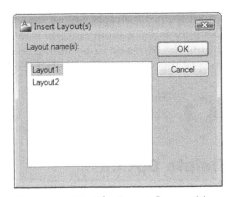

*Figure 11-21 The **Insert Layout(s)** dialog box*

Rename Option

This option allows you to rename a layout. On choosing this option, you will be prompted to specify the name of the layout to be renamed. On specifying the name, you will be prompted to specify the new name of the layout. The layout names have to be unique and can contain up to 255 characters, out of which only 32 are displayed in the tab. The characters in the name are not case-sensitive. You can also right-click on the **Model** or the **Layout** tab or on the **Quick View Layouts** tiles and choose **Rename** from the shortcut menu to rename the selected layout.

Tip
*You can also double-click on the **Layout** tab to rename it.*

SAveas Option

This option is used to save a layout in the drawing template file. On choosing this option, you will be prompted to specify the layout that has to be saved. If you specify the name of the layout to be saved, the **Create Drawing File** dialog box will be displayed. In this dialog box, you can enter the name of the template in the **File name** edit box. The layout templates can be saved in the *.dwg*, *.dwt*, or *.dxf* format.

Set Option

This option is used to set a layout as the current layout. When you invoke this option, you will be prompted to specify the name of the layout that has to be made current.

? Option

This option is used to list all the layouts available in the current drawing. The list is displayed in the Command line. You can open the AutoCAD LT Text Window to view the list by pressing the F2 key.

INSERTING A LAYOUT USING THE WIZARD

Command: LAYOUTWIZARD

This command displays the **Layout Wizard** that guides you step-by-step through the process of creating a new layout.

DEFINING PAGE SETTINGS

Ribbon: Output > Plot > Page Setup Manager **Command:** PAGESETUP
Toolbar: Layouts > Page Setup Manager

This tool is used to specify the layout and plot device settings for each new layout. You can also right-click on the **Model** or the current **Layout** tab and choose **Page Setup Manager** from the shortcut menu to invoke this command. When you invoke this command, the **Page Setup Manager** dialog box is displayed, which will be discussed in Chapter 12.

EXAMPLE 2   *Plot*

In this example, you will create a drawing in the model space and then use the paper space to plot the drawing. The drawing to be plotted is shown in Figure 11-22.

1. Increase the limits to 75, 75 and then draw the sketch shown in Figure 11-22.

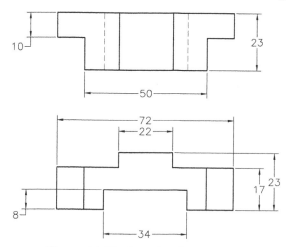

Figure 11-22 Drawing for Example 2

2. Choose the **Layout1** tab; AutoCAD LT displays **Layout1** with the default viewport. Delete this viewport. Right-click on the **Layout1** tab and then choose **Page Setup Manager** from the shortcut menu to display the **Page Setup Manager** dialog box. **Layout1** is automatically selected in the **Current page setup** list box.

3. Choose the **Modify** button to display the **Page Setup - Layout1** dialog box. Select the printer or plotter from the **Name** drop-down list in the **Printer/plotter** area. In this example, **HP Lasejet4000** is used. From the drop-down list in the **Paper size** area, select the paper size that is supported by your plotting device. In this example, the paper size is **A4 (210 x 297mm)**. Choose the **OK** button to accept the settings and exit the dialog box. Close the **Page Setup Manager** dialog box.

4. Choose the **New** tool from the **Viewports** flyout in the **View** menu; the **Viewports** dialog box is displayed. Select the **Single** option from the **Standard viewports** list box and choose **OK**. The prompt sequence is as follows:

   Tab index <0>: 0
   Specify first corner or [Fit] <Fit>: *Specify the first corner of the viewport near the bottom left corner of the drawing window.*
   Specify opposite corner: *@210,297*
   Regenerating model.

5. Use the **ZOOM** command in the paper space to zoom to the extents of the viewport.

6. Double-click in the viewport to switch to the temporary model space and use the **ZOOM** command to zoom the drawing to 2XP. In this example, it is assumed that the scale factor is 2:1; therefore, the zoom factor is 2XP.

7. Create the dimension style with the text height of 1.5 and the arrowhead height of 1.25. Define all the other parameters based on the text and arrowhead heights and then select the **Annotative** check box and the **Scale dimensions to layout** radio button from the **Scale for dimension features** area of the **Fit** tab in the **New Dimension Style** dialog box.

Chapter 11

8. Using the new dimension style, dimension the drawing. Make sure that you do not change the scale factor. You can use the **Pan** tool to adjust the display.

9. Double-click in the paper space to switch back to the paper space. Choose the **Plot** tool from the **Quick Access** toolbar to display the **Plot** dialog box.

10. Choose the **Window** option from the **What to plot** drop-down list in the **Plot area**; the dialog box will be closed temporarily and you will be prompted to specify the first and second corners of the window. Define a window close to the boundary of the viewport such that the viewport is not included in it.

11. As soon as you define both the corners of the window, the **Plot** dialog box will be redisplayed on the screen. Select **1:1** from the **Scale** drop-down list of the **Plot scale** area.

12. Select the **Center the plot** check box from the **Plot offset (origin set to printable area)** area.

13. Choose the **Preview** button to display the plot preview. You can make any adjustments, if required, by redefining the window.

14. After you are satisfied with the preview, right-click and choose **Plot** from the shortcut menu; the drawing will be printed with the scale of 2:1. This means that two plotted units will be equal to one actual unit. Save this drawing with the name *Example2.dwg*.

CONTROLLING THE DISPLAY OF ANNOTATIVE OBJECTS IN VIEWPORTS

Some new buttons have been added to the status bar to control the annotation scale in viewports and model space separately. When you activate a floating viewport, a new **Viewport Scale** button is added to the status bar. The **Viewport Scale** button lists the same set of scales as the **Annotation Scale**. You can set an annotation display scale either from the **Viewport Scale** button or the **Annotation Scale** button, and the other scales will be updated accordingly. The viewport will zoom to an appropriate scale so that the annotation objects can be displayed at the specified scale.

Also, when you activate a floating viewport, the **Lock/Unlock Viewport** button is added to the status bar. With the help of this button, you can toggle between the lock and unlock states of the viewport. The **Viewport Scale** and **Annotation Scale** buttons are not accessible when the viewport is locked. If the viewport is unlocked and you zoom the drawing instead of specifying the viewport scale, the annotation scale will not be changed and the current scale representation will remain intact and visible. But, the viewport scale will be changed to display the actual scale of the viewport.

The example given next will explain various concepts related to creating and controlling the display of annotations in viewports.

 Note
When the paper space is active, the annotation scale is always 1:1 and it cannot be modified.

EXAMPLE 3	*Annotative Text*

In this example, you will draw the object, as shown in Figure 11-23, and create the floating viewports, as shown in Figure 11-24. The left viewport has a scale of 3/8"=1'-0" and the right viewport has a scale of 1-1/2"=1'-0". All the annotations that are created in the model space should be displayed with a text height of 0.08" on the sheet even if the same annotation appears in multiple viewports.

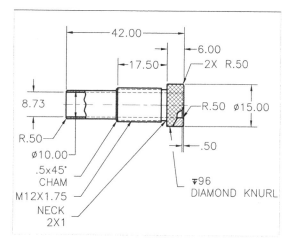

Figure 11-23 *Model for Example 3*

1. Start a new file in the **Drafting & Annotation** workspace and draw the object as shown in Figure 11-23.

2. Set the **Annotation Scale** to 3/8"=1'-0" from the Status Bar.

3. Create an annotative text style with the **Paper Text Height** equal to **0.08**.

4. Create an annotative dimension style with the values given next and draw the dimensions, refer to Figure 11-23.

   Arrow size = **0.07**
   Text height = **0.08**

5. Create an annotative multileader style with the values given next and draw the multileaders, refer to Figure 11-23.

   Landing distance = **0.075**
   Arrowhead size = **0.07**
   Text height = **0.08**

6. Change the annotation scale to 1-1/2"=1'-0", select all the dimensions from the right of the object, and then choose the **Add Current Scale** tool from the **Annotation Scaling** panel of the **Annotate** tab; the annotation scale of 1-1/2"=1'-0" is added to the selected dimensions. You will notice that the selected dimensions and multileaders appear smaller than the other annotations because they reflect the current annotation scale of 1-1/2"=1'-0".

7. Turn the **Annotation Visibility** button off. Now you can see the annotations that support a scale of 1-1/2"=1'-0". This helps you to find out the dimensions to which the scale of 1-1/2"=1'-0" has been assigned.

8. Select the annotations from the right of the object and adjust their locations with the help of grips, such that the placement of dimensions remains similar to the one shown in Figure 11-23. Notice that when you select the annotation object, its different scale representations are displayed with faded dashed lines.

9. In the Status Bar, set the annotation scale to 3/8"=1'-0" and then change it back to 1-1/2"=1'-0". Now you will notice that the same annotation objects not only change the size, but also change the location.

10. Choose the **Layout1** tab to switch to the layouts. A rectangular viewport is automatically created in this layout.

11. Choose the **Erase** tool from the **Modify** panel of the **Home** tab; you will be prompted to select the object. Enter **L** in this prompt to delete the last object, which in this case is the viewport.

12. Draw two rectangles of dimensions **3'X3.5'** and **2.25'X3.5'** side-by-side, refer to Figure 11-24.

13. Choose the **Convert Object to Viewport** tool from **View > Viewports > Create Viewports** drop-down; you will be prompted to select the object. Select one of the rectangles; it will be converted into a viewport. Similarly, convert the second rectangle into a viewport.

14. Activate the viewport on the left and set its annotation scale to 3/8"=1'-0" from the Status Bar.

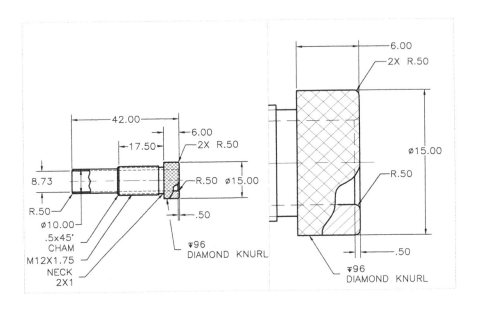

Figure 11-24 Displaying the drawing in two viewports

11. Similarly, activate the viewport on the right and set its annotation scale to 1-1/2"=1'-0". Pan the view so that it looks similar to Figure 11-24.

Self-Evaluation Test

Answer the following questions and then compare them to those given at the end of this chapter:

1. Viewports in the model space can be of any shape. (T/F)

2. Viewports in the model space can overlap each other. (T/F)

3. You can join two different tiled viewports. (T/F)

4. You cannot insert any additional layout in the current drawing. (T/F)

5. The _____ tool is used to create the tiled viewports.

6. The viewports in layouts are called _____ viewports.

7. The two working environments provided by AutoCAD LT are _____ and _____.

8. The _____ command is used to insert a title block in the current layout.

9. When you join two adjacent viewports, the resultant viewport is _____ in shape.

10. The default viewport that is created in a new layout is _____ in shape.

Review Questions

Answer the following questions:

1. Only the viewports that are created in layouts can be polygonal in shape. (T/F)

2. You cannot lock the display of a floating viewport. (T/F)

3. An existing closed loop can be converted into a viewport in the model space. (T/F)

4. Which of the following commands can be used to control the display of objects in viewports?

   (a) **MVIEW**   (b) **DVIEW**
   (c) **LAYOUT**   (d) **MSPACE**

5. Which of the following commands can be used to switch to the temporary model space?

   (a) **MVIEW**   (b) **DVIEW**
   (c) **LAYOUT**   (d) **MSPACE**

6. Which of the following options of the **MVIEW** command in the paper space can be used to hide the hidden lines of solid models in printing?

   (a) **Hide**   (b) **Shadeplot**
   (c) **Create**   (d) **None**

7. Which of the following commands can be used to clip an existing floating viewport?

   (a) **MVIEW**   (b) **DVIEW**
   (c) **VPCLIP**   (d) **MSPACE**

8. Which of the following options of the **VPLAYER** command is used to create a layer that will be frozen in all viewports?

   (a) **Freeze**   (b) **Thaw**
   (c) **Newfrz**   (d) **Reset**

9. You can work only in the _____ tiled viewport.

10. The _____ command can be used to set similar linetype scale for all viewports.

11. The _____ command is used to switch back to the paper space from the temporary model space.

12. The _____ dialog box is used to save a viewport configuration in the model space.

EXERCISE 1   *Tiled Viewport*

In this exercise, you will perform the following operations:

a. In the model space, make the drawing of the shaft shown in Figure 11-25.
b. Create three tiled viewports in the model space and then display the drawing in all the three tiled viewports.
c. Create a new layout with the name **Title Block** and insert a title block of ANSI A size in this layout.
d. Create two viewports, one for the drawing and one for the detail "A". See Figure 11-25 for the approximate size and location. The dimensions in detail "A" viewport must not be shown in the other viewport. Also, adjust the LTSCALE factor for hidden and center lines.
e. Plot the drawing.

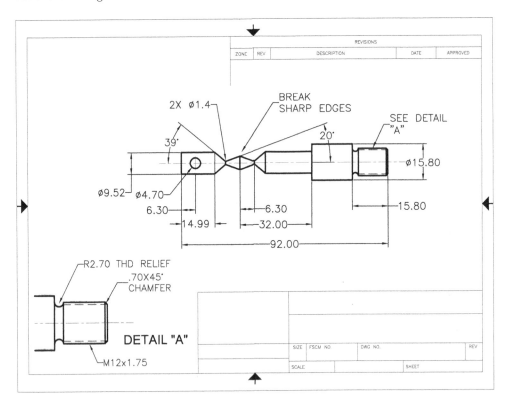

Figure 11-25 Drawing for Exercise 1

Answers to Self-Evaluation Test

1. F, **2. F**, **3.** T, **4.** F, **5. VPORTS**, **6.** floating, **7.** model space and paper space/layouts, **8. MVSETUP**, **9.** rectangular, **10.** rectangular

Chapter *12*

Plotting Drawings

CHAPTER OBJECTIVES

In this chapter, you will learn:
- *To plot drawings.*
- *To add plotters.*
- *To add plot styles.*

KEY TERMS

- *Plot*
- *Page Setup*
- *Plot Style*
- *Plotter Manager*
- *Styles Manager*

PLOTTING DRAWINGS IN AutoCAD LT

After you have completed a drawing, you can store it on the computer storage device such as the hard drive or diskette. However, to get its hard copy, you should plot the drawing on a sheet of paper using a plotter or printer. A hard copy is a handy reference for professionals working on site. With pen plotters, you can obtain a high-resolution drawing. Basic plotting has already been discussed in Chapter 2, Getting Started with AutoCAD LT. You can plot drawings in the **Model** tab or any of the layout tabs. A drawing has a **Model** and two layout tabs (**Layout1**, **Layout2**) by default. Each of these tabs has its own settings and can be used to create different plots. You can also create new layout tabs using the **LAYOUT** command. This is discussed in Chapter 11.

PLOTTING DRAWINGS USING THE PLOT DIALOG BOX

Quick Access Toolbar: Plot	**Toolbar:** Standard > Plot	**Command:** PLOT
Application Menu: Print > Plot	**Ribbon:** Output > Plot > Plot	

The **Plot** tool is used to plot a drawing. When you invoke this tool, the **Plot** dialog box is displayed. This dialog box can also be invoked by right-clicking on the **Model** tab or any of the **Layout** tabs and choosing the **Plot** option from the shortcut menu. Figure 12-1 shows the expanded **Plot** dialog box.

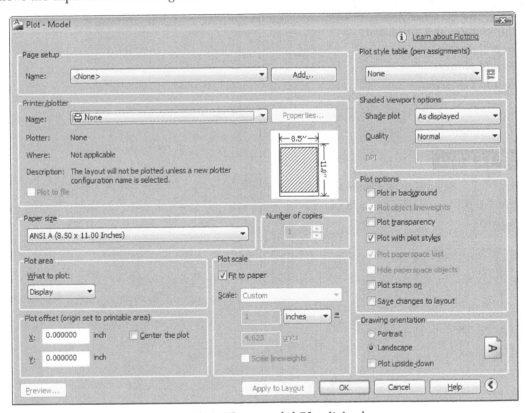

Figure 12-1 *The expanded* **Plot** *dialog box*

In this dialog box, some values were set when AutoCAD LT was first configured. You can examine these values and if they conform to your requirements, you can start plotting directly. Otherwise, you can alter these values to define plot specifications by using the options in the **Plot** dialog box. The available plot options are discussed next.

Page setup Area

The **Name** drop-down list in this area displays all the saved and named page setups. A page setup contains the settings required to plot a drawing on a sheet of paper to create a layout. It consists of all the settings related to the plotting of a drawing such as the scale, pen settings, and so on, and also includes the plot devices being used. These settings can be saved as a named page setup, which can be later selected from this drop-down list and used for plotting a drawing. If you select **Previous plot** from the drop-down list, the settings used for the last drawing plotted are applied to the current drawing. You can also import the existing page setup from the other files by selecting the **Import** option from the drop-down list. The page setup can be imported from any drawing file(*.dwg*), from a template file(*.dwt*), or from a drawing interchange format file(*.dxf*). You can choose the base for the page setup on a named page setup, or you can add a new named page setup by choosing the **Add** button, which is located next to the drop-down list. When you choose this button, AutoCAD LT displays the **Add Page Setup** dialog box, as shown in Figure 12-2.

Enter the name of the new page setup in this dialog box and choose **OK**. All the settings that you configure in the current **Plot** dialog box will be saved under this page setup.

*Figure 12-2 The **Add Page Setup** dialog box*

Tip
*To create a new page setup based on the existing one, select the existing page setup from the **Name** drop-down list and make modifications in it. Next, choose the **Add** button; the modified page setup will be saved.*

Printer/plotter Area

This area displays all information about the configured printers and plotters currently selected from the **Name** drop-down list. It displays the plotter driver and the printer port being used. It also displays the physical location and some description text about the selected plotter or printer. All the currently configured plotters are displayed in the **Name** drop-down list.

Note
*To add plotters and printers to the **Name** drop-down list, choose the **Plotter Manager** tool from the **Plot** panel in the **Output** tab; a window will be displayed. Double-click on the **Add-A-Plotter Wizard** icon in this window to display the **Add Plotter** wizard. You can use this wizard to add a plotter to the list of configured plotters. Once the plotter is added, the plotter configuration file (PC3) for the plotter will be created. This file consists of all settings needed by the specific plotter to plot the drawing. (The **Plotters** window will be discussed later in this chapter in the section Adding Plotters).*

Properties

To check information about a configured printer or plotter, choose the **Properties** button. When you choose this button, the **Plotter Configuration Editor** dialog box will be displayed. This dialog box lists all the details of the selected plotter under three tabs: **General**, **Ports**, and **Device and Document Settings**. The **Plotter Configuration Editor** will be discussed later in the "Editing Plotter Configuration" section of this chapter.

Plot to file

If you select this check box, AutoCAD LT plots the output to a file rather than to the plotter. Depending on the plotter selected, the file can be plotted in the *.dwf*, *.plt*, *.jpg*, or *.png* format. On selecting this check box and choosing **OK** from the **Plot** dialog box, the **Browse for Plot File** dialog box will be displayed. Specify the file name and its location in this dialog box.

Partial Preview Window

The window displayed below the **Properties** button is called the **Partial Preview** window. The preview in this window dynamically changes as you modify the parameters in the **Plot** dialog box. The outer rectangle in this window is the paper you selected. It also shows the size of the paper. The inner hatched rectangle is the section of the paper that is used by the image. If the image extends beyond the paper, a red border is displayed around the paper.

Paper size Area

The drop-down list in this area displays all standard paper sizes for the selected plotting device. You can select any size from the list to make it current. If **None** has been selected currently from the **Name** drop-down list in the **Printer/plotter** area, AutoCAD LT will display the list of all standard paper sizes.

Number of copies Area

You can use the spinner available in this area to specify the number of copies that you want to plot. If multiple layouts and copies are selected and some of the layouts are set for plotting to a file or AutoSpool, they will produce a single plot. AutoSpool allows you to send a file for plotting while you are working on another program.

Plot area Area

Using the **What to plot** drop-down list provided in this area, you can specify the portion of the drawing to be plotted. You can also control the way the plotting will be carried out. The options in the **What to plot** drop-down list are described next.

Display

If you select this option, the portion of the drawing that is currently being displayed on the screen is plotted.

Extents

This option resembles the **Extents** option of the **ZOOM** command and prints the drawing to the extents of the objects. If you add more objects to the drawing, they are also included in the plot and the extents of the drawing are recalculated. If you reduce the drawing extents by erasing, moving, or scaling the objects, the extents of the drawing are again recalculated. You can use the **Extents** option of the **ZOOM** command to determine which objects shall be plotted. If you use the **Extents** option when the perspective view is on and the position of the camera is not outside the drawing extents, the following message is displayed: **The annotation scale is not equal to the plot scale.**

Limits

This option is available only if you plot from the **Model** tab. Selecting this option plots the complete area defined within the drawing limits.

Note
*To be able to clearly view the differences between the three previously listed plotting options, it may be a good idea to make sure that the default scale options have been selected. Alternatively, select the **Fit to paper** check box from the **Plot scale** area of the dialog box if you are in the **Model** tab, and select **1:1** if you are working in any one of the layout tabs.*

Window

On selecting this option, you need to specify the section of the drawing to be plotted by defining a window. To define a window, select the **Window** option from the **What to plot** drop-down list.

The **Plot** dialog box will be temporarily closed and you will be prompted to specify two points on the screen to define a window; the area within this window will be plotted. Once you have defined the window, the **Plot** dialog box is redisplayed on the screen. You will notice that the **Window** button is now displayed on the right of the **What to plot** drop-down list. To reselect the area to be plotted, choose the **Window** button. If the **Model** tab is chosen, you will notice that the previously selected area is displayed in white and the remaining area is displayed in gray. After selecting the area to be plotted, you can choose the **OK** button in the dialog box to plot the drawing.

Note

*Sometimes, while using the **Window** option, the area you have selected may appear clipped off. This may happen because the objects are too close to the window you have defined on the screen. You need to redefine the window in this situation. Such errors can be avoided by using the **Preview** option discussed later.*

View

Selecting the **View** option enables you to plot a view that was created with the **VIEW** command. The view must be defined in the current drawing. If no view has been created, the **View** option is not displayed. When you select this option, a drop-down list is displayed in this area. You can select a view for plotting from this drop-down list and then choose **OK** in the **Plot** dialog box. While using the **View** option, the specifications of the plot will depend on the specifications of the named view.

Layout

This option is available only when you are plotting from the layout. This option prints the entire content of the drawing that lies inside the printable area of the paper selected from the drop-down list in the **Paper size** area.

Plot offset (origin set to printable area) Area

This area allows you to specify an offset of the plotting area from the lower left corner of the paper. The lower left corner of the specified plot area is positioned at the lower left margin of the paper by default. If you select the **Center the plot** check box, AutoCAD LT automatically centers the plot on the paper by calculating the X and Y offset values. You can specify an offset from the origin by entering positive or negative values in the **X** and **Y** edit boxes. For example, if you want the drawing to be plotted 4 units to the right and 4 units above the origin point, enter **4** in both the **X** and **Y** edit boxes. Depending on the units you have specified in the **Paper size** area of the dialog box, the offset values are either in inches, in millimeters, or in pixels.

Plot scale Area

This area controls the drawing scale of the plot area. Apart from **Custom** option, the **Scale** drop-down list has thirty-three architectural and decimal scales by default. The default scale setting is **1:1** when you are plotting a layout. However, if you are plotting in a **Model** tab, the **Fit to paper** check box is selected. The **Fit to paper** option allows you to automatically fit the entire drawing on the paper. It is useful when you have to print a large drawing using a printer that uses a smaller size paper.

Whenever you select a standard scale from the drop-down list, the scale is displayed in the edit boxes as a ratio of the plotted units to the drawing units. You can also change the scale factor manually in these edit boxes. When you do so, the **Scale** edit box displays **Custom**. For example, for an architectural drawing, which is to be plotted at the scale 1/4"=1'-0", you can enter either 1/4"=1'-0" or 1=48 in the edit boxes.

Note

*The **PSLTSCALE** system variable controls the paper space linetype scaling and has a default value of 1. This implies that irrespective of the zoom scale of the viewports, the linetype scale of the objects in the viewports remains the same. If you want the linetype scale of the objects in different viewports with different magnification factors to appear different, you should set the value of the **PSLTSCALE** variable to 0. This has been discussed in detail in Chapter 11 (Model Space Viewports, Paper Space Viewports, and Layouts).*

The **Scale lineweights** check box is available only if you are plotting in a layout. This option is not available in the **Model** tab. If you select the **Scale lineweights** check box, you can scale lineweights in proportion to the plot scale. Lineweights generally specify the linewidth of the printable objects and are plotted with the original lineweight size, regardless of the plot scale.

Note

*You can save the custom scales that you use during plotting or in layouts in the **Edit Drawing Scales** dialog box. To invoke the **Edit Drawing Scales** dialog box, choose the **Scale List** tool from the **Annotation Scaling** panel in the **Annotate** tab. The **Scale List** area lists the default scales in AutoCAD LT. Choose the **Add** button to invoke the **Add Scale** dialog box. Enter a name for the custom scale in the **Name appearing in the scale list** edit box. Next, enter the scale in the **Scale Properties** area and choose the **OK** button; the name specified for the custom scale will be listed in the **Scale List** area. In this way, you can keep a track of the custom scales used.*

Plot style table (pen assignments) Area

This area will be available when you expand the **Plot** dialog box. This area allows you to view and select a plot style table, edit the current plot style table, or create a new plot style table. A plot style table is a collection of plot styles. A plot style is a group of pen settings that are assigned to an object or layer and that determine the color, linetype, thickness, line ending, line joining and the fill style of drawing objects when they are plotted. It is a named file that allows you to control the pen settings for a plotted drawing.

Shaded viewport options Area

The options in this area are used to print a shaded or a rendered image.

Plot options Area

This area displays six options that can be selected as per the plot requirements.

Drawing orientation Area

This area provides options that help you specify the orientation of the drawing on the paper for the plotters that support landscape or portrait orientation. You can change the drawing orientation by selecting the **Portrait** or **Landscape** radio button, with or without selecting the **Plot upside-down** check box. The paper icon displayed on the right side of this area indicates the media orientation of the selected paper and the letter icon (A) on it indicates the orientation of the drawing on the page. The **Landscape** radio button is selected by default for AutoCAD LT drawings and orients the length of the paper along the *X* axis. If we assume this orientation to be at a rotation angle of 0°, then while selecting the **Portrait** radio button, the plot is oriented with the width along the *X* axis, which is equivalent to the plot being rotated through a rotation angle of 90°. Similarly, if you select both the **Landscape** radio button and the **Plot upside-down** check box at the same time, the plot gets rotated through a rotation angle of 180° and if you select both the **Portrait** radio button and the **Plot upside-down** check box at the same time, the plot gets rotated through a rotation angle of 270°. The AutoCAD LT screen conforms to the landscape orientation by default.

Preview

When you choose the **Preview** button, AutoCAD LT displays the drawing on the screen just as it would be plotted on the paper. Once the regeneration is performed, the dialog boxes on the screen disappear, and an outline of the paper size is shown. In the plot preview (Figure 12-3), the cursor is replaced by the **Zoom Realtime** icon. This icon can be used to zoom in and out interactively by pressing and moving the left mouse button. You can right-click to display a shortcut menu and then choose **Exit** to exit the preview or press the ENTER or ESC key to return to the dialog box. You can also choose **Plot** to plot the drawing right away or choose the other zooming options available.

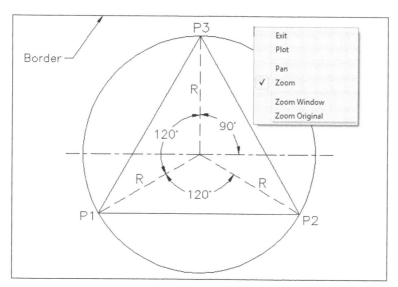

Figure 12-3 Full plot preview with the shortcut menu

Tip
*You can also choose **Plot Preview** from the **Quick Access Toolbar** to preview the plot, and at the same time, bypass the **Plot** dialog box.*

After finishing all the settings and other parameters, if you choose the **OK** button in the **Plot** dialog box, AutoCAD LT starts plotting the drawing in the file or plotters as specified. Also, the **Plot Job Progress** dialog box, where you can view the actual progress of plotting will be displayed.

ADDING PLOTTERS

Application Menu: Print > Manage Plotters	**Command:** PLOTTERMANAGER
Ribbon: Output > Plot > Plotter Manager	

In AutoCAD LT, the plotters are added using the **Plotter Manager** tool. This tool is discussed next.

The Plotter Manager Tool

When you invoke the **Plotter Manager** tool, AutoCAD LT will display the **Plotters** window, see Figure 12-4.

The **Plotters** window is basically a Windows Explorer window. It displays all the configured plotters and the **Add-A-Plotter Wizard** icon. You can right-click on any one of the icons belonging to the plotters that have already been configured to display a shortcut menu. You can choose **Delete** from the shortcut menu to remove a plotter from the list of available plotters in the **Name** drop-down list in the **Plot or Page Setup** dialog box. You can also choose **Rename** from the shortcut menu to rename the plotter configuration file or choose **Properties** to view the properties of the configured device.

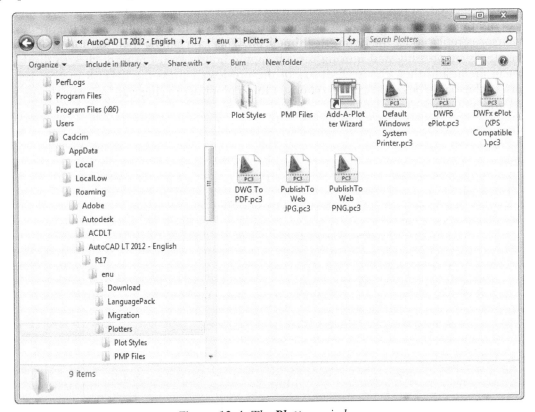

*Figure 12-4 The **Plotters** window*

Add-A-Plotter Wizard

If you double-click on the **Add-A-Plotter Wizard** icon in the **Plotters** window, AutoCAD LT guides you to configure a nonsystem plotter for plotting your drawing files. AutoCAD LT stores all the information of a configured plotter in configured plot (PC3) files. The PC3 files are stored in the *C:\Users\<owner>\AppData\Roaming\Autodesk\AutoCAD LT 2012\R17\enu\Plotters* folder by default. In AutoCAD LT 2012, you can add your own folder to store information of a configured plotter. To do so, add path of the folder in the **Support Files Search Path** given in the **Files** tab of the **Options** dialog box. The steps for configuring a new plotter using the **Add-A-Plotter Wizard** are as follows:

1. Open the **Plotters** window by choosing the **Plotter Manager** tool from the **Plot** panel and double-click on the **Add-A-Plotter Wizard** icon.

2. In the **Add Plotter - Introduction** page, read the introduction carefully, and then choose the **Next** button to advance to the **Add Plotter - Begin** page.

3. On the **Add Plotter - Begin** page, the **My Computer** radio button is selected by default. Choose the **Next** button; the **Add Plotter - Plotter Model** page is displayed.

4. On this page, select a manufacturer and model of your nonsystem plotter from the **Manufacturers** and **Models** list boxes, respectively. Now, choose the **Next** button. The **Add Plotter - Import Pcp or Pc2** page is displayed.

If your plotter is not present in the list of available plotters, and you have a driver disk for your plotter, choose the **Have Disk** button to locate the *.hif* file from the driver disk, and install the driver supplied with your plotter.

5. In the **Add Plotter - Import Pcp or Pc2** page, if you want to import configuring information from a PCP or a PC2 file created with a previous version of AutoCAD LT, you can choose the **Import File** button and select the file. Otherwise, simply choose the **Next** button to advance to the next page.

6. On the **Add Plotter - Ports** page, select the port from the list to be used while plotting, and choose **Next**.

7. On the **Add Plotter - Plotter Name** page, specify the name of the currently configured plotter or retain the default name. Choose **Next**.

8. When you reach the **Add Plotter - Finish** page, choose the **Finish** button to exit the **Add-A-Plotter Wizard**.

    You can also choose the **Edit Plotter Configuration** button to display the **Plotter Configuration Editor** dialog box where you can edit the current plotter's configuration. Also, in this page, you can choose the **Calibrate Plotter** button to display the **Calibrate Plotter** wizard. This wizard allows you to calibrate your plotter by setting up a test measurement. After test plotting, it compares the plot measurements with the actual measurements and computes a correction factor.

Once you have chosen **Finish** to exit the wizard, a PC3 file for the newly configured plotter will be displayed in the **Plotters** window. This PC3 file contains all the settings needed by the plotter to plot. Also, the newly configured plotter name is added to the **Name** drop-down list in the **Plotter configuration** area of the **Plot Device** tab in the **Plot** dialog box. You can now use the plotter for plotting.

USING PLOT STYLES

The plot styles can change the complete look of a plotted drawing. You can use this feature to override a drawing object's color, linetype, and lineweight. For example, if an object is drawn on a layer that is assigned the red color and no plot style is assigned to it, the object will be plotted as red. However, if you have assigned a plot style to the object with the color blue, the object will be plotted as blue, irrespective of the layer color it was drawn on. Similarly, you can change the Linetype, Lineweight, end, join, and fill styles of the drawing, and also change the output effects such as dithering, grayscales, pen assignments, and screening. Basically, you can use **Plot Styles** effectively to plot the same drawing in various ways.

Every object and layer in the drawing has a plot style property. The plot style characteristics are defined in the plot style tables attached to the **Model** tab, layouts, and viewports within the layouts. You can attach and detach different plot style tables to get different looks for your plots. Generally, there are two plot style modes. They are **Color-dependent** and **Named**. The **Color-dependent** plot styles are based on object color and there are **255** color-dependent plot styles. It is possible to assign each color in the plot style a value for the different plotting properties and these settings are then saved in a color-dependent plot style table file that has a *.ctb* extension. Similarly, **Named** plot styles are independent of the object color and you can assign any plot style to any object regardless of that object's color. These settings are saved in a named plot style table file that has *.stb* extension. Every drawing in AutoCAD LT is in either of the plot style modes.

Adding a Plot Style

Application Menu: Print > Manage Plot Styles	Command: STYLESMANAGER

All plot styles are saved in the *C:\Users <owner>\AppData\Roaming\Autodesk\AutoCAD LT 2012\ R17\enu\Plot Styles* location. On choosing **Print > Manage Plot Styles** from the **Application Menu**, the **Plot Styles** window will be displayed, see Figure 12-5. This window displays icons for all available plot styles, in addition to the **Add-A-Plot Style Table Wizard** icon. You can double-click on any of the plot style icons to display the **Plot Style Table Editor** dialog box and edit the selected plot style. When you double-click on the **Add-A-Plot Style Table Wizard** icon, the **Add Plot Style Table** wizard is displayed and you can use it to create a new plot style.

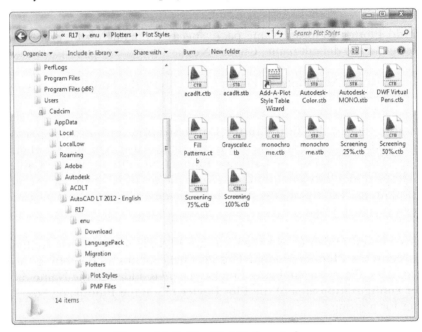

*Figure 12-5 The **Plot Styles** window*

Add-A-Plot Style Table Wizard

If you want to add a new plot style table to your drawing, double-click on the **Add-A-Plot Style Table Wizard** in the **Plot Styles** window to display the **Add Plot Style Table** wizard. The following steps are required for creating a new plot style table using the wizard.

1. Read the introduction page carefully and choose the **Next** button.

2. In the **Begin** page, select the **Start from scratch** radio button and choose **Next**. Selecting this option creates a new plot style table. Therefore, the **Browse File** page is not available.

   In addition to the **Start from scratch** option, this page has three more options: **Use an existing plot style table**, **Use My R14 Plotter Configuration (CFG)**, and **Use a PCP or PC2 file**. When you use the **Use an existing plot style table** option, an existing plot style table is used as a base for the new plot style table you are creating. In such a situation, the **Table Type** page of the wizard is not available and is not displayed because the table type will be based on the existing plot style table you are using to create a new one. With the **Use My R14 Plotter Configuration (CFG)** option, the pen assignments from the Release 14 *acadlt.cfg* file are used as a base for the new table you are creating. If you are using the **Use a PCP or PC2** option, the pen assignments saved earlier in the Release 14 PCP or PC2 file are used to create the new plot style.

3. The **Pick Plot Style Table** page allows you to select the **Color-Dependent Plot Style Table** or the **Named Plot Style Table** according to your requirement. Select the **Color-Dependent Plot Style Table** radio button and then choose the **Next** button.

4. Since you have selected the **Start from scratch** radio button in the **Begin** page, the **Browse File** page is not available and the **File name** page is displayed. However, if you had selected any of the other three options on the **Begin** page, the **Browse File** page would have been displayed. You can select an existing file from the drop-down list available in this page or choose the **Browse** button to display the **Select File** dialog box. You can then browse and select a file from a specific folder and choose **Select** to return to the wizard. You can also enter the name of the existing plot style table on which you want to base the new plot style table, directly in the edit box. After you have specified the file name, choose **Next** to display the **File name** page of the wizard. In the **File name** page, enter a file name for the new plot style table and choose **Next**. The **Finish** page is displayed.

Note

*If you are using the pen assignments from Release 14 acadlt.cfg file to define the new plot style table, you also have to specify the printer or plotter to use from the drop-down list available in the **Browse File** page of the wizard.*

5. The **Finish** page gives you the option of choosing the **Plot Style Table Editor** button to display the **Plot Style Table Editor** and then edit the plot style table you have created. If you select the **Use this plot style table for new and pre-AutoCAD LT 2012 drawings** check box in this page of the wizard, the plot style table that you have created will become the default plot style table for all the drawings you create. This check box is available only if the plot style mode you have selected in the wizard is the same as the default plot style mode specified by you in the **Default plot style behavior for new drawings** area of the **Plot Style Table Settings** dialog box. This dialog box can be invoked by choosing the **Plot Style Table Settings** button from the **Plot and Publish** tab of the **Options** dialog box. Choose **Finish** in the **Finish** page of the wizard to exit the wizard. A new plot style table gets added to the **Plot Styles** window and can be used for plotting.

Note

*You can also choose **Add Plot Style Table/ Add Color-Dependent Plot Style Table** from the **Tools > Wizards** menu to display wizards that are similar to the **Add Plot Style Table** wizard However, in the **Begin** page, the **Use an existing plot style table** option will not be available. Also the **Table Type** page will not be available and the **Finish** page will have an additional option to use the new plot style table for the current drawing.*

EXAMPLE 1   *Plot Style*

Create the drawing shown in Figure 12-6. Next, create a named plot style with the name *My First Table.stb* with a plot style having the following parameters:

1. Screening   :   65%
2. Object line weight   :   0.6000 mm
3. Line Type   :   ISO Dash
4. Object Color   :   Blue (5)

Additionally, plot the drawing using the **Date and Time** and **Paper size** stamps.

Chapter 12

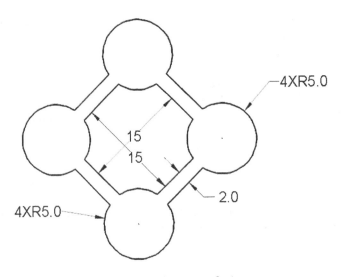

Figure 12-6 Drawing for Example 1

1. Create the drawing, as shown in Figure 12-6. You can create the drawing by making an octagon and then converting its alternate edge into an arc with the given radius.

2. Choose the **Print > Manage Plot Styles** from the **Application Menu**; a window is displayed with all plot styles available. Double-click on the **Add-A-Plot Style Table Wizard** shortcut icon; the **Add Plot Style Table** wizard will be displayed. Choose the **Next** button; the **Begin** page is displayed.

3. Select the **Start from scratch** radio button and choose the **Next** button; the **Pick Plot Style Table** page will be displayed. Now, select the **Named Plot Style Table** radio button and then choose the **Next** button. A window is displayed prompting to enter the file name. Enter *My First Table* in the **File name** text box and then choose the **Next** button.

4. In the **Add Plot Style Table - Finish** window, select **Plot Style Table Editor** button; a window named **Plot Style Table Editor - My First Table.stb** is displayed with the **Table View** tab chosen by default.

5. Choose the **Add Style** button in the bottom left of the window; a new column named **Style 1** is added in the **Add Style** area. Now, enter the following values in the database:

Row	Value
• Screening	65
• Lineweight	0.6000 mm
• Linetype	ISO Dash
• Color	Blue

Next, choose the **Save & Close** button and then choose the **Finish** button in the displayed window.

6. Now, set the **PSTYLEPOLICY** to 0 to make **Named Plot Style Table** as default. You have to restart the AutoCAD LT to select the *My First Table* plot style. After restarting, type the command **PLOT** at the Command prompt; a plot window is displayed. Now, select the plot style **My First Table.stb** in the **Plot style table** drop-down list; the **Question** window will be displayed. Choose the **Yes** button.

7. Select the layout to be printed/plotted.

8. Select the **Plot stamp on** check box; the **Plot Stamp Settings** button is displayed on the right of the check box. Choose this button; the **Plot Stamp** dialog box is displayed. In this dialog box, select the **Date and Time** and **Paper size** check boxes; clear all other check boxes. Choose the **OK** button to exit the dialog box, and then choose the **Preview** button from the **Plot-Model** dialog box to preview the plot. If the plot seems to be fine, right-click to invoke the shortcut menu. Choose the **Plot** option from the menu to take print.

EXERCISE 1   *Plot Style*

Create the drawing shown in Figure 12-7. Create a named plot style table *My Named Table.stb* with three plot styles: Style 1, Style 2, and Style 3, in addition to the Normal plot style. The Normal plot style is used for plotting the object lines. These three styles have the following specifications:

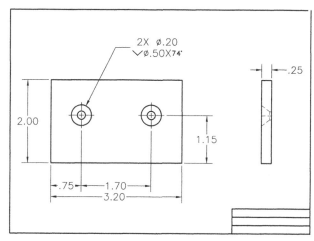

Figure 12-7 *Drawing for Exercise 1*

Style 1. This style has a value of Screening = 50. The dimensions, dimension lines, and the text in the drawing must be plotted with this style.

Style 2. This style has a value of Lineweight = 0.800. The border and title block must be plotted with this style.

Style 3. This style has a linetype of Medium Dash. The centerlines must be plotted with this plot style.

Self-Evaluation Test

Answer the following questions and then compare them to those given at the end of this chapter:

1. All settings of a plotter are saved in the *.PC3* file. (T/F)

2. Different objects in the same drawing can be plotted in different colors with different linetypes and line widths. (T/F)

3. You can partially or fully preview a drawing before plotting. (T/F)

4. The **PSLTSCALE** system variable controls the paper space linetype scaling and has a default value of 1. (T/F)

5. The size of a plot can be specified by selecting any paper size from the _____ drop-down list in the **Plot** dialog box.

6. If you want to store a plot in a file and not have it printed directly on a plotter, select the _____ check box in the **Printer/plotter** area.

7. The scale for a plot can be specified in the _____ edit box in the **Plot** dialog box.

8. If you select the _____ option from the **What to plot** drop-down list, the portion of the drawing that is in the current display is plotted.

9. Before you plot sheets in the sheet set, it is important that you set the _____ for the individual sheets in their page setups.

10. You can set the quality of a plot using the _____ drop-down list in the **Shaded viewport options** area.

Review Questions

Answer the following questions:

1. The **Page Setup Manager** dialog box is displayed when you invoke the **Page Setup Manager** tool. (T/F)

2. By selecting the **View** option from the **What to plot** drop-down list in the **Plot** area, you can plot a view that was created with the **VIEW** command in the current drawing. (T/F)

3. If you do not want the hidden lines of a 3D object created in the **Model** tab, you can select the **Hidden** option from the **Shade plot** drop-down list in the **Shaded viewport options** area. (T/F)

4. The orientation of a drawing can be changed using the **Plot** dialog box. (T/F)

5. Which of the following check boxes is available in the **Plot options** area of the **Plot** dialog box, while plotting in a **Layout** tab?

   (a) **Plot paperspace last**   (b) **Hide objects**
   (c) **Plot with plot styles**   (d) None of these

6. On invoking which of the following tools, the **Plotters** window will be displayed?

    (a) **Plot**   (b) **Manage Plotters**
    (c) **Plot Style**   (d) None of these

7. With which command is it possible to bypass the **Plot/Page Setup** dialog box and directly import a page setup from an existing drawing into a new drawing layout?

    (a) **PSETUPIN**   (b) **PLOTTERMANAGER**
    (c) **PLOTSTYLE**   (d) None of these

8. Which of the following commands is used to create a new plot style?

    (a) **Style**   (b) **Manage Plot Styles**
    (c) **Plot Style**   (d) None of these

9. Which of the following commands can be used to import a PCP file or PC2 file?

    (a) **PCINWIZARD**   (b) **PCIN**
    (c) **PLOTSTYLE**   (d) None of these

10. You can view a plot on the specified paper size before actually plotting it by choosing the _____ button from the **Plot** dialog box.

EXERCISE 2

Create the drawing shown in Figure 12-8 and plot it according to the following specifications. Also, create and use a plot style table with the specified plot styles.

1. The drawing is to be plotted on 10 X 8 inch paper.
2. The object lines must be plotted with a plot style Style 1. Style 1 must have a lineweight = 0.800 mm.
3. The dimension lines must be plotted with plot style Style 2. Style 2 must have a value of screening = 50.
4. The centerlines must be plotted with plot style Style 3. Style 3 must have a linetype of Medium Dash and screening = 50.
5. The border and title block must be plotted with plot style Style 4. The value of the lineweight should be =0.25 mm.

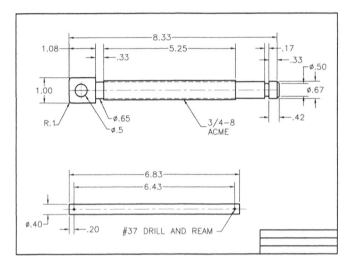

Figure 12-8 *Drawing for Exercise 2*

EXERCISE 3

Create the drawing shown in Figure 12-9 and then plot it according to your specifications.

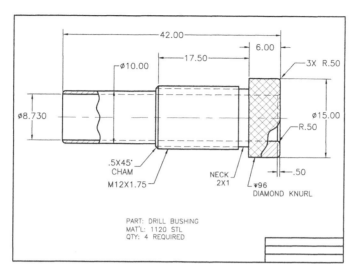

Figure 12-9 *Drawing for Exercise 3*

Problem-Solving Exercise 1

Make the drawing shown in Figure 12-10 and plot it according to your specifications.

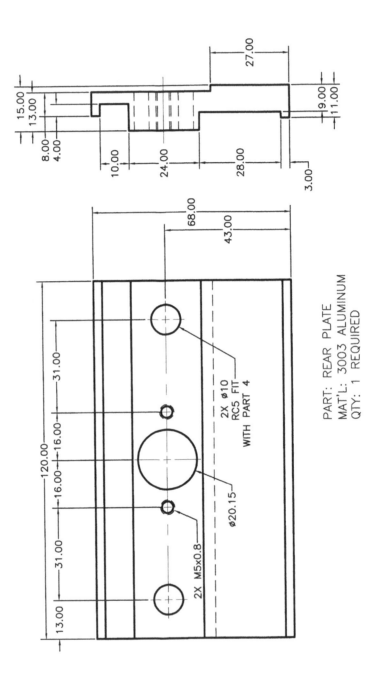

PART: REAR PLATE
MAT'L: 3003 ALUMINUM
QTY: 1 REQUIRED

Figure 12-10 Drawing for Problem-Solving Exercise 1

Answers to Self-Evaluation Test

1. T, **2.** T, **3.** F, **4.** T, **5. Paper size**, 6. **Plot to file**, 7. **Custom**, 8. **Display**, 9. Paper size
10. **Quality**

Chapter *13*

Hatching Drawings

CHAPTER OBJECTIVES

In this chapter, you will learn:

- *To hatch an area by using the Hatch tool.*
- *To use boundary hatch with Predefined, User defined, and Custom hatch patterns.*
- *To specify pattern properties.*
- *To preview and apply hatching.*
- *To create annotative hatching.*
- *To edit associative hatch and hatch boundary.*
- *To hatch inserted blocks.*
- *To align hatch lines in adjacent hatch areas.*

KEY TERMS

- *Hatching*
- *Pattern*
- *Gradient*
- *Boundaries*
- *Islands*
- *Edit Hatch*

HATCHING

In many drawings, such as sections of solids, the sectioned area needs to be filled with some pattern. Different filling patterns make it possible to distinguish between different parts or components of an object. Also, the material of which an object is made can be indicated by the filling pattern. You can also use these filling patterns in graphics for rendering architectural elevations of buildings, or indicating the different levels in terrain and contour maps. Filling objects with a pattern is known as hatching (Figure 13-1). This hatching process can be accomplished by using the **Hatch** tool in the **Draw** panel of the **Home** tab or the **Tool Palettes**.

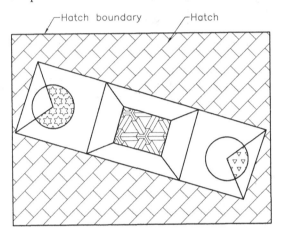

Figure 13-1 *Illustration of hatching*

Before using the **Hatch** tool, you need to understand some terms related to hatching. The following subsection describes some of the terms.

Hatch Patterns

AutoCAD LT supports a variety of hatch patterns (Figure 13-2). Every hatch pattern consists of one or more hatch lines or a solid fill. The lines are placed at specified angles and spacing. You can change the angle and the spacing between the hatch lines. These lines may be broken into dots and dashes, or may be continuous, as required. The hatch pattern is trimmed or repeated, as required, to fill exactly the specified area. The lines comprising the hatch are drawn in the current drawing plane. The basic mechanism behind hatching is that the line objects of the pattern you have specified are generated and incorporated in the desired area in the drawing. Although a hatch can contain many lines, AutoCAD LT normally groups them together into an internally generated object and treats them as such for all practical purposes. For example, if

Figure 13-2 *Some hatch patterns*

you want to perform an editing operation, such as erasing the hatch, all you need to do is select any point on the hatch and press ENTER; the entire pattern gets deleted. If you want to break a pattern into individual lines to edit them, you can use the **EXPLODE** command.

Hatch Boundary

Hatching can be used on parts of a drawing enclosed by a boundary. This boundary may be lines, circles, arcs, polylines, 3D faces, or other objects, and at least part of each bounding object must be displayed within the active viewport.

HATCHING DRAWINGS USING THE HATCH TOOL

Ribbon: Draw > Hatch   **Toolbar:** Draw > Hatch
Command: HATCH or H

The **Hatch** tool is used to hatch a region enclosed within a boundary (closed area) by selecting a point inside the boundary or by selecting the objects to be hatched. This tool automatically designates a boundary and ignores other objects (whole or partial) that may not be a part of this boundary. When you choose the **Hatch** tool, the **Hatch Creation** tab will be displayed, as shown in Figure 13-3. Also, you will be prompted to pick internal point. Select the type of hatch pattern in the **Pattern** panel, set the properties of the hatch pattern in the **Properties** panel, and move the cursor inside a closed profile; the preview of the hatch pattern will be displayed. Now, pick the internal point; the hatch will be applied. Alternatively, when you are prompted to pick an internal point, select the type of hatch pattern in the **Pattern** panel, set the properties of the hatch pattern in the **Properties** panel, and then pick an internal point; the hatch will be applied.

*Figure 13-3 The **Hatch Creation** tab*

EXAMPLE 1   *Hatch*

In this example, you will hatch a circle using the default hatch settings. Later, in the chapter you will learn how to change the settings to get the desired hatch pattern.

1. Choose the **Hatch** tool from the **Draw** panel; the **Hatch Creation** tab is displayed and you are prompted to pick an internal point. Move the cursor over the circle; the preview of the hatch pattern is displayed.

2. Select a point inside the circle (P1) (Figure 13-4) and press ENTER; the hatch is applied, as shown in Figure 13-5.

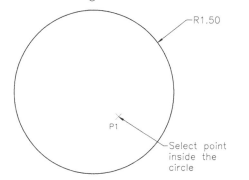

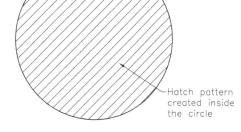

Figure 13-4 Specifying a point to hatch the circle   *Figure 13-5 Drawing after hatching*

Tip
*The **FILLMODE** system variable is set to On by default (value of the variable is 1) and hence the hatch patterns are displayed. In case of large hatching areas, you can set the **FILLMODE** to Off (value of the variable is 0), so that the hatch pattern is not displayed and the regeneration time is saved.*

PANELS IN THE HATCH CREATION TAB

Before or after specifying the pick points, you can change the parameters of a hatch pattern using various options in the panels of the **Hatch Creation** tab. These panels and their options are discussed next.

Boundaries Panel

The options in the **Boundaries** panel are used to define the hatch boundary. This is done by selecting a point inside a closed area to be hatched or by selecting the objects. You can also remove islands, create hatch boundary, and define the boundary set by using the options in this panel, as discussed next.

Pick Points

This option is chosen by default and used to define a boundary from the objects that form a closed area. After invoking the **Hatch** tool, move the cursor over a closed region; the preview of the hatch will be displayed. Click inside the closed object; a boundary will be defined around the selected point and the hatch will be applied, as shown in Figure 13-6. The following prompts appear when you click inside the closed object.

Pick internal point or [Select objects/seTting]: *Select a point inside the object to hatch.*
Selecting everything visible...
Analyzing the selected data...
Analyzing internal islands...
Pick internal point or [Select objects/seTting]: *Select another internal point or press ENTER to end selection.*

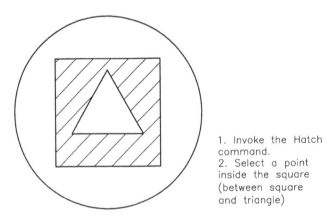

1. Invoke the Hatch command.
2. Select a point inside the square (between square and triangle)

Figure 13-6 Defining multiple hatch boundaries by selecting a point

Tip
*Suppose, you have selected a point within an area for hatching and later you realize that you have selected the wrong area, in such a case, you can enter **U** or **Undo** at the Command prompt to undo the last selection. You can also undo a hatch pattern that you have already applied to an area by entering **Undo** at the Command prompt.*

Boundary Definition Error. Sometimes, while selecting the boundary to be hatched, AutoCAD LT displays an error. This error may occur due to various reasons. AutoCAD LT displays different types of Boundary Definition Error message boxes, depending on the kind of error occurred while selecting the boundary. For example, if you pick a point inside any boundary that is not closed, a message box will be displayed, as shown in Figure 13-7, informing that the hatch boundary is not valid. Choose the **Close** button and then create a closed area as boundary. You can also specify the gap tolerance value in the **Gap Tolerance** edit box in the **Options** panel so that hatch is created, if the gap is within the permissible limit. If you select the same boundary twice, the message that the boundary duplicates an existing boundary will be displayed.

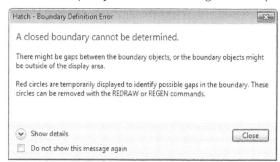

*Figure 13-7   The **Boundary Not Valid** message box*

Select

This option lets you select objects that form the boundary for hatching. It is useful when you have to hatch an object and disregard objects that lie inside it or intersect with it. When you select this option, AutoCAD LT will prompt you to select objects. You can select the objects individually or use the other object selection methods. In Figure 13-8, the **Select** option is used to select the triangle. It uses the triangle as the hatch boundary, and everything inside it is hatched. The text inside the triangle, in this case, also gets hatched. To avoid hatching of such internal objects, select them at the next **Select objects** prompt. In Figure 13-9, the text is selected to exclude it from hatching. While using the **Pick points** option, the text automatically gets selected to be excluded from the hatching.

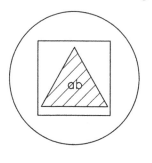

1. Choose the Select button.
2. Select the triangle for hatching and press ENTER.

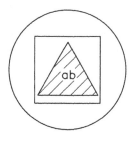

1. Choose the Select button.
2. Select the triangle for hatching
3. Select the text.
4. Press ENTER

*Figure 13-8   Using the **Select Objects** button to specify the hatching boundary*

*Figure 13-9   Using the **Select Objects** button to exclude the text from hatching*

Tip

If you have an area to be hatched that has many objects intersecting with it, it is easier to select the entire object to be hatched rather than choosing the internal points within each of the smaller regions created by the intersection.

You can also turn off layers that contain text or lines that make it difficult for you to select hatch boundaries.

Remove Boundary Objects

This option is used to remove boundaries and islands from the hatching area. Boundaries inside another boundary are known as islands. If you choose the **Pick Points** option to hatch an area, the inside boundaries, which are known as islands, will not be hatched by default. But, if you want to hatch the islands, you can choose the **Select** option and then the **Remove** option in the **Boundaries** panel. For example, if you have a rectangle with circles in it, as shown in Figure 13-10, you can use the **Pick points** option to select a point inside the rectangle. On choosing this option, AutoCAD LT will select both the circles and the rectangle. To remove the circles (islands), you can use the **Remove** option. When you select this option, AutoCAD LT will prompt you to select the islands to be removed. Select the islands to be removed and press ENTER to return to the dialog box. Choose **OK** to apply the hatch. Similarly, you can remove boundaries.

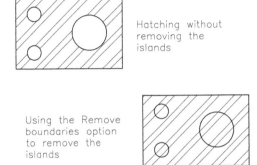

Hatching without removing the islands

Using the Remove boundaries option to remove the islands

*Figure 13-10 Using the **Remove Boundary** option to remove islands from the hatch area*

Tip
*It may be a good idea to use the **Select Objects** option to select the object containing islands, if you want to remove the islands from the hatching area.*

Recreate

This option is available while editing a hatch and is used to recreate boundaries around the existing hatch pattern. On choosing this option, you will be prompted to specify whether you want to recreate boundaries as a region or as a polyline. You can also associate the hatch to the new boundary.

Retain Boundary Objects drop-down list

When you select an internal point in a region to be hatched, a boundary is created around it. By default, this boundary will be removed as soon as the hatch pattern is applied. The **Retain Boundary Objects** drop-down list (see Figure 13-11) provides options to specify whether the boundary is to be retained as object or not. You can also specify the type of object it can be saved as.

Select the **Don't Retain Boundaries** option, if you do not need the boundary to be saved. In case. if you need to retain the boundary, you can retain it as a polyline or region. If you select the **Retain Boundaries - Polyline** option, the boundary created around the hatch area will be a polyline. Similarly, when you select **Retain Boundaries - Region**, the boundary of the hatch area will be a region. Regions are two-dimensional areas that can be created from closed shapes or loops.

Display Boundary Objects drop-down list

If you have chosen any one of the **Retain Boundaries** option, then you can choose this option to display the resulting boundary, while editing. However, the boundary will merge with the profile of the drawing object. You can use the **Move** command to view the resulting hatch boundary.

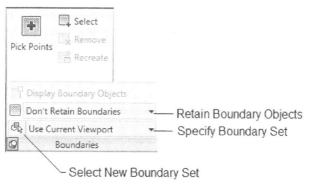

— Retain Boundary Objects

— Specify Boundary Set

— Select New Boundary Set

*Figure 13-11   Options in the expanded **Boundaries** panel*

Defining Boundary Set Area

When you invoke the **Hatch** tool and you have not formed a boundary set, the **Use Current Viewport** option will be available in the **Specify Boundary Set** drop-down list (see Figure 13-11). The benefit of creating a selection set is that when you select a point or select the objects to define the hatch boundary, AutoCAD LT will search only for the objects that are available in the selection set.

The default boundary set is **Use Current Viewport**, which comprises everything that is visible in the current viewport. Hatching is made faster by specifying a boundary set because, in this case, AutoCAD LT does not have to examine everything on screen. This option allows you to define a boundary area so that only a specific portion of the drawing is considered for hatching. You use this option to create a new boundary set.

When you choose the **Select New Boundary Set** button, you are prompted to select the objects to be included in the new boundary set. While constructing the boundary set, AutoCAD LT uses only those objects that you select and that are hatchable. If a boundary set already exists, it is replaced by the new one. If you do not select any hatchable objects, no new boundary set is created. AutoCAD LT retains the current set, if there is any. Once you have selected the objects to form the boundary set, press ENTER; you will notice that **Use Boundary Set** gets added to the drop-down list.

Remember that by confining the search to the objects in the selection set, the hatching process is faster. If you select an object that is not a part of the selection set, AutoCAD LT ignores it. When a boundary set is formed, it becomes the default for hatching until you exit the **Hatch** tool or select the **Use Current Viewport** option from the **Specify Boundary Set** drop-down list.

Tip
To improve the hatching speed in large drawings, you should zoom into the area to be hatched, so that defining the boundary to be hatched is easier. Also, since AutoCAD LT does not have to search the entire drawing to find hatch boundaries, the hatch process gets faster.

Pattern Panel

The **Pattern** panel displays all predefined patterns available in AutoCAD LT. However, the list depends upon the option selected in the **Hatch Type** drop-down list in the **Properties** panel. By default, the **Pattern** option is selected in this drop-down list and the predefined patterns are listed in the **Pattern** panel. A predefined pattern consists of ANSI, ISO, and other pattern types. The hatch pattern selected in this panel will be applied to the object. The selected pattern will be stored in the **HPNAME** system variable. ANSI31 is the default pattern in the **HPNAME** system variable. If you need to hatch a solid by using a solid color then choose the **Solid** option and set the color in the **Hatch Color** option in the **Properties** panel. Similarly, if you need to create a user-defined pattern, choose the **User** option from the **Pattern** panel and set the properties.

Properties Panel

The options in this panel (see Figure 13-12) are used to set the properties of the pattern selected in the **Pattern** panel. The different options are discussed next.

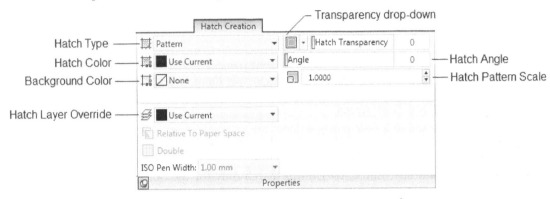

*Figure 13-12 Options in the **Properties** panel*

Hatch Type

The **Hatch Type** drop-down list displays the types of patterns that can be used for hatching drawing objects. The four types of hatch patterns available are **Solid, Gradient, Pattern**, and **User defined**. The predefined type of patterns come with AutoCAD LT and are stored in the *acadlt.pat* and *acadltiso.pat* files. The default type of hatch pattern is **Pattern**. If you select the **Gradient** option from this drop-down list, the corresponding options will be listed in the **Hatch Creation** tab. These options are discussed later.

Hatch Color

Specify the color of the hatch in this drop-down list. On selecting the **Use Current** option, the color set in the **Properties** panel of the **Home** tab will be applied to the hatch.

Background Color

If you need to apply a background color to a hatch, then set a color in the **Background Color** drop-down list.

Hatch Transparency

If you need a hatch to be displayed in a transparent mode, set the transparency value in this edit box. You can also set the value by using the slider or by double-clicking in the edit box. By default, it uses the transparency value set in the **Properties** panel of the **Home** tab. If you need to change the value, then select the required option in the **Transparency** drop-down. The other options available are **By Layer Transparency** and **By Block Transparency**.

Hatch Angle

The **Hatch Angle** slider is used to set the angle by which you can rotate the hatch pattern with respect to the X axis of the current UCS. The angle value is stored in the **HPANG** system variable. The angle of hatch lines of a particular hatch pattern is governed by the values specified in the hatch definition. For example, in the **ANSI31** hatch pattern definition, the specified angle of hatch lines is 45-degree. If you select an angle of 0, the angle of hatch lines will be 45°. If you enter an angle of 45-degree, the angle of the hatch lines will be 90°.

Hatch Pattern Scale

The **Hatch Pattern Scale** drop-down list is used to set the scale factors by which you can expand or contract the selected hatch pattern. You can enter the scale factor of your choice in the edit box by double-clicking in it. The scale value is stored in the **HPSCALE** system variable. The value 1 does not mean that the distance between the hatch lines is 1 unit. The distance between the hatch lines and other parameters of a hatch pattern is governed by the values specified in the hatch definition. For example, in the ANSI31 hatch pattern definition, the specified distance between the hatch lines is 0.125. If you select a scale factor of 1, the distance between the lines will be 0.125. If you enter a scale factor of 0.5, the distance between the hatch lines will be 0.5 X 0.125 = 0.0625.

Double

This option is available only for user-defined patterns. When you choose this option, AutoCAD LT doubles the original pattern by drawing a second set of lines at right angle to the original lines in the hatch pattern. For example, if you have a parallel set of lines as a user-defined pattern and if you select the **Double** option, the resulting pattern will have two sets of lines intersecting at 90-degree. You can notice the effect of selecting the **Double** option in Figure 13-13. If the **Double** option is selected, the **HPDOUBLE** system variable is set to 1.

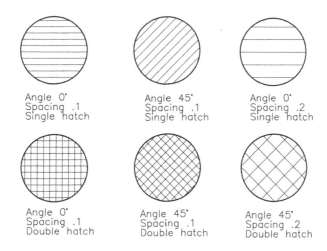

Figure 13-13 Specifying angle and spacing for user-defined hatch patterns

Relative to Paper Space

This option is available only in a layout. If this option is selected, then AutoCAD LT will automatically scale the hatched pattern relative to the paper space units. This option can be used to display the hatch pattern at a scale that is appropriate for your layout.

ISO Pen Width

The **ISO Pen Width** drop-down list is available only for ISO hatch patterns. You can select the desired pen width value from the **ISO Pen Width** drop-down list. The value selected specifies the ISO-related pattern scaling.

Origin Panel

Hatch pattern alignment is an important feature of hatching, as on many occasions, you need to hatch adjacent areas with similar or sometimes identical hatch patterns while keeping the adjacent hatch patterns properly aligned. Proper alignment of hatch patterns is taken care of automatically by generating all lines of every hatch pattern from the same reference point. The reference point is normally at the origin point (0,0). Figure 13-14 shows two adjacent hatch areas. The area on the right is hatched using the pattern ANSI32 at an angle of 0-degree and the area on the left is hatched using the same pattern at an angle of 90-degree. When you hatch these areas, the hatch lines may not be aligned, as shown in Figure 13-14(a). The options in the **Origin** panel allow you to specify the origin of hatch so that they get properly aligned, as shown in Figure 13-14(b). The options in this panel are discussed next.

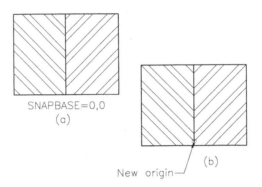

Figure 13-14 Aligning hatch patterns using the SNAPBASE variable

By default, the **Use Current Origin** button is chosen. This implies that the origin of the hatch pattern to be created is the origin of the current drawing. On choosing **Set Origin**, you need to specify the origin point for the hatch pattern in the drawing area.

You can also choose the other buttons to set the origin. For example, if you choose the **Bottom left** button from this panel, the origin of the hatch pattern will be at the bottom left corner of the boundary. Choose the **Store as Default Origin** button to store the origin just selected as the default origin for all the hatch patterns to be created now onwards.

Note
*The reference point for hatching can also be changed using the **SNAPBASE** system variable.*

Options Panel

The options in this area allow you to specify the draw order and some commonly used properties of the hatch pattern.

Associative

This button is chosen by default; therefore, when you modify the boundary of a hatch object, the hatch patterns will be automatically updated to fill up the new area. But, if the hatch boundary is a region, you cannot edit the shape of the hatch boundary. One of the major advantages with the associative hatch feature is that you can edit the hatch pattern or edit the geometry that is hatched without having to modify the associated pattern or boundary separately. After editing, AutoCAD LT automatically regenerates the hatch and the hatch geometry to reflect the changes. To edit the hatch boundary, select it and edit it by using grips.

Annotative

Choose this button to create an annotative hatch. An annotative hatch is defined relative to the paper space size. The scale of the annotative hatch objects changes in the viewport or layout according to the annotation scale assigned to the hatch objects and the annotation scale specified for that particular layout or viewport.

Gap tolerance

The **Gap tolerance** edit box is used to set the maximum value of gap for which the open area will be considered closed when selected for hatching, using the **Pick Points** method. The default value of the gap tolerance is 0. As a result, an open area will not be selected for hatching. You can set the value of the gap tolerance using the **Gap tolerance** edit box. If the gap in the open area is less than the value specified in this edit box, the area will be considered closed and will be selected for hatching.

Create Separate Hatches

If you hatch multiple closed areas that are not nested together, then on selecting this option, a separate hatch will be created for each closed area. As a result, you can edit the hatches separately. If this option is not selected, the hatch created in all the selected closed areas will be treated as single entity and can be edited together.

Island Detection Style

The drop-down list below the **Create Separate Hatches** option is used to select the style of the island detection during hatching. There are four styles available in this drop-down list. The effect of using a particular style is displayed in the form of an illustration in the image tile placed before the name and is also shown in Figure 13-15. To set a particular style, select the corresponding option. The four styles available in this drop-down list are discussed next.

Note
The selection of an island detection style carries meaning only if the objects to be hatched are nested (that is, one or more selected boundaries are within another boundary).

Normal Island Detection. This style is selected by default. This style hatches inward starting at the outermost boundary. If it encounters an internal boundary, it turns off the hatching. An internal boundary causes the hatching to turn off until another boundary is encountered. In this manner, alternate areas of the selected object are hatched, starting with the outermost area. Thus, areas separated from the outside of the hatched area by an odd number of boundaries are hatched, while those separated by an even number of boundaries are not.

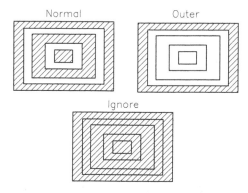

Figure 13-15 Using hatching styles

Outer Island Detection. This particular option also lets you hatch inward from an outermost boundary, but the hatching is turned off if an internal boundary is encountered. Unlike the previous case, it does not turn on the hatching again. The hatching process, in this case, starts from both ends of each hatch line; only the outermost level of the structure is hatched, hence, the name **Outer Island**.

Ignore Island Detection. In this option, all areas bounded by the outermost boundary are hatched. The option ignores any hatch boundaries that are within the outer boundary. All islands are completely ignored and everything within the selected boundary is hatched.

No Island Detection. In this option, even if the object is nested, the individual closed boundary is hatched separately.

Tip
*It is also possible to set the pattern and the island detection style at the same time by using the **HPNAME** system variable. AutoCAD LT stores the Normal style code by adding **N** to the pattern name. Similarly, **O** is added for the Outer style, and **I** for the Ignore style to the value of the **HPNAME** system variable. For example, if you want to apply the BOX pattern using the outer style of island detection, you should enter the **HPNAME** value to the **BOX, O**. Now, when you apply the hatch pattern, the BOX pattern is applied using the outer style of hatching.*

Match Properties

The **Match Properties** drop-down list is used to hatch the specified boundaries using the properties of an existing hatch.

EXERCISE 1	Hatch Scale & Hatch Angle

In this exercise, you will hatch the given drawing using the hatch pattern named **STEEL**. Set the scale and the angle to match the drawing shown in Figure 13-16.

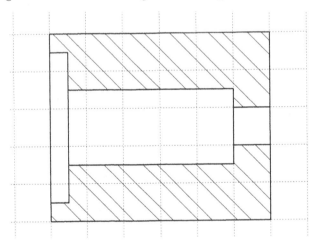

Figure 13-16 Drawing for Exercise 1

EXERCISE 2	Hatch Pattern

In this exercise, you will hatch the front section view of the drawing in Figure 13-17 using the hatch pattern for brass. Two views, top and front are shown. In the top view, the cutting plane indicates how the section is cut and the front view shows the full section view of the object. The section lines must be drawn only where the material is actually cut.

EXERCISE 3	Align Hatch

In this exercise, you will hatch the given drawing using the hatch pattern ANSI31. Align the hatch lines as shown in the drawing (Figure 13-18).

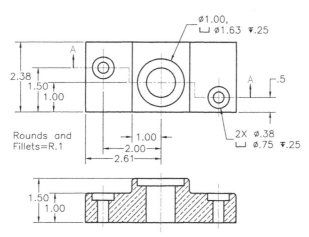

Figure 13-17 Drawing for Exercise 2

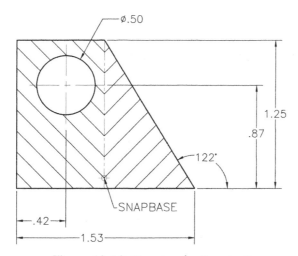

Figure 13-18 Drawing for Exercise 3

Setting the Parameters for Gradient Pattern

During hatching, you can select the **Gradient** option in the **Hatch Type** drop-down list to fill the boundary in a set pattern of colors. On selecting the **Gradient** option in the **Hatch Type** drop-down list, nine fixed patterns will be listed in the **Pattern** panel and their corresponding options will be displayed in the **Hatch Creation** tab, as shown in Figure 13-19. You can select the required gradient or specify the gradient pattern by entering its value in the **GFNAME** system variable. The default value of this variable is 1. As a result, the first gradient pattern is selected.

*Figure 13-19 The **Hatch Creation** tab with the options for the **Gradient** pattern*

You can set the colors for the Gradient in the **Gradient Color 1** drop-down list available in the **Properties** panel. By default, you can set one color to the gradient. You can set the angle and the tint of the color by using the corresponding sliders. If you need to set two colors then choose the **Gradient Colors** button available on the left of the **Gradient Colors 2** drop-down list. On doing so, the **Gradient Colors 2** drop-down list will be enabled. Now, you can set the other color in this drop-down list. In this case, the **Tint** slider will not be available.

The **Gradient Angle** slider displays the angles by which you can rotate the gradient fill with respect to the *X* axis of the current UCS. You can select any angle from this slider or you can double-click and enter an angle of your choice in the edit box. The angle value is stored in the **GFANG** system variable.

The symmetricity of the gradient is set by choosing the **Centered** button in the **Origin** panel. If this button is not chosen, then the gradient fill is moved up and to the left.

Note
The other options are same as discussed earlier.

Tip
*To snap the hatch objects, set the **OSOPTIONS** system variable to **1**. You can also invoke the **Options** dialog box and choose the **Drafting** tab. Then, clear the **Ignore hatch objects** check box from the **Object Snap Options** area.*

CREATING ANNOTATIVE HATCH

You can create annotative hatch having similar annotative properties like text and dimensions. The annotative hatch are defined relative to the viewport scaling, you only have to specify the hatch scale according to its display on the sheet. The display size of the hatch in the model space will be controlled by the current annotation scale multiplied by the paper space height. You can also control the annotative properties of the hatch pattern as discussed in Chapter 7.

To create an annotative hatch, choose the **Hatch** tool from the **Draw** panel; the **Hatch Creation** tab will be displayed. Choose the **Select** option from the **Boundaries** panel, select the objects that you want to hatch, and press the ENTER key; the **Hatch and Gradient** dialog box will be displayed again. In the **Options** area of this dialog box, select the **Annotative** check box and choose the **OK** button. You can also convert the existing non-annotative hatch into the annotative hatch. To do so, select the non-annotative hatch in the drawing and select **Yes** from the **Annotative** drop-down list in the **Pattern** list of the **Properties** palette.

Note
*While creating the hatch, the annotative hatch pattern will only be displayed in the drawing area for the annotative scale that is set current. To display that hatch pattern at any other annotative scale, you have to add that scale to the selected hatch using the **OBJECTSCALE** command.*

HATCHING THE DRAWING USING THE TOOL PALETTES

Ribbon: View > Palette > Tool Palettes	**Command:** TOOLPALETTES
Toolbar: Standard Annotation > Tool Palettes Window	

You can use the **Tool Palettes** window shown in Figure 13-20 to insert predefined hatch patterns and blocks in the drawings. By default, AutoCAD LT displays **Tool Palettes** as a window on the right of the drawing area. A number of tabs such as **Command Tool Samples**, **Hatches and Fills**, **Civil**, **Structural**, **Electrical**, and so on are available in this window. In this chapter, you will learn to insert **Imperial Hatches** and **ISO Hatches** in the **Hatches and Fills** tab of the **Tool Palettes** window. The **Imperial Hatches** list provides the options to insert the hatch patterns that are created using the Imperial units. The **ISO Hatches** list provides the options to insert the hatch patterns that are created using the Metric units. You will notice that the hatch patterns provided in both these lists are similar. The basic difference between the two lists is their scale factor.

Tip
The Tool Palettes window can be turned on and off by pressing the CTRL+3 keys.

AutoCAD LT provides two methods to insert the predefined hatch patterns from the **Tool Palettes** window: **Drag and Drop** method and **Select and Place** method. Both these methods are discussed next.

Drag and Drop Method

To insert the predefined hatch pattern from the **Tool Palettes** using this method, move the cursor over the desired predefined pattern in the **Tool Palettes**. You will notice that as you move the cursor over the hatch pattern, the hatch icon gets converted into a 3D icon. Also, a tooltip is displayed that shows the name of the hatch pattern. Press and hold the left mouse button and drag the cursor within the area to be hatched. Release the left mouse button, and you will notice that the selected predefined hatch pattern is added to the drawing.

Select and Place Method

You can also add the predefined hatch patterns to the drawings using the **Select and Place** method. To add the hatch pattern, move the cursor over the desired pattern in the **Tool Palettes**; the pattern icon will be changed to a 3D icon. Next, click the left mouse button; the selected hatch pattern will be attached to the cursor and you will be prompted to specify the insertion point of the hatch pattern. Now, move the cursor within the area to be hatched and click the left mouse button; the selected hatch pattern will be inserted at the specified location.

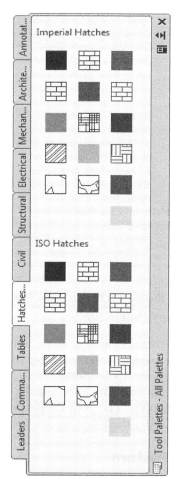

Figure 13-20 The Hatch tab of the Tool Palettes

Modifying the Properties of the Predefined Patterns available in Tool Palettes

To modify the properties of the predefined hatch patterns, move the cursor over the hatch pattern in the **Tool Palettes** and right-click on it to display the shortcut menu. Using the options available in this shortcut menu, you can cut or copy the desired hatch pattern available in one tab of **Tool Palettes** and paste it on the other tab. You can also delete and rename a selected hatch pattern using the **Delete** and **Rename** options, respectively. To update and change the image displayed on the selected hatch pattern, choose the **Update tool image** or **Specify image** option. To modify the properties of the selected hatch pattern, choose **Properties** from the shortcut menu, as shown in Figure 13-21; the **Tool Properties** dialog box will be displayed, as shown in Figure 13-22.

In the **Tool Properties** dialog box, the name of the selected hatch pattern is displayed in the **Name** edit box. You can also rename the hatch pattern by entering a new name in the **Name** edit box. The **Image** area available on the left of the **Name** edit box displays the image of the selected hatch pattern. You can change the displayed image by choosing the **Specify image** option.

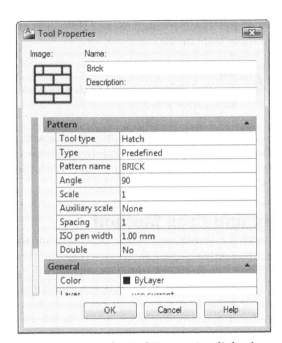

*Figure 13-21 Choosing **Properties** from the shortcut menu*

*Figure 13-22 The **Tool Properties** dialog box*

from the shortcut menu that will be displayed when you right-click on the image. If you enter a description of the hatch pattern in the **Description** text box, it is stored with the hatch definition in the **Tool Palettes**. Now, when you move the cursor over the hatch pattern in **Tool Palettes** and pause for a second, the description of the hatch pattern appears along with its name in the tooltip. The **Tool Properties** dialog box displays the properties of the selected hatch pattern under the following categories.

Pattern

In this category, you can change the pattern type, pattern name, angle, and scale of the selected pattern. You can modify the spacing of the **User defined** patterns in the **Spacing** text box. Also, the ISO pen width of the ISO patterns can be redefined in the **ISO pen width** text box. The **Double** drop-down list is available only for the **User-defined** hatch patterns. You can select **Yes** or **No** from the **Double** drop-down list to determine the hatch pattern to be doubled at right angles to the original pattern or not. When you choose the [...] button in the **Type** property field, AutoCAD LT displays the **Hatch Pattern Type** dialog box. You can select the type of hatch pattern from the **Pattern Type** drop-down list. If the **Predefined** pattern type is selected, you can specify the pattern name by either selecting it from the **Pattern** drop-down list or from the **Hatch Pattern Palette** dialog box displayed on choosing the **Pattern** button. Similarly, if you select the **Custom** pattern type, you can enter the name of the custom pattern in the **Custom Pattern** edit box. If you select the **User defined** pattern type, both the **Pattern** drop-down list and the **Custom Pattern** edit box are not available.

General

In this category, you can specify the general properties of the hatch pattern such as color, layer, linetype, plot style, transparency, and line weight for the selected hatch pattern. The properties of a particular field can be modified from the drop-down list available on selecting that field. Choose **OK** to apply the changes and close the dialog box.

HATCHING AROUND TEXT, DIMENSIONS, AND ATTRIBUTES

When you select a point within a boundary to be hatched and if it contains text, dimensions, and attributes then, by default, the hatch lines do not pass through the text, dimensions, and attributes present in the object being hatched by default. AutoCAD LT places an imaginary box around these objects that does not allow the hatch lines to pass through it. Remember that if you are using the select objects option to select objects to hatch, you must select the text/attribute/ shape along with the object in which it is placed when defining the hatch boundary. If multiple line text is to be written, the **Multiline Text** tool is used. You can also select both the boundary and the text when using the window selection method. Figure 13-23 shows you how hatching takes place around multiline text, attributes, and dimensions.

EDITING HATCH PATTERNS

Using the Hatch Editor Tab

On selecting a hatch pattern, the **Hatch Editor** tab will be displayed in the **Ribbon**, as shown in Figure 13-24. The panels and their options in this tab are similar to that of the **Hatch** tab. Change the parameters of the hatch pattern in the corresponding panels; the hatch pattern will be modified instantaneously. Press ESC to exit the **Hatch Editor** tab.

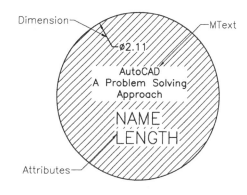

Figure 13-23 *Hatching around dimension, multiline text, and attributes*

Figure 13-24 *The **Hatch Editor** tab with the options for the **Gradient** pattern*

Using the HATCHEDIT Command

Ribbon: Home > Modify > Edit Hatch	**Tool Palette:** Modify > Edit Hatch
Toolbar: Modify II > Edit Hatch	**Command:** HATCHEDIT

The **Edit Hatch** tool is used to edit a hatch pattern. When you invoke this tool and select the hatch for editing, the **Hatch Edit** dialog box will be displayed, as shown in Figure 13-25.

The **Hatch Edit** dialog box is used to change or modify a hatch pattern. This dialog box is the same as the **Hatch and Gradient** dialog box, except that only the options that control the hatch pattern are available. The available options work in the same way as they do in the **Hatch and Gradient** dialog box.

The **Hatch Edit** dialog box has two tabs, just like the **Hatch and Gradient** dialog box. They are **Hatch** and **Gradient**. In the **Hatch** tab, you can redefine the type of hatch pattern by selecting another type from the **Type** drop-down list. If you are using the **Predefined** pattern, you can select a new hatch pattern name from the **Pattern** drop-down list. You can also change the scale or angle by entering new values in the **Scale** or **Angle** edit box. While using the **User defined** pattern, you can redefine the spacing between the lines in the hatch pattern by entering a new

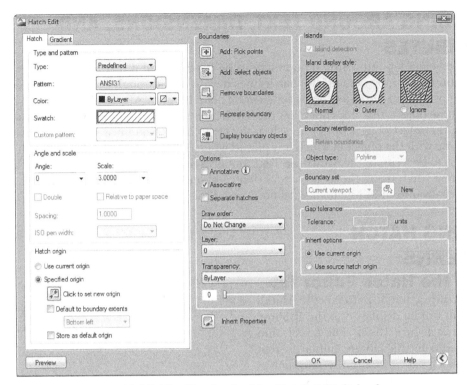

Figure 13-25 *The **Hatch** tab of the **Hatch Edit** dialog box*

value in the **Spacing** edit box. If you are using the **Custom** pattern type, you can select another pattern from the **Custom pattern** drop-down list. You can also redefine the island detection style by selecting either of the **Normal**, **Outer**, or **Ignore** styles from the **Islands** area of the dialog box. You can also convert a non-annotative hatch into an annotative hatch and vice-versa. If you want to copy the properties from an existing hatch pattern, choose the **Inherit Properties** button, and then select the hatch whose properties you want to be inherited. You can also change the draw order of the hatch pattern using the options available in the **Draw order** area. If the **Associative** radio button in the **Options** area of the dialog box is selected, the pattern is associative. This implies that whenever you modify the hatch boundary, the hatch pattern is automatically updated. The appearance of the gradient fill can be specified using the **Gradient** tab of the dialog box. You can specify the gradient fill comprising different shades and tints of a single color or double colors by selecting the **One color** and **Two color** radio buttons, respectively. You can also specify the color of the gradient fill or the shade and tint of a single color using the color swatch and the **Shade and Tint** slider. If the **Centered** button is chosen, AutoCAD LT will apply a symmetrical gradient fill. Also, AutoCAD LT provides you with an option to select the desired display pattern of the gradient fill by selecting any one of the nine fixed patterns for the gradient fill.

Note
If a hatch pattern is associative, the hatch boundary can be edited using grips and editing commands and the associated pattern is modified accordingly. This is discussed later.

In Figure 13-26, the object is hatched using the **ANSI31** hatch pattern. With the **HATCHEDIT** command, you can edit the hatch using the **Hatch Edit** dialog box, refer to Figure 13-27. You can also edit an existing hatch through the command line by entering **-HATCHEDIT** at the Command prompt.

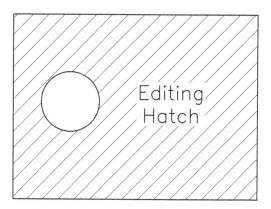

Figure 13-26 ANSI31 hatch pattern

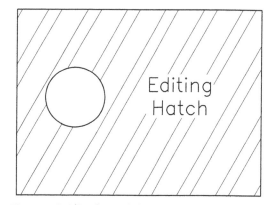

Figure 13-27 The modified hatch pattern using the
Edit Hatch tool

Trimming the Hatch Patterns

You can trim the hatch patterns by using a cutting edge. For example, Figure 13-28 shows a drawing before trimming the hatch. In this drawing, the outer loop was selected as the object to be hatched. This is the reason the space between the two vertical lines on the right is also hatched. Figure 13-29 shows the same drawing after trimming the hatch using the vertical lines as the cutting edge. You will notice that even after trimming some of the portions of the hatch, it is a single entity.

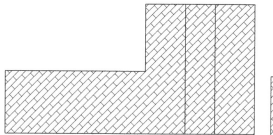

Figure 13-28 Before trimming the hatch

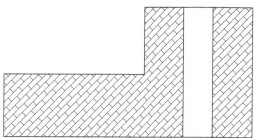

Figure 13-29 After trimming the hatch by using
the vertical lines as the cutting edge

EXAMPLE 2   *Hatch*

In this example, you will hatch the drawing, as shown in Figure 13-30, using various hatch patterns.

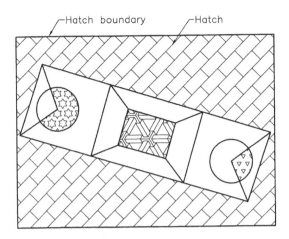

Figure 13-30 Drawing for Example 2

1. Make a drawing as shown in Figure 13-30.

2. Choose the **Hatch** tool from the **Draw** panel in the **Home** tab; the **Hatch Creation** tab is displayed.

3. Select the **AR-BRSTD** pattern from the **Pattern** panel and click inside the outer rectangle's boundary to select the internal pick point.

4. Next, you need to change the angle of the hatch pattern to 45°. To do so, drag the **Angle** slider in the **Properties** panel. Also, adjust the **Hatch Pattern Scale** using the **Hatch Pattern Scale** spinner.

5. Select the **Outer Island Detection** option from the **Island Detection** drop-down list in the **Options** panel, if it is not selected by default.

6. Exit the **Hatch Creation** tab by pressing ENTER.

7. Again, choose the **Hatch** tool and select the **STARS** pattern from the **Pattern** panel; you are prompted to pick an internal point in the object. Select a point in the right section of the left circle, refer to Figure 13-30; preview of the pattern is displayed. You have to specify the values of the **Hatch Angle** and **Hatch Pattern Scale** options. After making the required changes, exit the **Hatch Creation** tab.

8. Choose the **Hatch** tool and select the **ESCHER** pattern from the **Pattern** panel; you are prompted to pick an internal point in the object. Select a point in the middle of the innermost rectangle, refer to Figure 13-30; a preview will be displayed. Adjust the scale of the hatch pattern, if required and then exit.

9. Invoke the **Hatch** tool once again and select **TRIANG** from the **Pattern** panel; you are prompted to pick an internal point in the object. Select a point in the right section of the right circle, refer to Figure 13-30; preview of the pattern is displayed. Set the desired values for **Hatch Angle** and **Hatch Pattern Scale** and then exit.

EXAMPLE 3   *Hatch*

In this example, you will hatch the drawing, as shown in Figure 13-31. But, ensure that the hatching results in two entities.

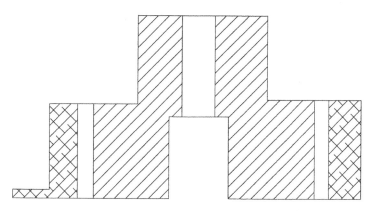

Figure 13-31 *Drawing for Example 3*

To make this kind of hatching, you have to follow the steps given below:

1. Make a drawing as shown in Figure 13-31.

2. Choose the **Hatch** tool from the **Draw** panel in the **Home** tab; the **Hatch Creation** tab is displayed. Make sure that the entities having different hatch patterns are drawn as different entities.

3. Select **ANSI38** from the **Pattern** panel; you will be prompted to pick an internal point. Select any internal point of the two outermost entities. Set the scale of the pattern, if required.

4. Press SPACEBAR to exit the command.

5. Choose the **Hatch** tool and select the **ANSI31** pattern from the **Pattern** panel; you will be prompted to pick an internal point in the object.

6. Select the internal points of the remaining two entities; a preview is displayed. Set the scale of pattern, if required. After making required adjustments, exit the command by choosing the **Close Hatch Creation** button in the **Close** panel.

Using AutoCAD LT Editing Tools

When you use the editing tools such as **Move**, **Rotate**, **Scale**, and **Stretch**, associativity is maintained, provided all objects that define the boundary are selected for editing. If any of the boundary-defining objects is missing, the associativity will be lost and AutoCAD LT will display the message **Hatch boundary associativity removed**. When you rotate or scale an associative hatch, the new rotation angle and the scale factor are saved with the hatch object data. This data is then used to update the hatch. While using the **Array**, **Copy**, and **Mirror** tools, you can array, copy, or mirror just the hatch boundary, without the hatch pattern. Similarly, you can erase just the hatch boundary, using the **Erase** tool and associativity is removed. If you explode an associative hatch pattern, the associativity between the hatch pattern and the defining boundary is removed. Also, when the hatch object is exploded, each line in the hatch pattern becomes a separate object.

When the original boundary objects are being edited, the associated hatch gets automatically updated, but new boundary objects do not have any effect. For example, when you have a square island within a circular boundary and then you erase the square, the hatch pattern is updated to fill up the entire circle. But, once the island is removed, another island cannot be added, since it was not calculated as a part of the original set of boundary objects.

HATCHING BLOCKS AND XREF DRAWINGS

When you apply hatching to inserted blocks and xref drawings, their internal structure is treated as if the block or xref drawing were composed of independent objects. This means that if you have inserted a block that consists of a circle within a rectangle and you want the internal circle to be hatched, you need to invoke the **Hatch** tool and then specify a point within the circle to generate the hatch, refer to Figure 13-32. However, if you choose the **Select** option from the **Boundaries** panel of the **Hatch Creation** tab, you will be prompted to select an object. Select an object; the entire block will be selected and a hatch will be created, as shown in Figure 13-32.

When you xref a drawing, you can hatch any part of the drawing that is visible. Also, if you hatch an xref drawing and then use the **XCLIP** command to clip it, the hatch pattern is not clipped, although the hatch boundary associativity is removed. Similarly, when you detach the xref drawing, the hatch pattern and its boundaries are not detached, although the hatch boundary associativity is removed.

Hatch created by choosing the Pick Points button

Hatch created by choosing the Select button

Figure 13-32 Hatching inserted blocks

OTHER FEATURES OF HATCHING

1. In AutoCAD LT, the hatch patterns are separate objects. The objects store the information about the hatch pattern boundary with reference to the geometry that defines the pattern for each hatch object.

2. When you save a drawing, the hatch patterns are stored with the drawing. Therefore, the hatch patterns can be updated even if the hatch pattern file that contains the definitions of hatch patterns is not available.

3. If the system variable **FILLMODE** is 0 (Off), the hatch patterns are not displayed. To see the effect of a changed **FILLMODE** value, you must use the **REGEN** command to regenerate the drawing after the value has been changed.

4. You can edit the boundary of a hatch pattern even when the hatch pattern is not visible (**FILLMODE**=0).

5. The hatch patterns created in the earlier releases are automatically converted into AutoCAD LT 2012 hatch objects when the hatch pattern is edited.

6. When you save an AutoCAD LT 2012 drawing in Release 12 format (DXF), the hatch objects are automatically converted to Release 12 hatch blocks.

7. You can use the **CONVERT** command to change the pre-Release hatch patterns to AutoCAD LT 2012 objects. You can also use this command to change the pre-Release 13 polylines to AutoCAD LT 2012 optimized format to save memory and disk space.

EXERCISE 4   *Boundary*

See Figure 13-33 and then create the drawing shown in Figure 13-34 using the **Boundary** tool to create a hatch boundary. Copy the boundary from the drawing shown in Figure 13-34, and then hatch.

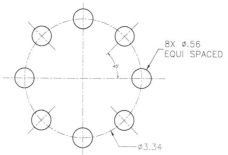

8X ∅.56
EQUI SPACED

45°

∅3.34

Figure 13-33 *Drawing for Exercise 4*

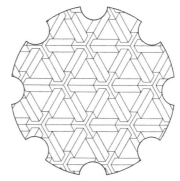

Figure 13-34 *Final drawing for Exercise 4*

Self-Evaluation Test

Answer the following questions and then compare them to those given at the end of this chapter:

1. Different filling patterns make it possible to distinguish between different parts or components of an object. (T/F)

2. If AutoCAD LT does not locate the entered pattern in the *acadlt.pat* file, it searches for it in a file with the same name as the pattern. (T/F)

3. When a boundary set is formed, it does not become the default boundary set for hatching. (T/F)

4. You can edit the hatch boundary and the associated hatch pattern by using grips. (T/F)

5. If you need to hatch a drawing that has a gap, then specify the gap value in the _____ edit box in the **Hatch Creation** tab.

6. One of the ways to specify a hatch pattern from the group of stored hatch patterns is by selecting one from the _____ drop-down list.

7. The value that you enter in the _____ edit box lets you rotate a hatch pattern with respect to the *X* axis of the current UCS.

8. The _____ option in the **Hatch Creation** tab lets you select the objects that form a boundary for hatching.

9. While hatching, you can select the _____ option in the **Hatch Type** drop-down list to fill the boundary in a set pattern of colors.

Review Questions

Answer the following questions:

1. The **Hatch** tool does not allow you to hatch a region enclosed within a boundary (closed area) by selecting a point inside the boundary. (T/F)

2. A Boundary Definition Error message box is displayed if AutoCAD LT finds that the selected point is not inside the boundary or that the boundary is not closed. (T/F)

3. When you use editing tools such as **Move**, **Scale**, **Stretch**, and **Rotate**, associativity is lost, even if all the boundary objects are selected. (T/F)

4. The hatching procedure in AutoCAD LT does not work on inserted blocks. (T/F)

5. Patterns drawn using the **Hatch** tool are associative. (T/F)

6. Which of the following system variables has to be set to 1, if the **Double** hatch box is selected?

   (a) **HPSPACE**   (b) **HPDOUBLE**
   (c) **HPANG**   (d) **HPSCALE**

7. For which of the following hatch patterns will the **ISO pen width** drop-down list be available?

   (a) **ANSI**   (b) **Predefined**
   (c) **Custom**   (d) **ISO**

8. Which of the following variables can be used to align the hatches in adjacent hatch areas?

   (a) **SNAPBASE**   (b) **FILLMODE**
   (c) **SNAPANG**   (d) **HPANG**

9. In which of the following system variables will the specified hatch spacing value be stored?

   (a) **HPDOUBLE**   (b) **HPANG**
   (c) **HPSCALE**   (d) **HPSPACE**

10. To select a custom hatch pattern, first select **Custom** from the **Hatch Type** drop-down list and then select the name of a previously stored hatch pattern from the _____ drop-down list.

11. If you select the _____ style, all areas bounded by the outermost boundary are hatched, ignoring any hatch boundaries that lie within the outer boundary.

EXERCISE 5   Hatch Pattern

Hatch the drawings shown in Figures 13-35 and 13-36 using the hatch pattern as shown in figure.

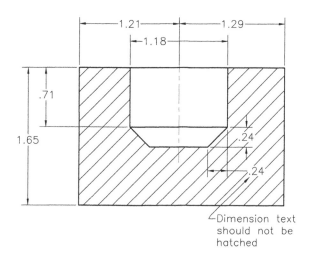

Figure 13-35 *Drawing for Exercise 5*

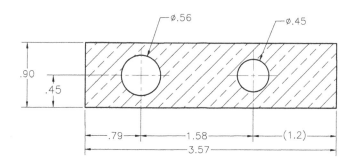

Figure 13-36 *Drawing for Exercise 5*

EXERCISE 6   *Hatch Align*

Hatch the drawing, as shown in Figure 13-37, using the hatch pattern **ANSI31**. Use the **SNAPBASE** variable to align the hatch lines, as shown in the drawing.

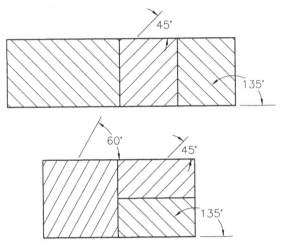

Figure 13-37 *Drawing for Exercise 6*

EXERCISE 7   *Hatch*

Figure 13-38 shows the top and front views of an object. It also shows the cutting plane line. Based on the cutting plane line, hatch the front views in section. Use the hatch pattern of your choice.

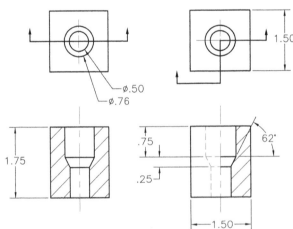

Figure 13-38 *Drawing for Exercise 7*

EXERCISE 8   *Hatch*

Figure 13-39 shows the top and front views of an object. Hatch the front view in full section. Use the hatch pattern of your choice.

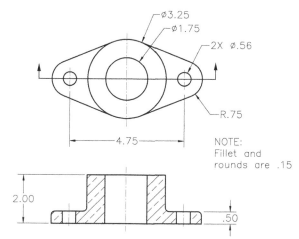

Figure 13-39 *Drawing for Exercise 8*

EXERCISE 9   *Hatch*

Figure 13-40 shows the front and side views of an object. Hatch the side view in half section. Use the hatch pattern of your choice.

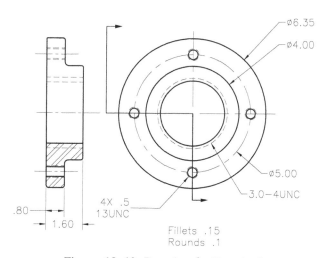

Figure 13-40 *Drawing for Exercise 9*

EXERCISE 10 Hatch

Figure 13-41 shows the front view with the broken section and top views of an object. Hatch the front view as shown. Use the hatch pattern of your choice.

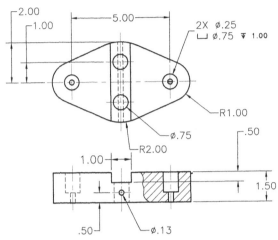

Figure 13-41 Drawing for Exercise 10

EXERCISE 11 Hatch

Figure 13-42 shows the front, top, and side views of an object. Hatch the side view in section using the hatch pattern of your choice.

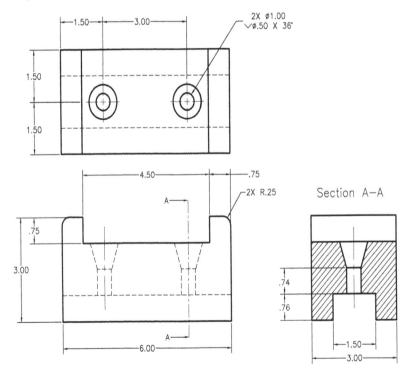

Figure 13-42 Drawing for Exercise 11

Problem-Solving Exercise 1

Figure 13-43 shows an object with front and side views with aligned section. Hatch the side view using the hatch pattern of your choice.

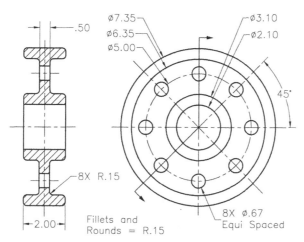

Figure 13-43 *Drawing for Problem-Solving Exercise 1*

Problem-Solving Exercise 2

Figure 13-44 shows the front view, side view, and the detail "A" of an object. Hatch the side view and draw the detail drawing as shown.

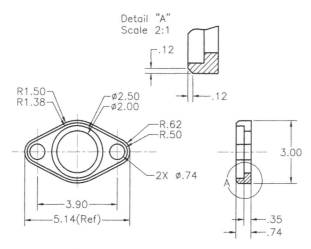

Figure 13-44 *Drawing for Problem-Solving Exercise 2*

Problem-Solving Exercise 3

Create the drawing shown in Figure 13-45. Assume the missing dimensions.

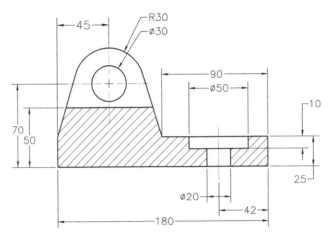

Figure 13-45 Drawing for Problem-Solving Exercise 3

Problem-Solving Exercise 4

Draw a detail drawing whose top, side, and section views are given in Figure 13-46. Then, hatch the section view. **

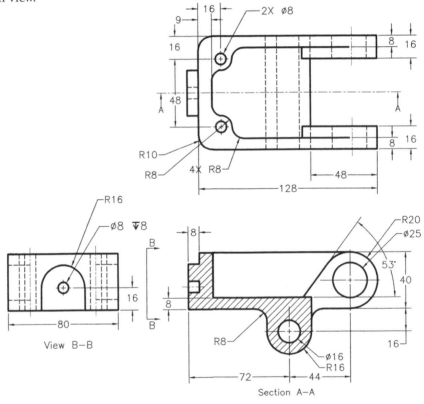

Figure 13-46 Views and dimensions of the drawing for Problem-Solving Exercise 4

Answers to Self-Evaluation Test

1. T, **2.** T, **3.** F, **4.** T, **5. Tolerance, 6. Pattern, 7. Angle, 8. Select objects, 9. Gradient, 10.** ISO hatch

Chapter *14*

Working with Blocks

CHAPTER OBJECTIVES

In this chapter, you will learn:
- *To create and insert blocks.*
- *To create drawing files by using the Write Block dialog box.*
- *To use the Tool Palettes to insert blocks.*
- *To edit blocks.*
- *To split a block.*
- *To rename blocks and delete unused blocks.*

KEY TERMS

- *Blocks*
- *Annotative Blocks*
- *WBLOCK*
- *XPLODE*
- *Constraints to Blocks*

THE CONCEPT OF BLOCKS

The ability to store parts of a drawing, or the entire drawing, such that they need not be redrawn when required in the same drawing or another drawing is a great benefit to the user. These parts of a drawing, entire drawings, or symbols (also known as **blocks**) can be placed (inserted) in a drawing at the location of your choice, with the desired orientation, and scale factor. A block is given a name (block name) and is referenced (inserted) by its name. All objects within a block are treated as a single object. You can move, erase, or list the block as a single object, that is, you can select the entire block simply by selecting anywhere on it. As for the edit and inquiry commands, the internal structure of a block is immaterial, since a block is treated as a primitive object, like a polygon. If a block definition is changed, all references to the block in the drawing are updated to incorporate the changes.

A block is created by using the **Create Block** tool in the **Block Definition** panel. You can also save objects in a drawing, or an entire drawing as a drawing file using the **WBLOCK** command. The main difference between the two is that a wblock can be inserted in any other drawing, but a block can be inserted only in the drawing file, in which it was created.

One of the important feature of AutoCAD LT is the annotative blocks that can be used as symbol to annotate your drawing. The annotative blocks are defined in terms of paper space height. The annotative blocks are displayed in floating viewports and their respective size in model space is calculated by multiplying the current annotation scale set for those spaces and the paper space height of the block.

Another feature of AutoCAD LT is that instead of inserting a symbol as a block (which results in the addition of the content of the referenced drawing to the drawing in which it is inserted), you can reference the other drawings (Xref) in the current file. This means that the contents of the referenced drawing are not added to the current drawing file, although they become part of that drawing on the screen.

Advantages of Using Blocks

Blocks offer the following advantages:

1. Drawings often have some repetitive features. Instead of drawing the same feature again and again, you can create its block and insert it wherever required. This helps you to reduce drawing time and better organize your work.
2. Blocks can be drawn and stored for future use. You can thus create a custom library of objects required for different applications. For example, if your drawings are concerned with gears, you could create their blocks and then integrate them with custom menus. In this manner, you could create an application environment of your own.
3. The size of a drawing file increases as you add objects to it. AutoCAD LT keeps track of information about the size and position of each object in the drawing, for example, the points, scale factors, annotation scale, radii, and so on. If you combine several objects into a single object by forming a block by using the **Create Block** tool in the **Block Definition** panel, there will be a single scale factor, annotation scale, rotation angle, position, and so on, for all objects in the block, thereby saving storage space. Each object, repeated in the multiple block insertions, needs to be defined only once in the block definition. Ten insertions of a gear, made of forty-three lines and forty-one arcs, require only ninety-four objects (10+43+41), while ten individually drawn gears require 840 objects [10 X (43+41)].
4. If the specification for an object changes, the drawing needs to be modified. This is a very tedious task, if you need to detect each location where the change is to be made and edit it individually. But, if this object has been defined as a block, you can redefine it. Also, wherever that object appears, it is revised automatically.

5. Attributes (textual information) can be included in blocks. Different attribute values can be changed in each insertion of a block.
6. You can create symbols and then store them as blocks by using the **Create Block** tool. Later on, with the **Insert** tool, you can insert the blocks in the drawing, in which they were defined. There is no limit to the number of times you can insert a block in a drawing.
7. You can store symbols as drawing files using the **WBLOCK** command and later insert them into any other drawing, using the **Insert** tool.
8. The X, Y, and Z scale factors and rotation angles of blocks may vary from one insertion to another (Figure 14-1).
9. You can insert multiple copies of a block about a specified path, using the **Divide** or **Measure** tool from the **Point** drop-down in the **Draw** panel.

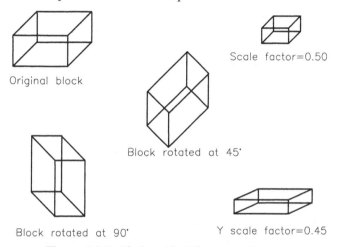

Figure 14-1 Blocks with different specifications

FORMATION OF BLOCKS
Drawing Objects for Blocks

The first step for creating blocks is to draw the object(s) to be converted into a block. You can consider any symbol, shape, or view that may be used more than once for conversion into a block (Figure 14-2). Even a drawing, that is to be used more than once, can be inserted as a block.

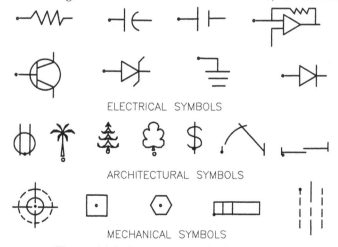

Figure 14-2 Some common drafting symbols

Tip

Examine the sketch of the drawing you are about to begin and carefully look for any shapes, symbols, and components that are to be used more than once. They can then be drawn once and stored as blocks.

CONVERTING ENTITIES INTO A BLOCK

Ribbon: Insert > Block Definition > Create Block
Toolbar: Draw > Make Block   **Command:** BLOCK

You can convert the entities in the drawing window into a block by using the **BLOCK** command or by choosing the **Create Block** tool from the **Block Definition** panel in the **Insert** tab or the **Home** tab. Alternatively, you can do so by choosing the **Make Block** tool from the **Draw** toolbar. When you invoke this tool, the **Block Definition** dialog box will be displayed, as shown in Figure 14-3. You can use the **Block Definition** dialog box to save any object or objects as a block.

In the **Name** edit box of the **Block Definition** dialog box, enter the name of the block you want to create. All the block names present in the current drawing are displayed in the **Name** drop-down list in an alphabetical and numerical order. This way you can verify whether a block you have defined has been saved. By default, the block name can have up to 255 characters. Also, it can contain letters, digits, blank spaces as well as any special characters including the $ (dollar sign), - (hyphen), and _ (underscore), provided they are not being used for any other purpose by AutoCAD LT or Windows.

Note
*The block name is controlled by the **EXTNAMES** system variable and its default value is 1. If the value is set to 0, the block name will be only thirty-one characters long and will not include spaces or any other special characters, apart from a $ (dollar sign), - (hyphen), or _ (underscore).*

If a block already exists, with the block name that you have specified in the **Name** edit box, and you choose **OK** in the **Block Definition** dialog box, the **Block - Redefine Block** message box will be displayed informing you that the block with this name is already defined. It will also prompt you to specify if you want to redefine the block. In this dialog box, you can either redefine the existing block by choosing the **Redefine** button or you can exit it by choosing the **No** button. You can then use another name for the block in the dialog box.

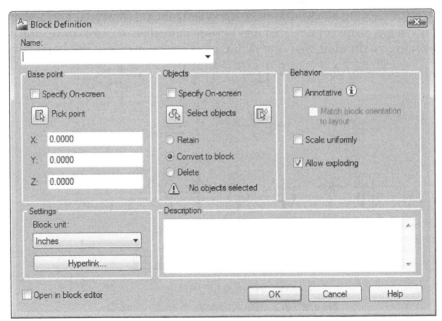

*Figure 14-3 The **Block Definition** dialog box*

After you have specified a block name, you are required to specify the insertion base point, which will be used as a reference point to insert the block. Usually, either the center or the lower left corner of the block is defined as the insertion base point. Later on, when you insert the block, you will notice that it appears at the insertion point, and you can insert it with reference to this point. The point you specify as the insertion base point is taken as the origin point of the block's coordinate system. You can specify the insertion point by choosing the **Pick point** button in the **Base point** area of the dialog box. The dialog box is temporarily removed, and you can select a base point on the screen. Alternatively, you can also enter the coordinates in the **X**, **Y**, and **Z** edit boxes. Once the insertion base point is specified, the dialog box reappears and the *X*, *Y*, and *Z* coordinates of the insertion base point are displayed in the **X**, **Y**, and **Z** edit boxes respectively. If no insertion base point is selected, AutoCAD LT assumes the insertion point coordinates to be 0,0,0, which are the default coordinates.

Tip
In drawings where the insertion point of a block is important, for example, in the case of inserting the block of a door symbol in architectural plans, it may be a good idea to first specify the requisite scale factors and rotation angles and then the insertion point. This way, you are able to preview the block symbol as it is to be inserted.

After specifying the insertion base point, you are required to select the objects that will constitute the block. Until the objects are selected, AutoCAD LT displays a warning: **No objects selected**, at the bottom of the **Objects** area. Choose the **Select objects** button; the dialog box is temporarily removed from the screen. You can select the objects on the screen using any selection method. After completing the selection process, right-click or press the ENTER key to return to the dialog box. The number of objects selected is displayed at the bottom of the **Objects** area of the dialog box.

The **Objects** area of the **Block Definition** dialog box also has a **QuickSelect** button. On choosing this button, the **Quick Select** dialog box is displayed, which allows you to define a selection set based on the properties of objects. **Quick Select** is used in cases where the drawings are very large and complex. The **Quick Select** dialog box has been discussed earlier in Chapter 6, Editing Sketched Objects-II.

In the **Objects** area, if you select the **Retain** radio button, the selected objects that form the block, are retained on the screen as individual objects. If you select the **Convert to block** radio button, the selected objects are converted into a block and will not be displayed on the screen after the block has been defined. Rather, the created block will be displayed in place of the original objects. If you select the **Delete** radio button, the selected objects will be deleted from the drawing, after the block has been defined.

Tip
*When you select the **Delete** radio button from the **Objects** area while defining a block, the selected objects are removed from the drawing. To restore them, you can use the **OOPS** command. On entering **U** at the Command prompt or choosing the **Undo** button from the **Standard** toolbar, the block definition will be restored from the drawing.*

If you select the **Annotative** check box in the **Behavior** area, the block created will become annotative. The block will now acquire annotative properties like text, dimension, hatch, and so on. On selecting the **Annotative** check box, the **Match block orientation to layout** check box will get highlighted. If you select the **Match block orientation to layout** check box, the orientation of the block in paper space viewport will always remain aligned to the orientation of the layout, while inserting the block. If you select the **Scale uniformly** check box, the block can only be scaled uniformly in all directions, while inserting. In such cases, if you create an annotative block, you can scale it only uniformly, while inserting. The **Scale uniformly** check box will be selected by default and remains unavailable for modification when you select the **Annotative** check box. If you select the **Allow exploding** check box, the block can be exploded into separate entities using the **Explode** tool, whenever required.

In the **Settings** Area, the **Block unit** drop-down list displays the units that will be used when inserting the current block. For example, if the block is created with inches as the units and you select **Feet** from the **Block unit** drop-down list, the block will be scaled to feet. You can also invoke the **Insert Hyperlink** dialog box by choosing the **Hyperlink** button in the **Settings** Area. This dialog box allows you to link any specific files, websites, or named views with the current drawing. You can also link the drawing to a default email address or you can select one from the recently used email addresses.

The **Open in block editor** check box is available at the bottom of **Block Definition** dialog box. If this check box is selected, the **Block Editor** will be opened as soon as you close the **Block Definition** dialog box. Also, the entities of the block will be displayed in the authoring area of the block editor. You will learn more about the **Block Editor** in the next section.

After setting all parameters in the **Block Definition** dialog box, choose the **OK** button to complete defining the block.

Tip
It is a good idea to create a unit block, especially for drawings where the same block is to be inserted with various scale factors. A unit block can be defined as a block that is created within a unit square area (1 unit x 1 unit). This way, every time you specify a scale factor, the block simply gets enlarged or reduced by the said amount directly, since the multiplication factor is 1.

Note
You can also create blocks by entering -BLOCK at the Command prompt.

EXERCISE 1   *Block*

Draw a circle of 1unit radius and then draw multiple circles inside it, as shown in Figure 14-4. Next, convert them into a block and name the entity as CIRCLE. Refer to the following figure for details.

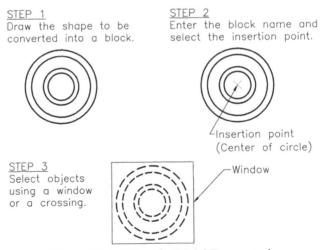

*Figure 14-4 Using the **BLOCK** command*

INSERTING BLOCKS

Ribbon: Insert > Block > Insert
Toolbar: Insert > Insert Block or Draw > Insert Block   **Command:** INSERT

The blocks created in the current drawing are inserted using the **Insert** tool. An inserted block is called a block reference. You should determine the layer and location to insert the block, and also the angle by which you want the block to be rotated prior to its insertion. If the layer on which you want to insert the block is not the current layer, select the appropriate option from the **Layer** drop-down list in the **Layers** panel of the **Home** tab or choose the **Set Current** button in the **Layer Properties Manager** palette to make it current. When you invoke the **Insert** tool, the **Insert** dialog box is displayed, as shown in Figure 14-5. You can specify different parameters of the block or external file to be inserted in the **Insert** dialog box.

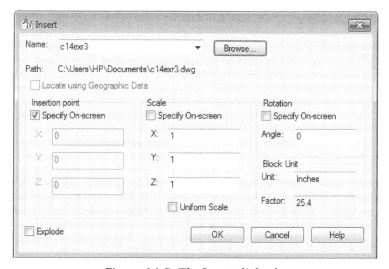

Figure 14-5 *The **Insert** dialog box*

Name

This drop-down list is used to specify the name of the block to be inserted. Select the name from this drop-down list. You can also enter a name for it. All blocks, created in the current drawing, are available in the **Name** drop-down list.

Note
*The last block name inserted becomes the default name for the next insertion and is displayed in the **Name** drop-down list.*

The **Browse** button is used to insert external files. When you choose this button, the **Select Drawing File** dialog box is displayed, as shown in Figure 14-6.

This dialog box is similar to the standard **Select File** dialog box, which has been discussed earlier in Chapter 1. You can select a drawing file from the files listed in the current directory. You can also change the directory by selecting the desired directory from the **Look in** drop-down list. Once you select the drawing file, choose the **Open** button; the drawing file name is displayed next to the **Name** drop-down list of the **Insert** dialog box. The **Path** option displays the path of the external file selected to be inserted. Now, if you want to change the block name, just change the name in the **Name** drop-down list. In this manner, the drawing can be inserted with a different name. Changing the original drawing does not affect the inserted drawing.

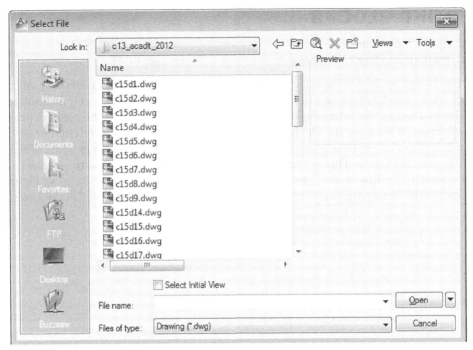

*Figure 14-6 The **Select Drawing File** dialog box*

Note
*If the name you have specified in the **Name** edit box does not exist as a block in the current drawing, AutoCAD LT will search the drives and directories on the path (specified in the **Options** dialog box) for a drawing of the same name. If the block is found, it will be inserted.*

*Also, suppose you have inserted a block in a drawing and then you want to insert a drawing with the same name as the block, AutoCAD LT will display a message saying that XX is already defined as a block and asks what do you want to do. If you choose **Redefine**, the block in the drawing will get replaced by the drawing with the same name, that is, the block gets redefined.*

Tip
*You can create a block in the current drawing from an existing drawing file. This saves the time, by avoiding redrawing the object as a block. Locate and select an existing drawing file using the **Browse** button. Next, choose the **Open** button after selecting the existing drawing. Next, choose the **OK** button; the **Insert** dialog box will be closed, prompting you to specify the insertion point. Now, instead of specifying the insertion point, press the ESC key; the selected file will be converted into a block, but will not be inserted into the drawing.*

Insertion point Area

When a block is inserted, its coordinate system is aligned parallel to the current UCS. In the **Insertion point** area, you can specify the *X*, *Y*, and *Z* coordinate locations of the block insertion point in the **X**, **Y**, and **Z** edit boxes, respectively. If you select the **Specify On-screen** check box, the **X**, **Y**, and **Z** edit boxes will not be available. You can specify the insertion point on the screen. By default, the **Specify On-screen** check box is selected, and hence, you can specify the insertion point on the screen.

Scale Area

In this area, you can specify the X, Y, and Z scale factors of the block to be inserted in the **X**, **Y**, and **Z** edit boxes, respectively. By selecting the **Specify On-screen** check box, you can specify the scale of the block at which it has to be inserted on the screen. The **Specify On-screen** check box is cleared by default and the block is inserted with the scale factors of 1 along the three axes. Also, if the **Uniform Scale** check box is selected, the X scale factor value is assumed for the Y and Z scale factors also. This means that if this check box is selected, you need to specify only the X scale factor. All dimensions in the block are multiplied by the same scale factors that you specify. These scale factors allow you to stretch or compress a block along the *X* and *Y* axes, respectively. You can also insert 3D objects into a drawing by specifying the third scale factor (since 3D objects have three dimensions), the Z scale factor. Figure 14-7 shows a block with different X and Y scale factors.

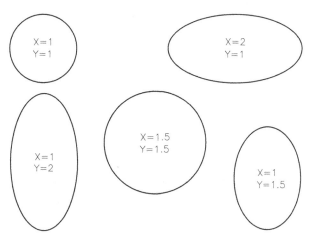

Figure 14-7 Block inserted with different scale factors

Tip

By specifying negative scale factors, you can insert a mirror image of a block along a particular axis. A negative scale factor for both the X and Y axes is the same as rotating the block reference through 140-degree, since it mirrors the block reference in the opposite quadrant of the coordinate system. The effect of the negative scale factor on the block (DOOR) can be marked by a change in position of the insertion point marked with an (X), as shown in Figure 14-8.

Also, specifying a scale factor of less than 1 inserts the block reference smaller than the original size. A scale factor greater than 1 inserts the block reference larger than its original size.

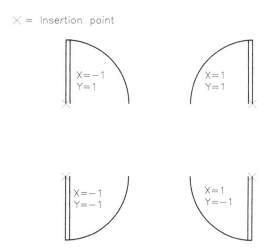

Figure 14-8 Block inserted using negative scale factors

Rotation Area

You can enter the angle of rotation for the block to be inserted in the **Angle** edit box. The insertion point is taken as the location about which the rotation takes place. Selecting the **Specify**

On-screen check box enables you to specify the angle of rotation on the screen. This check box is cleared by default and the block is inserted at an angle of zero-degree.

Block Unit Area

This area displays the information related to the block unit specified in the **Block Definition** dialog box and the scale factor used for the unit to insert the block. For example, if you have defined a block with the block unit as feet and you insert the same block in a drawing whose unit is inches, the **Block Unit** area will display **Unit** as feet and **Factor** as 12. The information displayed in this area is read-only.

Note
*You can control the units for the insertion of the block through the **INSUNITS** system variable. While doing so, the **Factor** information displayed in the **Block Unit** area will change accordingly.*

Explode Check Box

By selecting this check box, the block is inserted as a collection of individual objects. The function of the **Explode** check box is identical to that of the **Explode** tool. Once a block is exploded, the X, Y, and Z scale factors become identical. Therefore, you are provided access to only one scale factor edit box (**X** edit box), the **Y** and **Z** edit boxes are not available, and the **Uniform Scale** check box also gets selected. The X scale factor is assigned to the Y and Z scale factors too. You must enter a positive scale factor value.

Note
*If you select the **Explode** check box before insertion, the block reference will be exploded and the objects will be inserted with their original properties such as layer, color, and linetype.*

Once you have entered the relevant information in the dialog box, choose the **OK** button. The **Insert** dialog box is removed from the screen. If you have selected the **Specify On-Screen** check boxes, you can specify the insertion point, scale, and angle of rotation with a pointing device. Whenever the insertion point is to be specified on the screen (by default), you can specify the scale factors and rotation angle values. These values will override the values specified in the dialog box using the command line. Before specifying the insertion point on the screen, you can right-click to display the shortcut menu, which has all the options available through the command line. You can choose the options for insertion from the dynamic preview. On being prompted to specify the insertion point, press the down arrow key to see the options in the dynamic preview. However, if you have already specified an insertion point in the dialog box and have selected the **Specify On-screen** check boxes in the **Scale** or **Rotation** areas of the **Insert** dialog box, you are allowed to specify only the scale factors or the rotation angle at the Command line. The following Command prompt will be displayed when all three **Specify On-screen** check boxes are selected:

Specify insertion point or [Basepoint/Scale/X/Y/Z/Rotate]: *You can specify an insertion point on the screen or select an option.*
Enter X scale factor, specify opposite corner, or [Corner/XYZ] <1>: *Specify scale factor in X- axis or select an option or ENTER to accept the default scale factor of 1.*
Enter Y scale factor <use X scale factor>: *Specify scale factor in Y- axis or press ENTER to use the X scale factor.*
Specify rotation angle <0>: *Specify the angle of rotation of the inserted block.*

Tip
Using the Command line, you can override scale factors and rotation angles already specified in the dialog box.

The Command line options are discussed next.

Basepoint

If you enter **B** at the **Specify insertion point** prompt, or select the option from the dynamic preview, you are again prompted to specify the base point. Specify the base point, by clicking the cursor at the desired location. This point will now act as the insertion point. All prompts are also displayed at the cursor input so there is no need to always take a look on the command prompt. The prompt sequence for this option is given next.

> Specify insertion point or
> [Basepoint/Scale/X/Y/Z/Rotate]: **B** [Enter]
> Specify base point: *Specify base point*
> Specify insertion point or [Basepoint/Scale/X/Y/Z/Rotate]: *Specify insertion point.*

Scale

On entering **S** at the **Specify insertion point** prompt, you are asked to enter the scale factor. After entering it, the block assumes the specified scale factor, and AutoCAD LT lets you drag the block until you locate the insertion point on the screen. The *X*, *Y*, and *Z* axes are uniformly scaled by the specified scale factor. The prompt sequence for this option is given next.

> Specify insertion point or [Basepoint/Scale/X/Y/Z/Rotate]: **S**
> Specify scale factor for XYZ axes<1>: *Enter a value to preset general scale factor.*
> Specify insertion point or [Basepoint/Scale/X/Y/Z/Rotate]: *Specify insertion point.*

X, Y, Z

With X, Y, or Z as the response to the **Specify insertion point** prompt, you can specify the X, Y, or Z scale factors before specifying the insertion point. These options are only available when the **Uniform Scale** check box is cleared from the **Insert** dialog box. The prompt sequence when you use the **X** option is given next.

> Specify insertion point or [Basepoint/Scale/X/Y/Z/Rotate]: **X**
> Specify X scale factor<1>: *Enter a value for the X scale factor.*
> Specify insertion point or [Basepoint/Scale/X/Y/Z/Rotate]: *Select the insertion point.*
> Specify rotation angle <0>: *Specify angle of rotation.*

Rotate

On entering **R** at the **Specify insertion point** prompt, you are asked to specify the rotation angle. You can enter the angle of rotation or specify it by specifying two points on the screen. Dragging is resumed only when you specify the angle. Also, the block assumes the specified rotation angle. The prompt sequence for this option is given next.

> Specify insertion point or [Basepoint/Scale/X/Y/Z/Rotate]: **R**
> Specify rotation angle<0>: *Enter a value for the rotation angle.*
> Specify insertion point or [Basepoint/Scale/X/Y/Z/Rotate]: *Select the insertion point.*

The XYZ and Corner Options

When you specify the insertion point and scale factors on the screen, the following prompt appears after you have selected an insertion point.

> Enter X scale factor, specify opposite corner or [Corner/XYZ]<1>: *Enter X scale factor, specify opposite corner or select an option.*

Here, the **XYZ** option can be used to enter a 3D block reference and the successive prompts allow you to specify the X, Y, and Z scale factors individually.

With the **Corner** option, you can specify both X and Y scale factors at the same time. When you invoke this option, and **DRAGMODE** is turned off, and you are prompted to specify the other corner (the first corner of the box is the insertion point). You can also enter a coordinate value, instead of moving the cursor. The length and breadth of the box are taken as the X and Y scale factors for the block. For example, if the X and Y dimensions (length and width) of the box are the same as that of the block, the block will be drawn without any change. The points selected should be above and to the right of the insertion block. Mirror images will be produced if points selected are below or to the left of the insertion point. The prompt sequence is given next.

> Enter X scale factor, specify opposite corner or [Corner/XYZ]<1>: **C**
> Specify opposite corner: *Select a point as the corner*.

The **Corner** option also allows you to use a dynamic scaling technique when **DRAGMODE** is turned to **Auto (default)**. You can also move the cursor at the **Enter X scale factor** prompt to change the block size dynamically and, when the size meets your requirements, select a point.

Note

*1. You should avoid the use of the **Corner** option, if you want to have the same X and Y scale factors, because it is difficult to select a point whose X distance equals its Y distance, unless the **SNAP** mode is on. If you use the **Corner** option, it is better to specify the X and Y scale factors explicitly or select the corner by entering coordinates.*

*2. If the **Uniform Scale** check box is selected in the **Insert** dialog box, then the **X/Y/Z** options will not be available at the Command prompt.*

*3. You can also insert blocks using the command window either by entering the **-INSERT** command or by simply writing **-I** .*

EXERCISE 2   *Basepoint Insertion*

Create a block with the name SQUARE at the insertion base point 1,2. Insert this block in the drawing. The X scale factor is 2 units, the Y scale factor is 2 units, and the angle of rotation is 35-degree. It is assumed that the block SQUARE is already defined in the current drawing.

EXERCISE 3   *Scaled Insertion*

a. Insert the block CIRCLE created in Exercise 1. Use different X and Y scale factors to get different shapes after inserting this block.
b. Insert the block CIRCLE created in Exercise 1. Use the **Corner** option to specify the scale factor.

EXERCISE 4   *Scaled Insertion*

a. Construct a triangle and form a block of it. Name the block as TRIANGLE. Now, set the Y scale factor of the inserted block as 2.
b. Insert the block TRIANGLE with a rotation angle of 45-degree. After defining the insertion point, enter the X and Y scale factor of 2.

CREATING AND INSERTING ANNOTATIVE BLOCKS

You can create an annotative block by selecting the **Annotative** check box from the **Behavior** area of the **Block Definition** dialog box. The annotative block acquires the annotative properties like text, dimension, hatch, and so on. To convert an existing non-annotative block into an annotative one, choose the **Create Block** tool from the **Block Definition** panel of the **Insert** tab. Select the block to be converted to annotative from the **Name** drop-down list of the **Block Definition** dialog box. Select the **Annotative** check box from the **Behavior** area and then choose the **OK** button. AutoCAD LT will display a message box stating that the selected block is already defined as a block. If you want to redefine the block, choose the **Redefine** button; the specified block will be converted to annotative.

The annotative blocks are indicated by an annotative symbol attached to the block in the preview displayed in the **Insert** dialog box. While inserting the annotative block in the AutoCAD LT session for the first time, the **Select Annotation Scale** dialog box will be displayed on the screen, see Figure 14-9. Select the annotation scale from the drop-down list and then choose the **OK** button; the block will be inserted at the specified annotation scale. The annotative blocks are inserted at a scale value decided by the multiplication of the current annotation scale and the block scale specified in the **Scale** area of the **Insert** dialog box.

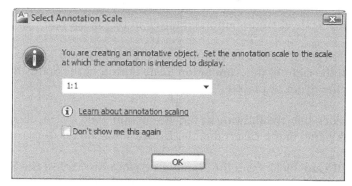

Figure 14-9 The Select Annotation Scale dialog box

Note
*While inserting the annotative blocks, the settings specified for the **INSUNITS** system variable are ignored. Also, the **Block Unit** area of the **Insert** dialog box will display no change in the factor value.*

EXAMPLE 1   *Annotative Block*

In this example, you will draw the object shown in Figure 14-10, and convert it into an annotative block, named NOR Gate. Next, you will insert the NOR Gate block into the drawing at the annotation scales of 1:1, 1:2, and 1:8 and notice the changes in the size of the annotative blocks inserted in the drawing.

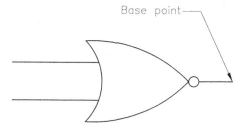

Figure 14-10 Drawing of block for Example 1

1. Start a new file in the **Drafting & Annotation** workspace and draw the object, as shown in Figure 14-10.

2. Invoke the **Block Definition** dialog box by choosing the **Create Block** tool from the **Block Definition** panel in the **Insert** tab.

3. Enter **NOR Gate** as the name of the block in the **Name** edit box. Next, choose the **Select objects** button from the **Objects** area; the **Block Definition** dialog box will disappear. Select the object drawn and press the ENTER key; the **Block Definition** dialog box will appear. Next, select the **Delete** radio button from the **Objects** area.

4. Choose the **Pick point** button from the **Base point** area; the **Block Definition** dialog box will disappear from the screen. Specify the base point, as shown in Figure 14-10.

5. Select the **Annotative** check box from the **Behavior** area. Next, choose the **OK** button from the **Block Definition** dialog box; the selected objects disappear from the screen and an annotative block is defined with the name **NOR Gate**.

Before proceeding further, ensure that the **Automatically Add Scales to annotative objects when the annotation scale changes** button is chosen in the Status Bar.

6. Now, you need to change the annotation scale of the drawing to 1:8. To do so, click on the down-arrow on the right of the **Annotation Scale** button in the Status Bar, and choose the scale 1:8 from the flyout displayed.

7. To insert the block into the drawing at the annotation scale of 1:8, choose the **Insert** tool from the **Block** panel in the **Insert** tab; the **Insert** dialog box is displayed.

8. Select the **NOR Gate** block from the **Name** drop-down list. Select the **Specify On-screen** check box from the **Insertion point** area and choose the **OK** button.

9. Specify the insertion point for the block by clicking on the screen; the block is inserted into the drawing at an annotation scale of 1:8.

10. Similarly, set the annotation scale to **1:2** in the Status Bar and insert the block. Then, set the annotation scale to **1:1** and insert the block.

11. Notice the difference in the sizes of the inserted blocks, see Figure 14-11. This automated variation in the size occurs due to annotative blocks. You will notice that the **Annotation Visibility** button on the right of the **Annotation Scale** button is on.

12. Now, set the current annotation scale to **1:8**. Choose the **Add/Delete Scales** tool from the **Annotation Scaling** panel in the **Annotate** tab. Select the block displayed at the annotation scale of 1:8 and press ENTER; the **Annotation Object Scale** dialog box is displayed. Choose the **Add** button; the **Add Scales to Object** dialog box is displayed. Press and hold the CTRL key and select the scale of 1:2 and 1:1 from the **Scale List** area.

13. Next, choose **OK**; the selected annotation scales get associated with the selected block. In this way, you can associate different annotation scales to a single annotative block.

14. Select the block to which you had added the annotation scales; the preview of the block with all annotation scales associated to the block is displayed, as shown in Figure 14-12. The bigger block with the current annotation (1:8) scale is displayed with dark dotted lines and the smaller blocks with other annotation scales (1:1, 1:2) are displayed with the faded dashed lines.

15. To move the block with the current annotation scale (1:8) to the other locations, select the blue grip displayed at the insertion point and move the block to the desired location. This way you can place the block with different annotation scales to any desired location.

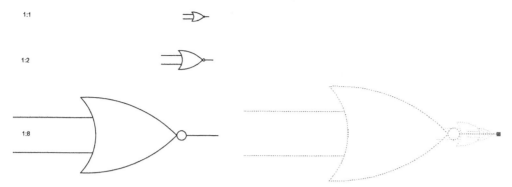

Figure 14-11 *Annotative blocks inserted at different annotation scales*

Figure 14-12 *Different annotation scales associated to a single block*

Block Editor

Ribbon: Insert > Block Definition > Block Editor or Home > Block > Edit
Toolbar: Standard > Block Editor   **Command:** BEDIT

The **Block Editor** is an important feature. This application is used to edit existing blocks or create new blocks. To invoke the **Block Editor**, choose the **Block Editor** tool from the **Block Definition** panel of the **Insert** tab or enter **BE** (shortcut for the **BEDIT** command) at the Command line. You can also double-click on the existing block to edit the block. On doing so, the **Edit Block Definition** dialog box will be displayed, as shown in Figure 14-13.

If you want to create a new block, enter its name in the **Block to create or edit** text box and choose **OK**; the **Block Editor** will be invoked where you can draw the entities in the new block. Similarly, if you want to

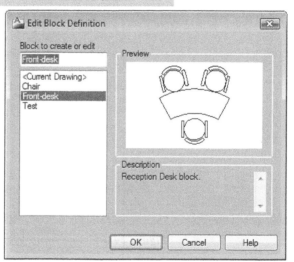

Figure 14-13 *The **Edit Block Definition** dialog box*

edit a block, select it from the list box provided in this dialog box; its preview will be displayed in the **Preview** area. Also, its related description, if any, will be displayed in the **Description** area. Choose the **OK** button; the **Block Editor** is invoked.

The default appearance of the **Block Editor** is shown in Figure 14-14. The drawing area of the **Block Editor** has a dull background and is known as the authoring area. You can edit existing entities or add new ones to the block in the authoring area. In addition to the authoring area, the **Block Editor** tab and **Block Authoring Palettes** are provided in the **Block Editor** that contain tools to create dynamic blocks. This will be discussed in detail later in this chapter. Now, you can edit a block using any tool, as you did in the drawing. When you are finished with the editing, choose the **Save Block** tool in the **Open/Save** panel of the **Block Editor** tab to save the changes. Then, choose the **Close Block Editor** button from the **Close** panel to return to the drawing again. Like this, you can edit the block at any time of your design process.

ADDING BLOCKS IN TOOL PALETTES

By default, the **Tool Palettes** window displays the predefined blocks in AutoCAD LT. You can also add the desired block and the drawing file to the **Tool Palettes** window. This is done using the **DesignCenter**. AutoCAD LT provides two methods for adding blocks from the **DesignCenter** to the **Tool Palettes**: **Drag and Drop** method and **Shortcut menu**. These two methods are discussed next.

Drag and Drop Method

To add blocks from the **DesignCenter** in the **Tool Palettes**, move the cursor over the desired block in the **DesignCenter**. Press and hold the left mouse button on the block and drag the cursor to the **Tool Palettes** window. You will notice that a box with a + sign is attached to the cursor and a black line appears on the **Tool Palettes** window, as shown in Figure 14-14. If you move the cursor up and down in the **Tool Palettes**, the black line also moves between the two consecutive blocks. This line is used to define the position of the block to be inserted in the **Tool Palettes** window. Release the left mouse button and you will notice that the selected block is added to the location specified by the black line in the **Tool Palettes**.

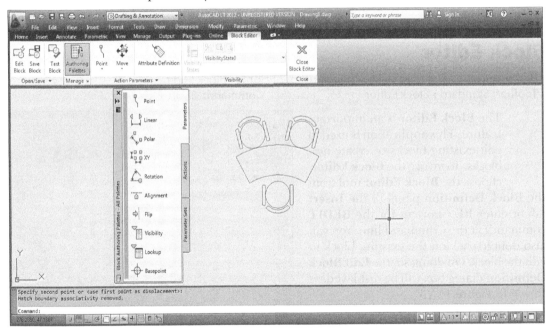

*Figure 14-14 Appearance of the drawing area in the **Block Editor***

Shortcut Menu

You can also add the desired block from the **DesignCenter** to the **Tool Palettes** using the shortcut menu. To add the block, move the cursor over the desired block in the **DesignCenter** and right-click on it to display a shortcut menu. Choose **Create Tool Palette** from it. You will notice that a new tab with the name **New Palette** is added to the **Tool Palettes**. And, the block is added in the new tab of the **Tool Palettes**. Also, a text box appears that displays the current name of the tab. You can change its name by entering a new one in this text box.

You can also add a number of blocks in a drawing to the **Tool Palettes** using the following two methods:

Select the **Blocks** folder of any drawing in the **DesignCenter** and right-click in the **Tree View** area of the **DesignCenter**; a shortcut menu will be displayed. Choose **Create Tool Palette** from the shortcut menu; a new tab will be added to the **Tool Palettes** with the same name as that of the drawing file selected in the **DesignCenter**. This new tab contains all blocks which were in the folder that you selected from the **DesignCenter**.

You can also add all the blocks in a drawing by right-clicking on the drawing in the **tree view** of the **DesignCenter**; a shortcut menu is displayed. Choose **Create Tool Palette** from it; you will notice that a new tab is added to the **Tool Palettes**, which contains all the blocks that were available in the selected drawing. You will also notice that the new tab has the same name as that of the selected drawing.

MODIFYING EXISTING BLOCKS IN THE TOOL PALETTES

If you modify an existing block that was added to the **Tool Palettes** and then insert it using the **Tool Palettes** in the same or a new drawing, you will notice that the modified block is inserted and not the original block. However, if you insert the modified block from the **Tool Palettes** in the drawing in which the original block was already inserted, AutoCAD LT inserts the original block and not the modified one. This is because the file already has a block of the same name in its memory.

To insert the modified block, you first need to delete the original block from the current drawing, using the **Erase** tool. Next, you need to delete the block from the memory of the current drawing. The unused block can be deleted from the memory of the current drawing, using the **PURGE** command. To invoke this command, enter **PURGE** at the command window. The **Purge** dialog box is displayed. Choose the (+) sign located on the left of **Blocks** in the tree view available in the **Items not used in drawing** area. You will notice that a list of blocks in the drawing is shown. Select the original block to be deleted from the memory of the current drawing and then choose the **Purge** button. The **Confirm Purge** dialog box is displayed, which confirms the purging of the selected item. Choose **Yes** in it and then choose the **Close** button to exit the **Purge** dialog box. Next, when you insert the block using the **Tool Palettes**, the modified block is inserted in the drawing.

Note
You will learn more about deleting unused blocks using the command line is, however, discussed later in this chapter.

*If you create a block with the name that is defined in the **Tool Palettes**, the block in the **Tool Palettes** is redefined in the current drawing. However, when you open a new drawing and insert the block using the **Tool Palettes**, the original block will be inserted.*

LAYERS, COLORS, LINETYPES, AND LINEWEIGHTS FOR BLOCKS

A block possesses the properties of the layer on which it is drawn. The block may be composed of objects drawn on several different layers, with different colors, linetypes, and lineweights. All this information is preserved in the block. At the time of insertion, each object in the block is drawn on its original layer with the original linetype, lineweight, and color, irrespective of the current drawing layer, object color, object linetype, and object lineweights. You may want all instances of a block to have identical layers, linetype properties, lineweight, and color. This can be achieved by allocating all the properties explicitly to the objects forming the block. On the other hand, if you want the linetype and color of each instance of a block to be set according to the linetype and color of the layer on which it is inserted, draw all the objects forming the block on layer 0 and set the color, lineweight, and linetype to **By Layer**. Objects with a **By Layer** color, linetype, and lineweight can have their colors, linetypes, and lineweights changed after insertion by changing the layer settings. If you want the linetype, lineweight, and color of each instance of a block to be set according to the current explicit linetype, lineweight, and color at the time of insertion, set the color, lineweight, and linetype of its objects to **By Block**. You can use the **Properties** palette to change some of the characteristics associated with a block (such as layer).

Note
The block is inserted on the current layer, but the objects comprising the block are drawn on the layers on which they were drawn when the block was being defined.

For example, assume block B1 includes a square and a triangle that were originally drawn on layer X and layer Y, respectively. Let the color assigned to the layer X be red and to layer Y be green. Also, let the linetype assigned to layer X be continuous and for layer Y be hidden. Now, if we insert B1 on layer L1 with color yellow and linetype dot, block B1 will be on layer L1, but the square will be drawn on layer X with color red and linetype continuous. The triangle will be drawn on layer Y with the color green and the linetype hidden.

The **By Layer** option instructs AutoCAD LT to assign objects within the block the color and linetype of the layers on which they were created. There are three exceptions:

1. If objects are drawn on a special layer (layer 0), they are inserted on the current layer. These objects assume the characteristics of the current layer (the layer on which the block is inserted) at the time of insertion, and can be modified after insertion by changing that layer's settings.

2. Objects created with the special color **By Block** are generated with the color that is current at the time of insertion of the block. This color may be explicit or **By Layer**. You are thus allowed to construct blocks that assume the current object color.

3. Objects created with the special linetype **By Block** are generated with the linetype that is prevalent at the time the block is inserted. Blocks are thus constructed with the current object linetype, which may be **By Layer** or explicit.

Note
If a block is created on a layer that is frozen at the time of insertion, it is not shown on the screen.

Tip
*If you provide drawing files to others for their use, using only **BYLAYER** settings provide the greatest compatibility with varying office standards for layer/color/linetype/lineweight. This is because they can be changed more easily after insertion.*

NESTING OF BLOCKS

The concept of having one block within another block is known as the **nesting of blocks**. For example, you can insert several blocks by selecting them, and then, with the **Create Block** tool, create another block. Similarly, if you use the **Insert** tool to insert a drawing, containing several blocks, into the current drawing, it creates a block containing nested blocks in the current drawing. There is no limit to the degree of nesting. The only limitation in nesting of blocks is that blocks that reference themselves cannot be inserted. The nested blocks must have different block names. Nesting of blocks affects layers, colors, and linetypes. The general rule is given next.

If an inner block has objects on layer 0, or objects with linetype or color **By Block**, these objects may be said to behave like fluids. They "float up" through the nested block structure until they find an outer block with fixed color, layer, or linetype. These objects then assume the characteristics of the fixed layer. If a fixed layer is not found in the outer blocks, then the objects with color or linetype **By Block** are formed; which means, they assume the color white and the linetype CONTINUOUS.

EXAMPLE 2   *Nested Blocks*

To clarify the concept of nested blocks, let us do the following example.

1. Draw a rectangle on layer 0, and form a block with the name X using this block.
2. Change the current layer to OBJ, set its color to red, and linetype to hidden.
3. Draw a circle on OBJ layer.
4. Insert the block X in the OBJ layer.
5. Combine the circle with the block X (rectangle) to form a block Y.
6. Now, insert block Y in any layer (say, layer CEN) with the color green and linetype continuous.

You will notice that block Y is generated in red and its linetype is hidden. However, the block X, which is nested in block Y and created on layer 0, is not generated in the color (green) and linetype (continuous) of the layer CEN. This is because, the object (rectangle) on layer 0 floated up through the nested block structure and assumed the color and linetype of the first outer block (Y) with a fixed color (red), layer (OBJ), and linetype (hidden). If both the blocks (X and Y) were on layer 0, the objects in the block Y would assume the color and linetype of the layer on which the block was inserted.

EXAMPLE 3   *Nested Blocks*

1. Change the color of layer 0 to red.
2. Draw a circle with color **By Block** and then form its block, B1. It appears white because its color is set to **By Block** (Figure 14-15).
3. Set the color to **By Layer** and draw a square. The color of the square is red.
4. Insert block B1. Notice that the block B1 (circle) assumes red color.
5. Create another block B2 consisting of the Block B1 (circle) and square.
6. Create a layer L1 with green color and hidden linetype. Make it current. Insert block B2 in layer L1.
7. Explode block B2. Notice the change.
8. Explode block B1, circle. You will notice that the color of the circle changes to white because it was drawn with the color set to **By Block** .

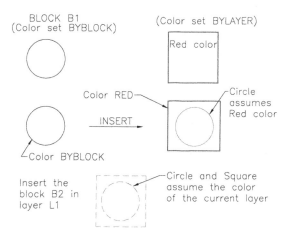

Figure 14-15 *Blocks versus layers and colors*

EXAMPLE 4   *Nested Blocks*

Part A
1. Draw a unit square on layer 0 and make it a block named B1.
2. Draw a circle of radius 0.5 and change it into a block named B2.
3. Insert block B1 into the drawing with an X scale factor of 3 and a Y scale factor of 4.
4. Now, insert the block B2 in the drawing and position it at the top of B1.
5. Make a block of the entire drawing and name it Plate.
6. Insert the block **Plate** in the current layer.
7. Create a new layer with different colors and linetypes and insert blocks B1, B2, and Plate.
Keep in mind the layers on which the individual blocks and the inserted block were made.

Part B
Try nesting the blocks drawn on different layers and with different linetypes.

Part C
Change the layers and colors of the different blocks you have drawn so far.

CREATING DRAWING FILES USING THE WRITE BLOCK DIALOG BOX

Command: WBLOCK

The blocks are symbols created by the **BLOCK** command and can be used only in the drawing, in which they were created. This is a shortcoming because you may need to use a particular block in different drawings. The **WBLOCK** command is used to export symbols by writing them to new drawing files that can then be inserted in any drawing. With the **WBLOCK** command, you can create a drawing file (*.dwg* extension) of the specified blocks, selected objects in the current drawing, or the entire drawing. All the used named objects (linetypes, layers, styles, and system variables) of the current drawing are inherited by the new drawing created with the **WBLOCK** command. This block can then be inserted in any drawing.

When you invoke the **WBLOCK** command, the **Write Block** dialog box is displayed, as shown in Figure 14-16. This dialog box converts the blocks into drawing files and also saves objects as drawing files. You can also save the entire current drawing as a new drawing file.

The **Write Block** dialog box has two main areas: **Source** and **Destination**. The **Source** area allows you to select objects and blocks, specify insertion base points and convert them into drawing files. In this area of the dialog box, different default settings are displayed, depending upon the selection you make. By default, the **Objects** radio button is selected. In the **Destination** area, the **File name and path** edit box displays *new block.dwg* as the new file name and its location. The **Block** drop-down list is also not available. Now, you can select objects in

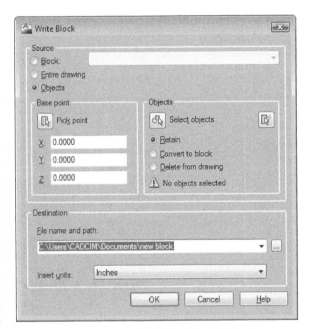

*Figure 14-16 The **Write Block** dialog box*

a drawing and save them as a wblock, and can enter a name and a path for the file. Sometimes the current drawing consists of blocks. To save a block as a wblock, you can select the **Block** radio button. When the **Block** radio button is selected, the **Block** drop-down list is available. The **Block** drop-down list displays all the block names in the current drawing and you can select a block name to convert it into a wblock. The **Base point** and **Objects** areas are not available, since the insertion points and objects have already been saved with the block definition. Also, you will notice that in the **Destination** area, by default, the **File name and path** edit box displays the name of the selected block. This means that you can keep the name of the wblock the same as the selected block or you can change it. Selecting the **Entire drawing** radio button, selects the current drawing as a block and saves it as a new file. When you use this option, the **Base point** and **Objects** areas are not available.

The **Base point** area allows you to specify the base point of a wblock, which is used as an insertion point. You can either enter values in the **X**, **Y**, and **Z** edit boxes or choose the **Pick point** button to select it on the screen. The default value is 0, 0, 0. The **Objects** area allows you to select objects to save as a file. You can use the **Select Objects** button to select objects or use the **QuickSelect** button to set parameters in the **Quick Select** dialog box to select objects in the current drawing. The number of objects selected is displayed at the bottom of the **Objects** area. If the **Retain** radio button is selected in the **Objects** area, the selected objects in the current drawing are kept as such, after they have been saved as a new file. If the **Convert to block** radio button is selected, the selected objects in the current drawing will be converted into a block with the same name as the new file, after being saved as a new file. Selecting the **Delete from drawing** radio button deletes the selected objects from the current drawing after they have been saved as a file.

Note

*Both the **Base point** and **Objects** areas are available in the **Write Block** dialog box only when the **Objects** radio button is selected in the **Source** area of the dialog box.*

The **Destination** area sets the file name, location, and units of the new file, in which the selected objects are saved. In the **File name and path** edit box, you can specify the file name and the path of the block or the selected objects. You can choose the [...] button to display the **Browse for Drawing File** dialog box, where you can specify the path where the new file will be saved. From the **Insert Units** drop-down list, you can select the units, the new file will use when inserted as a block. The settings for units are stored in the **INSUNITS** system variable and the default option **Inches** has a value of 1. On specifying the required information in the dialog box, choose **OK**. The objects or the block is saved as a new file in the path specified by you. A **WBLOCK Preview** window with the contents of the new file is displayed. This preview image is stored and displayed in the **DesignCenter**, when using it to insert drawings and blocks.

Note

Whenever a drawing is inserted into the current drawing, it acts as a single object. It cannot be edited unless exploded.

Tip

*You can reduce the size of the current drawing by using the **Entire Drawing** radio button in the **Write Block** dialog box so that all unused blocks, layers, linetypes, text styles, dimension styles, multiline styles, shapes, and so on are removed from the newly generated drawing. The new drawing does not contain any information that is no longer needed. The **Entire drawing** option is faster than the **-PURGE** command (which also removes unused named objects from a drawing file) and can be used whenever you have completed a drawing and want to save it. The **-PURGE** command has been discussed later in this chapter.*

EXERCISE 5   *WBLOCK*

1. Create a drawing file named CHAIR using the **WBLOCK** command. Make a listing of your *.dwg* files and make sure that *CHAIR.dwg* is listed. Quit the drawing editor.
2. Begin a new drawing and insert the drawing file into it. Save the drawing.

Exploding Blocks Using the XPLODE Command

Command: XPLODE

With the **XPLODE** command, you can explode a block or blocks into component objects and simultaneously control their properties such as layer, linetype, color, and lineweight. The scale factor of the object to be exploded should be equal. Note that if the scale factor of the objects to be exploded is not equal, you need to change the value of the **EXPLMODE** system variable to 1. Note that, if the **Allow exploding** check box in the **Behavior** area of the **Block Definition** dialog box was cleared while creating the block, you will not be able to explode the block. The command prompts for this command are as follows:

> Command: **XPLODE**
> Select objects to XPlode
> Select objects: *Select objects by using any object selection method, and then press ENTER.*

On pressing ENTER, AutoCAD LT reports the total number of objects selected and also the number of objects that cannot be exploded. If you select multiple objects to explode, AutoCAD LT further prompts you to specify whether the changes in the properties of the component objects should be made individually or globally. The prompt is given next.

> XPlode Individually/<Globally>: *Enter i, g, or press ENTER to accept the default option.*

If you enter **i** at the above prompt, AutoCAD LT will modify each object individually, one at a time. The next prompt is given below.

> Enter an option [All/Color/LAyer/LType/LWeight/Inherit from parent block/Explode] <Explode>: *Select an option.*

The options available at the Command line are discussed next.

All

This option sets all the properties such as color, layer, linetype, and lineweight of the selected objects, after exploding them. AutoCAD LT prompts you to enter new color, linetype, lineweight, and layer name for the exploded component objects.

Color

This option sets the color of the exploded objects. The prompt is given next.

> New color [Truecolor/COlorbook]<BYLAYER>: *Enter a color option or press ENTER.*

When you enter **BYLAYER**, the component objects take on the color of the exploded object's layer and when you enter **BYBLOCK**, they take on the color of the exploded object.

Layer

This option sets the layer of the exploded objects. The default option is inheriting the current layer. The command prompt is as follows.

Enter new layer name for exploded objects <current>: *Enter an existing layer name or press ENTER.*

LType

This option sets the linetype of the components of the exploded object. The Command prompt is given next.

Enter new linetype name for exploded objects <ByLayer>: *Enter a linetype name or press ENTER to accept the default options.*

LWeight

This option sets the lineweight of the components of the exploded object. The Command prompt is given next.

Enter new lineweight: *Enter a lineweight or press ENTER to accept the default option.*

Inherit from parent block

This option sets the properties of the component objects to that of the exploded parent object, provided the component objects are drawn on layer 0 and the color, lineweight, and linetype are **BYBLOCK**.

Explode

This option explodes the selected object exactly as in the **EXPLODE** command.

Selecting the **Globally** option, applies changes to all the selected objects at the same time. The options are similar to the ones discussed in the **Individually** option.

RENAMING BLOCKS

Command: RENAME

Blocks can be renamed using the **RENAME** command. To rename a block, enter **RENAME** at the Command prompt and press ENTER; the **Rename** dialog box will be displayed, see Figure 14-17. This dialog box allows you to modify the name of an existing block. In the **Rename** dialog box, the **Named Objects** list box displays the categories of object types that can be renamed, such as blocks, layers, dimension styles, linetypes, Multileader styles, material, table styles and text styles, UCSs, views, and viewports. You can rename all of these except layer 0 and continuous linetype. When you select **Blocks** from the **Named Objects** list, the **Items** list box displays all the block names in the current drawing. When you select a block name to rename from the **Items** list box, it is displayed in the **Old Name** edit box. Enter the new name to be assigned to the block in the **Rename To** edit box. Choosing the **Rename To** button applies the change in name to the old name. Choose **OK** to exit the dialog box. For example, to rename a block named Bracket to **Valve-3**, select **Bracket** from the **Items** list box; it is displayed in the **Old Name** edit box. Enter **Valve-3** in the **Rename To** edit box and choose the **Rename To** button; the **Valve-3** block appears in the **Items** list box. Now, choose **OK** to exit the dialog box.

Note
*The layer 0 and Continuous linetype cannot be renamed and therefore, they do not appear in the **Items** list box, when **Layers** and **Linetypes** are selected in the **Named Objects** list box.*

*To rename a block, enter **-RENAME** or **-REN** at the Command window.*

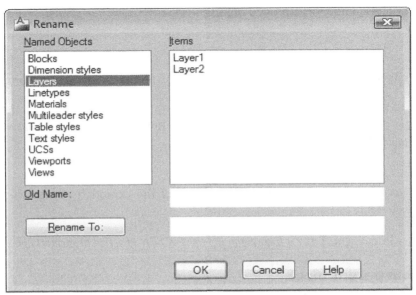

*Figure 14-17 The **Rename** dialog box*

DELETING UNUSED BLOCKS

Sometimes, after completing a drawing, you may notice that the drawing contains several named objects, such as dimstyles, textstyles, layers, blocks, and so on that are not being used. Since these unused named objects unnecessarily occupy disk space, you may want to remove them. Unused blocks can be deleted with the **-PURGE** command. For example, to delete an unused block named Drawing2, the prompt sequence is given next.

Command: **-PURGE**
Enter type of unused objects to purge
[Blocks/Dimstyles/LAyers/LTypes/MAterial/MUltileaderstyles/Plotstyles/SHapes/textSTyles/
Mlinestyles/Tablestyles/Visualstyles/Regapps/Zero-length geometry/Empty Text Objects/
All]: **B**
Enter name(s) to purge <*>: **Drawing2**
Verify each name to be purged? [Yes/No] <Y>: ⏎
Purge block "Drawing2"? <N>: **Y**

If there are no objects to be removed, AutoCAD LT displays a message "No unreferenced visual styles found.".

Note
*The unused blocks can also be deleted using the **PURGE** command as discussed earlier.*

*If you put an (*) asterisk before the name of the wblock while using the **-WBLOCK** command, it will work in the same manner as the **-PURGE** command. Also, you can select the **Entire drawing** radio button in the **Write Block** dialog box when creating a block using the **WBLOCK** command to get the same effect. But, the **WBLOCK** command is faster and deletes the unused named objects automatically, while the **-PURGE** command allows you to select the type of named objects you want to delete, and it also gives you an option to verify the objects before the deletion occurs.*

EDITING CONSTRAINTS TO BLOCKS

While creating assembly drawings, you may need some parts that have same geometry but different sizes. AutoCAD LT 2012 allows you to create the drawings of these parts by using geometric and dynamic constraints, if you could control these constraints in a block table. Note that you need to apply the geometric and dynamic constraints to blocks in the **Block Editor**.

To create the parts having same geometry but different sizes, draw the sketch of the parts and then convert them into a block. Next, invoke the **Block Editor** to edit the block. In the **Block Editor**, apply the necessary geometric and dimensional constraints and make the sketch a fully-defined sketch. Now, choose the **Block Table** tool from the **Dimensional** panel of the **Block Editor** tab; you will be prompted to specify the location of the parameter. Specify a suitable location; you will be prompted to specify the number of grips. If you enter **0**, no grip will be displayed in the drawing area. It is recommended to have atleast one grip. After specifying the number of grips, the **Block Properties Table** will be displayed, as shown in Figure 14-18.

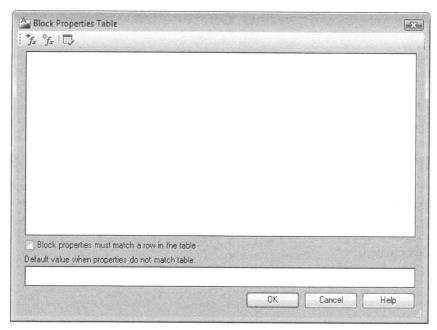

*Figure 14-18 The **Block Properties Table***

In the **Block Properties Table**, choose the **Adds properties which appear as columns in the table** button to add all or some of the dimensional constraints added to the block. On choosing this button, the **Add Parameter Properties** dialog box will be displayed, as shown in Figure 14-19. Next, select the parameter properties to be added to the **Block Properties Table** by pressing and holding the CTRL key and then choose **OK**; the selected properties will be listed in the **Block Properties Table**. If you need to add any new parameter to the table, choose the **Creates a new user parameter and adds it to the table** button from the **Block Properties Table**; the **New Parameter** dialog box will be displayed, as shown in Figure 14-20. Specify the parameters and choose the **OK** button; the new parameter will be added to the **Block Properties Table**. You can also check the errors in the table. To do so, choose the **Audits the block property table for errors** button from the **Block Properties Table**. After specifying all parameters, choose the **OK** button from the **Block Properties Table**. Next, save the changes and exit the **Block Editor**. Now, if you select the block, the lookup grip will be displayed. Click on the grip; different values will be displayed, as shown in Figure 14-20. Next, choose the required value; the block will change accordingly. Note that if you have selected the **Block properties must match a row in the table** check box in the **Block Properties Table**, then the lookup grip will not be displayed and you cannot change the block sizes dynamically.

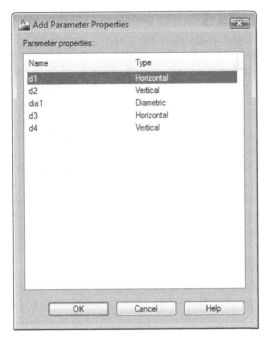

Figure 14-19 The **Add Parameter Properties** dialog box

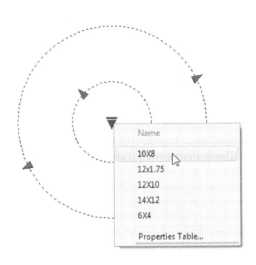

Figure 14-20 Shortcut menu displayed on selecting the lookup grip

EXAMPLE 5   *Constraints to Blocks*

In this example, you will edit the dimensional constraint of a bolt that has been created as a dynamic block. The original sketch is shown in Figure 14-21(a) and the sketch after editing the dimensional constraint is shown in Figure 14-21(b). After editing the dimensional constraints of the sketch, you will apply the constraints such that the bolts of diameter 6, 10, 12.5, 15, 18, 24, and 25 are created.

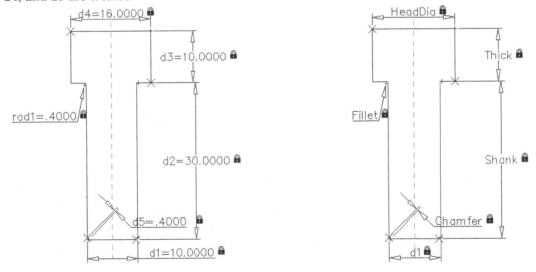

Figure 14-21(a) *Sketch with all dimensional constraints*   Figure 14-21(b) *New name of the constraints*

Note
The bolt shown in Figure 14-21 does not have any standard dimension or annotation. It is given for the purpose of example. However, you can follow the procedure given next to design a standard bolt.

1. Start a new file with the *acad.dwt* template in the **Drafting & Annotation** workspace. Draw the sketch assuming that the value of d=10 and it satisfies other relations shown in Figure 14-21(a). Make sure that the **Infer Constraints** button is chosen in the Status bar and the endpoints are snapped so that it becomes a closed sketch, as shown in Figure 14-21(b).

2. Choose the **Create Block** tool from the **Block** panel in the **Home** tab and convert the sketch into a block. Name the block as **Bolt**.

3. Choose the **Block Editor** tool from the **Block** panel in the **Home** tab; the **Edit Block Definition** dialog box is displayed. Select **Bolt** and choose **OK**; the **Block Editor** environment is displayed.

4. Draw a vertical line passing through the midpoint of the bottom horizontal line.

5. Choose the **Construction Geometry** tool from the **Manage** panel of the **Block Editor** tab, select the vertical line drawn in the previous step, and press ENTER; you will be prompted to enter an option.

6. Enter **C** and press ENTER; the vertical line is converted to a construction line, as shown in Figure 14-21(a). Note that you can also create a centerline in the drawing mode but for the purpose of example, this method is given.

7. Choose the **Equal** tool from the **Geometric** panel and apply the equal constraints between fillets, chamfers, vertical lines tangential to fillets, horizontal lines tangential to fillets, and vertical lines at the top.

8. Choose the **Symmetric** tool from the **Geometric** panel and apply the symmetric constraints between all entities on either side of the construction line.

9. Hide all geometric constraints by choosing the **Hide All** button from the **Geometric** panel of the **Block Editor**.

10. Apply the dimensional constraints by using the tools in the **Dimensional** panel of the **Block Editor**. Figure 14-21(b) shows the sketch with all dimensional constraints applied. Also, make sure that you snap the endpoints of the vertical line while applying constraints to the base diameter and to the length of the bolt.

You can observe the grips (arrow) for every dimensional constraint but you need to hide them so that you can easily select the dimensional constraints in the drawing.

11. Select all dimensional constraints and invoke the **Properties** palette. In the **Misc** rollout, change the **Number of Grips** to 0.

12. Choose the **Parameters Manager** button from the **Manage** panel; the **Parameters Manager** palette is displayed.

Next, you need to rename the constraints in the **Name** column of the **Properties Manager** palette.

13. To rename a constraint, select it in the **Name** column and press the F2 key or double-click on the respective field; an edit box will be displayed. Change the name of the constraint.

14. Apply a new expression to each renamed constraint, as shown in Figure 14-21(b).

15. Choose the **Block Table** tool from the **Dimensional** panel of the **Block Editor**; you are prompted to specify the parameter location.

16. Select the midpoint of the horizontal line at the bottom; you are prompted to specify the number of grips.

17. Enter **1** and press ENTER; the **Block Properties Table** is displayed.

18. Choose the **Creates a new user parameter and adds it to the table** button; the **New Parameter** dialog box is displayed.

19. Enter **Size** in the **Name** edit box. Next, select the **String** option from the **Type** drop-down list and choose the **OK** button; a new column named **Size** is added to the **Block Properties Table**.

20. Choose the **Add properties which appear as columns in the table** button from the **Block Properties Table**; the **Add Parameter Properties** dialog box is displayed.

21. Select the **d1** parameter and choose the **OK** button; the selected parameter is added to the **Block Properties Table**.

22. Clear the **Block properties must match a row in the table** check box, if not cleared already.

23. Enter the following values in the **Size** and **d1** columns:

Size	d1
M6	6
M10	10
M12.5	12.5
M15	15
M18	18
M24	24
M25	25

24. Choose the **Audits the block property table for errors** button; a message box is displayed stating that no errors have been found.

25. Close the message box and choose **OK** in the **Block Properties Table**; the **Size** parameter is added to the **Parameters Manager** palette under the **User Parameters** node.

26. Now, you need to test the block by invoking the **Test Block Window**. To do so, choose the **Test Block** tool from the **Open/Save** panel of the **Block Editor**; the **Test Block Window** is opened. You can view the name of the new window at the title bar.

27. Select the block; the block is displayed in dashed lines and two grips are also displayed, one at the insertion point of the block and other at the midpoint of the horizontal line at the bottom. The triangular grip at the midpoint is known as lookup grip.

28. Click on the lookup grip; a shortcut menu is displayed.

29. Choose different sizes and check whether the block resizes without any error.

30. After checking the block, choose the **Close Test Block Window** button from the **Close** panel; the **Block Editor** is displayed.

31. Choose the **Close Block Editor** button to close the block editor; a message box is displayed.

32. Choose the **Save changes and exit the Block Editor** option from the message box.

33. Select the block and click on the lookup grip; different possible sizes are displayed. Select the required size.

34. Save the drawing and exit.

Note

In this example, the block has been created without creating a fully-defined sketch. But it is recommended to create a fully-defined sketch while working with dynamic blocks.

Self-Evaluation Test

Answer the following questions and then compare them to those given at the end of this chapter:

1. Individual objects in a block cannot be erased using the **Block Editor**. (T/F)

2. The blocks created by the **Create Block** tool in the **Block** panel can be used in any drawing. (T/F)

3. You cannot redefine any existing block. (T/F)

4. The _____ command lets you create a drawing file (*.dwg* extension) of a block defined in the current drawing.

5. The _____ command can be used to change the name of a block.

6. The _____ tool is used to place a previously created block in a drawing.

7. You can delete the unreferenced blocks using the _____ command.

8. The _____ command is used for in-place reference editing.

Review Questions

Answer the following questions:

1. An entire drawing can be converted into a block. (T/F)

2. The objects in a block possess the properties of the layer on which they are drawn, such as color and linetype. (T/F)

3. If the objects forming a block were drawn on layer 0 with color and linetype **BYLAYER**, then at the time of the insertion, each object that makes up a block is drawn on the current layer with the current linetype and color. (T/F)

4. The objects created with the special color **BYBLOCK** are generated with the color that is current at the time the block was inserted. (T/F)

6. Which of the following commands should you use to get back the objects that consist of the block and have been removed from the drawing?

       (a) **OOPS**   (b) **BLIPS**
       (c) **BLOCK**   (d) **UNDO**

7. When you insert a drawing into the current drawing, how many blocks belonging to the inserted drawing are brought into the current drawing?

       (a) One   (b) None
       (c) All   (d) Two

8. The **Entire drawing** option of the **WBLOCK** command has the same effect as the **PURGE** command. (T/F)

9. The automatic save feature is _____ during in-place reference editing.

10. You cannot use the **REFEDIT** command on blocks inserted using the _____ command.

11. The Layer 0 and the Continuous linetype _____ be renamed using the **RENAME** command.

EXERCISE 6   *Block*

Draw part (a) of Figure 14-22 and define it as a block named A. Then, using the **Insert** tool, insert the block in the plate, as shown.

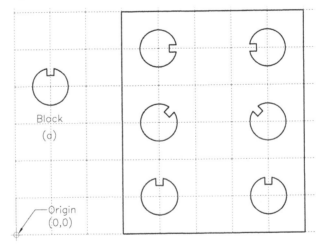

Figure 14-22 *Drawing for Exercise 6*

EXERCISE 7   *Block*

Draw the diagrams shown in Figure 14-23 using blocks.
a. Create a block for the valve, Figure 14-23(a).
b. Use a thick polyline for the flow lines.

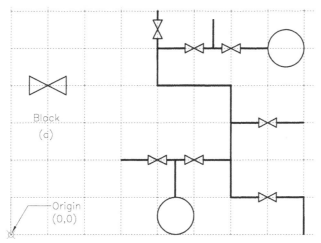

Figure 14-23 *Drawing for Exercise 7*

EXERCISE 8   *Block*

Draw part (a) of Figure 14-24 and define it as a block named B. Then, using the relevant insertion method, generate the pattern as shown. Note that the pattern is rotated at 30-degree.

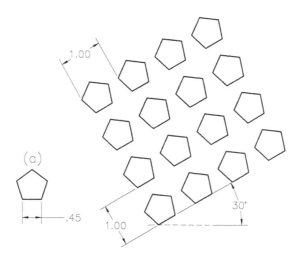

Figure 14-24 *Drawing for Exercise 8*

EXERCISE 9   *Block*

Draw Block A given in Figure 14-25 and define it as a block named Chair. The dimensions of the chair can be referred from the Problem Solving Exercise 3 of Chapter 5. Then, using the block insert command, insert the chair around the table as shown in the same figure.

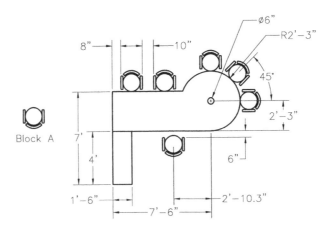

Figure 14-25 Drawing for Exercise 9

EXERCISE 10   *Constraints to Block*

Create the sketch of a bolt as shown in Figure 14-26. Then, convert it to a block and apply constraints such that you can create bolts of diameter 6, 10, 12.5, 15, 18, 24, and 25.

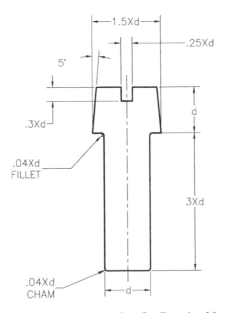

Figure 14-26 Drawing for Exercise 10

Answers to Self-Evaluation Test

1. F, **2.** T, **3.** F, **4.** WBLOCK, **5.** RENAME, **6.** Insert, **7.** PURGE, **8.** REFEDIT

Student Project

Draw the two dimensional (2D) drawings shown in Figure 1 through 21. Add dimensions and annotations to the drawings, as shown in the figures. Assume the missing dimensions.

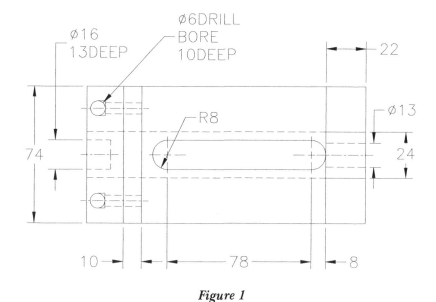

Figure 1

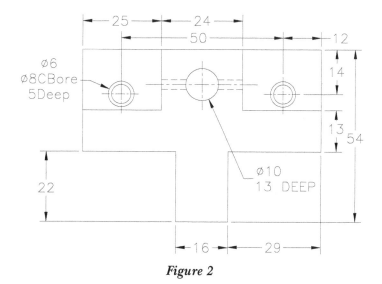

Figure 2

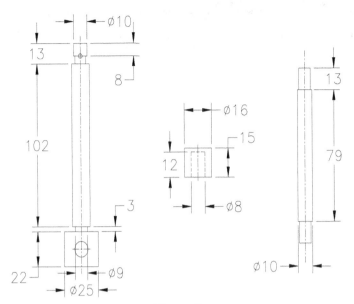

Figure 3

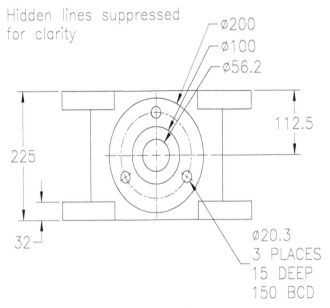

Figure 4

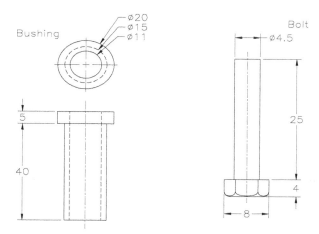

Figure 5

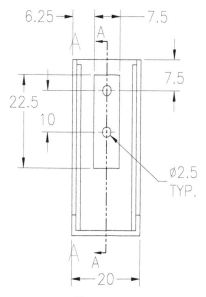

Figure 6

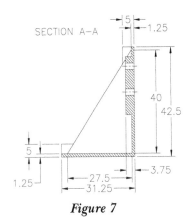

Figure 7

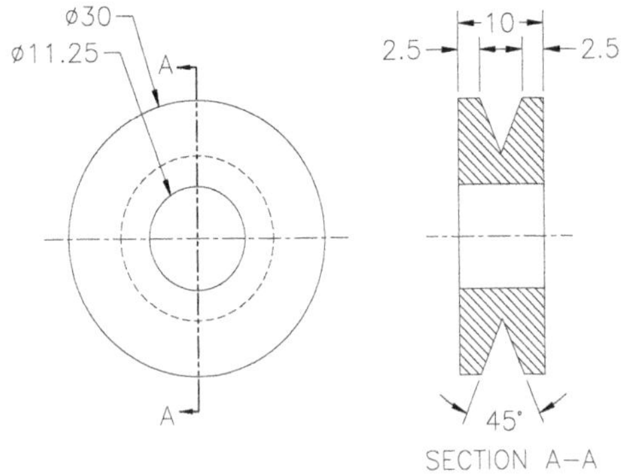

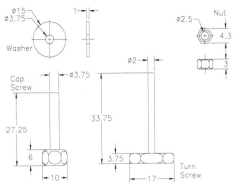

Figure 8

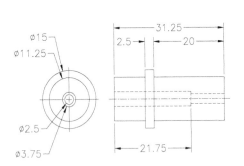

Figure 9

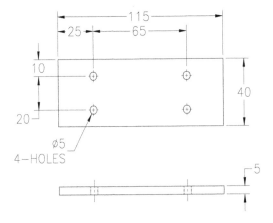

Figure 10

Figure 11

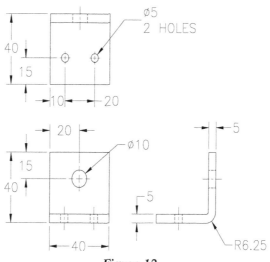

Figure 12

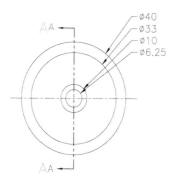

Figure 13

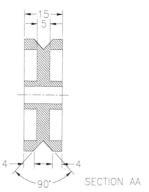

SECTION AA

Figure 14

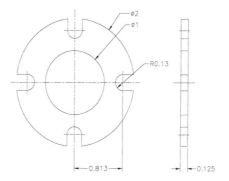

Figure 15

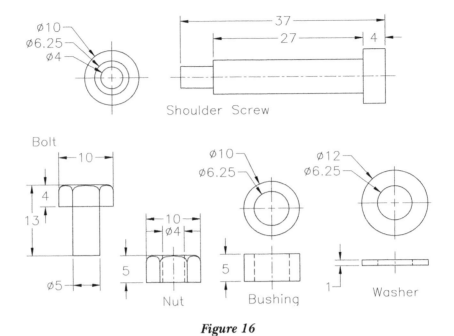

Figure 16

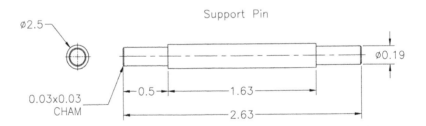

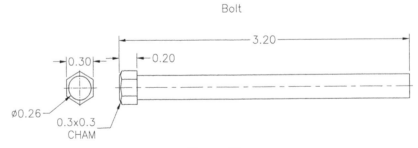

Figure 17

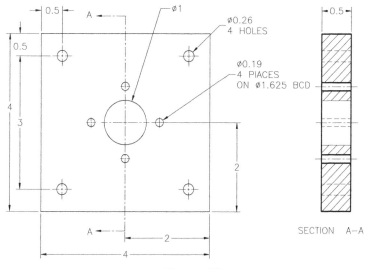

Figure 18

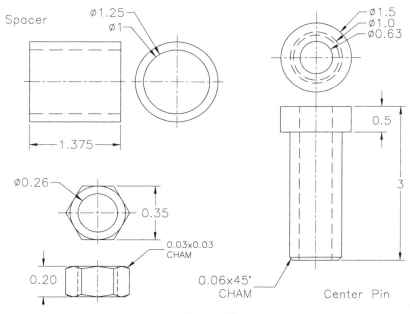

Figure 19

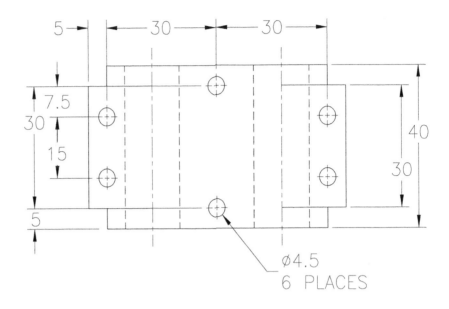

Figure 20

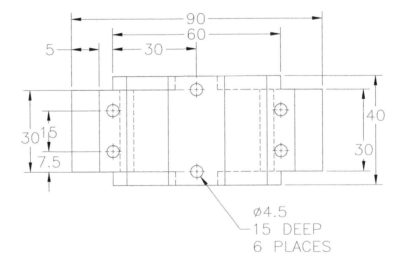

Figure 21

Index

Symbols

2-Point tool 2-23
3-Point tool 2-23, 3-2
-DIMSTYLE command 9-7
-PURGE command 14-24

A

Absolute Coordinate System 2-9
ADCENTER command 6-6
Add-A-Plot Style Table Wizard 12-10
Add-A-Plotter Wizard 12-8
Add/Delete Scales tool 7-3
Add Leaders tool 8-34
Add Page Setup dialog box 12-3
Add Parameter Properties dialog box 14-26
Adjust Space tool 8-24
Advanced Setup wizard 1-17
Aligned tool 8-12, 8-34
Align Option 7-7
ANNOAUTOSCALE system variable 7-4
ANNORESET command 7-5
Annotation Object Scale dialog box 7-4
Annotation Scale button 8-44
Annotation Visibility button 1-6
Annotative Dimensions 8-7
Application Menu 1-9
ARC command 3-2
Arc drop-down 3-2

B

Background Mask dialog box 7-12
BEDIT command 14-15
BLOCK command 14-4
Block Definition dialog box 14-4
Block Editor 14-16
Block Editor tool 14-15
Block Properties Table 14-25

C

Cell Border Properties dialog box 7-35
Center, Diameter tool 2-22
Center Mark tool 8-22
Center, Radius tool 2-22
Center, Start, Angle tool 3-3
Center, Start, End tool 3-3
Center, Start, Length tool 3-4
Center tool 3-8
CHAMFERA system variable 5-14
CHAMFERB system variable 5-14
CHAMFER command 5-12
CHAMFERC system variable 5-14
CHAMFERD system variable 5-14
Chamfer tool 5-12
CHAMMODE system variable 5-14
Circle drop-down 2-22
Clean Screen button 1-8
Column Settings dialog box 7-17
Constraints to Blocks 14-25
Copy tool 11-10
Create New Drawing dialog box 1-14
Create New Table Style dialog box 7-31
Create Block tool 14-4
Create Viewports drop-down 11-7

D

DDEDIT command 7-24
DDPTYPE command 3-22
Definition Points 8-6
DEFPOINTS layer 8-6
DesignCenter 3-8
Diameter tool 8-20
DIMADEC system variable 8-8
DIMALIGNED command 8-12
DIMALT system variable 10-20
DIMALTTD system variable 10-24
DIMANGULAR command 8-17
DIMARC command 8-13
DIMASSOC system variable 8-6
DIMASZ system variable 10-8
DIMAZIN system variable 10-20
DIMBASELINE command 8-15
DIMBLK1 system variable 10-7
DIMBLK2 system variable 10-7
DIMCEN system variable 8-4, 10-9

DIMCENTER command 8-22
DIMCLRD system variable 8-39, 10-4
DIMCLRE system variable 10-5
DIMCLRT system variable 8-40, 10-11
DIMCONTINUE command 8-16
DIMDEC system variable 8-8, 10-17
DIMDIA command 8-20
DIMDISASSOCIATE command 8-6
DIMDLE system variable 10-4
DIMDLI system variable 10-4
DIMDSEP system variable 10-18
DIMEDIT command 9-4
Dimension, Dimjogline tool 8-21
Dimension drop-down 8-9
Dimension Edit tool 9-4
Dimension Line 8-3
Dimension Style Manager dialog box 10-2
Dimension Text 9-6
Dimension Text Edit tool 9-6
Dimension Update tool 9-7
DIMEXE system variable 10-5
DIMEXO system variable 10-6
DIMFRAC system variable 10-17
DIMGAP system variable 10-11, 10-13
DIMINSPECT command 8-25
DIMJOGLINE command 8-21
DIMLFAC system variable 10-19
DIMLINEAR command 8-9
DIMLUNIT system variable 10-17
DIMLWD system variable 10-4
DIMLWE system variable 10-5
DIMORD command 8-23
DIMPOST system variable 10-18
DIMRAD command 8-21
DIMREASSOCIATE 8-27
DIMRND system variable 10-18
DIMSCALE system variable 10-16
DIMSD1 system variable 10-4
DIMSD2 system variable 10-4
DIMSE1 system variable 8-21
DIMSE2 system variable 8-24
DIMSOXD system variable 10-15
DIMSPACE command 9-8
DIMSTYLE command 10-2
DIMSTYLE system variable 9-6
DIMTAD system variable 10-12
DIMTEDIT command 9-6
DIMTFAC system variable 10-11
DIMTIH system variable 8-23, 10-13
DIMTIX system variable 10-15
DIMTMOVE system variable 10-15
DIMTM system variable 10-22, 10-23

DIMTOFL system variable 10-16
DIMTOH system variable 8-23, 10-13
DIMTOLJ system variable 10-23
DIMTOL system variable 10-22
DIMTP system variable 10-22, 10-23
DIMTXSTY system variable 10-11
DIMTXT system variable 8-40
Direct Distance Entry 2-16
Direction Control dialog box 6-12
DRAGMODE system variable 14-12

E

EDGEMODE system variable 5-19
Edit Block Definition dialog box 14-15
Edit Drawing Scales dialog box 7-3
Edit Hatch tool 13-17
Edit tool 14-15
ELLIPSE command 3-12
Ellipse drop-down 3-12
Elliptical Arc tool 3-14
ERASE command 2-19
Erase tool 2-19
EXPLMODE system variable 14-22
EXTNAMES system variable 14-4

F

Field dialog box 7-18
Fillet/Chamfer drop-down 5-9
FILLET command 5-9
FILLETRAD system variable 5-9
Fillet tool 5-9
FILLMODE system variable 13-4
Find and Replace dialog box 7-19
FONTALT system variable 7-39

G

GDT 8-37
Geometric Tolerance dialog box 8-39
GFANG system variable 13-14
GFNAME system variable 13-13
Gradient Pattern 13-13

H

Hardware Acceleration On button 1-7
Hatch Angle 13-8
Hatch Creation tab 13-3
HATCHEDIT Command 13-17
Hatch Edit dialog box 13-18
Hatch Editor Tab 13-17
Hatch tool 13-3
Hatch Transparency 13-8

HPANG system variable 13-8
HPDOUBLE system variable 13-9
HPNAME system variable 13-7, 13-12
HPSCALE system variable 13-9

I

IMAUNIT system variable 10-19
Insert a Block in a Table Cell dialog box 7-35
INSERT command 14-7
Insert dialog box 14-7
Insert Layout(s) dialog box 11-18
Insert Table dialog box 7-26
Insert tool 14-7
INSUNITS system variable 14-10, 14-13, 14-21

J

Join Viewports tool 11-5

L

Layer Properties Manager dialog box 11-15
LAYOUT command 11-16
LAYOUTWIZARD command 11-18
Leader Settings dialog box 5-20
Lengthen tool 5-20
LIMITS command 2-30

M

Manage Cell Styles dialog box 7-33
Manage Plot Styles tool 12-10
Manage Xrefs icon 1-8
MATCHPROP command 6-5
Match Properties tool 6-5
Material Condition dialog box 8-40
Measure tool 3-23
Mirror tool 5-37
MLEADERALIGN command 8-34
MLEADER command 8-31
MLEADEREDIT command 8-34
MLEADERSTYLE command 10-26
Model button 1-6
Modify Dimension Style dialog box 9-11
Modify Multileader Style dialog box 10-26

N

Named tool 11-3
Navigation Bar 1-4
Nesting of Blocks 14-18
New Dimension Style dialog box 10-10
New Excel Data Link dialog box 7-27
New Layout button 11-16

O

OBJECTSCALE command 7-3
Object Selection Methods 2-20
Object Snap button 1-5
Object Snap Tracking button 4-30
OFFSET command 5-4
Ordinate tool 8-23
OSOPTIONS system variable 13-14

P

PAGESETUP command 11-18
PAN command 3-17
Pan tool 6-19
Paragraph dialog box 7-13
PLINE command 3-18
PLOT command 12-2
Plot Styles window 12-10
PLOTTERMANAGER command 12-7
Plotter Manager Tool 12-7
Plot tool 12-2
PROPERTIES command 4-3

Q

QDIM command 8-8
QLEADER command 8-27
QNEW command 1-14
QSAVE command 1-20
Quick Dimension tool 8-8
Quick Properties button 1-6

R

Radius tool 8-21
RAY command 3-26
Ray tool 3-26
Reassociate tool 8-6, 8-27
Rectangle tool 3-9
Rectangular Array 5-22
REDRAWALL command 6-13
REDRAW command 6-12
REGENALL command 2-12
REGEN command 6-13
Relative Coordinate System 5-6
Relative Polar Coordinates 2-14
Relative Rectangular Coordinates 6-3
RENAME command 14-23
Rename dialog box 14-24

S

SAVEAS command 1-20
SAVE command 1-20
Save Drawing As dialog box 1-21

SCALE command 5-7
SCALETEXT command 7-25
Scale tool 7-25
Select a Data Link dialog box 7-27
Select Annotation Scale dialog box 14-13
Select File dialog box 1-23
SELECTIONANNODISPLAY system
      variable 7-5
Selection Cycling button 6-5
Selection list box 6-6
Select template dialog box 11-17
Show/Hide Lineweight button 1-6
Show/Hide Transparency button 1-6
Sign Convention 2-12
Single Line tool 3-26
SNAPBASE system variable 13-10
Snap Mode button 1-5
Status Bar 1-5
Status Toggles option 1-8
SteeringWheels 1-4

T

Table Cell tab 7-34
TABLEINDICATOR system variable 7-36
TABLESTYLE command 7-30
Table Style dialog box 7-31
Table Style tool 7-30
Table tool 7-25
Tan, Tan, Radius tool 2-23
Tan, Tan, Tan tool 2-24
TEXT command 3-26, 7-5
Text drop-down 7-6, 7-9
TEXTSIZE system variable 7-41
Text Style dialog box 7-39
Tiled Viewports 11-3
TILEMODE system variable 11-3
TOLERANCE command 8-38
Tolerance tool 8-38
Tool Palettes button 13-14
TOOLPALETTES command 13-16

U

Update tool 9-7

V

Viewports dialog box 11-4

W

WBLOCK command 14-20
Welcome Screen of AutoCAD LT 2012 1-3
Window Crossing Method 2-21
Window Selection 2-20
Write Block dialog box 14-20

X

XPLODE Command 14-22

Z

ZOOM command 6-13
Zoom drop-down 6-14
Zoom Extents tool 2-25
Zoom In 6-19
Zoom In tool 2-26
Zoom Out 6-19
Zoom Out tool 2-26
Zoom Previous tool 2-26, 6-17
Zoom Realtime tool 2-26, 6-14
Zoom tool 6-13
Zoom tools in the Navigation Bar 6-14
Zoom Window tool 2-25

Other Publications by CADCIM Technologies

The following is the list of some of the publications by CADCIM Technologies. Please visit *www.cadcim.com* for the complete listing. To order any of these textbooks online, please visit the following link: *www.cadcimtech.com*

Autodesk Inventor Textbooks
- Autodesk Inventor 2012 for Designers
- Autodesk Inventor 2011 for Designers
- Autodesk Inventor 2010 for Designers
- Autodesk Inventor 2009 for Designers

Solid Edge Textbooks
- Solid Edge ST3 for Designers
- Solid Edge ST2 for Designers
- Solid Edge ST for Designers
- Solid Edge V20 for Designers

NX Textbooks
- NX 7 for Designers
- NX 6 for Designers

Autodesk Alias Textbooks
- Learning Autodesk Alias Design 2010
- Autodesk AliasStudio 2009 for Designers

SolidWorks Textbooks
- SolidWorks 2011 for Designers
- SolidWorks 2010 for Designers
- SolidWorks 2009 for Designers

CATIA Textbooks
- CATIA V5R20 for Designers
- CATIA V5R19 for Designers

EdgeCAM Textbooks
- EdgeCAM 11.0 for Manufacturers
- EdgeCAM 10.0 for Manufacturers

Pro/ENGINEER Textbooks
- Pro/ENGINEER Wildfire 5.0 for Designers
- Pro/ENGINEER Wildfire 4.0 for Designers

ANSYS Textbook
- ANSYS 11.0 for Designers

AutoCAD LT Textbooks
- AutoCAD LT 2011 for Designers
- AutoCAD LT 2010 for Designers
- AutoCAD LT 2009 for Designers

AutoCAD Electrical Textbook
- AutoCAD Electrical 2011 for Electrical Control Designers
- AutoCAD Electrical 2010 for Electrical Control Designers

Autodesk Revit Textbooks
- Autodesk Revit Architecture 2012 for Architects & Designers
- Autodesk Revit Architecture 2011 for Architects & Designers
- Autodesk Revit Architecture 2010 for Architects & Designers

AutoCAD Civil 3D Textbook
- AutoCAD Civil 3D 2012 for Engineers
- AutoCAD Civil 3D 2009 for Engineers

AutoCAD Map 3D Textbook
- Exploring AutoCAD Map 3D 2012
- Exploring AutoCAD Map 3D 2011

3ds Max Design Textbooks
- Autodesk 3ds Max Design 2012: A Tutorial Approach
- Autodesk 3ds Max Design 2011: A Tutorial Approach
- Autodesk 3ds Max Design 2010: A Tutorial Approach
- Max Design 2009: A Tutorial Approach

3ds Max Textbooks
- Autodesk 3ds Max 2012: A Comprehensive Guide
- Autodesk 3ds Max 2011: A Comprehensive Guide
- Autodesk 3ds Max 2009: A Comprehensive Guide
- 3ds Max 2008: A Comprehensive Guide

Maya Textbooks
- Autodesk Maya 2012: A Comprehensive Guide
- Autodesk Maya 2011: A Comprehensive Guide
- Character Animation: A Tutorial Approach
- Autodesk Maya 2010: A Comprehensive Guide
- Autodesk Maya 2009: A Comprehensive Guide

Paper Craft Book
- Constructing 3-Dimensional Models: A Paper-Craft Workbook

Computer Programming Textbooks
- Learning Oracle11g
- Learning ASP.NET AJAX

- Learning Java Programming
- Learning Visual Basic.NET 2008
- Learning C++ Programming Concepts
- Learning VB.NET Programming Concepts

AutoCAD Textbooks Authored by Prof. Sham Tickoo and Published by Cengage-Delmar Press (Autodesk Press)
- AutoCAD 2012: A Problem-Solving Approach
- AutoCAD 2011: A Problem-Solving Approach
- Customizing AutoCAD 2011
- AutoCAD 2010: A Problem-Solving Approach
- Customizing AutoCAD 2010
- AutoCAD 2009: A Problem-Solving Approach
- Customizing AutoCAD 2009
- AutoCAD 2008: A Problem-Solving Approach
- Customizing AutoCAD 2008

Textbooks Authored by CADCIM Technologies and Published by Other Publishers

3D Studio MAX and VIZ Textbooks
- Learning 3ds max5: A Tutorial Approach
  (Complete manuscript available for free download on *www.cadcim.com*)
- Learning 3Ds Max: A Tutorial Approach, Release 4
  Goodheart-Wilcox Publishers (USA)
- Learning 3D Studio VIZ: A Tutorial Approach
  Goodheart-Wilcox Publishers (USA)
- Learning 3D Studio R4: A Tutorial Approach
  Goodheart-Wilcox Publishers (USA)

CADCIM Technologies Textbooks Translated in Other Languages

SolidWorks Textbooks
- SolidWorks 2006 for Designers (Russian Edition)
  Piter Publishing Press, Russia
- SolidWorks 2008 for Designers (Serbian Edition)
  Mikro Knjiga Publishing Company, Serbia

NX Textbooks
- NX 6 for Designers (Korean Edition)
  Onsolutions, South Korea
- NX 5 for Designers (Korean Edition)
  Onsolutions, South Korea

CATIA Textbooks
- CATIA V5R18 for Designers (Serbian Edition)
  Mikro Knjiga Publishing Company, Serbia
- CATIA V5R18 for Designers (Korean Edition)
  Onsolutions, South Korea

3ds Max Textbook
- 3ds Max 2008: A Comprehensive Guide (Serbian Edition)
  Mikro Knjiga Publishing Company, Serbia

Pro/ENGINEER Textbooks
- Pro/ENGINEER Wildfire 4.0 for Designers (Korean Edition)
  HongReung Science Publishing Company, South Korea
- Pro/ENGINEER Wildfire 3.0 for Designers (Korean Edition)
  HongReung Science Publishing Company, South Korea

Coming Soon: New Textbooks from CADCIM Technologies

- ANSYS Workbench 14.0 for Designers
- SolidWorks 2012: A Tutorial Approach
- Exploring Revit Structure 2012
- AutoCAD Plant 3D 2012 for Designers
- Creo Parametric 1.0 for Designers
- NX 8 for Designers
- Solid Edge ST4 for Designers
- Adobe Premiere CS5.5: A Tutorial Approach
- Adobe Flash CS5.5: A Tutorial Approach

Online Training Program Offered by CADCIM Technologies

CADCIM Technologies provides effective and affordable virtual online training on various software packages such as CAD/CAM/CAE, Animation, Civil, GIS, and computer programming languages. The training will be delivered 'live' via Internet at any time, any place, and at any pace to individuals, students of colleges, universities, and training centers. For more information, please visit the following link:
http://www.cadcim.com